1 - 7

12 - 17

36, 37

40

42

24, 25

Handbook on

AGRICULTURAL EDUCATION

in Public Schools

Handbook on

AGRICULTURAL

THE INTERSTATE
Printers & Publishers, Inc.

DANVILLE, ILLINOIS

EDUCATION

in Public Schools

LLOYD J. PHIPPS

Professor Emeritus
Agricultural Education Division
University of Illinois

 Prior editions: 1965, 1966, 1972. Printed in the United States of America.

Library of Congress Catalog Card No. 79-89023

ISBN 0-8134-2094-6

PREFACE

The *Handbook on Agricultural Education in Public Schools* tells how to conduct a program and develops an understanding of the philosophy supporting the procedures recommended. Suggestions pertaining to all phases of agricultural education at the secondary and post–high school level, but below the baccalaureate level, are included. Programs and courses with vocational objectives and programs and courses with non-vocational objectives are discussed. Implications of the Vocational Education Act of 1963 and its 1976 amendments are considered for high school courses and for courses for young and older adults needing education in agriculture.

Supervised agriculture experience programs, which include supervised farming programs, are considered for students who have entered or are preparing to enter any occupation requiring knowledge and skill in agriculture. The broadened objectives of vocational agriculture are presented, and practical suggestions are outlined for accomplishing these broadened objectives without neglecting the program to educate present and prospective farmers.

Special attention is given to the new programs in agricultural education which are now reimbursable with federal funds, such as agricultural technology, ornamental horticulture, and agriculture for persons who cannot profit from the regular vocational agriculture program. The courses for adults working in occupations requiring knowledge and skill in agriculture, which are now reimbursable under legislation for vocational education, are also given special attention.

This handbook should be of primary interest to present and prospective teachers of agriculture, teacher educators, and supervisors. It should also be of value to superintendents and principals who administer programs of agricultural education in the secondary schools, area vocational and technical schools, and community colleges. It is hoped that this book will be helpful in the development and conduct of programs of agricultural education throughout the United States and elsewhere where courses in agriculture are offered.

LLOYD J. PHIPPS

ACKNOWLEDGMENTS

The assistance and advice received from co-workers in agricultural education and teacher education at the University of Illinois, from co-workers in agricultural education, Department of Adult, Vocational and Technical Education, Illinois State Board of Education, and from teachers of agriculture are greatly appreciated. Appreciation is also expressed to the many teachers of agriculture and the many teacher educators and supervisors in agricultural education in other states and countries who assisted in providing materials and ideas. The agricultural education personnel, Vocational and Technical Division, U.S. Office of Education, were especially helpful.

CONTENTS

Part I

INTRODUCING AGRICULTURAL EDUCATION

Part II

TEACHING PROCEDURES

Part III

DEVELOPING AGRICULTURAL EDUCATION PROGRAMS

Part IV

ORGANIZING AND PLANNING A HIGH SCHOOL PROGRAM

Part V

SUPERVISED OCCUPATIONAL EXPERIENCE PROGRAMS

Part VI

FFA

Part VII

PROVIDING AN AGRICULTURE MECHANICS PROGRAM

Part VIII

CONDUCTING A GUIDANCE PROGRAM

Part IX

CONDUCTING POST-SECONDARY AND ADULT EDUCATION IN AGRICULTURE

Chapter | Page

Part X

PROVIDING AND USING FACILITIES, EQUIPMENT, SUPPLIES, AND TEACHING AIDS

Part XI

ADMINISTERING AND EVALUATING AGRICULTURAL EDUCATION

PART I

Introducing Agricultural Education

CHAPTER

1

What Is the Content, Philosophy, and Scope of Education in Agriculture?

TYPES OF AGRICULTURAL EDUCATION IN PUBLIC SCHOOLS

Agricultural education is a relatively new addition to the program of the public schools. The best known type of agricultural education in the public schools is vocational education in agriculture. Other types of agricultural education, however, have been present in the programs of the public schools since the beginning of public education. The first courses taught were academic, non-vocational courses. Thirty states had established agriculture courses in their public schools prior to 1917, when the Smith-Hughes Act was passed. The Smith-Hughes Act provided funds to promote vocational education in agriculture for present and prospective farmers. The funds provided had to be matched by local and state funds. The Smith-Hughes Act and subsequent acts were very effective in promoting the establishment of courses of vocational education in agriculture. At present more than 10,000 school systems in the United States offer education in agriculture. The vocational education in agriculture program has been so successful that it has overshadowed other types of agricultural education.

Alert citizens see the need for a more comprehensive and higher quality program of vocational education in agriculture. They recognize that production agriculture and agribusiness is becoming highly technical and that both employers and employees need more vocational education in agriculture. They recognize that this education must be of high quality.

Persons who understand vocational education in agriculture know that although this type of education is firmly established in the public schools, the program needs further emphasis. More than half of the schools in rural areas do not offer any type of course in agriculture. There have never been enough young persons with education in agriculture, willing or able to enter production agriculture and agribusiness to replace those leaving the work of agriculture.

In addition to vocational education in agriculture for production, several other types of agricultural education are needed. Vocational education in agriculture programs for occupations requiring knowledge and skills in agriculture are needed. Our society is becoming increasingly dependent on those agriculturally oriented businesses necessary for the efficient and effective supply of food and fiber products for the exploding population. Many workers in these agriculturally oriented businesses need special types of vocational education in agriculture if they are to make a maximum contribution to the economy of the nation. Vocational education in agriculture programs at the secondary and post–high school levels have developed and are developing rapidly in occupations other than production agriculture which require knowledge and skills in agriculture. These programs have developed and are developing because of the encouragement provided by the Vocational Education Act of 1963 and the Vocational Education Amendments of 1968 and 1976.

Agricultural education is also needed and should be supplied for those interested in agriculture as an avocation. Education in agriculture as a practical arts subject should be a part of the program of all public junior and senior high schools. Practical arts subjects are considered a part of general education. The content of practical arts includes those things which a person needs to know to perform successfully the practical activities in which nearly everyone engages in the process of living. The subject matter areas usually included in the practical arts are agricultural arts, industrial arts, household arts, and business arts.

Another type of agriculture taught in the public schools is related to education for citizenship. All persons need to know the role and functions of agriculture if they are to behave as effective citizens. Still another type of education in agriculture is that designed to teach people what they need to know about agriculture to be intelligent consumers of agricultural products. Instruction in agriculture is needed by all students, as it relates to career education.

Recently interest has been shown in education in agriculture for its value as physical and mental therapy. Finally, some specialized courses in agriculture in the public schools may be required to provide the basic education in agriculture needed by persons who plan to continue their education in this field at institutions of higher learning. At the elementary and junior high school levels agricultural education is needed for occupational orientation and exploration for agricultural careers.

COMPREHENSIVE PROGRAM OF AGRICULTURAL EDUCATION

A public school with a comprehensive program of agricultural education would provide, if appropriate, the following:

1. Agriculture as a part of the school's career education program.
2. Agriculture as a part of the school's education for citizenship.
3. Agriculture as a part of the school's consumer education program.
4. Agriculture as a part of the school's special education program.
5. Agriculture as a part of the school's applied science program.
6. Agriculture as a part of the school's practical arts program.
7. Agricultural education for students planning to enter a college of agriculture.
8. Vocational education in agriculture for present and prospective producers of agricultural products.
9. Vocational education in agriculture for persons in occupations other than farming which require knowledge and skills in agriculture.

A public school with a comprehensive program of agriculture would offer many different types of courses in agriculture, and the agriculture teachers would be involved in the team teaching of many other courses.

A comprehensive program of agricultural education for a community necessitates a comprehensive school system dedicated to serving the best interests of all the people. It necessitates a school system of adequate size which is well financed and staffed. It necessitates, as a part of the system, access to an area post–high school program where the more specialized types of agricultural education would be provided, and it necessitates multiple-teacher departments of agriculture.

Vocational Education in Agriculture for Farming—The purpose of vocational education in agriculture for farming is to educate present and prospective farmers for proficiency in farming. Such education provides systematic instruction in agriculture of less than college grade in the public schools for those persons who have entered upon, or who are preparing to enter upon, the work of the farm or the farm home. Federal aid is available for vocational education in agriculture for farming.

There are three well recognized groups served by vocational agriculture for farming, namely:

1. High school youth preparing to farm.
2. Out-of-school young persons engaged in farming, usually on their home farms, or employed as farm workers looking forward to full establishment as independent farm operators.
3. Adult farmers fully established as operators and employees on farms.

Landowners may also profit from some types of vocational agriculture courses for farming.

In order to provide systematic instruction for the groups served by vocational agriculture for farming, educators have developed four kinds of courses as follows:

1. *Adult farmer courses* for farmers and their employees who are operating farms.
2. *Young farmer courses* for out-of-school farm youth who are becoming established in farming.
3. *Courses for in-school youth* who are enrolled in high schools and who meet daily during the school year.
4. *Courses for in-school youth* at the thirteenth and fourteenth grade levels.

The following are commonly included as integral parts of the instruction in vocational agriculture for farming:

1. Classroom activities.
2. Supervised occupational experience programs of the students.
3. Agriculture mechanics activities.
4. School-sponsored organizations, such as FFA and Young Farmers.

Classroom activities provide opportunities for high school students, young farmers, and older adult farmers to study and discuss problems related to farming programs and farm living. Activities in areas such as animal science, dairy science, poultry science, field crops, horticulture, soils, marketing, rural economics, farm management, accounting, and agriculture mechanics are included in the instruction.

Supervised occupational experience programs provide opportunities for the students to apply the knowledge and skills learned at school to farm situations. The occupational experience programs of high school students include *productive projects, improvement projects, supplementary farm practices, placement for experience*, and *exploratory experiences.* These programs are an integral part of the instruction in vocational agriculture for farming, and they are under the guidance and supervision of the teacher of vocational agriculture. They provide many opportunities for the students to progress toward establishment in production agriculture. All persons enrolled in young farmer courses are expected to apply on farms the knowledge and skills gained as a result of the instruction and to conduct occupational experience programs, under the supervision of the teacher of vocational agriculture, which will help them to become successfully established in production agriculture. Likewise, farmers enrolled in adult courses in agriculture are expected to adopt and put into effect a number of approved practices as a result of the instruction which will help them to become more efficient in their farming operations.

Agriculture mechanics activities involve areas such as *shop work*, including carpentry, painting, glazing, ropework, home shop work, sheet metal work, forge work, arc welding, and oxyacetylene welding; *farm power and machinery*, including transmission of power, motors, trucks and tractors, and agricultural machinery; *buildings and conveniences*, including concrete work, buildings, plumbing, water systems, sewage disposal, heating, and lighting; *rural electrification*, including selection of materials and equipment and care and maintenance of equipment; and *soil and water management*, including terracing, contouring, drainage, and irrigation.

Many of the agriculture mechanics jobs and problems in the courses for farmers, young farmers, and high school students are based on the occupational experience programs of the students. The establishment of good farm shops may be one of the desirable outcomes of the programs.

"*The FFA* [Future Farmers of America] is the national organization of, by, and for students studying vocational agriculture in public secondary schools which operate under the provisions of the National Vocational Education Acts. It is an educational, nonprofit, nonpolitical youth organization of voluntary membership designed to develop agricultural leadership, character, thrift, scholarship, cooperation, citizenship, and patriotism. Its members learn through participating experiences to conduct and take part in public meetings, to speak in public, to buy and sell cooperatively, and to assume civic responsibility. The FFA is an intra-curricular part of vocational education in agriculture in the public school system of America. It constitutes one of the most effective devices for teaching through participating experiences."[1] The FFA is recognized as an integral part of the program of vocational education in agriculture. It serves both production agriculture students and students preparing for off-farm agricultural occupations.

(Photo from Jasper Lee, Mississippi)

Fig. 1.1. Students receiving instruction related to agricultural sales in a simulated farm supply store located in the facilities of a vocational agriculture department.

School-sponsored organizations of the members of young farmer courses are a part of many young farmer programs. Such organizations provide opportunities for many types of learning that otherwise would not be possible.

Many school-sponsored organizations composed of members of older-adult farmer courses have developed as a means of facilitating the teaching of certain abilities. These organizations develop out of the educational needs made apparent through adult farmer courses. Membership is limited to enrolled members of a course, and each organization is terminated when the course is over, or sooner, if the educational purpose of the organization has been accomplished.

Vocational Education for Off-Farm Occupations Requiring Knowledge and Skills in Agriculture—Many present and prospective workers in off-farm jobs need agricultural education of a vocational nature. Courses of the following types are needed:

1. *Preparatory courses* of specialized types at the high school and post-high school levels designed to provide the agricultural abilities needed for each of the logical clusters of off-farm agriculturally oriented businesses.

[1]*The FFA Foundation Incorporated*, Bul. 1, U.S. Office of Education, Washington, D.C., p. 4.

2. *Upgrading courses* of specialized types designed to provide the agricultural abilities needed by employed workers in off-farm businesses.
3. *Retraining courses* of specialized types designed to provide adults the agricultural abilities they need for employment in off-farm businesses.

The Vocational Education Act of 1963 and the Vocational Education Amendments of 1968 and 1976 broadened the objectives of vocational education in agriculture to permit and encourage the providing of vocational education in agriculture for persons, other than present and prospective farmers, in occupations requiring knowledge and skills in agriculture. Courses of the types listed in the preceding paragraphs have been organized and are being organized rapidly as a result of this legislation. In many schools more than half the students enrolled are in programs for off-farm agricultural workers.

Legislation now mandates that vocational education in agriculture and renewable natural resources prepare students for the world of work in the following occupational areas:

1. Agricultural production.
   a. Animal science.
   b. Plant science.
   c. Farm mechanics.
   d. Farm business management.
2. Agricultural supply and service business.
   a. Agricultural chemicals.
   b. Feeds.
   c. Seeds.
   d. Fertilizers.
3. Agricultural mechanics businesses.
   a. Agricultural power and machinery.
   b. Agricultural structures and conveniences.
   c. Soil management.
   d. Water management.
   e. Agriculture mechanics skills.
   f. Agricultural construction and maintenance.
   g. Agricultural electrification.
4. Agricultural products businesses.
   a. Food products.
   b. Non-food products.
5. Ornamental horticulture.
   a. Arboriculture.
   b. Floriculture.
   c. Greenhouse operation and management.
   d. Landscaping.
   e. Nursery operation and management.
   f. Turf management.
6. Agricultural resources.
   a. Forests.
   b. Recreation.
   c. Soil.
   d. Water.
   e. Air.
   f. Fish.
   g. Range.
7. Forestry.
   a. Forests.
   b. Forest protection.
   c. Logging.
   d. Wood utilization.
   e. Recreation.
   f. Special products.
   g. Forestry technology.

8. Agricultural technology.
9. Agriculture related technology.
10. Agricultural, other.

MAJOR OBJECTIVES OF AGRICULTURAL EDUCATION

General Education Objectives—Vocational education in agriculture is an integral part of public school education and contributes to the general objectives of education. It contributes to the development in students of the ability to think and study and the ability to solve problems efficiently, which requires skill in collecting and interpreting data. Public school agricultural education also aids in the development of desirable attitudes and interests and in the development of social sensitivity and resourcefulness of students.

According to *Educational Objectives in Vocational Agriculture* (Vocational Division Monograph 21, Office of Education, Washington, D.C., pp. 4–5), public school education in agriculture should attempt:

"1. *To develop the individuals as completely as possible.*" The students should understand their capacities, limitations, and abilities and their relationships to other individuals, homes, and society. They must be concerned about their vocations, business affairs, and personal development. They need to be aided in acquiring desirable personal qualities and characteristics. In their struggle for successful accomplishment they must cultivate all of their desirable native qualities.

"2. *To promote personal-group relationships with emphasis upon home and family life as fundamental to the individual's growth and to the public welfare.*" Individuals and groups living in a society are dependent upon the family for group relationships.

"3. *To make individuals and groups responsive to the needs of other individuals and groups, of communities, of governments, and of other desirable social agencies.*" Individuals in a society must be concerned with the welfare of others in the solution of their own problems. Social life is essential to the development of individuals, of homes, and of life's interests in general. There are many social problems in a constantly changing, progressive society. Individuals and groups have great responsibility in the determination of the direction of that change.

Agricultural Education Objectives—A comprehensive program of agricultural education, in addition to contributing to the objectives of all types of education, should do the following:

1. Assist American citizens to develop the attitudes, understandings, and abilities regarding agriculture necessary for their future welfare and the welfare of agriculture.
2. Develop appreciation of America's rural heritage and its influence on our literature, art, drama, and music.
3. Develop understanding of the influence of research on agriculture and on other aspects of our society, such as medicine, statistics, and consumer products.
4. Develop understanding of interrelationships of agriculture and other segments of society.
5. Develop understanding of the influence of public policy on agriculture.
6. Develop understanding and appreciation of agriculture for avocational and leisure interests.
7. Assist and make meaningful for the students involved the special education program in schools.
8. Promote creative activities of students.

9. Promote meaning and practical applications of the content of other subject matter areas, such as science.
10. Provide guidance regarding the occupational opportunities in farm and off-farm occupations requiring knowledge and skills in agriculture.
11. Assist in improving the economic efficiency of agriculture and individuals in agriculture.
12. Promote balance and meaning in the total educational program of the school and of individuals.
13. Develop understanding of the contributions of agriculture to society.
14. Assist present and prospective farmers in improving their efficiency in farming.
15. Assist present and prospective workers in off-farm agricultural jobs in improving their efficiency.
16. Promote environmental quality.

Vocational Education in Agriculture—Courses in agriculture for farming or for off-farm occupations requiring knowledge and skills in agriculture should contribute both to the general objectives of education and to the overall objectives of agricultural education. In addition, they should have as a major objective the development of those abilities necessary for proficiency in farming or in an off-farm agricultural job.

Educational Objectives in Vocational Agriculture (pp. 2–3) lists as the major objectives of vocational education in agriculture for farming the development of effective ability to:

"1. *Make a beginning and advance in farming.*
"2. *Produce farm commodities efficiently.*
"3. *Market farm products advantageously.*
"4. *Conserve soil and other natural resources.*
"5. *Manage a farm business effectively.*
"6. *Maintain a favorable environment.*
"7. *Participate in rural leadership activities.*"

In vocational education in agriculture for farming, and for off-farm agricultural occupations, the development of essential abilities depends upon individuals having real situations in agriculture as a basis for developing sound judgment and understanding of the various agricultural disciplines. There should be a definite relationship between the course of study and the supervised occupational experience programs of the students.

The major objectives of vocational education in agriculture for off-farm occupations requiring knowledge and skills in agriculture are to develop ability to:

1. Select intelligently a cluster of agricultural occupations for study.
2. Make a beginning and advance in an off-farm occupation requiring knowledge and skills in agriculture.
3. Understand the relationships between the agricultural abilities and the other abilities necessary for success in the occupation.
4. Participate in leadership activities in the occupation.
5. Adapt to changes in the occupation due to changes in the agricultural disciplines involved.
6. Maintain a favorable environment for work in the occupation.

In addition to the major objectives of vocational education in agriculture, there are numerous contributory objectives essential to the successful attainment of the major objectives. A teacher should, with the help of others who are concerned, carefully select and adopt a list of contributory objectives needed for each major objective.

Some examples of the ways that vocational education in agriculture contributes to the seven cardinal principles of an education are indicated in the following statements:

1. Vocational agriculture provides for many activities through individual occupational programs, the FFA, field trips, and numerous other outdoor activities which contribute to the *health* of the students.
2. Vocational agriculture instruction develops abilities in constructive thinking and problem-solving which enable the students to have a better *command of the fundamental processes*.
3. Vocational agriculture provides desirable training for *worthy home membership* in that the instruction includes many problems closely related to home and family living.
4. Vocational agriculture contributes to a *vocation* by affording students opportunities to receive guidance regarding the occupations in agriculture and to apply through their occupational experience programs the knowledge and skills gained at school.
5. Vocational agriculture provides for many activities through the FFA and other school-sponsored organizations for the development of abilities essential to *desirable citizenship*.
6. Vocational agriculture, through the activities of the FFA and other school-sponsored organizations, provides for the development of many abilities essential to *worthy use of leisure time*.
7. Vocational agriculture contributes to the development of an *ethical character* through the pattern set by the teacher who spends considerable time with the students in many activities, such as those in leadership, cooperation, savings, recreation, and supervised occupational experiences.

These lists of objectives should not be considered by teachers of agriculture as final statements of the aims of education but rather as areas in which they should work with their students in developing individual goals which are adapted to their students' needs.

SCOPE AND DEVELOPMENT OF AGRICULTURAL EDUCATION

Scope—Agricultural education courses are taught in public schools throughout the country, and courses are found in school systems varying in size from the smallest to the largest. Since many public school systems in rural areas do not offer agricultural education and since there has never been more than half the needed amount of individuals with high school vocational agriculture education willing to enter farming for the farmer replacements needed, it is apparent that there is need for the continuing growth of vocational education in agriculture for farming.

It is also apparent that the opportunity for growth of agricultural education programs in urban areas is greater than it is in many rural areas. Growth of agricultural education is occurring in urban areas. The Board of Education for Los Angeles has a policy of having the architects plan facilities for practical arts agriculture in each new junior high school. The population of Los Angeles is growing rapidly and so is agricultural education.

Education in agriculture for the off-farm occupations requiring knowledge and skills in agriculture increases materially the opportunity for growth of agricultural education in school systems of all sizes. Most states have several post–high school institutions with agricultural technology programs designed to educate workers for off-farm agricultural occupations. Many schools in metropolitan areas are offering or planning to offer vocational agriculture courses in ornamental horticulture. Ornamental horticulture is one of the fastest growing segments of American agriculture and offers many job opportunities. Leaders in agricultural education have estimated that a 50 per cent increase in the number of teachers of agriculture will be needed in the near future to make possible the development of agricultural education for off-farm occupations requiring knowledge and skills in agriculture.

The recent emphasis on career education at the elementary and junior high school levels, with its attention to occupational orientation and exploration for careers in agriculture, increases further the scope of the program. There has been a steady growth in total enrollments in vocational agriculture from the beginning of the program in 1918, except for the period during World War II.

Developments in Agricultural Education—Recent developments in agricultural education are twofold. There is an upsurge of interest in broadening agricultural education in the public schools to include all the types of agricultural education listed earlier in this chapter. The second development is the improvement of the quality of vocational education in agriculture. The agricultural knowledge and skills essential for careers in agriculture have increased in geometric proportions. A program with high standards is necessary to meet the demands of present and prospective workers in both farm and off-farm agricultural jobs.

AGRICULTURAL EDUCATION LEGISLATION

Vocational Acts[2]—The need for the development of vocational education has been recognized on numerous occasions by Congress, as indicated by the passage of a number of acts. The following is a list of these acts providing for vocational education in agriculture of less than college grade:

1. Smith-Hughes Act of 1917.
2. An act to extend the benefits of the Smith-Hughes Act to Hawaii, 1924.
3. George-Reed Act of 1929.
4. An act to extend the benefits of the Smith-Hughes Act and supplementary acts to Puerto Rico, 1931.
5. George-Ellzey Act of 1934.
6. George-Deen Act of 1936.
7. National Defense War Training Acts.
   a. Public Law 812, 1940.
   b. Public Law 647, 1941.
   c. Public Law 146, 1942.
   d. Public Law 135, 1943.
   e. Public Law 373, 1944.
8. George-Barden Act of 1946.
9. Area Redevelopment Act.
10. Manpower Act of 1962.

[2]The details of these acts pertaining to agricultural education are given in the Appendix.

11. Vocational Education Act of 1963.
12. Vocational Education Amendments of 1968.
13. Vocational Education Amendments of 1976.

President Kennedy's Panel on Vocational Education, reporting in January 1963, recommended a broadening of vocational education in agriculture to include education for off-farm occupations requiring knowledge and skills in agriculture. This recommendation was implemented by the passage of the Vocational Education Act of 1963 and the Vocational Education Amendments of 1968 and 1976.

Smith-Hughes Act—A national vocational education act known as the Smith-Hughes Act was approved February 23, 1917. It was designated by this name because Senator Hoke Smith and Representative Dudley M. Hughes, both of Georgia, were instrumental in its passage.

The act was designed to encourage states to promote and further develop programs of vocational education of certain kinds which otherwise might not be adequately provided in our state systems of education. This act provided for vocational education in agriculture, trades and industries, and homemaking.

It annually appropriated $3 million for the purpose of cooperating with the states in paying the salaries and transportation costs of teachers, supervisors, and directors of agricultural subjects and of agricultural teacher educators.

The controlling purposes of the act were:

1. *that "such education shall be to fit for useful employment,*
2. *that such education shall be less than college grade,*
3. *that such education be designed to meet the needs of persons over fourteen years of age who have entered upon or who are preparing to enter upon the work of the farm or of the farm home."*[3]

Only public schools were eligible for aid under the act. Instruction in vocational agriculture under the terms of the act provided for directed or supervised practice in agriculture. A copy of the Smith-Hughes Act appears in the Appendix.

George-Barden Act—This act, designated as Vocational Bill S. 619, was passed by Congress and was signed by President Truman on August 1, 1946

It was an act to replace the George-Reed, George-Ellzey, and George-Deen acts, which supplemented the Smith-Hughes Act. It was designed to provide for the further development of vocational education in the states and territories.

Vocational Education Act of 1963—This act, Public Law 88-210, was passed by Congress in December 1963. Its purpose was to strengthen and improve the quality of vocational education and to expand the vocational education opportunities in the nation.

The monies authorized may be used to:

1. Maintain, extend, and improve existing programs.
2. Develop new programs of vocational education.

[3]Smith-Hughes Act (Public Law 347, Sixty-fourth Congress—S. 703).

3. Provide part-time employment for youths who need earnings from such employment to continue their vocational education full-time.

The act provides monies for vocational education for:

1. High school students.
2. Persons who have completed or discontinued their formal education and are preparing to enter the labor market.
3. Persons who have entered the labor market but need to upgrade their skills or learn new ones.
4. Persons with special educational handicaps.

The act amended the George-Barden and Smith-Hughes acts in the following important way for vocational agriculture:

> "Any amounts allotted (or apportioned) under such titles, Act, or Acts for agriculture may be used for vocational education in any occupation involving knowledge and skills in agricultural subjects, whether or not such occupation involves work of the farm or of the farm home, and such education may be provided without directed or supervised practice on a farm."

This amendment made possible, with federal monies, many vocational education in agriculture courses. It granted many additional persons, who need agricultural education for their work, the opportunity of obtaining systematic instruction in agriculture in public schools. The Vocational Education Act of 1963 opened a whole new "box" of opportunities in vocational education in agriculture.

Vocational Education Amendments of 1968 and 1976—The Vocational Education Amendments of 1968 and 1976 further emphasized and mandated certain aspects of vocational and technical education. The 1976 act stated that its purpose was "to authorize federal grants to states to assist them to maintain, extend, and improve existing programs of vocational education, to develop new programs of vocational education, to develop and carry out programs of vocational education to overcome sex discrimination and sex stereotyping in vocational education programs and thereby furnish equal opportunities in vocational education to persons of both sexes, and to provide part-time employment for youths who need the earnings from such employment to continue their vocational training on a full-time basis, so that persons of all ages in all communities of the state—those in high school, those who have completed or discontinued their formal education and are preparing to enter the labor market, those who have already entered the labor market but need to upgrade their skills or learn new ones, those with special educational handicaps, and those in post-secondary schools—will have ready access to vocational training or retraining which is of high quality, which is realistic in the light of actual or anticipated opportunities for gainful employment, and which is suited to their needs, interests, and ability to benefit from such training."[4]

The Vocational Education Amendments of 1976 hold vocational education programs responsible for:

1. Eliminating sex discrimination and sex stereotyping.

---

[4]Vocational Education Amendments of 1976, Ninety-fourth Congress (P.L. 94-482). See Appendix for selected portions of this act.

2. Using local advisory councils for vocational education.
3. Evaluating the vocational education program.
4. Providing vocational education in job and content areas where there is a labor market need for prepared workers.
5. Improving vocational education opportunities for women.

Additional aspects of vocational education of interest to agricultural educators which were emphasized in the Vocational Education Amendments of 1976 are as follows:

1. Cooperative vocational education programs.
2. Exemplary and innovative programs.
3. Vocational guidance and counseling.
4. Special programs for the disadvantaged.

PHILOSOPHY OF VOCATIONAL EDUCATION IN AGRICULTURE

A definite philosophy has been evolved by agricultural educators in the twentieth century. And, this philosophy differs at certain points with the philosophy of other educators, even educators in other areas of vocational education.

Agricultural educators put much emphasis on pragmatism. The instruction, the methodology, the program, and the courses are based on the problems involved in the various tasks in the agricultural world of work. Thus the content is flexible and changing. At least it is often more flexible and changing than it is in many areas of education such as English, mathematics, and history.

Agricultural educators emphasize learning by doing. This emphasis is apparent in the attention given to laboratory work, field trips, problem-solving, and supervised occupational experience programs. Often, much less attention is given to learning by doing in many general education courses.

Agricultural educators place much emphasis on the individual. This emphasis is in evidence by the importance placed on home and job visits by the teachers, by the importance placed on supervised study, and by the basing of the content of instruction on the individual problems of the students.

Agricultural educators accept seriously their role in vocational guidance and counseling. They provide career education through their instructional activities related to agriculture. They emphasize self-awareness, work awareness, career awareness, education awareness, career orientation, career exploration, and career decision making in addition to career preparation. Their attention to these areas often far exceeds the attention given by teachers of other content areas.

Agricultural educators firmly believe in the importance of leadership and citizenship development. They believe that the instructional program in agriculture provides an excellent vehicle for teaching regarding leadership, citizenship, and the other values of our society. They believe in the importance of student organizations such as the FFA in furthering education in agriculture and in broadening the impact of agricultural education. They see student organization work as an excellent vehicle for providing agricultural education according to its broadest definition.

Agricultural educators, having always worked with the disadvantaged, recognize the importance of providing agricultural education to the disadvantaged and the handicapped. They have learned how to work with the disadvantaged and the handicapped by emphasizing the individualization of instruction, by placing emphasis on the agricultural problems of the students, and by giving attention to supervised study, laboratory work, field trips, supervised occupational experience, and student organizations.

Agricultural educators, in working with the disadvantaged, discovered early that some of the disadvantaged were academically talented. Agricultural educators through their activities have learned how to work effectively with the academically talented, and welcome them in the program. They believe that production agriculture and agribusiness careers need the academically talented and that careers in agriculture will be challenging and satisfying to them.

Agricultural educators at the ninth to fourteenth grade levels believe that some of their students should continue their education to the baccalaureate level or beyond and that the education in agriculture they provide is good preparation for further education. And they try to teach so that it will be. Agricultural educators attempt to encourage thinking by emphasizing problem-solving. This type of instruction broadens the value of agricultural education to most types of future situations in which the students may find themselves.

Agricultural educators are community oriented. They believe that they should serve the community in which they work and that the program they provide should also serve the community. Agricultural educators are strong believers in adult education. They believe that agricultural education should be provided to all adults who want it and can profit from it. As a result, many communities have equally strong programs in agriculture for both in-school and out-of-school individuals in the area.

CHAPTER 2

What Are the Values, Prospects, and Opportunities for Education in Agriculture?

The agricultural education program in the public schools is still growing. This is true for both the vocational and the non-vocational aspects of the program. The vocational education in agriculture program will need to expand rapidly due to broadening of the program to include the off-farm occupations requiring knowledge and skills in agriculture. Since many public schools, especially in urban areas, do not offer vocational education in agriculture, there also remains room for further expansion in the number of schools offering agricultural education.

Agricultural education is being extended downward into the junior high schools and upward into the post-secondary schools. Some school systems are providing agricultural education coordinators as consultants to elementary school and other teachers to assist them in teaching agriculture. School systems are also employing agriculture teachers full-time to teach agriculture to adults. Agricultural education is being broadened both horizontally and vertically.

NEED INCREASING

Changes are occurring rapidly in all dimensions of our society. The changes in agriculture have been especially rapid. These changes have created needs for more and different types of agricultural education in the public schools.

Vocational Education in Agriculture—Changes in agriculture have created a demand for a more technically oriented type of agricultural education for farmers and off-farm agriculture workers. They must receive technician level training in agriculture. Since the technological development of agriculture is continuous, the need for formal, systematic adult education in agriculture is increasing and continuous.

Today farming is a business which involves many scientific practices, and it has become highly organized, specialized, and mechanized. The soil is rapidly becoming depleted in many areas; the country is becoming densely populated; many pests have been introduced; production, management, and marketing problems are more complex than before; and competition is becoming keener each year. Consequently, farmers and off-farm agriculture workers must cope with many complex problems. They must be able to form judgments, evaluate the problems carefully, and arrive at proper conclusions in solving their problems.

A large number of the jobs previously done on farms are now done off the farms. The workers in these occupations often need specific education in agriculture if they are to be proficient in their jobs.

Agricultural Education for Everyone—The need for agricultural education, other than in vocational agriculture for farming and for off-farm occupations requiring knowledge and skills in agriculture, is increasing and becoming more apparent. When farming was the occupation of the majority of the population, much basic agricultural knowledge was commonplace or easily obtained. The agricultural knowledge and abilities necessary for the practical affairs of living, for effective citizenship, and for avocational interests are no longer commonplace or easily obtained.

This situation accounts for the upsurge of interest in providing agricultural education at all levels in the public schools for everyone. Vocational education in agriculture for farming and for off-farm occupations requiring knowledge and skills in agriculture is no longer the only type of agricultural education needed.

VALUES AND FUNCTIONS OF AGRICULTURAL EDUCATION

Values—Attention in education recently has been centered on the importance of career guidance for young people. Agricultural education programs in schools have certain inherent advantages and opportunities for guidance for youth. The teachers, because of their background and education, understand the interests, problems, and concerns of youth interested in agriculture. With an increasing number of public school teachers with backgrounds and interests foreign to agriculture, the teachers of agriculture are often the teachers best qualified to counsel youth regarding agriculture careers.

Research studies indicate that if our economy continues to develop in an upward direction, the economic opportunities in farming, in off-farm jobs requiring knowledge and skills in agriculture, and in professional disciplines of agriculture are going to become increasingly attractive. These research studies also indicate that the competition to become established in agriculture is increasing rapidly. In the future only the best qualified and most motivated will be able to survive the competition.

Research studies relating to the aspirations of youth and adults indicate that many have unrealistic ambitions relating to agriculture. These youth and adults, if enrolled in agriculture courses with good teachers, have opportunities for guidance and counseling second to none. They have a chance to assess the opportunities to become established in farming, in an off-farm occupation requiring knowledge and skills in agriculture, and in a professional position in agriculture. They have a chance to determine personal and other prerequisites for entry into the various agricultural occupations. They have an opportunity to compare their qualifications and abilities, in a realistic way, with the prerequisites for the various occupations requiring agricultural education. They have these meaningful guidance experiences while they are having meaningful learning experiences in an applied science, which will be of value to them whether they engage in an agricultural or non-agricultural occupation.

Agriculture courses in schools serve society and individuals by guiding out of farming or off-farm occupations persons who, for various reasons, would not be successul in these fields. This is done in a humane and meaningful way. Agriculture courses in schools also serve society and individuals by assisting those students who are most needed and most likely to be successful in farming and in off-farm occupations requiring knowledge and skills in agriculture to prepare themselves adequately in the science of agriculture.

Agricultural education permits many young people to earn while they learn. Through their occupational experience programs they are able to accumulate capital to finance further education. This further education may or may not be for an agricultural occupation. No matter what their ultimate vocational objectives, earning while learning in an agriculture course provides these students with the best vehicle for effective education yet known. It promotes meaning and interest in the total school program. It provides a real-life experience in the world of work, which so many young people in our present culture miss while in school. Earning while learning in agriculture courses may provide the incentive and opportunity needed by many future scientists, doctors, lawyers, business executives, farmers, professional agriculturalists, and teachers to motivate them to remain in school. The opportunity in agricultural education to earn while learning may for many be a deterrent to quitting school. With the dropout problem in schools becoming more serious, measures for decreasing the number of school dropouts need more attention.

Beginning courses in agriculture for high school students may, in summary, (1) ease the transition from elementary school to high school for many youth, (2) make school more meaningful and interesting, (3) provide guidance services relating to occupations, especially agricultural occupations, (4) provide opportunities to earn while learning, (5) provide opportunities to ac- cumulate capital to finance future education, (6) provide vocational exp ences for farming and off-farm occupations requiring knowledge and sk agriculture, and (7) provide pre-occupational experiences in the v work.

Advanced courses in agriculture in schools may also serve

(Photo from Robert W. Walker, Pennsylvania)

Fig. 2.1. Students in a vocational education in agriculture program, receiving individualized instruction.

tions. They may continue to serve, without regard to ultimate vocational objectives, the students who are farming and are improving and increasing their farming programs. They may serve the students committed to becoming established in farming. They may serve the students preparing for off-farm, nonprofessional occupations requiring knowledge and skills in agriculture, and they may serve students who plan to attend colleges of agriculture.

Agricultural instruction at the post–high school level has several important values and functions. It is at this level that the really vocational education in agriculture is conducted. A post–high school institution needs to offer many types of agriculture courses to provide the agricultural education needed by persons preparing for the large number of agriculturally oriented jobs. The task of providing the agricultural education needed by persons preparing for off-farm agriculturally oriented jobs which demand specialized competencies in agriculture will become larger than the task of providing agricultural education for farming.

Upgrading and retraining courses in agriculture are also needed at the post–high school level for the persons currently employed in agriculture. Since many of the off-farm agriculturally oriented jobs are found in rural areas, this type of adult education is also highly important in nonmetropolitan centers.

This kind of agricultural education needs increased emphasis. Adult education for the agricultural occupations has always been conducted on such a marginal basis that there are unlimited possibilities for expansion. The need is still much greater than the manpower and finances in agricultural education can handle. The need and opportunities for adult education for agricultural occupations are actually increasing due to the necessity of providing enrollees with more technical, more systematic, more formal, and longer courses. It also appears that more of the adult education for agricultural occupations in the future must be provided by local schools and by area post–high school institutions. The colleges of agriculture seem to be less and less concerned with agricultural education for farming and off-farm agricultural occupations and more and more concerned with education for the agricultural professions.

Rural Community—Agriculture courses in a rural community and the teachers of these courses can and should serve many functions. Agriculture courses usually are and should be the most meaningful and interesting courses in the public schools for many, and perhaps most, students.

Why does this situation exist when studies indicate that a large percentage of the youth in rural communities may migrate to urban communities? A fundamental principle of good education is that education starts where the student is. It is difficult or impossible to start elsewhere.

Rural youth are surrounded by agricultural activities. Agriculture is the most important ingredient of their experience. Most of the everyday concerns of the adults of the community are related to agriculture. Agriculture permeates the total existence of rural youth. Rural youth, whether they want, or will have, an opportunity to engage in farming or an off-farm agricultural occupation, become involved at an early age in the production of plants and animals. During their preschool and early elementary school years, they have "gardens" and assist in the feeding and care of livestock.

At 10 years of age they usually enroll in 4-H clubs and obtain ownership of crop and livestock projects. By the time they start high school, many of them have substantial farming programs. They are farming on a small scale.

These youth want to enroll in agriculture courses. Should they have the opportunity to study agriculture? Observance of sound educational principles would necessitate an affirmative answer to the question. According to studies, these youth often come from homes where the parents do not understand the value of education or promote further education as much as the parents of children living in metropolitan areas. This gap is closing rapidly, but it still exists. Rural parents have less formal schooling than the average formal schooling of all adults.

The study of agriculture may serve several functions for these rural youth. Since the agriculture teachers who provide on-job instruction often work at least 11 months a year in the community instead of 9, and are a part of the community, they are often the teachers best known by rural youth. With their rural backgrounds and interests, it is easy for rural youth and their parents to develop rapport with these teachers.

An important function of agricultural education for rural youth is the easing of the transition from elementary school to high school. The percentage of dropouts between elementary school and high school is decreasing, but it still is rather high. A good agricultural education program in a high school may make a significant contribution toward decreasing this dropout percentage, especially in rural areas where the dropout rate at this transitional period is the highest.

There is ample opportunity and need for expansion of agricultural education for out-of-school young men and women living on farms. Agricultural education for these persons may serve two important functions: (1) it can help some of them obtain the educational help they need to become successfully established in farming, and (2) it can provide the educational help others need to decide that they do not have the competencies or other qualifications necessary for becoming successfully established in farming. For these persons it may also provide some of the agricultural knowledge necessary for entry into off-farm jobs requiring knowledge and skills in agriculture.

An extremely important function and need in agricultural education in rural areas, because of the increasing level of technology and management problems, is adult education in agriculture for both farmers and workers in off-farm agricultural occupations.

Urban Community—Agricultural instruction may serve several functions in an urban community. All high school students need some instruction in agriculture if they are to become intelligent consumers of agricultural products and if they are to exercise their citizenship responsibilities intelligently regarding agricultural policy. Much of this agricultural education must be given as units of instruction in required general education courses. A larger school system frequently designates an agriculture teacher as the coordinator of agricultural education for the system. It is this teacher's job to help the non-agriculture teachers offering units on agriculture in their courses to obtain the technical help they need. The consumer and citizenship functions of agricultural education may also be facilitated by elective courses in agriculture for students wanting to study the subject in greater depth.

These elective courses may serve other functions. They may serve a career guidance function relating to the opportunities in the agricultural occupations. Most nonrural youth will not be able to become established in farming, but many of them may be able to work in off-farm occupations requiring knowledge and skills in agriculture. For these persons, agriculture courses may serve as a prevocational experience.

Agriculture courses in an urban community may serve a secondary vocational function for some youth. There is a significant number of youth in metropolitan areas from families with financial interests in farming or agriculturally oriented businesses. These youth anticipate that they will eventually become involved with these financial interests in agriculture. Youth in this category will enroll in agriculture courses if suitable courses are offered.

Many youth living in metropolitan areas seem to have an affinity or interest in agriculture akin to their interest in a zoo or a circus. Perhaps they are emotionally starved for contact with living and growing things—plants and animals. If the agricultural education offered to them provides laboratory experiences with living plants and animals, they will enroll in and profit from agriculture taught as an applied science course. It will provide them with a creative experience. It will function as part of their general education. For some, it may also have a mental health function.

For persons living in suburban areas, agriculture courses have an increasing practical arts or avocational function to perform. They want to learn how to care for flowers, gardens, lawns, and pets. What better way is there to provide a meaningful experience in the biological sciences while serving the practical arts needs of the students? For some potential part-time agricultural producers, these agriculture courses may have a vocational function.

Agricultural instruction may serve an important function in the education of the problem students in a school, the potential dropouts. For emotionally disturbed students at all levels of intelligence, laboratory-centered agricultural instruction may have a calming or therapeutic value. Caring for and studying plants and animals has a desirable emotional influence on most persons. Care of growing plants is used in hospitals as mental therapy.

Laboratory-centered agricultural instruction may provide a meaningful work experience to youth who want to work but who have never had an opportunity to do useful work. Some agricultural content is very rigorous and technical, but there are elements of agriculture that can be comprehended in a meaningful way by mentally handicapped students. Agriculture courses for the educable mentally handicapped are feasible. Special agriculture courses may also be the vehicle for teaching many desired attitudes, understandings, and characteristics to students who are unable to profit from courses such as chemistry, physics, algebra, and foreign language.

Probably the most important function of agricultural education in an urban school is to prepare youth and adults for careers in agricultural occupations that exist in urban areas. These occupations require persons with specific abilities in agriculture, and many youth and adults in urban areas are interested in preparing for these occupations. Urban schools need to provide opportunities to prepare for agricultural occupations existing in urban areas in the same way they need to provide vocational courses in other occupational areas.

A neglected area of adult education in metropolitan areas is agriculture. Agriculture courses serving avocational functions are needed and would be successful. Instruction regarding agricultural policy would be functional for many adults. Those with agricultural interests welcome courses in the agricultural economics area. Agricultural instruction for many adults may function as part of their preparation for retirement, and for some it provides an additional opportunity to know and understand their world. Urban adults in off-farm agricultural occupations also need and deserve agricultural education.

FUTURE DEVELOPMENTS

The more education people experience, the more they want. As various types of agricultural education are experienced, the demand for them will increase. Experience with vocational education in agriculture for adults has shown an increasing demand for this type of educational service. As school administrators and citizens become acquainted with agricultural education other than vocational education in agriculture for farming, the demand for these types of agricultural education also will increase.

Desires Made Known Through Advisory Councils—People have not only been led to expect more from their departments of agricultural education, but these desires are being discovered more fully through the required use of advisory councils composed of a representative group of persons from the community who analyze the educational desires of the people. Advisory councils are discussed in detail in Chapter 10.

State and Federal Aid Increasing—States are providing more and more aid for education in agriculture. In some states, the monies appropriated by the state for the support of vocational education are considerably greater than the monies provided by federal legislation. This is an indication of the increasing awareness of states of the need for, and value of, vocational education being provided by public schools.

The Vocational Education Act of 1963 and the Vocational Education Amendments of 1976 provide substantial additional monies to maintain, improve, and extend vocational education, including vocational agriculture for production plus vocational education in agriculture for all occupations requiring knowledge and skills in agriculture. Increased funds for vocational education, coupled with the broadening of objectives, provides almost unlimited new opportunities in agricultural education.

Teachers Becoming More Professional—Teachers are becoming organized in professional associations dedicated to making agriculture programs more educationally worthwhile and more widespread. Through the efforts of professional organizations of teachers of agriculture, the public is being educated regarding the educational services and values of education in agriculture.

Facilities Improving—New building facilities for agricultural education have been provided in a large number of schools in recent years, and many more are planned. These new facilities will make it possible to provide agricultural education to a larger number of persons.

Research Showing the Way—Research is showing the way for more effective education in agriculture. Studies have identified the students most likely to profit from agricultural education. Research has indicated effective methods of teaching both youth and adults. With over 60 years of experience in vocational education in agriculture and thousands of research studies in the field, we can move ahead with assurance.

Needs for Adequate Staff Recognized—School administrators, boards of education, and the public are becoming increasingly aware of the need for, and the value of, an adequate staff. The good administrator is recognizing not only the time required to provide classroom instruction for high school students but also the time required for:

1. Supervised occupational experience programs.
2. FFA.
3. Adult education.

The next development in agricultural education may be a further and more rapid expansion in the number of multiple-teacher departments.

ADVANTAGES AND OPPORTUNITIES IN TEACHING AGRICULTURE

Advantages—All jobs have their advantages and disadvantages, and most provide opportunities for advancement. The teaching of agriculture is not an exception to this statement. However, the disadvantages of a job are often so apparent that workers forget to consider the values, advantages, or rewards inherent in the job. Workers have to learn to be content with a certain amount of routine and "red tape" in any job. Most jobs present problems of working with others. Teaching agriculture consists of a certain amount of routine, a certain amount of "red tape" work, and its fair share of problems involved in interacting with others. It does have certain advantages, however, that other types of jobs may not possess.

Teachers of agriculture are paid as well as, or better than, many public servants. In addition, the nonfinancial rewards, if recognized, in teaching agriculture are many. Following are some of these rewards:

1. *Tenure.* Many states have tenure laws that protect their teachers from being dismissed for political, partisan, capricious, or personal reasons.
2. *Pension.* Most states have pension plans for teachers. Many but not all types of employment provide pension plans for the employees.
3. *Year's contract.* Teachers of agriculture are often employed on a 12-month basis, and they have the security of a year's contract. Many employees in other occupations are subject to dismissal with only a short notice.
4. *Independence.* No employee has complete independence, but teachers of agriculture are relatively independent. They are professionally trained for their jobs, and most school administrators respect their training and allow them to "run their own show."
5. *Opportunity to use talents in agriculture.* It is a psychological fact that when a person has developed a particular skill, talent, or ability, he/she usually desires to use it. Teachers of agriculture have ample opportunity to use in their teaching activities all the various types of agricultural knowledge and skills they possess.
6. *Feeling of belonging.* Most communities quickly make their agriculture teachers feel needed and at home. A teacher of agriculture has friendly associations with an entire community.
7. *Feeling of worth, usefulness.* An agriculture teacher has many opportunities to be of educational service to the community. The feeling of worth, therefore, is bolstered frequently.
8. *Responsibility.* Most persons enjoy being able to reinforce their egos by accepting responsibilities. Agriculture teachers should recognize that their students are providing them with opportunities to accept important responsibilities daily.
9. *Healthfulness.* Agriculture teachers have the stimulating opportunity to spend part of each working day outside. They also have the enviable position of not being forced to work outside when the weather is exceptionally bad. When the weather is bad, teachers can usually arrange their work so that they can stay at school all day instead of providing instruction outdoors during part of the day.
10. *Safety.* Compared with many occupations, the teaching of agriculture is a safe occupation. The opportunities for accidents are not nearly as great as they are in farming. Teachers do not spend a large amount of time driving on the highways. The safe driving record of teachers of agriculture is reflected by the premium rates of some automobile insurance companies.
11. *Intellectual stimulation.* The new problems and new ways of solving problems encountered in teaching agriculture keep teachers mentally alert. Persons need not fear that they will become mentally stagnant while teaching agriculture.

12. *Social approval, status, respect.* There are very few persons, and in some communities none, who have more status and social approval than teachers of agriculture.
13. *Warm human relationships, companionship.* The agriculture teachers in a community should have many friends. There is little chance that they will ever by lonely.
14. *Action, novelty, variety.* In agriculture teaching, something new happens frequently. There is plenty of action, and the activities of teachers are sufficiently varied to prevent monotony.
15. *Long vacations.* Many teachers of agriculture receive a month's vacation with pay. The typical vacation with pay for new employees in most occupations is two weeks.
16. *Recreational opportunities.* In many places, the school is the recreational center for the community. Teachers working in a school have ready access to the recreational opportunities and facilities it provides.
17. *New agricultural information.* Teachers of agriculture need the latest agricultural information. Most states have developed special procedures to insure that their agriculture teachers do receive, in a useable form, such information.
18. *Controlled competition.* Many jobs force persons to compete constantly with others or with themselves. Teachers of agriculture have ample opportunity to compete with themselves or with others. They are sufficiently independent, however, to control the extent of the competitive activity in which they engage. Insurance agents, on the other hand, are usually forced to compete with other agents, and if they do not compete successfully, they may lose their jobs.
19. *Sick benefits.* Many schools have sick benefit plans which permit the teachers to take time off with pay while sick. A two-week sick leave with pay is common.
20. *Chance to be home nearly every night.* Teaching agriculture is a job that permits persons to be at home nearly every night. It may necessitate being away from home during the early evening, but it does not require being away from home and living in hotels as do many jobs that employ college agriculture graduates.
21. *Challenging work, personal growth.* The nature of the work is challenging and, therefore, promotes personal growth.

Teachers of agriculture are very fortunate because they have opportunities to work with and guide our most precious resource—human beings.

Opportunities—Teaching agriculture does create opportunities for advancement, if persons are good teachers. In the past a favored advancement opportunity for many teachers of agriculture has been the opportunity to grow in stature and status in their teaching communities and in the profession of teaching agriculture. Many persons have chosen to remain teachers of agriculture for their entire professional career, often in the same school system.

However, this is not the only opportunity for advancement. Good teachers have many opportunities for changing jobs within the field of teaching agriculture. Opinions can be obtained both pro and con regarding whether these changes are advancements.

Some of the different job classifications in the agricultural education profession are as follows:

1. Agriculture teacher at the elementary school level.
2. Agriculture teacher at the middle school and junior high level.
3. Agriculture teacher at the high school level in a single-teacher program.
4. Agriculture teacher at the high school level in a multiple-teacher program.
5. Specialized teacher of agriculture in areas such as horticulture, agriculture mechanics, agricultural business, and so forth.

6. Head teacher of agriculture in a multiple-teacher program.
7. Agriculture teacher in an area vocational school.
8. Agriculture teacher in a post-secondary institute or community college.
9. Supervisor or consultant in agriculture in a state department of education.
10. Teacher educator in agriculture in a university.
11. Teacher of agriculture in a university.
12. Extension specialist in agriculture in a university.

Good teachers of agriculture also have opportunities, with certain amounts of additional education and experience, for many different types of jobs outside the agricultural education field:

1. Within public education.
   a. Administrator.
      1) Principal.
      2) Superintendent.
   b. Guidance counselor.
   c. Specialist teacher, in an area such as career education.
2. Outside public education.
   The various opportunities outside public education are too numerous to mention. A few of the most available jobs are:
   a. Farm manager.
   b. Agricultural representative of a bank.
   c. Agricultural representative of a business.
   d. Manager of an agribusiness.

Good teachers of agriculture have many and frequent opportunities to change jobs. Their real challenge is to decide what makes them happy and what they want in a job before changing jobs.

CHAPTER

3

How to Become a Good Teacher of Agriculture

NECESSARY CHARACTERISTICS

Persons considering the profession of teaching agriculture have certain decisions to make. They should decide whether they have the following abilities, characteristics, or qualifications, and, if they do not have them, they should decide whether they have the ability and willpower to attain them. They are necessary for the successful teaching of agriculture.

Agriculture—Persons who plan to teach agriculture should have a background of experience in the agricultural occupation they will be teaching. They should have had at least two years of appropriate occupational employment experience since the age of 15. Many of the abilities learned on a farm will be helpful in teaching agriculture in a rural school. Farm experience, however, is not necessary for teachers who plan to teach, in an urban area, vocational agriculture courses such as ornamental horticulture.

Character and Personality—Unquestionable character is essential for every successful teacher. This is especially true of teachers of agriculture. In all probability, many students try to be like their agriculture instructors; consequently, what teachers do must be of the highest standard. Teachers must have distinctive and individual character indicative of forceful personality. They must know how to meet people and carry on a conversation. Often agriculture instructors fail simply because of the inability to meet people and to adapt themselves to their environments. A teacher with a pleasing personality can do a great deal in developing a good community attitude toward the program in agriculture.

Rural-mindedness—Instructors who plan to teach in rural areas should have the following characteristics:

1. They must be in sympathy with rural life.
2. They must have an attitude of friendliness toward farmers and other workers in agriculture.
3. They must have a technical, scientific, and practical knowledge of agricultural production.
4. They must be able to guide present and prospective agricultural workers in arriving at practical procedures that may be used on their jobs.
5. They must be able to help persons with a rural background prepare for off-farm jobs requiring knowledge and skills in agriculture. Many of these persons will perform their work in an urban environment.

Urban-mindedness—Instructors who plan to teach in urban areas should have the following attributes:

1. Understanding of and sympathy with the life styles of urban people.
2. Understanding of working conditions in off-farm occupations in urban areas requiring knowledge and skills in agriculture.
3. Understanding of employment needs in off-farm occupations requiring knowledge and skills in agriculture.
4. Understanding of abilities needed by the persons being taught.
5. Possession of competencies necessary to prepare prospective workers in the off-farm agricultural occupations.

Leadership—One of the most important qualifications of teachers of agriculture is leadership. They must be leaders of adults, as well as organizers and leaders of students. The following are 12 attributes of an agricultural leader stated by Dean Alfred Vivian of The Ohio State University:

1. Abounding *faith* in the importance of the work.
2. Infinite *tact* in meeting trying situations.
3. Unlimited *patience* in overcoming community inertia.
4. Endless *good nature* in face of all trials.
5. A saving *sense of humor* when nothing else will meet the situation.
6. A large *vision* of the work to be done.
7. Ability to *lose gracefully* and to *rebound* after each defeat.
8. Indomitable *courage* in standing for the right.
9. A grim *determination* to see the work put through to its completion.
10. A contagious *enthusiasm* that inspires local leadership.
11. Unquenchable *optimism* in spite of all discouragements.
12. Unreserved *belief in the importance of the family* to the commonwealth.

Commitment to Teaching—To be successful, teachers must believe in their work.

1. They must be believers in their programs and have the initiative to carry them out.
2. They must be willing to dedicate themselves to their jobs and render services efficiently.
3. They must be persons of perseverance, since success cannot be attained overnight.
4. They must have faith in their work and possess the enthusiasm and courage to continue, even though at times things do not appear the brightest.

Confidence—Some teachers are well trained and know their subject matter, but because of their lack of confidence they are unable to do good jobs. Other teachers have not made good records in college, but because of their initiative and confidence they have become good instructors.

Neatness—Teachers of agriculture must dress properly for all occasions. Some teachers are of the opinion that since they are teaching agriculture, they should dress differently from other teachers. In order to make a good impression, they feel they should wear only work clothes. This is not true except on special occasions, such as some field trips, some home visits, or certain demonstrations. Neatness of dress is as important for teachers of agriculture as for others in a school system. Most of the time agriculture teachers should dress the same as the other teachers in the school. They may have a pair of coveralls or other appropriate clothes for field trips and demonstrations.

Teachers of agriculture should also keep their classrooms and shops neat and well arranged. Students should form habits of good housekeeping, which must be stimulated by their instructors. There is not much incentive for the students to keep the agriculture classrooms in order unless the teachers set good examples.

Courtesy and Manners—Teachers are supposed to be educated persons, and educated persons are expected to be courteous. Some teachers are handicapped because they have not developed desirable habits of courtesy. When teachers do not practice the commonly accepted courtesies and manners, people may be offended. Manners and courtesy are the drops of oil that lubricate the machinery of wholesome human relationships.

Persons who want to become good teachers should become conscious of the commonly accepted courtesies, such as saying *please, excuse me,* and *thank you.* They should then practice until courteous behavior is automatic.

Correct Attitude—Teachers must have the proper attitude not only toward their work but also toward others in the school system. They must be professionally minded, take suggestions kindly, and work for the benefit of the students and the community.

Willingness to Cooperate—Teachers of agriculture must be willing to cooperate with the school officials at all times. They should realize that they are a part of a school system and that they must uphold school policies. A school depends not only upon its administrators but also upon all the teachers in the system. Like a chain, a school system is no stronger than its weakest link. Every teacher forms a link in the school system.

Professional Ethics—The following are some of the principles of professional ethics which should be followed by teachers of agriculture:

1. Conform to the regulations of the school.
2. Refuse to cast reflections on the activities of a fellow worker.
3. Consider a contract with the school binding, and fulfill it.
4. Refuse to be an applicant for a job held by a fellow teacher.
5. Abide by oral agreements as well as by those in writing.
6. Be a good winner or a good loser.
7. Refuse to make alibis for work.
8. Be fair and respect the rights of others.

Willingness to Work—Teachers of agriculture, to be successful, must be willing to work. Successful teachers often spend 50 to 60 hours per week on

(Photo from Jasper Lee, Mississippi)

Fig. 3.1. Teachers of vocational education preparing to teach a forestry class. Notice hard hats in picture. Safety instruction is important.

their jobs during busy periods. At the present time, all professions require long hours of work from their members. Teaching agriculture is no exception.

Intelligence—Teachers of agriculture do not have to be geniuses, but they need plenty of good, practical judgment and common sense. They need to be solid thinkers. Agriculture students do not expect their teachers to have a phenomenal memory, but they do expect them to be able to think through problems and use available sources of information. The best teachers are not necessarily those with the best memories or the ones with the largest accumulation of agricultural information.

Emotional Maturity—Teachers of agriculture must be secure individuals. They must be confident of their abilities and recognize their limitations. They must act as adults at all times. Their actions must be based on considered judgments and not on snap judgments. Emotional immaturity is most apparent in an individual's ability to work with others. Lack of ability to work with others is one of the principal causes of failure in teaching.

Physical Abilities—Teachers of agriculture need the ordinary physical attributes required for most professional jobs. They should have strong, clear voices so that the students can hear and understand them. Teachers whose hearing is impaired are handicapped. Teachers must, of course, have good vision because they are forced to use their eyes constantly.

Health—Teachers of agriculture must have stamina, which requires good health. The job requires long hours. It is occasionally nerve-wracking. Persons in poor health are irritable and soon lose patience with students. Good health is necessary for patience, ability to work long hours, confidence, and a secure feeling, which are prerequisites for success. Those in poor health should not enter teaching, or if they are teaching, they should be given leaves of absence until they regain good health.

General Education—Teachers of agriculture are educational leaders. Therefore, they need to be educated persons, speaking in the broadest sense. They need to exhibit the characteristics of educated persons in all areas of life. To be educated only in the area of agriculture is not sufficient.

It is especially important for agriculture teachers to use good English, both in speaking and in writing. A community expects all its teachers to be proficient in the use of the English language. Persons who misuse the English language, no matter how much technical knowledge or skill they possess, are assumed to be ignorant by many people.

Broad Interests—To be successful in teaching, instructors must start with the present interests of their students and develop their interests from there. This is nearly impossible for teachers with few interests, because it is difficult for them to understand the feelings of others. In addition, broad interests make for happier and more secure individuals, and happiness and security are two essential characteristics of teachers. Broad interests give teachers an advantage in associating with all types of people in their communities. They also give them a chance to look at their problems objectively.

ABILITIES NEEDED BY TEACHERS OF AGRICULTURE

Teachers of agriculture must possess or develop the abilities required to perform the many duties involved in conducting a successful program of vocational or non-vocational agriculture. The following are some of these abilities:

1. Ability to establish and maintain relationships.
2. Ability to determine community and individual needs.
3. Ability to develop and improve the local program of agricultural education.
4. Ability to organize and use advisory groups.
5. Ability to plan and maintain instructional facilities.
6. Ability to advise the local FFA chapter, young adult association, and other school-sponsored organizations.
7. Ability to develop and supervise occupational experience programs of all groups which receive instruction.
8. Ability to plan instruction and teach high school students and adults.
9. Ability to provide guidance, placement, and follow-up.
10. Ability to keep departmental records and make reports.
11. Ability to administer, supervise, and coordinate the activities of the local department.
12. Ability to relate agricultural education to the highest values.
13. Ability to behave as professional educators and as members of a professional group.

Ability to Establish and Maintain Relationships—Some of the activities of teachers of agriculture requiring this ability follow:

1. Working with the principal and superintendent on school policy and other matters.

2. Working with other faculty members on committees, at faculty meetings, at school activities, and in other situations.
3. Participating in school activities and community activities.
4. Working with other agricultural education agencies.
5. Participating in professional organizations and civic clubs.

Ability to Determine Community and Individual Needs—Teachers engage in many activities similar to the following which require this ability:

1. Using census data, soil reports, farm management reports, and programs of other agricultural education agencies.
2. Surveying the community.
3. Observing agricultural activities in the community.
4. Determining trends and recent developments in the community.

Ability to Develop and Improve the Local Program of Agricultural Education—A few of the activities of teachers requiring some proficiency in this ability are as follows:

1. Determining objectives of the department.
2. Planning the annual and long-time program of the department.
3. Evaluating outcomes of instruction.
4. Working with the advisory council in determining improvements needed in the local program.
5. Planning and instigating activities.

Ability to Organize and Use Advisory Groups—Teachers, to be successful, must have the ability to work with others. Some of the activities of teachers requiring proficiency in this ability follow:

1. Obtaining permission to organize advisory groups.
2. Selecting advisory council members.
3. Visiting with council members.
4. Participating in discussions of the local council.
5. Using advice of advisory groups.

Ability to Plan and Maintain Instructional Facilities—This ability involves the following activities plus many others:

1. Arranging the classroom and shop.
2. Planning for and maintaining visual aids and references.
3. Storing charts and other materials.
4. Adjusting lighting, heating, and ventilation as needed.
5. Inventorying present equipment and supplies.
6. Ordering new equipment and supplies.
7. Establishing procedures for keeping facilities orderly.

Ability to Advise the Local FFA Chapter, Young Adult Association, or Other School-sponsored Organizations—Some of the duties of teachers requiring competency in this ability are as follows:

1. Assisting members in developing a program of work.
2. Participating in meetings.
3. Advising regarding budget and financial records.
4. Assisting the treasurer with financial records.
5. Helping the secretary improve the records.
6. Instructing the reporter in preparing news articles.
7. Advising committees.

8. Assisting students in carrying out special activities.
9. Assisting students in making applications for advanced degrees.

Ability to Develop and Supervise Occupational Experience Programs of All Groups Which Receive Instruction—Teachers need competencies for many activities similar to the following:

1. Evaluating supervised occupational experience programs.
2. Guiding students in selecting and expanding their supervised occupational experience programs.
3. Holding meetings with parents to discuss supervised programs.
4. Assisting students in developing goals and objectives for their programs.
5. Guiding students in setting standards and evaluating progress in their programs.
6. Guiding students in keeping records.
7. Guiding students in analyzing and using their records.
8. Planning and conducting tours of supervised occupational experience programs.
9. Making supervisory visits.
10. Assisting young farmers in developing partnership agreements or leases.
11. Aiding adult farmers in selecting phases of farming and farm living to be improved.
12. Supervising and evaluating experiences of high school students and adults in off-farm jobs requiring knowledge and skills in agriculture.

Ability to Plan Instruction and Teach High School Students and Adults—Effective teaching requires competency in many activities. Some of these follow:

1. Developing course outlines.
2. Developing course calendars.
3. Planning units of instruction for use in teaching.
4. Developing short-time teaching plans.
5. Planning and conducting field trips.
6. Teaching classes.
7. Conducting supervised study.
8. Developing teaching aids.
9. Evaluating the results of instruction.

Ability to Provide Guidance, Placement, and Follow-up—Some of the activities involved in this ability are as follows:

1. Becoming familiar with the guidance program and the records of the school.
2. Interviewing prospective enrollees and their parents, employers, landlords, and others.
3. Making case studies of selected students.
4. Counseling students regarding problems and future career plans.
5. Assisting students in securing opportunities to become established in agricultural occupations.
6. Interviewing and counseling established students regarding progress and problems.

Ability to Keep Departmental Records and Make Reports—Some of the jobs which teachers must perform involving this ability are follows:

1. Making travel reports.
2. Preparing annual reports.
3. Filing references and other material.
4. Preparing forms and reports of young and older adult programs.

5. Assisting in making state reports for local school-sponsored organizations, such as the FFA.
6. Developing and maintaining cumulative records of students and former students.

Ability to Administer, Supervise, and Coordinate the Activities of the Local Department—Some of the activities of teachers of agriculture requiring this ability follow:

1. Participating in staff conferences to coordinate activities in the local department.
2. Planning schedules of activities for the department.
3. Assisting special teachers in using effective teaching procedures.
4. Developing report forms for visits to farms, homes, and agricultural firms and for other activities of teachers in the department.
5. Assisting in the formulation of budgets for the department.

PROFESSIONAL IMPROVEMENT OF TEACHERS

Teaching and administering a complete program of agriculture for high school students, young adults, and older adults in our complex society with the rapidly changing science of agriculture necessitates constant attention to professional improvement. It is impossible for students to become adequately proficient in performing all the diverse duties of teachers of agriculture through preservice preparation alone. Teachers of vocational or non-vocational agriculture must complete the preparation for their jobs and keep abreast of the changes in their work through professional improvement activities.

Methods of Improving Professionally—There are numerous activities that will aid teachers in improving themselves professionally. Teachers can:

1. Participate in in-service courses, workshops, and meetings.
2. Develop and make use of a library of good books, bulletins, magazines, and newspapers.
3. Do graduate work.
4. Participate in professional organizations.
5. Tune in to agricultural radio and television programs.
6. Attend district, state, and regional conferences for teachers of agriculture.
7. Visit other departments of agriculture.
8. Attend state and national conventions and meetings.
9. Attend leadership training meetings.
10. Make self-evaluations of teaching.
11. Travel widely.
12. Work on committees preparing instructional materials.

In-service Training—Teachers, teacher educators, and supervisors are realizing more and more the need for on-the-job training for teachers of agriculture. This is necessary because:

1. It is impossible under present college standards for adequate training to be given in a four-year college course to fit teachers for all the jobs they have to do.
2. Teachers are often more cognizant of the need for training after they are on the job.
3. Teachers need to keep up-to-date with the latest technical information and methods of teaching.

Some of the types of in-service education for teachers on the job are as follows:

1. Workshops on curriculum development, courses for adults, and agriculture mechanics.
2. Short, intensive courses held at colleges.
3. Courses from colleges given off-campus.
4. Courses which are given at colleges but which meet only once a week, in the evening or on Saturday.
5. Follow-up courses for beginning teachers of agriculture.
6. Summer conferences of teachers of agriculture.
7. Meetings in which a teacher educator or a subject matter specialist, or both, from a college meet with a group of teachers from a small area of the state for a few hours to discuss problems in agricultural education.
8. Service letters, plans, and bulletins from a teacher education institution and the state board for vocational education.
9. Radio and television broadcasts on agricultural education.
10. Special field trips.

Library—All teachers should have access to the new books and other publications in agriculture and education. They should also have access to new books of general cultural value. It will probably be necessary for teachers to budget some money for new books and other publications if they are to keep abreast of developments in education and agriculture. Some of these new books may be purchased by the school if they can be used as references.

Selected professional books and magazines should be available in teachers' libraries. All teachers should subscribe to the *Agricultural Education Magazine*, which is the national magazine for teachers of agriculture.

Graduate Study—Graduate study is the most systematic type of professional improvement program available to teachers. Since it is a systematic program, it is usually the best type of professional improvement program for teachers. Teachers of agriculture are engaging in graduate study in increasing numbers. This is probably true because many institutions have provided programs that do not require teachers to take leaves of absence from their jobs. Courses that correlate with their jobs have been provided, and these courses are offered at night in centers within driving distance of their schools. Summer school courses are offered in three- or four-week sessions, which teachers may attend during vacation. Special problem or independent study courses which do not require class attendance have also been provided. Some believe that in the near future, most teachers of agriculture will do graduate study for a master's degree. Many will study for advanced degrees beyond the master's degree.

Professional Organizations—There are a few professional organizations in which teachers of agriculture usually hold membership. They are:

1. The National Association of Vocational Agriculture Teachers.
2. The state organization of teachers of vocational agriculture.
3. The American Vocational Association.
4. The state vocational association.
5. A national education organization.
6. The state education organization.
7. The local education organization.

There are several reasons why teachers enroll in these organizations:

1. To improve themselves professionally.
2. To familiarize themselves with the problems of their states.
3. To become acquainted with the activities of other states.
4. To have a greater appreciation of education in general.
5. To make new contacts.
6. To promote agricultural education and other types of education.

Teachers' Conferences—Teachers should strive to attend as many as possible of the conferences representing the various professional organizations previously mentioned. They should also attend and participate in conferences for teachers of agriculture in their area, such as district, regional, and state meetings. These meetings provide opportunities for acquiring inspiration, new information, and skills helpful in teaching agriculture.

WHAT NEW TEACHERS SHOULD DO

Becoming Acquainted—New teachers should systematically attempt to become acquainted with:

1. Administrators and other teachers.
2. Supervisors of agricultural education.
3. Prospective high school students.
4. Parents.
5. Prospective young adult students.
6. Prospective older adult students.
7. Businesspersons in agriculturally oriented businesses.
8. Farmers in general.
9. Professional workers in agricultural education in the community.
10. Professional workers in agriculture.
11. Professional and business workers.

These have been listed somewhat in their order of importance. New teachers should eventually try to become acquainted with as many as possible of the people they work with or serve. A record of the names of individuals visited, by the classifications given, and other pertinent information about them assists teachers in remembering those whom they have met.

Teachers should not only become acquainted with persons in the communities, but they should also become acquainted with the needs and the mores of their communities. To do this they should study available literature about their communities, read the local newspapers, and seek information from persons in the communities. A teacher's advisory council is an excellent source of information about a community.

Educating the Public—New teachers should provide information regarding the program of agricultural education to the public and to the persons they meet in their communities. Some of the program's unusual or little known aspects, such as learning by doing, programs for off-farm agricultural occupations, and the adult program, may be highlighted. Information regarding agricultural education may be provided through the following media:

1. Newspaper articles.
2. Radio and television broadcasts.

3. Individual visits.
4. Advisory councils.
5. Meetings of parents.
6. Open houses.
7. Faculty meetings.
8. Meetings of organizations in the community.

Becoming acquainted in the community and using or starting an advisory council should be the first two things done by new teachers.

PART II

Teaching Procedures

CHAPTER

4

What Is Good Teaching?

This chapter is a discussion of general teaching procedures which are applicable in all types of teaching. These procedures apply to the teaching of adults as well as high school students. They apply in the teaching of agricultural skills as well as in the teaching of managerial abilities. Techniques for applying these general procedures are presented in the chapters on teaching that follow.

Good Teaching—Good teaching is recognized as being essential, but what is good teaching? There are numerous definitions of teaching, many of which indicate that *it is the direction of the learning process so that desirable changes of a relatively permanent nature are brought about within the learner as a result of the instruction.* The teaching of agriculture may be regarded as effective only to the extent that desired and desirable changes in the student have been realized. What are the desired changes which should be accomplished? Many educators agree that *effective instruction should result in the development of desirable attitudes, interests, ideals, appreciations, understandings, habits, and abilities.*

BASIC FACTORS OF GOOD TEACHING

Democracy—The first prerequisite of good teaching is democratic behavior by teachers. This means that teachers treat their students as they would like to be treated. It means that they behave as chairpersons and not as dictators. It means that they practice the "golden rule." Students are allowed to assist in planning. Instruction is based on their needs, which the teachers help them to recognize. Students assist in planning and in evaluating. Evaluation is not the sole prerogative of teachers.

Democratic teaching of adults is not difficult. Teachers of adults must be democratic, or their adult class members will quit coming. Democratic teaching of high school students is more difficult because teachers have to re-educate themselves not to teach as they have been taught. Because of tradition, the organization of our schools, and other factors, democratic teaching may be more difficult with high school students than with adults, but it is no less necessary.

Use—Teachers and students should be primarily concerned with knowledge and skills which may be used now or in the near future. If the general principles for good teaching to be outlined in this chapter are followed, this concept of teaching for use will be automatically followed. Use is mentioned because traditionally we have been teaching for the future. We try to teach students who may be preparing for off-farm agricultural jobs how to raise sheep, for example, because of a pious belief that someday they might raise sheep.

It is very difficult to teach for future use. Those who try disregard how fast people forget that which they do not use, and they find that their students soon lose interest and do not learn what is being taught. Instead, they learn to dislike what is being taught. An example might be record keeping. Record keeping taught without analysis and interpretation probably teaches students not to keep records instead of teaching them to keep records.

Readiness—Readiness is closely related to use. It is useless to try to teach something to students before they are ready to learn it. Students may not be ready to learn something because they have no immediate use for it. They may not be ready because of mental development, interest, or attitude. Teachers must guide their students to tackle those problems for which they are ready and which they are capable of handling. A minimum of success is necessary for continued interest. Another way of stating this principle is that students must be started where they are. They cannot be started anywhere else.

Learning by Doing—We learn what we do. If we merely talk about agricultural problems, we learn only to *talk* about agricultural problems. Instruction needs to be based on those activities which students anticipate doing or are doing, and the instruction is not complete until they have used the ability being taught. It is not enough to teach about some job in class. Information may not carry over from the classroom to the farm or agriculturally oriented business. Classroom instruction must be based on agricultural activities, and what is learned in class should be used in performing these activities. Learning by doing is closely related to *use* and *readiness.*

TEACHER-STUDENT PLANNING

Democratic teaching, instruction based on use now or in the near future, and instruction based on learning by doing and on readiness necessitate teacher-student planning. Teachers cannot be democratic and cannot adequately predict need and readiness unless they provide for teacher-student planning. Teacher-student planning is necessary for high school students as well as adults.

Teacher-student planning does not mean that teachers abdicate and turn the planning of the courses over to the students. They always have a part in the planning of groups, and they give the groups as much responsibility as they are capable of accepting. The younger the students or the less their experience in planning, the more responsibility teachers must accept. Planning should be restricted, within reason, to the framework of the course in agriculture in which the students are enrolled. The more experience students have in planning, the more responsibility they can accept in the development of a course. Young adults who have had experience in planning as high school students should be able to plan their courses effectively with a teacher acting only as a chairperson of the group. The question that bothers many teachers is how to initiate teacher-student planning.

Teacher-Student Objectives—The first step in teacher-student planning is the development of objectives. This is a continuous process throughout a period of instruction. More time is needed for this activity at the beginning of a course because, in addition to the development of short-time or immediate goals, overall or long-time objectives must be established, and the process of validating objectives must be learned. The time required in developing and validating objectives depends on the age and experience of the students. Adults need the least time, and high school students need the most time to formulate and validate objectives.

Teacher-student planning might begin by a brief review of the objectives of agricultural education and a review of the objectives of the department. Students may then be asked to revise or further define these objectives in relation to their own needs. The purpose of this activity is to develop a clear understanding of the overall objectives of agricultural education. Part of this activity may be omitted or modified with adult class members enrolled in a single course. It would not be repeated entirely each time there is teacher-student planning of objectives.

The following suggestions for teachers were developed by Leo L. Knuti for helping students develop their objectives:

1. Have students indicate what they need to do and know to become the best possible future farmers, employed farmers, self-employed farmers, or workers in agriculturally oriented jobs.
2. Have students indicate what they need to do and know to establish or maintain happy home lives.
3. Have students indicate what they need to do and know to get along with other people on the job, in the school, and in the community.
4. Have students indicate what they need to do and know to be good citizens.
5. Have students indicate what they need to do and know to be able to make the best use of their leisure time.
6. Have students indicate what they need to do and know to keep themselves healthy and physically fit.

This list should be summarized and analyzed.

The following are suggestions for determining the criteria for selecting and validating educational objectives for individual students.[1]

Have students determine the following:

A. Which objectives can help them achieve their psychological needs.
   1. Securing the approval and affection of friends and family.

[1]Also adapted from suggestions developed by Leo L. Knuti.

2. Providing for social and economic security.
3. Developing self-confidence and independence.
4. Acquiring the recognition and confidence of other persons in the group, class, and community.

B. Which objectives can help them achieve their biological needs.
1. Providing wholesome activity and recreation.
2. Maintaining body health.
3. Developing desirable health habits and practices.
4. Carrying out safety practices.
5. Developing wholesome relationships.

C. Which objectives can help them carry out their responsibilities for democratic citizenship.
1. Practicing critical judgment in economic and social issues.
2. Recognizing the need for implementation and change.
3. Accepting the democratic principles of economic and social equality.
4. Accepting civic responsibility and participation in group activities.
5. Acquiring skill in group work and group planning.

D. Which objectives or levels of achievement are in keeping with the principles of learning.
1. Knowing which objectives are appropriate for the high school or adult levels.
2. Knowing which objectives are in keeping with present and possible future interests.
3. Knowing what facilities, equipment, opportunities for agriculture-practice work, FFA programs, and class and shop instruction are available.
4. Knowing what use can be made of the learning experience in other situations or in the future.

The next step might be the consideration of ways and means of accomplishing the objectives adopted by students which pertain specifically to agriculture. At this point an instructor might inject some information on how people learn, such as the value of learning by doing. This should lead to a study of the establishment of supervised occupational experience programs. Assuming in a high school class, for example, that most of the students developed plans for obtaining a job, the next step would be to consider what abilities they wish to develop relating to obtaining a job.

Teacher-Student Evaluation—Planning for the evaluation of progress usually develops almost simultaneously with the planning of objectives. When students are attempting to formulate what they need to do and know in order to accomplish their objectives, the teacher should guide the class members in discovering what they already know about the job or problem. The learning process begins where a student is. Consideration of ways and means of evaluating progress toward accepted objectives is an excellent way of making the objectives really meaningful.

Teacher-Student Problems—The natural result of teacher-student planning is the development of anticipated problems or the recognition of real problems which the teacher and the class wish to solve.

Summary—The basic factors of good teaching may be more apparent after an illustration based on procedures with an adult class studying swine production. In this situation, the teacher-student planning of objectives may be started by an evaluation of the present ability of class members as pork producers. The next activity might be the comparison of their results in pork production with an ideal, with the results of superior farmers, and with those of average farmers. The natural process at this point is to consider further the factors that affect some of the specific results, such as number of pigs per litter or weight at 56 days, and what they can do to improve their results. Planning for evaluation of progress should begin at about this point. Several adult courses have organized sow testing associations to weigh pigs at 56 days as one evaluation of adult students' ability in swine production.

Many illustrations could be given of effective procedures of teaching, but if the procedures were reduced to their simple items, they could be summarized into the following general procedures:

1. The teacher and students work together democratically.
2. The teacher and students evaluate their present status and establish objectives.
3. The teacher and students, in working toward their objectives, discover problems to solve.
4. The teacher and students keep objectives meaningful and uppermost in their minds by planning and carrying out evaluations of their progress toward these objectives.
5. The teacher and students, by continuous planning, evaluation, and problem-solving, revise and expand their objectives as they progress.

ESSENTIALS IN EDUCATION

It is essential in education that the students develop desirable ideals, attitudes, interests, appreciations, understandings, and knowledge. It is desirable that students learn to think effectively and solve new problems efficiently. To be effective, education must also meet the needs of students. Education should assist the students in satisfying the following basic needs or desires:

1. Approval and affection from friends and family.
2. Social and economic security.
3. Self-confidence and independence.
4. Recognition and confidence from other persons in their group, class, and community.
5. New experiences.
6. Activity and recreation.
7. Body health.
8. Health habits and practices.
9. Safety.
10. Wholesome relations with the opposite sex.

Do the general procedures described in the preceding section meet these essentials of education? It is granted that the suggested procedures in teaching agriculture will not meet all the essentials of education, but education in agriculture is not all of education. The general procedures suggested will assist in developing desirable interests because the instruction starts where the students are, at their points of interest.

PROBLEM-SOLVING

In using the generalized procedures described in the preceding section, it is apparent that much of the instructional time in class, on the farm, or in an agriculturally oriented business is used in solving problems. Since problem-solving is so important, it will be discussed in some detail.

Value—Good teaching in agriculture is based to a considerable extent on problems that become meaningful because of the supervised occupational experience programs of the students.

Problem-solving procedure is recognized as being an effective means of developing and securing desirable learning. It stimulates interest; develops thinking ability; and helps students to evaluate, draw inferences from, and make decisions essential to the solution of, a problem.

It is usually conceded that facts gathered because they are necessary to the solution of a problem are more permanently learned. Problem-solving provides abundant opportunity to draw inferences from data. No amount of learning of facts for future use can provide this type of experience. Problem-solving provides opportunities for thinking, and people learn what they do. Ability to think is not inherited. Some worry about the amount of information learned in problem-solving. They claim this is a slow way to accumulate facts. But Dewey states, "The assumption that information which has been accumulated apart from use in the recognition and solution of a problem may later on be freely employed at will by thought is quite false. The only information which otherwise than by accident, can be put to logical use is that acquired in the course of thinking."[2]

Solution of problems as a means of obtaining useful knowledge is our most efficient learning procedure. Memorization of facts does not usually lead to action, but the thinking through of problems encountered in planning often leads to action. Action creates further problems which require further thought and knowledge, because knowledge is the basis of thinking.

Some even claim that no learning of a desirable nature takes place without a real problem in which a student is interested. Often our teaching results in problem-solving, but problem-solving of an undesirable type. When we demand that students learn something in which they are not interested, we create a problem for the students—a problem of how to outsmart or circumvent the teacher. Some students become very proficient in solving this type of problem. Dewey indicates the value of problem-solving over our traditional methods when he says: "Because their knowledge has been achieved in connection with the needs of specific situations, men of little book learning are often able to put to effective use every ounce of knowledge they possess; while men of vast erudition are often swamped by the mere bulk of their learning, because memory, rather than thinking, has been operative in obtaining it."[3]

Problem-solving provides students opportunities to acquire attitudes conducive to the solution of future problems. These are attitudes of questioning, comparison, and doubt.

Chapman and Counts, in their book *Principles of Education*, indicated that teachers have been so impressed with the need of imparting information that they have studied and reduced to a fine art the process of cramming unin-

---

[2]Dewey, John, *How We Think*, Boston: D. C. Heath, 1933, p. 53.

[3]*Ibid*.

teresting material into passively resisting or passively assisting minds. The use of problems encountered through teacher-student planning eliminates this situation. The information necessary for solving a problem is interesting, and the process of learning is assisted by active, not passive, minds.

In our highly developed society, propaganda is poured forth upon a worker in agriculture from many sources. The ability to solve problems effectively provides those attitudes of mind which tend to immunize one against propaganda.

Much instruction provided through lecture, telling, and recitation is not geared to the level of understanding of the students. Problems encountered through teacher-student planning which are attacked by a teacher-student group must be geared to the level of understanding of that group. Much instruction is not realistic or meaningful to students. Problem-solving by a group utilizes the real experiences of the members of the group, thus making the instruction real and meaningful.

Problem-solving leads to action. Persons who assist in solving a problem or who solve problems themselves develop naturally the attitude of acceptance of information learned and the desire to carry information to the point of use in the supervised occupational experience program. Problems encountered through teacher-pupil planning and attacked by a class group are often better solved than problems which the individuals try to solve.

Ability to solve problems will offset habits and protect against conservative old age. If we wish to have a progressive population in agriculture, one which is capable of change, these persons must be taught to use creative thought.

Problems are incentives to learning. Educators recognize that interest is essential for learning, and many techniques have been suggested to teachers for motivating their students. Problems encountered through teacher-student planning provide their own intrinsic incentives. One of the intrinsic incentives of problem-solving is the pleasure of creative activity. Problem-solving puts the learning of information in its proper role as a tool and not as an end in itself.

Learning is directly associated with active participation. Anyone who has had the opportunity to watch students wrestling with problems they have encountered through teacher-student planning or through their supervised occupational experience programs cannot deny that the amount of active participation is much greater than is found in classrooms where the teachers tell the students what they think they should know.

Problem-solving develops democratic abilities. When adults or high school students are actively planning, judging, executing, and coming to conclusions regarding a common problem, a miniature democracy is created. In such a miniature democracy, there is an opportunity for many clashes of personality with real assumption of responsibility. The proper guidance of these clashes of personality can result in much ethical and moral growth.

Teaching students to think is one of the major aims of education. It is almost universally true that the farmers and off-farm workers in agriculturally oriented businesses who are most efficient and successful are the best thinkers.

Those who pass by problem-solving in teaching assume that they are able to select the essentials in agriculture which students need to know and that students will retain what they are taught. But true agricultural education means a different thing. The changes in agriculture are rapid. The problems of the future will not be the same as the problems we face or the problems our fathers faced in agriculture.

If public school departments of agriculture cannot give their students the ability to solve the problems they meet, they are not providing agricultural education. "Problem-solving is one of our traits which most clearly separates us from the lower animals," so let's teach problem-solving and use problems in teaching.[4]

Definition of a Problem—A problem is a life situation which creates a difficulty or a state of suspense, confusion, and doubt. It requires thinking in its solution and not merely the finding of facts in a book. This is the distinction between a question and a problem. "What are the steps in the McLean County System?" is a question. It is not a problem. "Why is the McLean County System effective?" is a thought question. It requires some thinking and approaches a problem, but it is not a life situation. A problem presents a life situation that requires thinking or the use of facts in its solution. A teacher and students planning together may decide to consider how to manage hogs in order to keep them as healthy as possible. This would be a real problem. To solve this problem would require the finding of facts and the evaluation of these facts in terms of their situations.

Some have difficulty distinguishing between a project and a problem. Both are planned, purposeful, self-directed activities. The solution of a problem is primarily mental, although some problems do have manual aspects. A project involves both mental and manual activity. The principal difference is the scope of the activity. A project usually involves many problems. Most of the activities involved in a project occur on the farm or in an agriculturally oriented business. The activities involved in a problem may occur either in the classroom or on the job. Farming and other occupational experience programs are excellent sources of problems.

Types of Problems—Problems are usually classified by the type of thinking required in their solution. The problems encountered in teacher-student planning are usually *creative*. Creative problems require students to apply what they know to specific situations. They involve the use of facts and the evaluation of these facts as they pertain to a specific situation. Creative problems involve the highest type of thinking, and they are the type of problems an agricultural worker meets every day.

When students recognize a creative problem, the teacher's task is to guide them in discovering whether they have sufficient facts and sufficient skill in using these facts to find the answer to the problem. One way of doing this is to ask the group members what they need to know and do to solve the problem. This kind of question will usually bring out several *inductive* problems. Inductive problems require the discovery of unknown facts and principles. In

---

[4]Griffith, Coleman R., *Psychology Applied to Teaching and Learning*, New York: Farrar and Rinehart, Inc., 1939, p. 37. By permission from Rinehart & Company, Inc.

inductive thinking, we start with observed effects and work back to causes. The best inductive problems usually result from observing effects in a supervised occupational experience program and trying to discover their causes. Another good source of inductive problems is the analysis of past experiences to discover why observed effects happened. A group may also wish to consider a typical situation and try to anticipate the effect.

In the solution of a creative problem, decisions often have to be made requiring judgment as to the best procedure to follow in a particular situation. This is the *judgment* problem. Its solution answers the question of which, what, or how much. The solution of a judgment problem involves deductive thinking. This is a weighing of principles or facts as they apply to a set of conditions. An example of a judgment problem might be: Should the students in a class hedge in the commodity market at this time?

In actual practice, we often have problem situations that are a combination of inductive and judgment problems—problems that require both the discovery of principles and facts and the development of decisions or judgments regarding the use of these facts.

The fourth type of problem is the *reasoning* problem. It is the type of problem usually found at the end of chapters in texts on mathematics. It is the type of problem that the lay person thinks about when a teacher mentions problem-solving. A reasoning problem is similar to a judgment problem in that both involve deductive thinking.

Logical thinking is involved in the solution of a reasoning problem. The problem is solved in a series of steps. The correctness of each step can be proved. The final conclusion or proposed solution cannot be proved immediately. It is necessary to try out the proposed solution or conclusion to determine whether it is correct.

An example of a reasoning problem is: How many tons of hay can be stored in a barn of a specific size?

Use of Various Types of Problems—Farmers and off-farm agricultural workers encounter creative, inductive, judgment, and reasoning problems daily. They need training in solving all types of problems. Teacher-student planning usually results in creative problems, but in order for teachers and students to solve these creative problems, facts and principles must be discovered and skill in making decisions or judgments must be developed. Teachers need to guide their students toward the consideration of good inductive problems and good judgment problems in the process of solving their creative problems.

Formulation of Problems for Class Use—The first step in problem-solving is agreeing upon an objective through teacher-student planning. The objective may then be stated as a creative problem. This creative problem is then analyzed so that the factors to be considered in its solution may be discovered. This analysis will create many detailed creative, inductive, reasoning, and judgment problems.

A good problem-solving procedure usually involves:

1. Locating and defining a problem so that it may be stated as a clear, simple question or series of questions that the students understand and want to answer.

2. Attempting a trial solution of the problem.
3. Deciding on references and other sources of information that may be helpful in obtaining additional information or in validating hypotheses.
4. Searching during a directed study period for information that will be useful in solving the problem.
5. Arriving, through group discussion, at the best possible solution or conclusion to the problem.
6. Considering how the decisions reached may be applied by the students.

In individualized instruction there will be many opportunities for individual problem-solving. Translating group decisions to individual situations calls for much problem-solving. Students need to be trained how to study and how to think for themselves. There are many individual problems which have to be formulated and solved.

Good problems to consider in class or with individuals should have the following characteristics:

1. They should be stated clearly.
2. They should be divided or combined until they are of the proper scope and difficulty.
3. They should demand thinking of superior quality.
4. They should be interesting to the students.
5. They should develop from the experiences of the students.

Students should share in formulating the statement of a problem. This will promote their understanding of the problem and increase their interest in its solution. In formulating a problem in class, the teacher may get ahead of the students. The teacher may be asking the students to determine how to hedge in the commodity market before the students have decided whether such a move would be wise. Using students in formulating and stating the problem will help prevent this situation.

Techniques in Guiding Problem-solving Activities—There are many techniques of analyzing and developing problem-solving activities. Two illustrations will be given. A teacher should use ingenuity in encouraging students to use different procedures in solving their problems. Variety of activity is necessary for continuing interest. The first illustration follows a relatively formal approach.

Objective—In a simulated situation, to handle a short and long hedge in the commodity market and to calculate accurately profits and losses, using accepted procedures.

Problem—Determining when to hedge in the commodity market.

For this problem it is assumed that all the students in the class are in off-farm agribusinesses where they need to understand hedging in commodities. It is also assumed that the students participated in determining the objective and in stating the problem.

The teaching procedure: The teacher asks the class members what they need to know and be able to do to determine when to hedge in the commodity market. The members of the class suggest the following questions.

1. What is the purpose of hedging?
2. What is a hedge?

3. How can a hedge make you money? Lose you money?
4. What does it cost to make a hedge in the commodity market?
5. What is the purpose of a long hedge?
6. What is the purpose of a short hedge?
7. When, in general, should hedges be made?

The teacher may then lead a discussion in which the class members would attempt to determine the answers to the questions listed. They may go through the entire list of questions before time is taken for supervised study to verify their answers, or they may desire to verify their answers at the conclusion of the discussion of each question. This preliminary discussion prior to the supervised study period is often labeled the *trial solution*.

During the supervised study, the students review references to find the facts about each question suggested. They consult experiment station bulletins, reference books, project-record books, lists of market prices on feeds, and other available sources of information.

One of the purposes of a *trial solution* is to develop interest which will promote efficient work during the supervised study period. Another purpose is to discover how much information the class members possess. There is no reason for students to study something they already know. With adult students it is often not necessary to have a supervised study period. Usually the experience of the adults is sufficient to answer a majority of the questions considered. Many teachers feed in the information needed to solve questions or to verify the experiences of the adults. Some teachers let adult students consider a question or problem until the next class meeting before a conclusion is reached. This period between classes is substituted for a study period during the meeting. Teachers of agriculture are probably missing many excellent opportunities for supervised study in adult classes, because many teachers have found supervised study periods very profitable in the teaching of such classes.

After the supervised study period, the teacher leads a discussion in an attempt to arrive at some conclusions. This discussion may indicate that some factors for which decisions have to be made have been overlooked. It may also indicate that the problem is more involved than first anticipated and that more study is needed before a decision can be reached. If this is the situation, additional time should be used for supervised study. Eventually the group members will reach some conclusions. The following conclusions might be the ones reached by a class:

1. Pigs will begin eating grain at about 10 days of age.
2. Corn and skim milk are available on the home farms.
3. Soybean meal is the most economical protein supplement.
4. Alfalfa pasture is available.
5. A mineral mixture of equal parts of finely ground limestone, bone meal, and salt is best.
6. Creep feeding pigs with a self-feeder is best.
7. Slopping pigs will not be used because of additional labor.
8. The pigs will be weaned at eight weeks of age.

Members of the class need to recall and evaluate the facts gained from reading references and from the exchange of experiences in order to make these decisions.

The conclusions reached may be copied in the students' notebooks. The objective and problem may also be copied in the notebooks. Notes taken during the discussions and during the supervised study periods should not necessarily go into the students' notebooks. Portions of these notes may be copied into their notebooks at the discretion of the students. In an adult class, the teacher often mimeographs the objectives, problems, and conclusions and passes out the sheets at the next class meeting.

The following illustration presents a more informal classroom approach to a problem.

The teaching procedure: The teacher asks questions of the class members, concerning their practices, past and present. Results from these practices are considered. The teacher then asks the class members to suggest how they believe the job should be done. Suggestions are usually listed on the board. Disagreements will usually develop in the class. Some discussion regarding these points of disagreement is desirable to see whether an agreement can be reached. The teacher must not allow the discussion to develop into too much of an argument. Points of disagreement may be indicated on the board for further consideration during the supervised study period. When the class has reached tentative conclusions and points of disagreement, the teacher should summarize the discussion and suggest which points need further verification and which points of disagreement need further study.

The teacher then assists individuals during the supervised study period. After the study period, the teacher leads a discussion to determine whether a conclusion can be reached. This discussion may also indicate the need for more study. Eventually, as in the other illustration, the group members should reach some fairly definite conclusions which can be copied into the students' notebooks. Both procedures are equally good, as are many other procedures for guiding a group in solving its problems. Many procedures should be used. One other procedure is to ask the students, after they have decided on a problem, how they want to proceed toward its solution. A group may decide that it has so little information that the most efficient procedure would be to have a supervised study period immediately. Many ideas on guiding problem-solving activities are contained in the literature on conference procedure and group dynamics.

In Form 4.1, a chalkboard technique for guiding a group toward the solution of a problem is illustrated.

Skills in Problem-solving—Solving problems as an individual or as a member of a group requires the mastery of many skills and abilities. Teaching students to solve problems efficiently also requires skill. Efficient problem-solving is essentially the scientific method taken from the laboratory and adapted for use in the classroom.

The scientific method intellectualized consists of the following steps:

1. Recognizing a problem situation.
2. Defining the problem.
3. Developing hypotheses regarding a solution.
4. Testing hypotheses and gathering data.
5. Revising hypotheses and testing revised or new hypotheses.
6. Forming a conclusion.

Form 4.1. Chalkboard Pattern for Solving Problems[1]

JUST WHAT ARE WE TRYING TO ACCOMPLISH?

(Right Now) 1. ______________________________

(Eventually) 2. ______________________________

	Facts	Possible Courses of Action	Decision
1.			
2.			
3.			
4.			
5.			
6.			
Etc.			

[1]Sutherland, S. S., *The Problem Method of Teaching in Vocational Agriculture*, p. 23. (Mimeograph.)

Problem-solving in a classroom consists essentially of the same six steps:

1. Recognition of a problem situation through teacher-student planning of objectives, and consideration of ways and means of meeting these objectives.
2. Definition of a problem through teacher-student analysis of the problem situation.
3. An attempt by the class members to solve the problem by pooling experiences and ideas.
4. Validation or disproving of the hypotheses suggested by the class. With high school students this job is done during supervised study periods.
5. A class discussion for the purpose of reporting the results of attempts to validate hypotheses. At this point, it may be necessary to revise hypotheses or state new hypotheses which must be validated.
6. Arrival at a conclusion to the problem by the class members, which is accepted by all the class members and which is based on all available facts.

If students are to solve problems efficiently, they need to develop the following understandings, skills, habits, attitudes, and abilities:

1. Ability to recognize problem situations.
2. Ability to analyze problem situations and define a problem or problems.
3. Ability to state a hypothesis regarding the solution of a problem.
4. Ability to work with others, in group situations, in the pooling of information and ideas in formulating hypotheses.
5. Ability to withhold final judgment regarding hypotheses until they have been tested and validated (attitude of flexibility).
6. Ability to revise or accept new hypotheses when the original hypotheses have been proved to be incorrect (attitude of open-mindedness).
7. Ability to weigh data supporting a hypothesis.
8. Willingness to accept conclusions supported by reliable and valid facts.
9. Ability to test and validate hypotheses.
10. Ability to work with others in testing and validating hypotheses.
11. Ability to use imagination in the development of inferences and hypotheses.
12. Habit of using the problem-solving method and emotional allegiance to it.
13. Conscious understanding of the method of problem-solving.
14. Ability to solve long problems as well as short problems.
15. Ability to collect information to solve a problem.
16. Ability to self-criticize (an attitude of detecting and correcting one's mistakes).
17. Ability to express ideas with precision and force.

18. Ability to understand a problem before an attack is made, or the habit of insisting upon knowing definitely what is to be accomplished.
19. Ability to generalize from the solution of a problem or series of problems.
20. Ability to develop new hypotheses from new data.
21. Ability to separate facts from opinions.
22. Ability to evaluate the problem-solving technique being used.

Students make the following mistakes when trying to solve problems by themselves or as members of a group:

1. A problem situation is not defined. An attack is made on a problem situation and not on a problem. This leads to confusion and argument. Objectives are not clearly thought through, and the attack on the problem is aimless or poorly motivated.
2. Hypotheses are treated as conclusions. Students have to be taught that it is necessary to validate hypotheses.
3. The distinction between opinion and experimental results is not clear. Some students accept unwarranted conclusions because they have not learned how to evaluate their information.
4. Some students give attention to impressing the group instead of to thinking about the problem.
5. Instead of thinking independently and constructively about the solution to the problem, some students give attention to those in the group who, they think, know the answers.
6. Some students are afraid of making mistakes during a trial solution.
7. Some students may tend to jump to conclusions.
8. Bias due to interests, first impressions which linger and influence later judgments, previous experience, emotional excitement, and self-interest affect decisions.
9. Some students hold opinions tenaciously because they are accustomed to them and have adjusted their mental life to them.
10. Some individuals enjoy argument, and they are willing to discredit or distort facts during an argument.
11. Some individuals focus their attention on proving the answers of others wrong instead of thinking constructively toward a correct solution.
12. Some individuals give chief consideration to exceptional facts and cases instead of attempting to discover or establish general principles.
13. Some students often accept premature conclusions not warranted by facts.
14. Some individuals are prone to be distracted easily from the main problem to others that unexpectedly arise.
15. Some individuals may magnify in importance facts which support their hypotheses.

Teaching Problem-solving—Students have to be taught good problem-solving procedure. There are many ways of doing this. Following are some possible methods:

1. An evaluation by students of their problem-solving procedure during the process of problem-solving and after the process has been concluded.
2. A discussion of what is good problem-solving procedure and the development of standards to follow.
3. A discussion of the abilities, habits, attitudes, understandings, and knowledge needed in problem-solving.
4. A discussion of common errors in problem-solving.
5. A discussion of how to collect information and validate hypotheses.
6. A discussion of types of information of the most value. Development in class of a "yardstick" for measuring the quality of data is often helpful. Experiment or research data would be rated as most valid. Data such as golf scores and number of fish caught would probably be rated as least valid.
7. A discussion of the value of being able to solve problems efficiently.

8. A discussion of the similarities between the scientific method and good problem-solving procedure.
9. A discussion of how to analyze a problem situation and state a problem.
10. A discussion of how to work with others in solving problems and how to develop standards.
11. The preparation of charts to hang in the classroom showing the steps in problem-solving, the standards for good problem-solving procedure, the standards for working with others in solving problems, a scale of quality of data, and so forth.
12. A discussion of how to express ideas with precision and clarity.

Leading the Discussion of a Problem—When a problem has been defined and stated, the teacher should ask the group members for possible solutions to the problem. It is usually best to obtain all hypotheses before a discussion is held regarding the merits and demerits of each hypothesis. If the students have no ideas regarding a solution, the teacher may suggest two or three possible solutions in order to stimulate thinking; if interest is high, it may be desirable to go immediately into a supervised study period. This procedure should be used with caution, however, because it is often difficult to judge the amount of interest present. The development of several hypotheses is a good method of increasing the interest of a class in a problem.

If only one hypothesis is suggested, the teacher may suggest additional hypotheses. A simple problem may bring forth a single hypothesis which is the correct solution to the problem. If this is apparent to all the students, it is not always necessary to validate the hypothesis through supervised study before a final conclusion is reached.

In the discussion of a problem, all students in a class should be encouraged to participate. One way of doing this is for the leader not to ridicule any answer or show in any way that a comment is incorrect. A leader should not allow the class members to criticize too severely the comments of timid class members. The teacher can usually entice timid individuals into a discussion by maintaining suspense regarding the solution to the problem. Suspense may be developed by maintaining doubt regarding the correct solution. All hypotheses suggested must be given equal consideration. A teacher must not give any indication of the correct hypothesis, or the most nearly correct, by facial expression or comment. Lancelot suggests: "Evidence presented for any given conclusion [should] not greatly outweigh that offered in support of any other. To this end the teacher may properly resort to the plan of calling upon the stronger advocates of the weak or incorrect views and opinions, and the weaker exponents of the things that are right. Or he may even help those who find the argument going against them, or perhaps put questions whose purpose is to bring to light weaknesses in the argument that seems to be forging ahead."[5] This is an excellent way of maintaining suspense, but it must be used with judgment. This type of discussion belongs in the trial solution, and it should not be continued too long or the discussion will become a true argument—one of the errors in problem-solving procedure. A teacher may maintain suspense by keeping the discussion balanced during the trial solution, but when the discussion approaches the level of argument, the teacher

[5]Lancelot, W. H., *Handbook of Teaching Skills*, New York: John Wiley & Sons, Inc., 1929, pp. 72–73. Used by permission.

should suggest that it is time to validate the hypotheses in a supervised study period. The teacher can also increase interest in a problem by calling upon those who are interested. Their interest may be caught by those who are less interested.

A TEACHER'S RESPONSIBILITY

Use a Variety of Methods—A teacher should endeavor to use a variety of methods of teaching. There is no one best procedure in teaching, but there are some desirable techniques to use. The reason for using a variety is to stimulate interest and to relieve daily routine. Some of the methods to use in teaching are:

1. Conference and discussion procedure in problem-solving.
2. Job instruction training in developing manipulative skills.
3. Visual aids.
4. Topical reports.
5. Student debates.
6. Demonstrations.
7. Laboratory activities.
8. Field trips.

Have Everything Ready—Before class time a teacher should have all needed equipment, supplies, illustrative materials, and other teaching materials in place. If a field trip is to be taken, it should be carefully planned, and all arrangements should be made in advance.

Provide for Teaching on the Job—Whenever possible, teaching should be done in situations similar to those the students are encountering in their work. In the past too much teaching in many schools has been confined to the classroom. *Teachers should use every opportunity to carry the instruction to the doing level.* Jobs such as working in a parts department ordering repair parts, selling ornamentals, checking test weight of grains being sold, running contour lines, terracing, and the like should be performed. *Students learn by doing.*

Provide Suitable Conditions—It is important to have the room well ventilated and adequately heated to help keep the students alert and to provide suitable conditions for superior thinking and desirable learning. Likewise, it is necessary to have the room well lighted and the students comfortably seated, preferably at a table.

Stand While Teaching—In teaching an entire class, it is generally best for the teacher to be standing in front of the group and in the vicinity of the chalkboard. Standing helps to keep a teacher alert, and it enables the teacher to use the chalkboard. In some situations, when group or individual instruction is used, it is desirable for the teacher to sit at a table with the group, going to the chalkboard when necessary to record information needed in making decisions.

Formulate and Select Approved Practices—An approved practice is a practice which has been tried and tested by experiment stations, agricultural businesses, or successful farmers in the community and found to be a desirable practice to follow. Practices such as analyzing the potential market and competitors before pricing an agricultural product in a retail outlet, weighing a litter of pigs at 56 days, weaning pigs at eight weeks of age, placing guardrails in the farrowing pen, and providing 1 square foot of brooding space for every two chicks are recognized as desirable ones to follow.

Approved practices should be formulated and selected as a result of instruction, and plans should be made by the students for putting them into action. Their adoption should come as a result of instruction. When this is done, the students will understand the *why* and *how* of using a particular practice. It is an undesirable educational procedure merely to hand out a ready-made list of approved practices for the students to follow. *Insofar as possible, the conclusion to each question discussed should be stated in terms of an approved practice to be adopted.*

Use the Chalkboard—At the start of a discussion the teacher may write the problem situation on the board. As the discussion proceeds, the teacher may record on the board certain findings or opinions of the students for use in arriving at what seems to be the best decision. When a conclusion is reached, it should be briefly stated and written on the board.

Encourage Students to Use Notebooks—In teaching high school students, the teacher may write on the board the conclusions resulting from problem-solving for students to copy into notebooks. Adult students may also take some notes of conclusions reached. They usually do not, however, take extensive notes, and they appreciate having someone in the class take worthwhile notes which may be duplicated and given to them at the next class meeting.

Encourage Participation by All Students—All students should be encouraged and stimulated to enter into the discussion. The teacher should be open-minded, never make fun of a student, give praise when it can be justified, and make everyone feel free to enter into the discussion. Even if the answer is wrong, a student will have gained from having had the opportunity to participate.

Avoid Questions Calling for "Yes" or "No" Answers—Teachers should endeavor to ask questions pertaining to *when, how,* and *why* insofar as possible. Such questions usually require much more thinking than those which can be answered by "yes" or "no." If a "yes" or "no" question is asked and answered in this way, it may be followed with "why?"

Provide for Individualized Instruction—If group members have been discussing problems of individual students, there should be some time allowed at the close of the discussion for the students to evaluate the conclusions reached in terms of their particular situations.

Provide for Learning by Doing—Whenever possible, provision should be made for the instruction to be carried to the doing level. If a problem being discussed is strictly managerial, plans should be made for the students to adopt the approved practices recommended. If the problem involves a manipulative skill, such as selecting a sample of milk to be tested for mastitis, the students should perform the skill.

TEACHING MANIPULATIVE JOBS

Manipulative Jobs—Manipulative jobs may be taught in combination with managerial problems, or they may be taught separately. For example, in dealing with the problem of how to adjust the timing on a tractor, there may be a number of questions pertaining to the problem which the students will need to study and discuss before actually performing the task. They may want to know when to time, what procedures to follow, what equipment will be necessary, etc. In this case, a discussion may be conducted pertaining to these problems before manipulative skills are developed.

Developing Manipulative Skills—The job instruction training method can be successfully used in teaching skills. The four basic steps in job instruction training, with directions for their execution, are as follows:

Step 1. *Prepare the Learners.*
Get students' complete attention on the job.
Find out what they already know about the job.
Get them interested in learning the job. Show its importance.
Place them in the correct position.

Step 2. *Present the Operation.*
Tell, show, illustrate, and question.
Take up one point at a time.
Stress key points.
Point out safe working habits.

Step 3. *Try Out Performance.*
Have the students perform the job.
Have them tell and show you.
Have them explain key points.
Ask questions and correct errors.
Continue until you know they know.

Step 4. *Follow Up.*
Put the students on their own.
Advise them clearly regarding what to do in emergencies.
Check their work on the job to make certain they are performing the job correctly.

Using Visual Aids—Using motion pictures, filmstrips, and slides is very desirable in developing manipulative skills. They show how to perform skills and apply safety measures, and they help in developing appreciations, interests, attitudes, and understandings. Ordinarily such aids are used just prior to a demonstration by the teacher. However, they may be used a second time, later in the teaching process, if the students cannot recall what they have seen.

PLANNING AND CONDUCTING A FIELD TRIP

Aims and Purposes—A field trip is one of the best devices to use in making the instruction effective.

1. It develops student interest.
2. It provides opportunities for gaining new experiences and information.
3. It provides opportunities for learning by doing—teaching on the job.
4. It relieves the monotony of classroom instruction.
5. It helps to develop understandings.

Planning a Trip—A field trip needs to be carefully planned, and suitable arrangements must be made in advance. The instructor should contact the farm, organization, or concern where the trip will be taken and make the necessary arrangements. This may mean a personal trip by the teacher in advance of the instruction, or it may be possible to make the arrangements by phone or letter.

When the trip is for high school students, proper arrangements should be made with the school administration and school staff. The school administrator should know where the students are at all times. Even though the administrator has given the instructor permission to take field trips whenever desirable, the administrator's office should be informed of the trip. If adult students are being taken on a field trip, the teacher should inform the administration and make arrangements for someone else to perform the work at the school.

If high school students are to miss any other classes, the teachers of these classes should be informed in advance of the trip, and the students should arrange to make up their work. Teachers of agriculture should be as considerate of the work of others as possible, and they should not often take students out of the classes of others.

(Photo from Jasper Lee, Mississippi)

Fig. 4.1. Students studying meats. There are many off-farm agriculture jobs in which knowledge and skills related to meats are important.

Preparing the Students—Before leaving on a trip, the teacher should hold a discussion with the students to consider the purposes of the trip and what will be expected of them: what they will see, what they should do, what experiences they should gain, and what should be the final outcome. This helps to create interest and understanding which should result in desirable outcomes.

Determining When to Take Field Trips—Insofar as possible, field trips should be taken in seasonal sequence and in connection with problems being discussed at school. The time to take a field trip to study cleaning seed at a grain elevator or castrating pigs is at a suitable time for performing such jobs. Other types of field trips may be taken at appropriate times.

Providing Transportation—When school buses are available for field trips, they usually provide the most desirable type of transportation. In this way the students are kept together. This saves time and lessens the chance of discipline problems and accidents.

Conducting a Field Trip—It is important to conduct a trip in a businesslike manner. The class should be conducted as a group from the time of leaving the school to the time of returning. The instructor is responsible for the group and should have the class under close supervision at all times. All students should conduct themselves in an orderly manner. It is essential that high school students get back to the school in time to clean up and to arrive promptly at their next classes.

Evaluating a Field Trip—The students who participate in a field trip should discuss the trip as soon as possible after the trip is completed. In this discussion, the trip should be summarized and appropriate conclusions developed. The students should also participate in evaluating the trip regarding its contributions to their purposes.

INSTRUCTION ON THE FARM OR JOB

Teaching on the job or the farm during a visit should exhibit the same general methods recommended for use in the classroom. The difference is that much of the teaching is individual. The teaching on the farm or job should develop out of, and be an extension of, the teaching done in the classroom, and vice-versa. Some problems encountered should be brought back to the classroom for more extensive and intensive consideration. The application of this theory requires planning. Planning for on-job instruction can usually be done in advance during classes. If the students request the consideration of problems during individual instruction, preventing the use of the time for follow-up of previous instruction, it may be that the instruction in the other phases of the program is not geared to the real interests and needs of the group.

CHAPTER

5

How to Plan for Effective Instruction

Effective Planning Essential—Many jump to the conclusion that planning in advance is unnecessary when the students are utilized in developing objectives, defining problems, and developing procedures for evaluating results. Actually, when teacher-student planning is used, the planning required of the teacher is more extensive and more necessary than in a teacher-dominated situation. The teacher must plan to be ready for more eventualities. The teacher also must plan how to encourage students to accept as much responsibility for planning as they are capable of handling.

COURSE OUTLINES

General Principles of Course Planning—The details of course planning are presented in the chapters on the high school program and in the chapters on agricultural education for young and older adults. The following discussion concerns the general principles of course planning.

If the general principles of teaching outlined in Chapter 4 are followed, the course outline will have to be based on the needs, interests, and abilities of the students. Teachers can anticipate the content of courses as they will probably develop through teacher-student planning if they will consider the following:

1. General type of farms and agricultural business firms in the community.
2. Enterprises of most importance in the community.
3. Level of efficiency in these enterprises.
4. Agricultural problems in the community, the state, and the nation.

The following guides are suggested for the evaluation of anticipated outlines of courses:

1. Content is based on occupational experience programs of students and community study.
2. Content is arranged seasonally.
3. Content is developed psychologically instead of logically.
4. Proposed content is of primary importance for the age level of the students.
5. Proposed content is educationally sound.

(Photo from Robert W. Walker, Pennsylvania)

Fig. 5.1. Effective teaching is dependent on effective planning.

Values of Course Planning—Some of the reasons why course outlines should be developed are:

1. To enable instructors to think through what they propose to teach and how they will teach it.
2. To enable instructors to prepare themselves for effective teaching.
3. To help instructors meet better the needs of the students.
4. To allow instructors to have a record of what has been taught.
5. To save time and inconvenience for instructors.
6. To help instructors avoid hit-or-miss teaching. (When planning is not done, some activities which should be taught may be overlooked and some which are not especially needed may be taught.)
7. To allow instructors to gain respect of students, school administrators, and supervisors.
8. To enable instructors to provide for individual differences.
9. To help instructors avoid *textbook* teaching.
10. To provide for seasonal sequence of teaching and proper coordination and integration of activities.
11. To provide for desirable learning and outcomes.
12. To insure definite objectives and desirable teaching procedures.
13. To insure an adequate supply of suitable reference materials and teaching aids.
14. To help develop the confidence of instructors.

The purpose of a course outline is to help the teacher in anticipating the total task for the year and in allocating time for various areas. It is not a blueprint of what must be done. It should be departed from if it seems desirable to do so. A record of the content covered during a year should be maintained, however.

PERFORMANCE OBJECTIVES

Development—An important task in planning for effective instruction is the development of performance or behavioral objectives for the instruction. Through the teaching process, performance objectives developed by teachers should become the goals of the students.

There are three parts to a performance, behavioral, or measurable objective. They are (1) the outcome statement, (2) the conditions statement, and (3) the criteria statement. The *outcome statement* describes the activity, knowledge, attitude, or other accomplishment being sought. The *conditions statement* describes the circumstances under which the outcome expected will be observed or measured. It should indicate the tools, equipment, and materials the student will have available, plus any other special conditions that will exist. The *criteria statement* describes the standards, the level, and the quality of the outcome being sought. This statement will indicate the acceptable level of attainment of the outcome being sought.

Following are a few sample outcome statements:

1. The student will clean and prepare metal for welding.
2. The student will plan a wiring system.
3. The student will calculate the time required to seed a field.
4. The student will write a plan on how to prepare a seedbed.

Following are a few sample conditions statements:

1. Given a 10-minute demonstration and using a wire brush and grinder.
2. After three class periods of instruction and given a problem farmstead.
3. Given a drill of a certain model and size and a field of a certain size following a demonstration by the instructor.
4. Given three periods of instruction on seedbed preparation and a problem field and crop.

Following are a few sample criteria statements:

1. The product of the student's work will be equal in quality to the samples prepared by the teacher.
2. The wiring system planned by the student will conform to the National Electrical Code and to local codes.
3. The calculation must be accurate to one decimal point.
4. The plan prepared shall meet the criteria developed for seedbed preparation in preceding class sessions.

The outcome statements, conditions statements, and criteria statements put together would result in performance objectives such as the following:

1. Given a 10-minute demonstration and using a wire brush and grinder, the student will clean and prepare metal for welding, and the quality of the

work will be equal to the sample pieces of metal prepared for welding by the teacher.

2. Given three periods of instruction on seedbed preparation and a problem field and crop, the student will plan the seedbed preparation needed that will conform to the criteria of seedbed preparation developed in the preceding class sessions.

Domains of Objectives—The outcome statements have been divided into three domains by Bloom, Krathwahl, Simpson, and others. The three domains are:

1. Cognitive.
2. Affective.
3. Psychomotor.

The *cognitive* domain involves the mental processes and activities. It includes knowledge, comprehension, application, analysis, synthesis, and evaluation abilities.

The *affective* domain involves attitudes and feelings and includes abilities related to receiving stimuli willingly, responding to stimuli, valuing certain things, organizing a system of values, and developing an internal consistent system of values.

The *psychomotor* domain involves manipulative skills and includes the abilities related to perception, the preparatory set or readiness response, habitual responses, complex motor responses, adaptation of motor responses, and origination of new motor responses.

Verbs for Writing Outcome Statements—Writing outcome statements requires the use of descriptive, action-designating verbs. It is advisable to keep in mind many of these verbs. Following is a partial list of verbs that may be helpful.

Knowledge

cite	list	recognize	state
count	name	record	tabulate
define	point	relate	tell
draw	quote	repeat	trace
identify	read	select	write
indicate	recite		

Application

apply	illustrate	practice	schedule
calculate	interpolate	predict	sketch
complete	interpret	relate	solve
demonstrate	locate	report	translate
dramatize	operate	restate	use
employ	order	review	utilize
examine			

Snythesis

arrange	create	integrate	prescribe
assemble	design	manage	produce
collect	detect	organize	propose
compose	formulate	plan	specify
construct	generalize	prepare	

Comprehension

associate	differentiate	express	predict
classify	discuss	extrapolate	report
compare	distinguish	interpolate	restate
compute	estimate	interpret	review
contrast	explain	locate	translate
describe			

Analysis

analyze	debate	distinguish	inventory
appraise	detect	experiment	question
contract	diagram	infer	separate
criticize	differentiate	inspect	summarize

Evaluation

appraise	estimate	measure	revise
assess	evaluate	rank	score
choose	grade	rate	select
critique	judge	recommend	test
determine			

DEVELOPING SHORT-TIME TEACHING PLANS[1]

Why Have a Teaching Plan?—The most effective teachers are those who develop teaching plans in writing and use them. Any teaching plan that is not flexible enough to meet changes necessary to make it workable is not properly organized.

Kinds of Teaching Plans—There is no one best type of teaching plan. In fact, the better instructors use a variety of plans in their teaching. The type of teaching plan to develop will depend on the problem and the general plan of teaching. Any type of plan should provide for the development of problem-solving abilities. Several types of teaching plans which have been and are being successfully used by teachers are given in the chapter.

Teachers Should Decide on a Plan—Before starting to develop teaching plans, teachers should decide on the general plan of teaching to use most frequently in securing desirable learning. Many teachers still use the job as the unit of instruction. Others prefer to use the problem. Either will give good results if properly developed. The teaching procedures are more important than the terminology used. Good teachers use problem-solving procedures regardless of the terminology they employ. A job is usually broader in scope than a problem, since it may include a number of problems. In many instances the teaching observed by the author has been very similar, regardless of whether the unit of instruction was designated as a job or as a problem, since both provided for problem-solving.

Scope of Problem—A problem selected as the unit of instruction for a particular period should be of sufficient scope and difficulty to be challenging to the students, should be true-to-life, and should provide for the development

---

[1]As referred to here, a short-time plan pertains to teaching a unit of instruction requiring one to five days to complete.

of desirable thinking and problem-solving abilities. But it should not be so comprehensive as to cause the students to tire of it before it is completed. Many teachers have found that four to six consecutive hours is about the maximum time that should be devoted in the classroom to any one problem.

What a Teaching Plan Should Include—A well developed teaching plan for a problem should be complete enough for a substitute teacher to use in carrying out supervised study and classroom discussions. It may well include items such as the following: (1) enterprise or unit, (2) problem area or topic, (3) situations to be dealt with, (4) teaching objectives, (5) typical problems of students, (6) teaching procedures, (7) laboratory equipment, (8) demonstrations, (9) list of teaching aids, (10) testing and follow-up, and (11) references. A teaching plan should pertain to a problem which the students need to solve, are interested in, and are capable of understanding and solving, and one which the students will have an opportunity to carry to the *doing level*, preferably in connection with their supervised occupational experience programs. The first example illustrates a teaching plan for a managerial problem in an ornamental horticulture course. The teaching plan outline may also be used in other types of agriculture courses.

• • •

TEACHING PLAN

I. *Enterprise or unit:* Lawns.
II. *Problem area:* Maintaining a good lawn.
III. *Situation:*
    A. Several class members have jobs with ornamental horticulture firms.
    B. Most of the class members have lawn improvement projects.
    C. Most of the class members have lawns at home.
    D. Few of the homes of the class members have good lawns.
IV. *Teacher objectives:*
    A. To develop abilities in establishing lawns.
    B. To develop abilities in maintaining good lawns.
    C. To develop ideals, understandings, and appreciations for good lawns.
V. *Teaching procedures:*
    A. Determining present practices and past experiences:
        1. Lead questions:
            a. What kind of lawns do you work with in your job?
            b. What difficulties have you had with these lawns or with your home lawns?
            c. What improvements have you made on lawns?
        2. Anticipated responses:
            a.
            b.
            c.
    B. Determining goals and standards:
        1. Lead questions:
            a. Do you think you can satisfy your lawn customers at present?
            b. What are the qualities of good lawns? (Go on a field trip to observe good and poor lawns.)
            c. What kind of lawn would you like to be able to develop?
        2. Anticipated responses:
            a.
            b.
            c.

C. Identifying and defining problems:
   1. Lead questions:
      a. What difficulties will you have to overcome in developing the kind of lawn you would like to produce?
      b. What do you need to know and do to develop the kind of lawn you would like to produce?
   2. Anticipated responses:
      a. How should I grade lawns?
      b. How should I prepare the seedbed?
      c. What are some grass varieties I could use, and what are some of their advantages and disadvantages? What mixture should I use?
      d. How should I fertilize lawns? What would be the cost?
      e. When should I seed lawns? What would be the cost?
      f. How should I mow lawns?
      g. How can I control common lawn weeds? Insects and rodent pests?
      h. Should I use top dressing after the lawn has been established?
      i. Under what conditions should I sod lawn areas? What would be the cost?
      j. When should a new lawn be started?

D. Trial solutions of problems suggested by students.
   (For each of the questions suggested by the class, ask the class to give hypotheses regarding the answer. Discuss hypotheses briefly until the need for supervised study is apparent.)

E. Supervised study to collect information necessary for validating or revising the hypotheses developed during the trial solutions.

F. Concluding discussion:
   1. Lead questions:
      a. What hypotheses were correct?
      b. What hypotheses need revision?
      c. What approved practices for maintaining lawns have we developed?
   2. Anticipated responses:
      a.
      b.
      c.

G. Evaluation and application:
   1. How shall we evaluate our ability to use the approved practices developed?
   2. How shall we evaluate what we have learned?
   3. What plans do we need to make for adapting the approved practices developed to our particular situation?

VI. *Equipment needed:*
   A.
   B.
   C.

VII. *References:*
   A. Mich. Ext. Bul.—"Landscaping the Home Grounds."
   B. Missouri Cir.—"Development and Care of Lawns."
   C. Michigan Ext. Bul.—"Ant Control in Houses and Lawns."
   D. Farmers' Bul.—"Planning and Care of Lawns."

• • •

Daily Plan—The preceding plan was a teaching plan. It was not a daily plan. A teaching plan may require from one day to as much as a week to complete. Teachers need additional daily plans if their teaching plans last for more than one day. The daily plans needed in addition to the teaching plan may consist of a notation on the teaching plan of the stopping place plus a few notes regarding the method to be used to relate one day's work to the next day's work.

Teaching (Lesson) Plan Components—This chapter presents examples of teaching plans. Following is an outline of the important components of teaching plans.[2]

I. *Title:*

II. *Situation:*

The situations or conditions being encountered, as you see them, by the students or the community.

III. *Instructional objectives:*

What you want to accomplish. What you want the students to be able to do, under what conditions, using what criteria or standards of performance.

IV. *Teaching materials:*

What teaching materials you will need to teach the lesson.

V. *Teacher preparation needed:*

What skills you will need to develop or review before teaching the lesson. What knowledge you will need to obtain. What arrangements you will need to make before teaching the lesson.

VI. *Student references needed:*

What books and bulletins you will need to make available.

VII. *Teaching procedures:*

A. Preliminaries—roll checks, announcements, and so forth.

B. Introduction

How you will get the interest of students, motivate students, and determine the present situation.

C. Presentation

How you will help students determine goals. How you will help students define problems. How you will help students discuss problems (trial solution). How you will help students obtain needed information and skills.

D. Summary or conclusions

How you will help students reach conclusions and plan the next steps.

E. Evaluation and follow-up

How you will determine whether the objectives of the lesson have been accomplished.

Plan Covering Minimum Essentials—Experienced teachers may have their general plans of teaching so well established that it is not necessary to make detailed plans covering all activities. These teachers may develop plans covering only the minimum essentials for the instruction. While a teacher needs to think through all steps in the instructional process previous to the time of teaching, it may not be necessary to write out all of the steps in a teaching plan. This plan may include only the major items, such as the name of the problem area, objectives, problems or questions, and references. Teachers, however, should have in mind techniques to follow in creating interest. A written plan should not become so cumbersome as to consume too much time in preparation.

---

[2]Adapted from mimeograph used in the Department of Agricultural Education, Texas A & M University.

• • •

TEACHING PLAN

(Covering only the minimum essentials)

I. *Unit:*
II. *Problem area:*
III. *Objectives of teacher:*
  A. To develop desirable interests, ideals, and attitudes regarding______.
  B. To develop understandings regarding______.
  C. To develop abilities such as______.
IV. *Steps in teaching:*
  A. Survey present practices and past experiences.
  B. Select goals regarding what the students and the teacher want to accomplish.
  C. Define goals.
  D. Compare present and past results with goals developed.
  E. Determine what will need to be done in an attempt to reach goals.
  F. Determine approved practices required to accomplish goals.
V. *References:*
  A.
  B.
  C.

• • •

Probably an ideal teaching plan in agriculture contains not only a plan for teaching but also some agricultural information in outline form. A standard-size, three-ring notebook may be used very advantageously for this. On the left-hand page may appear the plan and on the right-hand page the notes on the agricultural information involved. These notes give the instructor a guide to follow in leading the discussion and prevent the leaving out of some points which might otherwise be overlooked. The teacher may divide the sheets used for plans and notes with a perpendicular line, leaving a space to the right of this line for additional information or for changes which he/she may care to make.

Teaching Plans for Manipulative Skills—In teaching manipulative skills, the teacher may develop teaching plans using the four following steps:

1. Prepare the learner.
2. Present the job.
3. Try out the student.
4. Follow up the instruction.

The plans should be sufficiently written out to indicate what the teacher plans to do under each step. The teacher may develop a job breakdown by dividing the plan sheet into two columns, one for the "important steps" and one for the "key points," as illustrated in Form 5.1.

Form 5.1. Job Breakdown

Name of Job ______________________

Important Steps (What you do)	Key Points (How you do it)
1.	
2.	
3.	
4.	
5.	

EXPLANATION OF TEACHING PLANS

To facilitate the use and understanding of the teaching plans presented on the preceding pages, a discussion of each major part of the plans will follow:

Enterprise or Unit—The term "enterprise or unit" is used as the heading for teaching plans because all content in agriculture may be classified as either enterprises or units.

Problem Area—A problem area is a subdivision of an enterprise or a unit. It indicates an area which may contain many problems, but it is small enough in size to be attacked by a class group. It is important not to subdivide an enterprise or a unit into too many problem areas or too few problem areas. Most enterprises or units may be divided into 10 to 12 problem areas that are of satisfactory size and scope. Another useable criterion for determining whether a problem area is of satisfactory size is the time needed to teach the area adequately. If a problem area requires less than one day to teach, it is probably too small. Problem areas should reflect the major activities involved in an enterprise or a unit. When a unit or an enterprise has been divided into the correct number of problem areas, the problem areas do not overlap to any great extent. Notice in the sample teaching plans presented earlier that the problem areas are stated as activities or they imply activities. See Chapter 13, "How to Develop Courses of Study," for examples regarding how to subdivide enterprises and units into problem areas.

Situation—The heading "situation" in the teaching plans refers to the situation as the teacher sees it. The statements under the heading are the opinions and statements of the teacher. The teacher's analysis of a situation before the determination of teaching objectives may help the teacher in establishing more realistic objectives for teaching.

Teacher Objectives—Often teachers become confused regarding teacher objectives and the goals and standards which result from teacher-student planning. The goals and standards which result from teacher-student planning are an outgrowth of group thinking in a class. Teacher objectives are the objectives of the teacher which are placed in the plan prior to its use in the classroom. The students do not participate in developing teacher objectives.

The teacher objectives and the situation statements are for the guidance of the teacher in determining teaching procedures.

Teaching Procedures—Under the heading "teaching procedures," the teacher places the lead questions for use in developing or guiding the progress of the class.

Determining Present Practices and Past Experiences—Often teachers call the first step in their teaching procedure an "interest approach." Many interest approaches, however, involve the determining of present practices and past experiences. Therefore, it seems advisable to give the first step in the teaching procedure as descriptive a name as possible. Also, the term "interest approach" is applicable to other situations in the teaching procedure. For example, in the sample teaching plans presented, one of the headings is "trial solution." A primary objective of a trial solution is to develop interest in the solution of a problem. Therefore, a trial solution could also be called an interest approach. Since the term "interest approach" is not very descriptive and may be used in more than one place in a teaching plan, the author prefers to use more descriptive terms for his headings instead of the general term "interest approach."

Most of the major headings under teaching procedures have two subheadings. They are "lead questions" and "anticipated responses." Lead questions are the questions which the teacher asks the class in order to initiate discussion. Anticipated responses are the responses expected from the class. Some beginning teachers feel more secure when they try to anticipate the responses they will receive from their lead questions. Most experienced teachers do not have to put in writing their anticipated responses.

Determining Goals and Standards—When members of a class determine present practices and past experiences, they usually determine "where they are." Class members, however, do not usually have many problems until they determine where they want to go or what they want to do. For example, persons are not concerned about road conditions until they decide to take a trip by automobile to a certain destination. They then become concerned about road conditions. Until students have developed goals and standards by which to measure progress toward their goals, they do not have problems.

It cannot be assumed that students do not have goals before they come to class. It is helpful in a teaching situation, however, to clarify and emphasize goals and standards. The process serves to help identify and define problems, and it helps to emphasize the importance of problems. When a teacher asks the members of a class group what their problems are in a problem area, they often present few or no problems. The teacher can motivate the identification of problems by first determining with the class the goals and standards for the problem area.

Identifying and Defining Problems—After the students in a group have determined "where they are and where they want to go," they are in a position to determine the problems which they are likely to encounter in progressing from "where they are to where they want to go." The anticipated responses under this heading in the sample teaching plans are the problems which the students have or anticipate.

Trial Solution—After the problems in a problem area are identified, the next logical step is to select a problem and attempt to solve it. In order to increase interest in the problem, it is usually wise to attempt to solve the problem with the knowledge and information which the class group possesses. If the members of the group can determine the answer to a problem, it is not necessary to have a supervised study period for that problem as a means of obtaining an answer to it. A trial solution often uncovers considerable differences of opinion regarding the correct solution to a problem. These differences of opinion motivate study during a supervised study period. Often teachers follow a trial solution of a problem with a supervised study period to find answers and solutions to the problem. A teacher may, however, want to conduct a trial solution on several problems before a supervised study period is allowed. The best technique depends on the size of the problems being discussed.

Supervised Study—A supervised study period is conducted for the purpose of collecting the information needed to solve the problems which were discussed during the trial solution period.

Concluding Discussion—In the concluding discussion, conclusions are reached regarding the problems discussed in the trial solution period. If valid conclusions and solutions are not obtained, another supervised study period is probably needed.

Evaluation and Application—In agriculture courses, the students learn by doing. If they cannot put into practice what they have been studying in class and if they cannot evaluate their ability to use what they have learned, much of the value of the class will be lost. A good teacher realizes that unless some plans are made for evaluating and applying what has been discussed in class, the carryover from the class work to real-life situations may be negligible.

Other Headings—A teacher may want to include other materials in the teaching plan, such as equipment needed for special activities or particular references which may be helpful during the supervised study period. A teacher may also wish to include a written test or other evaluation device as a part of the teaching plan.

DEVELOPING SOURCE UNITS

Definition and Use—Source units are collections of instructional materials assembled in advance by a teacher for the major divisions of the course outline. One of the difficulties of teachers in planning for effective instruction is the preparation of teaching materials that may be used in a flexible manner to meet emerging needs and developing interests of students. Source units provide the flexibility needed in planning for and anticipating these emerging needs and developing interests. A source unit provides a number of ideas and instructional materials for a major topic or problem area which may be used at any level of instruction. For example, there may be a source unit on operating a parts department in an agricultural machinery firm which may be used as a source of ideas and instructional materials whenever this topic is taught at any level.

A possible outline for assembling materials in a source unit is as follows:

1. Suggested objectives.
2. Approved practices to be developed.
3. Typical problems and concerns of students.
4. Possible kinds of activities and experiences.
5. Teaching aids and devices.
6. References for students.
7. Possible means of evaluation.

Short-time teaching plans which have been used may also be filed with the appropriate source unit.

A good source unit, an extensive collection of teaching materials that may be used in developing a short-time teaching plan, contains many more ideas than should be used at any one time with a class. Source units are added to from year to year as the teacher gains experience and secures new ideas for teaching the various units.

• • •

SOURCE UNIT ON LAND MANAGEMENT SERVICE

The *objectives* of a course or unit developed from the source materials that follow might include several or all of the following objectives:

1. The ability to sell land management services.
2. The ability to increase crop yields.
3. The ability to use soil conserving practices.
4. An appreciation of the value of grasses and pastures.
5. An appreciation of the value of tile drainage.
6. The ability to use better tillage practices.
7. The ability to keep and use accurate records of soil management practices.
8. The ability to control nutrient losses due to leaching.
9. The ability to reduce soil losses due to wind and water erosion.
10. The ability to replace nutrient losses due to crop removals.
11. The ability to devise suitable rotations.

Possible Problem Areas

Some of the problem areas that might be included in a unit on land management services are:

I. Introducing and developing the unit.
II. Demonstrating soil testing techniques.
III. Developing soil maps for farms.
IV. Increasing crop yields with fertilizers.
V. Selecting fertilizers to apply.
VI. Maintaining soil fertility.
VII. Selecting conservation practices to use.
VIII. Using crop rotation.
IX. Maintaining soil tilth.
X. Conducting tissue tests.
XI. Planning soil management programs for farms.
XII. Planning transition periods.

Typical Problems and Possible Activities

I. Introducing the unit and developing a unit outline.
   A. Typical problems of students.
      1. What are the lowest and highest yields known for the different crops grown in the community?
      2. What are good yields for the various crops grown in the community?
      3. What are desirable crop yields for the farm being managed?
      4. What do we need to know and do to obtain these yields?
      5. How can we measure progress in obtaining these higher yields?
      6. What problems are we likely to encounter in obtaining higher yields?
   B. Possible activities.
      1. List on the chalkboard the lowest and the highest yields for the different crops grown in the community. The yields for the community, county, and state might be compared.
      2. Ask enrollees to bring in data regarding yields of farms being managed.
      3. Elect committees to assist in the further detailed planning of the course.

II. Demonstrating soil testing techniques.
   A. Typical problems of students.
      1. Why do we test soils?
      2. What do soil tests show?
      3. How many soil samples are needed, and where should they be taken?
      4. How should soil samples be taken?
      5. How many soil samples are needed, and where should they be taken?
   B. Possible activities.
      1. Ask one of the enrollees to bring soil samples to class to be tested.
      2. Demonstrate the tests for lime and for phosphorus.
      3. Place the results of the demonstration tests on the chalkboard.
      4. Ask the enrollees to bring soil samples from their own farms the following week.

III. Developing soil maps for farms.
   A. Typical problems of students.
      1. How can a permanent record be kept of the location of each soil sample?
      2. What records are necessary in a soil fertility program?
      3. What is a land-use map?
      4. What should such a map show?
      5. What use could be made of such a map?
      6. What shading, coloring, and lettering should be used on a soil map to represent various soil conditions?
      7. How can a soil map serve as a guide for future cropping and soil conservation plans?
   B. Possible activities.
      1. Draw fields on the board and plot the locations where the soil samples should be taken.
      2. Distribute sample copies of soil maps and records which farm managers have used.
      3. Provide class members with blank soil maps on which they are to develop their own maps.

IV. Increasing crop yields with fertilizers.
   A. Typical problems of students.
      1. What kinds and amounts of fertilizers should we apply?
      2. If we apply these fertilizers, how long will the soil remain at its peak production?
      3. What are the ingredients of commercial fertilizers?
      4. What elements are necessary for plant life?
      5. What elements can we supply from the farm?
      6. What elements are abundant in the soil?

7. What elements do we have to buy?
8. What fertilizers contain these elements?
9. What nutrient elements will be removed by a rotation? In what amounts?
10. What nutrient elements will be lost by leaching? In what amounts?

B. Possible activities.
1. Analyze tags on commercial fertilizer bags and determine the amounts of fertilizer to apply, as shown by soil tests.
2. Observe the appearance of various types of commercial fertilizers.
3. Observe the results of fertilizer applications by holding a meeting of the class on a farm where various types and amounts of fertilizers have been used.
4. Visit a fertilizer factory.

V. Teaching aids, references.
A.
B.
C.
D.

VI. Possible evaluation activities.
A.
B.
C.
D.

• • •

Source units may be developed for any teaching unit and are not limited to managerial enterprises or shop units.

Keep a File of Source Unit Materials—A filing system may be developed for the source units in which a separate folder is used for each one. For example, there may be a unit on selling chemical fertilizers which will be properly labeled on a folder in the filing cabinet. Then as suitable materials become available on this activity, they may be filed in this folder. This material may be used when the teacher has time to develop, or more fully develop, a source unit on selling chemical fertilizers.

Many teachers have discovered that an efficient way to file a source unit is in a manila folder with separate sheets of paper devoted to (1) suggested objectives, (2) approved practices to be developed, (3) typical problems and concerns of students, (4) possible kinds of activities and experiences, (5) teaching aids and devices, (6) references for students, and (7) possible means of evaluation. Having each major heading on a separate sheet of paper provides space for additions to the source units as a teacher gains experience. Filing in a manila folder provides an opportunity for filing ideas and materials in back of a source unit until the teacher has an opportunity to add these materials to the source unit itself.

CHAPTER

6

How to Provide Career Education in Agriculture

INTRODUCTION

As a result of the impetus of recent legislation, vocational and technical education in agriculture is being offered from kindergarten through the thirteenth and fourteenth grades and in adult education. The education in agriculture at the elementary school level is to provide awareness and orientation experiences helpful in the developmental process related to making career choices. The education offered in junior high school, and in some cases the tenth grade, is to provide exploration and basic vocational education in the total field of agriculture to help students make decisions relating to whether or not to prepare for a career in production agriculture, agribusiness, and renewable natural resources. If the decision is to prepare for a career in agriculture and renewable natural resources, the exploration and orientation in agriculture is for the additional purpose of helping a student decide for which occupational cluster in agriculture to prepare.

OCCUPATIONAL AWARENESS AND ORIENTATION

Purpose—The choosing of a career in production agriculture, agribusiness, and renewable natural resources or the rejection of a career in these areas is a developmental process. It begins at the kindergarten level or earlier and continues throughout life. As with other types of education, early exposure is important if wise decisions, intellectually developed, are to be achieved.

Helping kindergarten and elementary school children to become aware and to learn progressively more about the world of work in agriculture and renewable natural resources is becoming increasingly important as our society becomes more complex. Kindergarten and elementary school children in earlier periods of time had ample opportunities to become aware of, and to be oriented to, the world of work in agriculture. They could learn about the world of work in production agriculture, agribusiness, and renewable natural resources by watching.

The farmer today is far removed from most children. Also, many jobs in agriculture are no longer performed on the farm and often are not visible to children. An occupational awareness and orientation program for agriculture and renewable natural resources attempts to make the whole world of work in agriculture and renewable natural resources visible to children in an organized and systematic way.

Making the world of work in production agriculture, agribusiness, and renewable natural resources visible to children is necessary because youth in America are being separated from the world of work at the elementary level, and they often develop negative biases relating to work, especially work in agriculture and renewable natural resources. There is much in production agriculture, agribusiness, and renewable natural resources that will appeal to and meet the needs of many persons if they become aware of the opportunities for work in this area.

A program to introduce children to such work in an organized and systematic way is essential. If a program is not provided, many persons will never, in our modern complex society, become aware of the world of work in agriculture and renewable natural resources. If they do become aware of this area of work, their limited knowledge and understanding of its characteristics and opportunities will prevent them from giving it serious consideration or will produce negative biases relating to it.

An occupational awareness and orientation program for kindergarten and elementary school children should do the following:

1. Make children aware of the many types of jobs in agriculture and renewable natural resources.
2. Make children aware that jobs in agriculture consist of more than farming.
3. Make children aware that some jobs in agriculture and renewable natural resources require little education and preparation and that some jobs require much vocational and technical or professional education.
4. Make children aware that different jobs in agriculture and renewable natural resources require workers with different talents, abilities, attitudes, and characteristics.
5. Make children aware of the environment in which different jobs in agriculture and renewable natural resources are performed.
6. Make children aware of the unique satisfactions that may be obtained from various jobs in agriculture and renewable natural resources.
7. Make children aware of the contribution that work in agriculture and renewable resources makes to the general welfare of society.
8. Provide elementary school teachers with a vehicle or "core of content" for teaching and making meaningful mathematics, English, and other content areas.
9. Provide children with opportunities for learning by participating in "hands-on" experiences.
10. Provide children with opportunities to communicate with adults in the world of work in agriculture and renewable natural resources.
11. Provide children with opportunities to make their schoolwork realistic, relevant, and enjoyable.

12. Provide children with opportunities to develop self-awareness regarding their attitudes and abilities as they relate to the characteristics and expectations of the world of work in agriculture and renewable natural resources.
13. Provide children with opportunities to learn about the world of work in agriculture and renewable natural resources in ways appropriate to their individual stages of development.
14. Assist children in assessing tentatively their abilities and limitations for various jobs in agriculture and renewable natural resources.
15. Provide children with an understanding of the dignity of work in agriculture and renewable natural resources and the understanding that agriculture performs a useful function.
16. Provide, when children are at an early age, accurate information about the world of work in agriculture and renewable natural resources.

Content—The content of an occupational awareness and orientation program in agriculture should attempt to introduce children, in ways appropriate to their age level, to the total spectrum of jobs in production agriculture, agribusiness, and renewable natural resources. It should provide "learning-by-doing" experiences, to create awareness and understanding and to provide a vehicle for the fundamental skills of learning. The content should not have as its primary purpose the development of job skills or abilities.

In planning an awareness and orientation program for the world of work in production agriculture, agribusiness, and renewable natural resources, the teacher should provide experiences to create awareness and understanding of work in the following areas:

1. Agricultural production.
   a. Animal science.
   b. Plant science.
   c. Farm mechanics.
   d. Farm business management.
2. Agricultural supply and service.
   a. Agricultural chemicals.
   b. Feeds.
   c. Seeds.
   d. Fertilizers.
3. Agriculture mechanics services.
   a. Agricultural power and machinery.
   b. Agricultural structures and conveniences.
   c. Soil management.
   d. Water management.
   e. Agriculture mechanics skills.
   f. Agricultural construction and maintenance.
   g. Agricultural electrification.
4. Agricultural technology.
5. Agricultural product processing and marketing.
   a. Food products.
   b. Non-food products.
6. Ornamental horticulture.
   a. Arboriculture.
   b. Floriculture.
   c. Greenhouse operation and management.
   d. Landscaping.
   e. Nursery operation and management.
   f. Turf management.
7. Agricultural resources.
   a. Forests.
   b. Recreation.
   c. Soil.

   d. Wildlife.
   e. Water.
   f. Air.
   g. Fish.
   h. Range.
8. Forestry.
   a. Forests.
   b. Forest protection.
   c. Logging.
   d. Wood utilization.
   e. Recreation.
   f. Special products.
   g. Forest technology.
9. Applied biology.
   a. Laboratory animals.
   b. Zoo animals.
   c. Birds.
   d. Parks.
   e. Environmental quality.
10. Agricultural, other.

Role of Agricultural Education—At the kindergarten and elementary school level the agriculture teacher will do little direct teaching. The teaching will be done by kindergarten and elementary school teachers. If the kindergarten and elementary school teachers are to do a good job, they must receive much assistance and encouragement from professionally prepared agricultural educators. Some school systems will provide an agricultural education supervisor or consultant. Other school systems may assign this duty as part of their workload to one or more of the agriculture teachers in the high schools.

The professional agricultural educator will need to do the following:

1. Plan and conduct a program to interest administrators and elementary teachers in an awareness and orientation program for the world of work in production agriculture, agribusiness, and renewable natural resources. This program needs to emphasize how an awareness program would help the teachers in their teaching of the fundamental tools of learning and how it would help the students.
2. Assist elementary school teachers in planning an awareness and orientation program.
3. Provide resource units or plans which elementary school teachers might use.
4. Provide multimedia resource materials.
5. Locate and secure workers in agriculture to serve as resource persons.
6. Plan and conduct field trips.
7. Plan and provide "hands-on," "learning-by-doing" experiences.
8. Serve as a consultant to elementary school teachers.
9. Serve as a special teacher for selected activities.

Kindergarten and elementary school teachers welcome this kind of assistance from agricultural educators. They usually want to include this type of content and experiences but lack the abilities and the time needed to implement their desires.

How to Teach—What activities to provide and how to teach are dependent to a considerable extent on the age level of the children. Remember that knowledge and understanding regarding jobs and work in production agriculture, agribusiness, and renewable natural resources need to be presented at simple or less complex levels for the younger children and then to be progressed to more complex levels as the children mature. This does not mean that the "hands-on" or "learning-by-doing" concept is not stressed at all levels. What is expected of children, however, must be scaled to their age levels and abilities.

For example, awareness experiences for the world of work in agriculture and natural resources would concentrate on the following large divisions in the early years of schooling:

1. Agricultural production.
2. Agricultural supply and service.
3. Agriculture mechanics service.
4. Agricultural technology.
5. Agricultural product processing.
6. Ornamental horticulture.
7. Agricultural resources.
8. Forestry.
9. Applied biology.

In the later years of elementary school, the subdivisions of these broad areas could be emphasized. Also, as the children mature, more emphasis may be given to the requirements and limitations of jobs, the abilities and attitudes needed, the characteristics of jobs, and the development of self-awareness of abilities and attitudes and how they correspond with requirements of various jobs.

In teaching children, it should be remembered that how they feel about a job is probably more important in helping them understand and become aware of the job than is their having cognitive knowledge about the job.

OCCUPATIONAL EXPLORATION

Introduction—Occupational exploration is usually provided at the seventh, eighth, and ninth grade levels. It is an extension of the occupational awareness and orientation program, at a more advanced level. It is designed to extend awareness and orientation into activities of an exploratory nature which will prepare a student to make decisions, based on firsthand knowledge and understanding, regarding the career cluster for which preparation will begin at the tenth or eleventh grade level.

Program—The program should emphasize "firsthand" learning by doing—experiences in the 10 areas and subdivisions of production agriculture, agribusiness, and renewable natural resources. The program should emphasize actual tryout experiences in various jobs to help the students develop a "feel" for each type of job. These tryout experiences may be provided at job sites, or they may be simulated at school. They should give the students opportunities to handle problems and situations that occur in various jobs.

Occupational exploration is to provide opportunities to develop a "feel" for a job through many different types of tryout experiences. The ways these tryout experiences may be provided are discussed in a following section of this chapter, "Occupational Awareness and Exploration Learning Activities."

(Photo from H. W. Gadda, South Dakota)

Fig. 6.1. The study of soils is important in production agriculture. It is also important for many students preparing for off-farm agricultural occupations. Such activities need to be included as a part of career exploration.

Role of the Agriculture Teacher—Exploration of the world of work in production agriculture, agribusiness, and renewable natural resources is provided in three ways:

1. Integration into the content of other courses.
2. Instruction in a separate course or as a part of an occupational exploration course designed to explore all career clusters.
3. Combination of the first two.

The best procedure is probably the combination of offering exploration of agriculture and renewable natural resources as a separate course and, at the same time, using it as a vehicle for making other courses more meaningful.

A teacher of agriculture should be assigned the job of providing exploration experiences in production agriculture, agribusiness, and renewable natural resources if these experiences are taught as a separate course or as a part of a more general course on occupational exploration. In addition, a teacher of agriculture should have responsibility for working with other teachers in integrating agriculture and renewable natural resource exploration into their teaching.

In working with other teachers, the teacher of agriculture should:

1. Help other teachers understand how occupational exploration in production agriculture, agribusiness, and renewable natural resources may be used as a vehicle for teaching the information and skills they are expected to teach.
2. Help other teachers understand how occupational exploration may be used to make their teaching more realistic, relevant, viable, and enjoyable.
3. Help other teachers plan and utilize occupational exploration activities in their teaching.

4. Provide consultant services to other teachers relative to occupational exploration in agriculture and renewable natural resources.
5. Provide resource materials.

OCCUPATIONAL AWARENESS AND EXPLORATION LEARNING ACTIVITIES

Many learning activities may be utilized to provide occupational awareness and exploration. The level of their use needs to be adjusted to the maturity of the students. Following is a partial list of learning activities and a brief discussion of each.

Role Playing—Role playing situations relating to jobs in production agriculture, agribusiness, and renewable natural resources are always popular activities for children. They may be varied to match the maturity level of the students, and they are excellent ways for students to develop a "feel" for a job.

Tryout Experiences—Because of the young age of the students there are many tryout experiences that must be avoided for safety reasons. However, portions of real activities which will give students a "feel" for a job may usually be found or simulated.

Demonstrations—Demonstrations may be used to create awareness of an occupation or to provide exploratory experiences related to an occupation. Workers in an occupation may be invited to demonstrate some portion of their job. Also, students with proper preparation may be utilized to demonstrate some portion of a job.

Development of Audio-Visuals—Students enjoy opportunities to develop audio-visuals relating to the world of work in agriculture and renewable natural resources.

Presentation of Radio and Television Programs—The preparation needed by students in order to present a radio or television program regarding the world of work in agriculture and renewable natural resources will provide many learning opportunities.

Dramatization—The use or development of occupational skits regarding agriculture and renewable natural resources is an excellent way of helping students understand the world of work in this area.

Supervised Visits—Visits to sites where work is being done is very important in awareness, orientation, and exploration programs.

Panels—Students enjoy being members of panels and will learn much about the world of work in agriculture and renewable natural resources in the process of preparing for a panel presentation. Adult workers also often prefer to be panel members rather than speakers regarding their jobs. It is often a good idea to use both students and adult workers on the same panel.

Surveys—Students enjoy surveying adult workers in production agriculture, agribusiness, and renewable natural resources regarding their jobs. It is a novel way for students to orient themselves or to explore occupations. The surveying may be done after school and on weekends. They can often survey family members.

Printed Materials—An abundance of printed materials has been prepared at the state and national levels regarding the job opportunities in agriculture. These materials should be secured in multiple copies. They may be used in many ways.

Interviews—An effective way to obtain firsthand information regarding the world of work is to invite both employers and employees to visit the class to be interviewed. The students should prepare interview questions in advance which could be provided to the adults to be interviewed. Time should also be provided for questions from students which occur to them as a result of the remarks of the person or persons being interviewed.

Correspondence—Students may learn much by corresponding with workers and employers in agriculture and renewable natural resources. Students prepare the letters in class and report answers in class. Correspondence is an excellent method for students to learn about jobs not present in the local community.

Scrapbooks—Elementary school children and junior high school students enjoy developing scrapbooks. They may be developed to illustrate and analyze jobs and clusters of jobs in agriculture. For example, the class could be divided into 10 committees, and each committee could select one of the 10 clusters in agriculture and renewable natural resources to illustrate and arrange in a scrapbook.

Quiz Contests—Quiz contests patterned after one of the quiz shows on television may be used to create awareness, orientation, and exploration of the world of work in agriculture and renewable natural resources. It is an enjoyable and painless method to orient students.

Interest Inventories—Several interest inventories in agriculture and applied biological sciences are on the market. These should be used to help students analyze their interests as they relate to the world of work in production agriculture, agribusiness, and renewable natural resources. The findings or results of the interest inventories should be discussed with the students. Their meaning or implication should be explored. The interest inventory by Walker and Stevens is often used.[1] Also, the interest inventory relating to ornamental horticulture is often used.[2]

Bulletin Board—An attractive bulletin board relating to the world of work in agriculture is an effective device. It is often desirable to have the students develop and maintain effective bulletin board displays. They learn more from this kind of participation than they learn from viewing a completed display.

Projects—Projects to simulate real jobs in production agriculture, agribusiness, and renewable natural resources are ideal for developing awareness or for exploring occupations. The difficulty of the project may be adjusted to the maturity level of the students. Following are a few projects that may be used:

---

[1]Walker, Robert W., and Glenn Z. Stevens, *The Applied Biological and Agribusiness Interest Inventory*, Danville, Illinois: The Interstate Printers & Publishers, Inc., 1971.

[2]Hamilton, William, *Ornamental Horticulture Interest Scale*, Agricultural Education Section, Purdue University.

Career Area	*Project*
Ornamental horticulture occupations.	Planting and maintaining a flower garden.
Agriculture supply and service occupations.	Purchasing and selling fertilizer and chemicals for a school garden.
	Cleaning and testing for germination the seed for a school garden.
Agricultural products (marketing and distribution) and processing occupations.	Distributing produce of a school garden. Processing produce of a school garden.
Agriculture mechanics occupations.	Constructing storage containers for produce of school garden.
Agricultural resource occupations.	Practicing environmental control of school land.
Forestry occupations.	Measuring tree production on school grounds.
Applied biology occupations.	Caring for laboratory animals.

Supervised Work Experience—An ideal tryout exploratory experience is a series of supervised work experiences. Such supervised work experiences, without pay, should be utilized to the extent that child labor laws and the Fair Labor Standards Act will permit. Careful study of such regulations will reveal many tryout supervised work experiences that are permissible.

CHAPTER

7

How to Teach Effectively

The general procedures outlined in Chapter 4 concerning what is good teaching should be followed in the teaching of high school students, post-secondary students in community colleges and technical institutes, and adult students.

KINDS OF INSTRUCTION

In general, there are three main kinds of instruction: (1) individual, (2) group, and (3) class.

Individual instruction should be used for students having problems not common to a group of students or to the class as a whole. For example, there may be a student in a class who has a job working on greens at a golf course. It may be that the student is the only one in the class with an occupational experience program of this kind. In such a case it would be unwise to expect the entire class to study the care of golf greens. Individual instruction should be used in such an instance. There must also be provisions made for students of different levels of ability. This will necessitate giving some students more individual help than is given to others in the class. It is also desirable to provide opportunities for students with greater abilities to do some advanced or additional work.

There are many opportunities for individual instruction through class instruction. In many instances an entire class will be working on a problem common to all members of the class. Individuals, however, will need to make suitable adaptations of the conclusions drawn by the class to meet their particular situations and needs. At this point there will be a need for some individual instruction to see that each member of the class decides on the best practices to follow. For example, the class may study a problem of one of its members to help him/her arrive at the best conclusion. This may be followed by all the members working out ways and means to solve their individual problems which may be similar to the one studied by the class.

Group instruction should be provided for groups of students having similar problems. This may apply to groups such as FFA committees, students having a group production project, students obtaining work experience in off-farm agriculturally oriented businesses, and other groups having common problems. In some instances there may be several different groups working in a classroom at one time. An example of this occurs in the fall of the year when groups of students planning the same kind of supervised occupational experiences are allowed to work together. There may be one group on working in a feed store, one on swine, one on dairy, one on experiences in farm equipment businesses, and the like.

Class instruction is most commonly used, since most students have problems related to the agricultural enterprises and businesses which occur most frequently in a community. These are the enterprises and businesses which in all probability will continue to be of major importance in the community, and they will probably be the enterprises and businesses in which the students will be engaged as adults. They will also be the enterprises and businesses represented in their supervised occupational experience programs. Many students who enter agricultural occupations do so in the area where they were raised; consequently, they need to develop abilities for the major agricultural enterprises and businesses in their area of the state.

A desirable guidance program is necessary to help students and parents understand the need for developing comprehensive supervised occupational experience programs in agriculture based on the major enterprises and businesses in their area of the state. If this guidance program is satisfactory, the instruction may pertain to many problems common to the class as a whole, which makes class instruction justifiable.

Whenever possible, it is desirable for an entire class to discuss the same problems. A conclusion drawn by the class members and the teacher should be much better than a conclusion drawn by any one individual. Such discussions stimulate interest and provide opportunity for much individual participation. As pointed out previously, there are many opportunities through class discussion for individual instruction. The teacher, in most instances, can do a more effective job of planning and teaching when class discussions are used.

FORMULATING GOALS

Goals are especially significant in connection with supervised occupational experience programs. Since these programs are recognized as forming the central core of the program in agricultural education, the attainment of the goals adopted in connection with the programs becomes an important basis for the instruction. Goals in connection with FFA activities are also especially desirable.

Occupational experience program goals are of value in the following ways:

1. They challenge students to achieve progressively higher records from year to year.

2. They stimulate students, under the guidance of their instructor, to make an intensive study of acceptable levels of attainment.
3. They motivate students to ask questions on how to attain goals.
4. They motivate students to keep accurate and complete records.
5. They help students evaluate progress.

The setting of goals is also desirable because students must study and evaluate standards now being reached. Standards should be studied and suitable goals anticipated by a teacher previous to the time goals are set.

The setting of desirable goals in connection with supervised occupational experience programs is discussed further in Chapter 14.

SELECTING AND DEFINING A PROBLEM

Importance—Defining a problem is the backbone of the teaching process, since it provides the teacher with an opportunity to create interest, develop a feeling of need for the instruction, and give other direction to the learning activity. It is a strong determining factor in the final outcome of the instruction.

Selecting Problems—In teacher-student planning for the purpose of selecting problems, the teacher should keep foremost factors such as individual interests, needs, and abilities and the supervised occupational experience programs.

Teachers should assist their students in defining their problems so that the problems are:

1. Clearly stated and easily understood.
2. Appropriate in scope and difficulty.
3. Related to supervised occupational experience programs.
4. Challenging.

Every member in a class should participate in the selection of a problem. It is democratic procedure; it enables each one to feel a part of the class in planning instruction which will best meet individual needs. Desirable teacher-student relationships, essential in effective teaching, are developed through such democratic procedures.

Defining the Problem—The following illustration for developing a problem in dairying has been drawn from a vocational education in agriculture for farming class and represents a procedure which has been successfully used by many teachers in all types of public school agricultural education courses. The procedure would be the same for teaching a problem or problem area in an off-farm agricultural occupation class.

Teacher: "Students, as you know, we have been studying problems in the dairy enterprise and have just completed the problem of *How to Care for a Cow and Calf at Calving Time*. What is the next problem in dairy which we have listed, Mary?"

Mary looked at her notebook.

Mary: "*How Shall I Feed My Cow for Milk Production?*"

Teacher: "That's right, but Ronald says he believes his cows have mastitis.

He would like to determine whether his cows do have mastitis. What do you think about considering Ronald's problem first and then taking up the one on feeding? A number of you have dairy production projects, and consequently, this problem is one in which you are all interested. All of you are testing in our D.H.I.A."

The class agreed to study this particular problem on mastitis but to follow it immediately with the one on how to feed for milk production.

The instructor wrote the problem on the chalkboard: *What Is Mastitis, and How Can I Test for It?* The students copied this in their notebooks.

In further preparing the students and creating interest in the need for the instruction on mastitis, the teacher asked questions such as the following:

1. How many of the students in this class have had any experience with mastitis?
2. Do you know of any farms where mastitis has occurred?
3. Have any of your cows been tested for mastitis?
4. Have you ever assisted in collecting milk samples to be tested for mastitis?
5. How many cows do you have in your farming programs? How many other cows at home?
6. Would you like to have your cows tested for mastitis?
7. Do you think testing cows for mastitis in this community would be a desirable community service to include in our FFA program?
8. How much financial loss may be expected when a cow has mastitis?

The instructor then proceeded.

Teacher: "*What should we know or be able to do if we are to solve this problem?* How about you, Ronald? This is your immediate problem. What questions come to your mind?"

Ronald: "How can you detect mastitis?"

The teacher wrote this question on the chalkboard, and the students copied it into their notebooks.

Fred: "What causes mastitis?"

Teacher: "Do you drink milk at home?"

Jean: "Is it safe to drink milk from a mastitis infected cow?"

The teacher continued to write questions on chalkboard, and the students copied them into their notebooks.

Teacher: "Jean raised a question concerning the drinking of milk from a cow infected with mastitis. Does that raise another question in any of your minds?"

Dale: "How do you collect a milk sample for testing?"

Ronald: "How often do you have to test for mastitis?"

Richard: "How can you control mastitis?"

Teacher: "If cows have mastitis, would you shoot them?"

Everybody laughed.

Anna: "What do you do with cows infected with mastitis?"

Teacher: "There are a number of approved practices we will want to follow in finding out whether Ronald's cows have mastitis."

Fred: "What approved practices should we follow?"

The teacher listed all the questions on the chalkboard, and the students recorded them in their notebooks. There may have been one or two questions which were not needed in solving the problem, but the students were exhibiting a high degree of interest, and the teacher felt justified in listing the questions because they related to the problem. There was a total of eight questions, which is not enough to hinder effective instruction.

The discussion presented here was based on the needs, interests, and abilities of the students. It was a problem common to the group. It was clear, concise, and understood by all members of the class. Approximately 25 minutes was used in defining this problem. The teacher did not permit a dull moment or a waste of time. In a few instances the teacher, through suggestive questioning, drew desirable questions from the class. There were no discipline problems; such problems seldom occur when the students are interested in, and busy at, worthwhile activities. There was just enough humor in the presentation to keep the students alert and interested.

The teaching plan developed for use in teaching this problem was similar to the one, "How can I maintain a lawn?" presented in Chapter 5.

THE TRIAL SOLUTION

The next step in the teaching process and for the illustration presented in preceding paragraphs is the trial solution regarding the questions raised. Conflicting hypotheses should be solicited regarding answers to the questions that have been raised. Another procedure is to try answering each question through class discussion as it is raised by a class member.

The teacher should summarize the discussion and point out the conflicting hypotheses and the questions not answered at the conclusion of a trial solution. The teacher may ask the students to suggest sources of information in verifying their hypotheses and validating their conclusions. Selected references should then be listed on the board. This listing on the board may not be necessary with advanced students.

Essentials in Summarizing a Trial Solution—In preparing students for verifying hypotheses and collecting information during their supervised study period, a teacher should observe the following precautions in summarizing a trial solution:

1. It must be clear.
2. It must be concise.
3. It must prepare the students for effective learning.
4. It must be interesting.
5. It must provide for student participation.
6. It should be placed on the chalkboard.

Too often an instructor summarizes hurriedly before a supervised study period, without placing anything on the chalkboard, and then asks the students whether they have any questions. When no response is received, the instructor assumes that the summary was adequate. The result is that some students do not read half of the references and perhaps select the wrong pages in the ones they do read. The students cannot be criticized for this when the summary has not been clear and concise. When a summary is developed by the teacher and the students, placed on the chalkboard, and copied into the notebooks by the class, everyone may be held responsible for knowing what to study.

When to Summarize a Trial Solution—There is no definite time during a class period to summarize a trial solution and begin the supervised study. A trial solution should be continued as long as it is fruitful. The summary of a trial solution may be near the beginning of the period, in the middle, or near the end of the period. It should never be attempted just at the close of the period when only two or three minutes are left. Hurried summaries often result in very ineffective outcomes. A trial solution is usually followed by supervised study and the concluding discussion. These steps will be discussed in the following sections of this chapter.

SUPERVISED STUDY

Importance of Directed Study—Under the supervised study system in agricultural education, the students study in the classroom under the guidance and direction of their teacher. The classroom is a desirable place for study because the laboratory, equipment, and reference materials are there, and the study is directed by the teacher of agriculture. Such study may be made very effective and result in desirable learning, or it may become a daily grind with very little constructive value. The results obtained in supervised study periods depend on the techniques used in directing the learning process. Many students, when entering high school, have very little idea of how to study effectively and how to solve problems. Consequently, they need considerable direction in evaluating materials, forming judgments, and reaching desirable decisions.

Some of the purposes of directed study in agriculture courses are:

1. To create and maintain *conditions conducive to effective learning*.
2. To provide for systematic and organized study under the guidance of a teacher.
3. To teach students how to study, read effectively, evaluate materials, draw inferences, and arrive at decisions in problem-solving.
4. To provide an adequate reference library and other aids, with suitable materials readily accessible to the students under the guidance of the teacher.
5. To provide opportunity for the teacher to counsel students and give aid when necessary.
6. To develop desirable teacher-student relationships.

What Should the Teacher Do?—A teacher should always have a well developed teaching plan before class time so that full time may be spent working with the students during directed study. The teacher should avoid spending the period in preparing teaching plans, writing letters, and the like. Without direction, the students will often sit and dream, create disturbances, or study for some other class. A directed study period cannot be justified unless the teacher gives the students adequate supervision and direction.

During directed study, teachers should:

1. See that all students are supplied with adequate and suitable references, charts, maps, and the like.

2. Provide suitable working conditions for effective learning, such as a well lighted and ventilated room, plenty of references, good order, and quiet working conditions.
3. Counsel students concerning their problems and give aid when needed in developing abilities in problem-solving or manipulative skills.
4. Move about the room quietly, and speak softly when giving individual help to avoid attracting the attention of others and interrupting their thinking. (Some teachers talk so loudly when helping individual students that all the others stop to listen.)
5. Encourage everyone to sit in a comfortable, businesslike position for effective learning.
6. Teach students how to study, show them how to skim through materials and pick out main thoughts necessary in problem-solving, and show them how to read and interpret experimental data.
7. Show students how to assemble ideas and record brief reading notes of information needed in problem-solving.
8. Provide for individual differences.
9. Direct students to references they otherwise might not find or might waste time in finding.
10. Introduce new materials.
11. Stimulate and encourage students.
12. Assist students in interpreting data, words, or phrases.

Reference Materials—Before a class enters the room, it is generally desirable for the instructor to check reference materials available. The instructor should see that each student, during the supervised study period, has the use of one or two references. When possible, it is a good plan for the instructor to withhold a few references to supply to the more rapidly working students after they have finished the regular list. Students should also be encouraged to look up additional references because they will have to find their own reference materials when they leave school.

Teaching Students How to Study—It is always a difficult task for teachers to teach students how to study, because individual differences must be observed and much individual help must be given. Many students have been accustomed to "textbook instruction" and have no idea of how to skim through a number of references and pick out the main thoughts. During the first few days of a course, the teacher should spend considerable time in giving the students suggestions on how to study; the habits formed during this early period will probably continue throughout the course. Students must be trained to solve problems, because many of the jobs in agriculture are of a problem-solving nature. An agricultural worker must be able to cope with perplexing situations and to think through the best procedures to follow. Students must train themselves to concentrate, to study systematically, to evaluate information, to make inferences, and to draw conclusions.

The first part of the year, the teacher should review experimental data and show how to interpret results. The teacher may also read several paragraphs with the students and pick out the main thoughts, showing how to evaluate them and arrive at desirable decisions. Often a student reads page after page or sits and gazes at the page with no thought of the information contained. A teacher should observe each student's notes to see whether the main thoughts are being recorded. Students need considerable training in evaluating materials and in writing notes; otherwise, they may merely copy words from the references and waste much time doing it. Most notes should be brief and recorded in outline form.

After the notes are taken, the teacher should encourage each student to review them, to evaluate the different points, and to draw conclusions. Students may be encouraged to underline the main thoughts in their personal books.

• • •

DIRECTING STUDY[1]

Which one are you?

"GET BY" TEACHER	"WIDE AWAKE" TEACHER
Pays no attention to physical conditions: room stuffy, shades partly pulled down, students facing light.	Provides desirable conditions for study. Room as well lighted and ventilated as facilities will permit.
Makes indefinite assignment: so many pages to read. Students do not know exactly what is expected of them.	Makes clear, definite assignments. Students know what they are to do and why.
Looks up references after class starts. Loss of time and confusion prevail in getting down to business.	Looks up references before class begins. Students start to work without fuss or loss of time.
Has insufficient references and illustrative material at hand. Two or more students attempt to use same reference.	Has plenty of references and illustrative material for class.
Ignores discipline problems, unnecessary talking, distracting noises; disorder prevails.	Retains control of class. Everyone is busy. Order pervails.
Sits at desk. Tries to get the lesson before the students do. Prepares lesson for next class. Writes letters. Acts as a stationary police officer.	Moves about room. Observes and checks work. Discovers difficulties of students. Finds opportunities to be of help. Gives suggestions and assistance where needed.
Talks and visits with students too much, hindering study and distracting attention from work.	Is careful not to interfere with students' work. Moves quietly, speaks softly.
Pays no attention to methods of study used. Satisfied if student has book open. Disregards misspelled words and poor expressions.	Teaches students how to study. Shows them how to pick out main points and take notes. Encourages use of dictionary and correct expression.
Solves students' problems for them.	Gives help only when needed. Helps students to help themselves.
Makes no provision for individual interests and abilities of students. Capable students finish assignment quickly and waste time. Slow students do not finish work.	Gives supplementary work, additional reports, etc., to superior or experienced students.
RESULTS	RESULTS
1. Students form careless study habits, are inefficient, and depend upon others to solve their problems.	1. Students are able to think for themselves, independent, self-confident, and effective in meeting real-life problems.
2. Students call instructor an easy mark, agriculture course a "snap."	2. Students respect their instructor and agriculture course. Community realizes value of agricultural education.
3. Community loses faith in agriculture courses. Agriculture teacher out of a job.	3. Agriculture teacher continues on job or is advanced to a better one.

• • •

Giving Aid to Students Who Need It—Students should not be given aid unless they really need it. They should be trained to solve their individual

[1]Adapted from material prepared by L. L. Scranton and G. C. Cook.

problems as they will have to do in life. There are times, however, when students need help, and it is their instructor's task to determine when this is the case and to give them any aid that they may need. For example, in interpreting experimental data, it is often necessary for an instructor to help a student. Some students will require very little aid; others will need a considerable amount.

CONCLUDING A PROBLEM

After a study period, there should usually be a concluding discussion. This discussion is for the development by the class of conclusions to the problem being studied. These conclusions can usually be worded as approved practices. The class members should be asked at this time to think through how they can make use of these approved practices.

Sometimes in the discussion after a supervised study period, it may be found that no conclusions can be reached. If this is true because of a lack of sources of information, the teacher may have to supply the needed information, or the class may want to take on the problem as a project and try to find the answers. For some problems, no final answer can be given at the time. For example, the problem in a vocational agriculture for farming course might be: *When should I sell my hogs in order to hit the highest market?* This problem can be thought through to its logical conclusion, but only time will reveal the correct answer.

If a conclusion or conclusions cannot be reached because the class discovered during the study period additional factors that should be considered or additional questions that need answering, it may be advisable to have another supervised study period for the problem.

Teaching Plans—Sample teaching plans (sometimes known as lesson plans) are presented in Chapter 5. These plans illustrate desirable procedures and techniques for implementing the generalized method of teaching described in the preceding paragraphs.

STUDENT NOTEBOOKS

Why Have a Notebook?—A well kept notebook, containing selected up-to-date information, plans, and procedures for use in a student's supervised occupational experience program, should be very valuable to the student. It should be considered as a guide to action and should be more useful to the student than any other reference book which might be purchased because it was developed as a result of the study of many books, bulletins, and other reference materials.

No one can retain everything which is read or taught, such as how to operate certain laboratory equipment in an off-farm agricultural firm, how to care for the cow and calf at calving time, how to test various seeds, and the like. A student needs a suitable place to record this information.

Type of Notebook to Keep—A three-ring, loose-leaf notebook, with paper of the standard 8½" x 11" size, is the best type. It provides for the rearrangement of materials if necessary; other materials which may be added will probably be 8½" x 11" in size.

Separate Notebook for Agriculture—It is desirable to have a separate notebook for agriculture for several reasons:

1. When algebra, English, and other class notes are mixed with the notes on agriculture, it requires more time to locate and check through the agriculture notes.
2. A combination notebook provides insufficient space for notes on all courses.
3. A special notebook is more apt to be filed for future use.
4. When a separate notebook is used, it may be kept in the agriculture classroom.

Fig. 7.1. Student notebook in agriculture. Included are problem sheets, conclusion and student plan sheets, division tabs, forms for problem areas in each of the enterprises, inventory blanks, form for calendar of activities, form for long-time occupational experience program, and form for objectives.[1]

[1]This particular notebook is the *Student Notebook in Agriculture* and may be secured from The Interstate Printers & Publishers, Inc., Danville, Illinois.

What to Include in the Notebook—There are several items that should be included in every notebook. The following are suggested:

1. A calendar of activities.
2. A list of the enterprises and units to be studied during the year.
3. A list of the problem areas within each enterprise or unit.
4. Objectives for each enterprise or unit of work.
5. Objectives and standards of efficiency for each problem area.
6. Problems and questions for each problem area.
7. Approved practices agreed upon in class.
8. Reading, laboratory, and field notes; pictures and clippings.

9. Plans for the student's supervised occupational experience program, including budgets, financing, jobs to be done, methods of performing, and the like.
10. Division sheets with tabs.

Calendar of Activities—Each student should develop a calendar of activities for his/her supervised occupational experience program. Several pages may be provided in the notebook for the calendar of activities. The approximate date of performing each activity should be recorded. The student plans (see Form 7.1) should be transferred to the calendar of activities.

List of Enterprises or Units—Near the beginning of a notebook, there should be a table of contents listing the enterprises or units which are included in the course. A page number should be listed for each enterprise or unit. This listing of page numbers should be delayed until the end of the year.

Division Sheets—A notebook should contain a series of medium weight division sheets with tabs for each enterprise or unit included in the course. A tab provides a place for the name of the enterprise or unit. The body of a division sheet provides space for listing the name of the unit and the problem areas included.

Form 7.1. Sample Page from a Student's Notebook

I. *Enterprise or unit:* Swine. *Date:* March 1.

II. *Problem area:*[1] Selling swine feed.

III. *Objectives and standards of efficiency:*[2]

A. To develop the ability to advise customers on feed to buy for pigs until weaning so that the following efficiency standards may be obtained:
   1. Weight of 40 pounds per pig at 56 days.
   2. Ninety per cent of pigs saved until weaning.
   3.

IV. *Problems and some questions to consider in solving them:*[3]

A. How to feed pigs until weaning.
   1. When should customer begin feeding grain and concentrate?
   2. What supplements should customer feed?
   3. What kinds of pasture should customer use?
   4. What minerals should customer feed?
   5. What home feeds should customer use?
   6. How should customer feed: self-feeder, hand feeding, creep?
   7. Should customer soak the feed?

V. *References:*

A. Ensminger's *Swine Science*.
B. Farmers' Bulletins.

VI. *Home Assignments:*

A. Find out what feeds customers have available at home.
B. Discuss with feedstore managers the practices they use.

[1]Some may prefer the term "job" instead of the term "problem area."
[2]Developed through teacher-student planning and discussion.
[3]Developed through teacher-student planning and discussion.

Problem Areas—A separate page in the notebook should be used for each problem area. It should provide space for listing the name of the enterprise or unit, the problem area, questions to be answered in reaching a solution to the problem, reference materials, and home assignments. Form 7.1 is a sample page from a notebook of a student enrolled in an off-farm agricultural business course which illustrates how notes may be recorded for a problem area being studied.

Approved Practices and Individual Plans—The approved practices agreed upon at the conclusion of a discussion may be kept on a page or pages separate from the problem sheet. A page for approved practices and individual plans may be placed so that it is on the right-hand side of the notebook when the notebook is open. The problem sheet should be on the left-hand side of the notebook when it is open. Form 7.2 is a sample page from a notebook of a student enrolled in a vocational agriculture for farming course which illustrates how notes on approved practices and individual plans may be recorded for each problem studied.

Notes—The individual notes of a student should be kept on a page or pages separate from the problem sheet and the sheet for approved practices

Form 7.2. A Sample Page from a Student's Notebook Showing Approved Practices and Individual Plans (To Be Placed on Right-Hand Side of Notebook When Open)

Conclusions and Approved Practices Agreed upon in Class[1]	Student's Plans[2]
1. When to begin feeding grain. a. As soon as pigs will eat grain. b. Usually at about 14 days.	I will start feeding my pigs grain on March 10, when they are 14 days old.
2. Supplements. a. Skim milk—good when available. b. Reliable commercial mixtures with antibiotics added—good.	I will feed a commercial supplement containing antibiotics.
3. Pasture. a. Alfalfa high in protein, one of the best. b. Clover, rye, rape, and bluegrass—good.	Saturday, March 7, I will move my sow and her litter to alfalfa pasture.
4. Minerals. a. Always feed salt. b. Mineral supplement needed.	I will provide a mineral mixture and place it in a self-feeder.
5. Home-grown feeds that may be used. a. Shelled yellow corn. b. Coarsely ground wheat. c. Broken oat kernels.	I will place shelled corn in one compartment of a self-feeder, which will be located inside the creep.
6. How to feed. a. Creep feeding—good. b. Hand feeding requires more time. c. Soaking feed does not pay for labor. d. Keep water before pigs at all times.	I will build a creep in the shop. I also plan to build a self-waterer in the shop.

[1]Conclusions may result from class, small-group, or individual instruction.
[2]For student's supervised occupational experience and FFA activities.

and individual plans. The reason for this is that a student may take notes regarding comments made during the discussion or notes from his/her reading that are not concise or relevant to the solution of the problem being studied. The notes recorded may be worthwhile but may be excess baggage if placed on the sheet for approved practices or the sheet for the definition of the problem.

Notes recorded by students will be more useable if they are written in a legible manner and in outline form. Students should not be permitted merely to copy paragraph after paragraph into their notebooks. This is time consuming, requires considerable space, and stimulates very little thinking. Instead, the notes should be specific and tell how, when, or why.

Notes on the Concluding Discussion—The students should be trained to take brief reading notes on scratch paper and to list briefly what they think are the best answers to the questions, thus formulating decisions and conclusions during the supervised study period. These notes need not be kept in the notebook, as they may contain poorly written materials and other materials which are not needed for future reference. *Students should not let the notebook get bulky with excess baggage.*

When to "Fill In" Notebooks—It is best to have the class notes on approved practices placed in the notebooks during the concluding discussion. The reason for this is that the students arrive at much better answers, decisions, and conclusions to the questions being studied when they are developed as a result of the experiences of the class and the teacher.

Reading notes may be recorded during the supervised study periods. One of the reasons for the increased class time per week which is often provided for agriculture courses is to provide time for study in class, which includes the taking of necessary notes, under the supervision of the teacher.

Plans for Supervised Occupational Experiences—Either in the notebooks or in another suitable place, space should be provided for long-time occupational experience plans and specific plans for individual activities. Objectives, goals, budgets, methods of financing, procedures used in carrying out jobs, and final outcomes should be recorded in this space.

Keep Notebooks in Classroom—The best place to keep the notebooks is in the classroom. This is where they will be used except when the students need to take them home or to the job. A suitable cabinet for notebooks should be provided in a convenient place in the classroom.

TEACHING STRATEGIES (METHODOLOGIES)

Problem-solving techniques provide the framework for teaching both skills and cognitive abilities. However, within this framework many strategies or methods need to be employed to provide variety and maintain interest in the teaching-learning process.

Discussion Techniques—An important ingredient of many teaching-learning situations is group discussion. Discussion may be promoted in various ways.

Teacher as discussion leader. The most frequently used model is for a teacher to act as the leader of the discussion. The teacher may vary this method by asking two or more students to lead the discussion of a problem or topic.

Buzz and huddle groups. A class may be divided into buzz and huddle groups to discuss goals, to discuss possible solutions to a problem, or to develop a plan of action.

Each group needs a leader of the discussion and a definite assignment. The leader or the secretary of each group reports the results of his/her group's discussion to the entire class.

Listening team or process observer. The teacher may improve discussions and introduce variety into the teaching process by designating one member of the class, or a team of class members, to observe and listen to the discussion. The task of the observer or team of observers is to listen to the discussion and report periodically what is being accomplished. Discussion listeners may evaluate the discussion process or question the group to help the discussion move forward. Listeners may also be used to summarize the discussion periodically.

Recorder. The teacher may wish to facilitate discussion productivity by designating a person in the class to serve as a recorder. The recorder keeps a record of the issues discussed, the decisions reached, and the percentage of the group participating in the discussion. The recorder may be asked to report to the class periodically.

Resource persons. The teacher may provide variety and enhance effectiveness in the teaching process by utilizing resource persons in the classroom. Resource persons may be used to generate interest in a topic or to provide information needed in the solution of problems. It is usually advisable to involve resource persons in a discussion instead of asking or permitting them to lecture the class.

Lectures. Lectures are not an effective teaching strategy unless the class members are adequately motivated to seek certain types of information and recognize that listening to a lecture is an effective way of obtaining the information desired.

Panels. A small group of persons may be used to discuss a problem in front of the rest of the class. The panel members need to be selected because of their special interest in the topic or because of their special knowledge of the area. They need to have a moderator who is the leader of the discussion. Panel members should discuss the topic among themselves and not be permitted to give a series of short speeches. Often the entire class is permitted to enter the discussion once the panel has generated interest in the topic.

Symposium. Panels and symposiums are often mistaken for each other. A symposium is the presenting of various points of view on a topic by a series of speakers. It consists of a series of short lectures. It is not a discussion as with a panel. The chairperson may permit a limited number of questions after all speakers have presented their points of view. A teacher using a symposium needs to designate the speakers in advance so they will have time to prepare their presentations.

Colloquy. A colloquy involves the use of two or three resource persons, who may be class members. These resource persons are presented with a problem and are questioned by two or three designated class members. After the resulting discussion has generated sufficient interest, the entire class group may be drawn into the discussion.

Role playing. In role playing, selected members of the class are asked to accept certain roles and act out in a spontaneous situation a certain human relations incident. It is an effective way for students to understand the feelings and attitudes of others. It is also an effective procedure to translate an intellectual activity into both an intellectual and an emotional experience.

Dramatic skit. A dramatic skit or play may be used for the same purposes as role playing. The difference is that this is not a spontaneous acting out of roles. With a dramatic skit, the dialogue is written in advance and presented by the participants. The parts are usually read instead of being memorized. A dramatic skit may be used as an appropriate part of the total problem-solving procedure.

Brainstorming. Brainstorming is an attempt to solicit from a class as many hypotheses as possible for the solution of a problem. It is a creative effort. Hypotheses or creative solutions to a problem are not evaluated when presented. All ideas are accepted and recorded. Ideas are not discussed regarding their feasibility or value. Brainstorming is a variation in the discussion procedure and may be used, when appropriate, to release inhibitions of class members and to create interest.

Laboratory Experience—The use of laboratory experience is an important tool in the overall problem-solving procedure. Laboratory experience varies class procedure and is an effective teaching tool. It utilizes many senses and provides for physical activity. Laboratory experiences may be used to point up problems or to find out solutions to problems. Such experiences may be provided in classroom laboratories, in greenhouses, on land laboratories, and in the community.

Field Trips—Within the framework of the problem-solving procedure, field trips are an important ingredient. Field trips may be used to help students recognize and define problems. They may also be used as a source of information to solve problems. Field trips involve directed observations.

Demonstrations—The problem-solving procedure involves much more than discussion. It often requires the use of demonstrations. Demonstrations may be needed to teach manipulative skills, or to assist in gaining acceptance of new ideas or practices. This latter type of demonstration is called a "result demonstration" and the former, a "method demonstration." A demonstration of a certain skill in welding might be used to illustrate a method. A demonstration of the strength of a certain weld might be used to illustrate a result.

Visuals—Within the framework of the problem-solving procedure, visuals of all kinds need to be used, such as overhead projectors, chalkboards, pictures, movies, TV, real objects, simulation visuals, and so forth. Visuals may be used to help students recognize or define problems. They may also be used to provide the information or skill necessary for solving problems.

Tape Recorder—Audio aids are often an important ingredient of the problem-solving procedure. Sounds may be recorded with a tape recorder and used in the classroom. For example, certain malfunctioning sounds of machinery may be recorded and introduced in the classroom at the appropriate time. Sometimes it is not possible to get certain resource persons to meet with a class. Often it is possible to record their contribution in advance with a tape recorder.

Tests—Tests, written or oral, may be used as a teaching strategy instead of as a summative evaluation device. A short test with an immediate feedback may be used to stimulate interest in an area. When tests are used in this way, the students must understand that they are being used not for summative evaluation purposes, but for diagnostic purposes.

PROVIDING FOR INDIVIDUAL DIFFERENCES

Teachers of agriculture are cognizant of the fact that there are wide differences in ability among students. Some students are capable of reading materials, interpreting the information, formulating judgments, and arriving at sound decisions in a minimum amount of time. Others have a low reading ability which may be below the sixth grade level.

A variety of practices have been used by teachers in solving the problem of how to provide for individual differences. The following represent some of the practices which have promising possibilities:[2]

1. Organizing course materials around units or broad divisions which provide problems and experiences for the class as a whole, together with opportunities for individuals to make applications in solving specific problems in their own supervised occupational experience programs.
2. Encouraging each student to develop a supervised occupational experience program in keeping with his/her capabilities and opportunities.
3. Utilizing as assistants or in other ways in group instruction and laboratory work individual students who have special abilities, being careful not to exploit or favor them unduly.
4. Encouraging students with special abilities to probe more thoroughly into various problems or phases of the subject; utilizing results of these special studies by having the students contribute to the group discussion at appropriate times.
5. Making effective use of supervised study to render individual assistance and provide motivation to each student to achieve, in keeping with his/her level of development and capacity.
6. Planning highly individualized assignments with the students for certain phases of the course, in keeping with varying individual differences.
7. Utilizing home or job visits as teaching situations in which the instruction or other assistance is pitched to the appropriate level for the individual student.
8. Utilizing conference periods to individualize certain phases of instruction, in keeping with special interests and capabilities of the students.

Some students may be given a specific question to report on; others may be given additional references to read, experimental data to report on, and the

[2]Adaptation of material prepared by G. P. Deyoe.

like. Reports, however, should not be confined to those students with the higher levels of ability. There is much educational value to be gained through the giving of reports, and all students should have this opportunity. It develops self-confidence and abilities in speaking and in the organization of materials for reporting.

Developing Individualized Instruction—Individual problems not common to a class or even to a group of students should be handled through individualized instruction. The instructor should encourage students to select and list in their notebooks those problems developing from their supervised occupational experience programs that are not common to the class or to a small group within the class.

Students should then select their most pressing problems and determine the questions they need to study to solve them. As a student determines what seem to be the best answers to the questions, the answers should be placed in a notebook, and the teacher should check them and make any recommendations needed. The student should then make a final decision on how to solve the problems and develop a plan of action.

This method of dealing with individual problems may also be used in group instruction. Group members may sit around a table, planning ways and means of performing skills and solving problems. The students, as a group, should define each problem and list the questions they will study in developing a solution to the problem. The teacher should check the progress of the group frequently and guide the students in the selection of questions for study and in the selection of suitable references.

TEACHING DESIRABLE BEHAVIOR

Good teaching promotes desirable student behavior. Undesirable behavior may be caused by fundamental deficiencies in methods of teaching; therefore, when behavior problems develop, teachers should immediately examine the teaching procedures being used. However, behavior problems may also be caused by the treatment a student receives in other classes, at home, or in the community. If the causes of undesirable behavior are found outside the agriculture course, good teaching in agriculture will in time produce more desirable behavior. This is true unless the student is a psychopathic case. Even then, good teaching may improve the situation.

Much of this handbook is a description of techniques of good teaching. Repeating these techniques will not be attempted in this section. Instead, suggestions will be offered regarding the teaching of desirable behavior, for desirable behavior has to be learned and can be learned the same as any skill in agriculture. Suggestions will also be offered regarding "stopgap" procedures for handling emergency behavior situations.

Understanding Students—Teachers may create behavior problems by insisting on unrealistic standards that group members do not understand. They cannot insist on standards for individuals not acceptable or understood by the group. Teachers' first task in managing undesirable behavior is understanding students' conception and standards of behavior. Standards of behavior vary from community to community. Teachers have to know where the students are and start from there. One value of group and individual discussions regarding desirable and undesirable behavior is that they make the students conscious of their own standards. Once they are conscious of their standards, they may analyze them.

Teachers often mistake insolence, arrogance, impertinence, sauciness, flippancy, bluster, haughtiness, highhandedness, or an overbearing and domineering attitude as an affront to them personally. When teachers take these actions as personal affronts, it is an indication that they do not understand high school students. These actions may be caused by tensions in the students' environment. Punishment of these actions usually increases the tensions.

These attitudes and actions are symptoms and not causes. In medicine we hardly ever treat symptoms. Ignoring these behavior symptoms seldom makes the situation worse. Teachers need to discover and treat causes. Milton J. Cohler states, "Often apparent insolence is lack of acculturation. Teachers are usually people with middle-class backgrounds and values. People from different class cultures do not cherish some aims and mores teachers hold basic to good behavior. The problem is to acculturate the pupil to the values and methods of the school. Punishment for not having those values is not designed to make them appear desirable."[3]

Secure teachers do not take the actions of students as personal affronts; consequently, the only types of behavior which teachers must immediately divert or change by "stopgap" procedures are those that are objectionable to the other students. In a democracy, behavior of an individual cannot be allowed to interfere with the welfare of the larger group. When the so-called personal affront is eliminated as a behavior problem calling for immediate action, much of the undesirable behavior demanding "stopgap" techniques is also eliminated.

Realistic Standards—It is easy for teachers to insist on unrealistic standards. Often teachers unconsciously adopt the standards used in schools they have attended, or unrealistic standards develop gradually without their being conscious of them. Unrealistic standards of behavior may also develop because of a teacher's intense desire to improve the agriculture of the community, to win the chapter FFA contest, and so forth. Every teacher should periodically evaluate the standards he/she promotes. Each standard should be evaluated in terms of what effect it is having on the students and the agricultural education program. Teachers should consider what would be the result, both immediate and long-time, if a standard were modified or dropped.

Teachers may learn a considerable amount about managing behavior by observing good supervisors handle workers in an agribusiness. Most good supervisors keep the morale of their workers high. This is sometimes done by ignoring a certain amount of horseplay among the workers.

Teachers' Understandings and Attitudes—Teachers often have to unlearn many of their understandings and attitudes regarding students' behavior. No

---

[3]Cohler, Milton J., "A New Look at the Old Problem of Discipline," *Education Digest*, Vol. 14, No. 4, pp. 1–4.

student is naturally bad. Undesirable behavior is learned. Desirable behavior must also be learned. It is futile to ask students to change their behavior immediately. Learning changes in behavior is gradual, the same as any other type of learning. Desirable behavior is learned through example, motivation, and practice.

Stopgap Techniques—Successful teachers are calm, dignified, and firm when managing behavior problems. They avoid anger and criticism. A behavior problem is often the result of tensions and anger on the part of a student. If the teacher becomes excited or angry, the situation is impossible.

Good rapport is necessary in teaching desirable behavior. The best way for teachers to establish rapport is by showing interest in students as human beings. Discussing a student's behavior in front of others is not conducive to good rapport. The other students nearly always take the side of the underdog. Discussions of behavior should be in private.

Teachers need to understand the futility of sarcasm, scolding, and insistence on apologies. They must train themselves to avoid the use of these ineffective procedures. Cohler states, "There is a 'law of parsimony' for dealing with disciplinary difficulties. If mere presence is enough, the teacher should do nothing. If an adominishing pointing of a finger is sufficient, do just that much. If the statement 'John' is also required, the teacher should limit the statement to the one word. If a long harangue is provided the students are rewarded by being informed that they have succeeded in upsetting the teacher."[4]

Most teachers can think back to their own school days and remember how ineffective the teachers were who scolded and harangued their students during class. Usually students become expert in instigating harangues from the teachers who resort to this practice. After all, they don't have to study while a teacher is engaged in such an activity.

Successful teachers minimize for the other students the undesirable behavior of an individual. One of the greatest mistakes in managing behavior in the classroom is the magnification of an undesirable action. Magnifying the action diverts the attention of others in the class from their true tasks. Undesirable action may also be catching.

Teachers should understand that they must be fair and that punishing the whole class for the misdeeds of a few is not being fair. Such punishment is often due to the inability of the teacher to discover the offenders. A sound principle to follow is to do nothing when not certain what to do. Having favorites is being unfair. Teachers constantly have to guard against this criticism.

Teachers may also use the following "stopgap" techniques:

Make a positive approach. Avoid suggesting misbehavior by pointing out what the students should not do. Parents soon learn that children often obtain ideas, which they would never have thought of themselves, through comments of what not to do. Threats are also in this category and should be avoided. When a teacher makes a threat, the students' curiosity will get the best of them, and they will have to test the teacher to determine whether the

---

[4]*Ibid.*

threat will be carried out. A teacher usually has to carry out any threat made. Threats invite trouble.

Study the seating of the class. If certain students seated near each other are potential sources of difficulty, separate them. Anticipate difficulties and prevent them. Stop the little things, but stop them as quietly as possible. Stop them by making a constructive proposal, such as giving the students new responsibilities, challenging them with a question, or asking them to do a chore. Avoid the use of *don't*. Vary your procedure of stopping the little things so that the students do not "catch on" to what you are doing.

Begin each class promptly and vigorously. Obtain the attention of the students before beginning a class discussion. Talk to the whole class at once and not to a series of individuals. Speak in an interesting tone of voice. Put some enthusiasm behind your voice. Avoid distracting mannerisms and idiosyncracies. Watch yourself in a mirror and see whether you have such mannerisms.

Give the students responsibility for the success of a course, a class, or an FFA meeting. Develop the "we" feeling. State your directions in the "we" form: "We will need to do this next," or "We need to perform it this way." Cooperation will be much better than if you use the "I" form: "I want you to do this next," or "I want you to perform it this way." Commands can create antagonism.

State your questions before calling a student's name. If the name is spoken first, the rest of the class may have a tendency to relax. Call first on those most interested. Their interest may spread to those less interested.

Stand up through most of the class period. It is usually not desirable to remain seated during much of a class. A standing teacher sees clearly what each student is doing. A teacher should try to hear and see all that is happening in a classroom.

Keep the room comfortable. Interest cannot remain high if the room becomes stuffy or hot. Present a pleasing appearance and attitude. High school students are greatly affected by the appearance of a teacher. Courtesy by a teacher is essential. Students respect and try to please the courteous teacher. Courtesy begets courtesy.

These immediate "stopgap" reactions to emergency situations will not eliminate the necessity of studying the causes of undesirable behavior. Symptoms will not disappear until causes are removed. Undesirable behavior may often be diverted, however, while a teacher determines and removes the underlying causes.

CHAPTER

8

How to Teach Young and Older Adults

INTRODUCTION

The principles of teaching are the same for adults as for high school students. Some of the details may differ. For these general principles, the reader should review Chapters 4, 5, 6, and 7 before reading this chapter.

Adult Learning—It is desirable for an instructor, in preparing to teach adult classes, to have some understanding of how adults learn. Young adults are at their prime in their ability to learn. As adults age, total ability to learn may decrease gradually. All factors involved in the ability to learn do not increase or decrease at the same rate, however. Judgment and reasoning ability develop slowly and reach their peak rather late in life. Their decrease is also slow. The ability to think through problems often increases with age, as long as a person is in good health. Creative imagination also apparently does not deteriorate appreciably with age when a person remains in good health. The ability peak in creative imagination is probably around 40 years of age. Those mental abilities most closely associated with physical functions deteriorate most rapidly. Perception abilities are the first to go. Hearing and sight among older adults are often impaired, especially sight after the age of 40. This means that the visual materials used in teaching must be larger so that all the older adults can see them.

If adults are interested, they can learn. Understanding comes more quickly because of their additional experience. A person of 80 in good health can learn as well as a 12-year-old. An adult of 40 may be able to learn as well as, if not better than, an 18-year-old, because the abilities in forming judgments, in reasoning, in attacking problems, and in creative imagination offset the loss of ability in the other factors which determine the ability to learn. Adults also depend less on memorization than do high school students because they recognize its weakness. Teachers of adults should decrease the need in their classes for keen perception and extensive and quick memorization. They should increase the importance of the abilities to reason, to form judgments, to think, and to use creative imagination. Teachers of adults must allow more time for the discussion of problems because of a decrease in memorization and perception abilities, and because of an increase in experience and the ability to think through problems. Adults do not arrive at hasty conclusions. They want to examine all sides of a problem. Some of the more important ways of learning used by adults are as follows:

1. *By doing:* performing a new job in the same way, with the same tools and equipment, and under the same conditions, as they will have to do this job in an actual life situation.
2. *By thinking:* solving a real-life difficulty or problem—getting the facts needed to solve it, discussing it with others, arriving at decisions, and putting the decisions into action and testing them.
3. *By seeing:* observing a thing being done and studying through words—written, spoken, or printed.
4. *By being told:* getting information and instruction through words—written, spoken, or printed.
5. *By being checked and corrected:* learning through mistakes brought to their attention by an alert, competent supervisor.

Follow Basic Principles of Teaching—In teaching adults, a teacher must follow the basic principles of good teaching. There must be suitable conditions provided for effective learning to take place.

1. The teacher must base the instruction on the interests and individual needs of the group.
2. The teacher must make provision for the development of interests, ideals, attitudes, appreciations, and habits.
3. The teacher must make provision for the development of understandings.
4. The teacher must make provision for the development of abilities in problem-solving and for the development of manipulative skills.
5. The teacher must make provision for "learning by doing."
6. The teacher must make provision for assisting adults in solving their problems.
7. The teacher must make provision for applying the knowledge obtained in class.

PLANNING

Planning Essential—It is very important for an instructor to plan carefully each meeting, and especially the first meeting, since first impressions are lasting and a successful opening meeting sets the pattern for more successful meetings. Regardless of the kind of course taught, it is essential for an instructor to:

1. Have clearly in mind the objectives of the course and the sequence of the instruction.
2. Learn the subject matter and skills to be taught.
3. Obtain references, charts, and other teaching materials. *The instructor should be sure to have a chalkboard.*

4. Obtain adequate facilities for effective instruction. This includes space, equipment, heat, lighting, and ventilation. *The instructor must make sure the room is clean and arranged appropriately for the type of instruction to be offered.*
5. Obtain all needed supplies.
6. Arrange for projects that will provide worthwhile activities for all the enrollees.
7. Obtain suitable clothes.
8. Plan suitable demonstrations.

The success or failure of a course depends largely on the instructor.

Planning a Lesson—In order to provide effective instruction, a teacher should do the following:

1. Carefully develop written plans for each meeting.
2. List in the plans items such as objectives, abilities to be developed, approved practices which should be adopted, problems common to the group, and reference materials.
3. Study the agricultural abilities of the persons who will be in the class.
4. Carefully select teaching devices to be used, such as charts, pictures, demonstrations, field trips, exhibits, experimental data, local data from high school students' occupational experience programs, films and slides, samples of feeds, parts of machines, and equipment.
5. Plan presentation of information so that the adults in a course do not have to do much reading of technical material. Adults have to be highly motivated before they will change their reading habits.

The following short-time teaching plan for an adult course was developed by a group of teachers enrolled in a graduate course at the University of Illinois. It illustrates a desirable procedure of planning for adult meetings.

• • •

TEACHING PLAN—ADULT EDUCATION

I. *Unit:* Swine production.
II. *Problem area:* Saving more pigs per litter.
III. *Situation:*
   A. Class membership is composed both of employees in agricultural business serving the community's swine industry and of swine producers.
   B. Adult course meets on Monday nights consecutively for at least 10 meetings and then at monthly intervals for the rest of the year.
   C. Instructor has met all class members personally.
   D. A survey of the swine programs on farms of area has been conducted.
   E. Spring farrowing time begins next month.
   F. Most gilts and sows are kept in confinement during the winter, getting no exercise.
   G. Producers of swine in area lose an average of four pigs per litter.
IV. *Objectives:*
   A. To develop realization of importance, in dollars and cents, of saving pigs.
   B. To develop ability to increase the number of pigs raised per litter.
V. *Procedure:*

(Before meeting time, arrange meeting room in group discussion fashion so that when members arrive they will seat themselves accordingly. As class members begin arriving, do not meet them at the door, and yet do not get too busy doing something else, such as reviewing notes. In other words, start early creating an atmosphere of friendliness and informality.)

First Meeting

A. Determining present situation:

Tonight we are beginning discussions in which we want to exchange ideas and gain new ones concerning the saving of baby pigs. During my visits, each of you indicated that you believe farrowing time to be very important in the production of swine—that failure at farrowing time is total failure. Since the spring farrowing season is near, tonight would be a good time to discuss the problems we may face at farrowing time.

1. How many pigs were farrowed per litter last year? (Class secretary or member should tally on chalkboard.)
2. How many pigs were lost at farrowing time? (Tally.)
3. How many pigs out of that total were raised to 56 days? (Tally.)

B. Determining goals:

1. How much is lost when a newly born pig dies?
2. Why did producers lose the number of pigs they did? (List on chalkboard reasons pigs died.)
3. How many pigs should be saved per litter this spring?
4. Do you think it is possible to raise 9 out of 10 pigs?

C. Defining problems and trial solution:

1. How could each of these losses have been prevented?
2. What are some of the practices now being used to save pigs?
3. How can you increase the average? (List practices suggested on the chalkboard.)

D. Validating hypotheses and supervised study:

1. Did any of you read the article in last week's *Prairie Farmer* concerning farrowing? It is one of the best articles on farrowing I have seen. It has some new ideas on saving pigs. If you get a chance, look it over before next time.

E. Summary.

Next Meeting

A. Introduction:

Saturday I visited Mr. E. Z. Farrow over in Swinedale Community and found that he had one sow to farrow last week. Twelve pigs were farrowed, but only four pigs were living. He attributed his losses to__________. Last week we were discussing some of the ways Mr. Farrow might have saved some of these pigs.

1. Do you recall some of the practices we discussed? (List on chalkboard.)
2. Did you discover any new practices in that article in *Prairie Farmer?*
3. Do you have any additional practices to add to these?

B. Presentation of additional information:

Next we will see a movie concerning some of the points we have been discussing. There may be other points in addition to those on our list, so watch for any new practice that is presented. The movie deals particularly with farrowing, and it presents some new ways of carrying out practices which might be profitable for us to adopt. (Show the film *Care of Sow at Farrowing Time*, 28 minutes, sound, color.)

1. Did you gather any new ideas from the movie? (Add to list.)

VI. *Conclusions:*

A. Are all the practices listed on the board practical and necessary? (All items have been listed as approved practices.)
B. Are they worth the additional effort and expense?
C. How many are you going to use or recommend?

VII. *References:*

A. *Swine Science* by Ensminger.
B. Better Farming Units, Nos. 16, 17, and 18.
C. Iowa Circ. 80.
D. Michigan Ext. Bul. 250.

VIII. *Needed supplies:*
  A. Chalkboard.
  B. Movie, *Care of Sow at Farrowing Time.*
IX. *Possible activities:*
  A. Field trip to farms of selected hog producers in the community to observe practices in operation.
X. *Evaluation:*
  A. Check on approved practices adopted by class members.

● ● ●

Someone has said that a teaching plan is a note from you to yourself. For a more complete discussion of planning for teaching, see Chapter 5, "How to Plan for Effective Instruction."

TEACHING CLASSES

Methods of Instruction—Too much emphasis cannot be placed on the selection of the proper types of instruction to use in teaching adult classes. The instruction must be adapted to the needs and abilities of an adult group. Following are some of the types of instruction or educational procedures which may be used in adult courses:

1. *The informing or lecture procedure,* in which new information is presented by the instructor through telling and illustration.
2. *The conference procedure,* in which a group discusses a problem under the direction of a competent leader. This is recognized as being one of the better procedures.
3. *The panel procedure,* in which a small group of persons discusses a given problem in the presence of all the persons assembled. This is especially desirable in meetings where a large number of persons are in attendance.
4. *The use of visual aids,* which supplements other procedures in teaching.
5. *The demonstration procedure,* which is especially desirable in teaching skills. It should be followed by student participation and doing on the job.

An alert teacher uses a variety of procedures, merging them whenever possible.

Informing Method—This procedure is also referred to as the lecture method. When used by itself, this is a very ineffective method of instruction. There are times when an instructur must supply new information and may need to resort to the lecture method for a few minutes in order to inform the enrollees. However, this information should be closely associated with the problem under discussion and presented at a logical time in the discussion.

Conference Procedure—In the conference method a systematic group discussion is conducted under the direction of a competent leader who, in agriculture courses, should be the teacher of agriculture or some other qualified instructor. This is recognized as the best procedure in teaching about managerial problems. The method provides for constructive thinking and the pooling of experiences on problems of interest to the group by the individuals enrolled. In the conference procedure it is assumed that no one person has the best answer to a problem. The conference leader encourages all class members to participate in the discussion in an informal and frank way, urging them to tell their experiences which relate to the problem being discussed. It is desirable in the conference procedure to have much of the discussion originate among the members. This means that a leader must stimulate and guide the group to ask questions and make statements pertaining to a problem.

After securing the viewpoints of the class members, the instructor should supply any new information necessary in helping the group agree on which approved practices should be adopted. This may be done through a variety of procedures, such as movies, field trips, or presentations. Following are the steps an instructor might utilize in leading a discussion:

1. Clearly state and introduce the problem area to be discussed.
2. Analyze the problem by asking questions pertaining to it, and *make sure the problem is understood by the group.*
3. Ask questions that will help the group members evaluate their past experiences or results.
4. Ask questions that will help the group determine standards and develop objectives.
5. Attempt to solve the problem. Call for experiences of the enrollees. Encourage all to participate.
6. Present scientific data, results obtained by local persons, and local data from students' supervised occupational experience programs.
7. Evaluate with the group the factual information and the experiences of the enrollees.
8. Decide on the best possible conclusions.
9. Decide on a *plan of action.*
10. Plan a follow-up program.

The plan of action should include a list of approved practices to be adopted as a result of the instruction.

The importance of adults understanding, selecting, and adopting approved practices which can be used cannot be overemphasized. *After a group discussion under the guidance of an instructor has been conducted and after definite conclusions based on experimental data and the experiences of local persons have been reached, the enrollees should carefully analyze their own situations and definitely decide which approved practices they can and will use.*

The conference procedure has several advantages which seem to substantiate faith in it. These include the following:

1. Learning is most effective when individuals participate actively, as in group discussion.
2. The instruction is geared to the level of understanding which prevails in the group, and it proceeds from there to higher levels as the result of thinking *within the group.*
3. Since practical experiences of the members are utilized, the discussion is kept on a realistic basis, and many suggestions for action are likely to evolve.
4. Persons are inclined to accept a solution which they have helped to find, and consequently they are likely to "do something about it" after the discussion is over.
5. The conference procedure frequently leads to better solutions to problems than would be possible otherwise.
6. The sharing of experiences and growth through group thinking are more democratic than more formal approaches to instruction.

It is important to provide physical facilities which contribute to an informal atmosphere. Members should be seated so that they can see the faces of all persons present, including the leader. If a group is small, the members can be seated in a semicircle or around a table. In larger groups, it is desirable to have several tables arranged to form a large rectangle, with the members seated around the outside. A chalkboard should be provided and placed so as to be in the range of vision of everyone present. Optimum conditions of temperature, lighting, and ventilation should be maintained at all times. Chairs should be comfortable, and the general surroundings should comprise a setting which will make everyone feel at ease.

Panels—One of the procedures used in adult classes in agriculture involves the panel. The panel procedure is a modified conference since only a few—usually four to eight—enter the discussion, rather than the entire group. The persons composing a panel are usually seated at a table, with the chairperson in the center of the group. This group generally sits in the front of the room, facing the audience.

The chairperson of a panel directs the discussion by asking different members of the panel their opinions on certain problems. The chairperson should be a good thinker, be quick to sense the trend of the discussion, and have the ability to lead a group. A chairperson may call a preparatory meeting of the panel, but some people believe that the best panel discussions are obtained without a preparatory meeting. The chairperson closes a panel discussion and gives a brief summary of what has been said.

The essential elements of a panel discussion are:

1. A problem about which there is some perplexity, difference of opinion, or confusion of thought.
2. A group that desires knowledge and a better understanding of the problem at hand.
3. A panel of four to eight persons chosen to represent the entire group.
4. A chairperson.

Effective Classes—The following suggestions for making effective use of a class period are offered:

1. *Start the meeting at the time scheduled, which should be at a time when the enrollees can and will be present.*
2. Have the secretary take the roll.
3. Call class members by name.
4. Briefly review problems and activities covered in the previous meeting.
5. Briefly review the plans for the class period which were suggested by the group at an earlier meeting, and allow the group to plan further regarding the problems to be discussed.
6. Clearly state the problems or activities to be considered in the meeting.
7. Phrase the topic for discussion as a problem.
8. Analyze the problems selected by the group for study.
   a. Ask questions to discover if the problems are of general concern.
   b. Ask questions to discover the experiences of others with the problems.
   c. Ask questions to make sure that all understand the problems.
9. Utilize experiences of the adult students as they relate to the solution of the problems of the group.
10. Determine the role of each member of the class.
11. Start the discussion with a procedural question.
12. Base instruction on problems and needs of the class.
13. Point up a problem by seeing that all understand and realize the importance of it.
14. Start discussions by asking a provocative or controversial question.
15. Watch visible responses of the group for an indication of readiness to participate in a discussion.

16. Direct the first question to those who appear visually to be interested.
17. Refer questions originating in the group back to the group members for their opinions.
18. Encourage class members to talk, but do not ask direct questions.
19. Phrase questions so that "yes" or "no" replies will not answer them.
20. Call for opinions and not facts. A question that begins with "What do you think about" will usually evoke an opinion.
21. Ask "reserved" members of the class before a meeting if they can present certain information to the class. (This procedure must be used with caution.)
22. Maintain suspense regarding the solution to a problem.
23. Let the group members feel that they have had more practical experience than you and that you would appreciate hearing about it. Let them understand that you can find and present new experimental and scientific information to them.
24. Be careful not to give away opinions or ideas before the group members have a chance to think through the problem.
25. Present facts as needed to assist the discussion in moving toward a conclusion.
26. Use language which the group members can understand.
27. Guide the discussion toward a conclusion by:
    a. Bringing the discussion back to the problem being discussed.
    b. Summarizing points of agreement.
    c. Focusing attention on points of disagreement.
28. Summarize points of agreement frequently.
29. Arrange for recognition of class members. Use class members to demonstrate and to teach the rest of the group.
30. Develop procedures so that all have at least occasional opportunities to participate in the discussion.
31. Change activities of the class frequently—discussion, demonstration, physical doing, seeing, hearing.
32. Provide for "learning by doing."
33. Teach the skills necessary for using the approved practices agreed upon by the class.
34. Continue philosophical problems, if necessary, over more than one meeting.
35. Allow all sides approximately equal opportunity to express their opinions when discussing controversial issues.
36. Summarize the points of agreement if tension develops.
37. Suggest, if necessary, that members not speak a second time until all have had an opportunity to express their opinions.
38. Stop the speaker, if necessary, and notice if the members are talking among themselves. If they are, it may mean that the material is being covered too quickly.
39. Analyze the discussion to see whether it is accomplishing anything.
40. Provide an evaluator.
41. Make reference to experiences of members of the class.
42. Provide the necessary supplies for class use and have them on hand before the meeting.
43. Do not do too much talking yourself.
44. See that certain members do not do all the talking.
45. Stand while teaching. *Be at ease*.
46. Use the chalkboard and other teaching devices.
47. Do not attempt to force an opinion on the group.
48. Be willing to remain the inconspicuous member of the group. Focus attention of the group on others.
49. Do not set yourself up as an expert, and do not apologize for what you do not know.
50. Respect the opinions of class members.
51. Fill the role of moderator and guide.
52. Keep poised. Do not be annoyed or surprised by any comments.
53. Be a good listener.
54. Recommend—do not demand.
55. Introduce humor.

56. Be democratic.
57. Promote informality.
58. Review the list of approved practices on which the members have agreed near the close of the class period.
59. State the problem to be discussed at the next meeting near the close of the class period, and list any questions which the group has pertaining to it.
60. Attempt to lead the group toward deciding on a plan of action.
61. Summarize the meeting.
62. Close the meeting before everyone is completely "talked out."

Teaching Manipulative Skills—The techniques of teaching manipulative skills are discussed in Chapter 4.

Form 8.1. Attendance Record

Course ______________________ School Year ______________________

Name of Individual	Month															
	Date															
	Session	1	2	3	4	5	6	7	8	9	10	11	12	13	14	15
1.																
2.																
3.																
4.																
5.																
6. etc.																
TOTAL																

Conducting an Agriculture Mechanics Class—The following procedure has been used in a number of states in conducting classes in agriculture mechanics:[1]

Step 1. *Open the class period.*

It is important that an instructor begin each instructional period in a businesslike way. It may be necessary to be at the shop some time in advance of the students to be sure that everything is ready for the instruction.

1. Dress in clothes suitable for the work to be done.
2. Begin work at the time scheduled. Encourage all students to be on time and to remain in class until closing time.
3. Plan in advance worthwhile jobs or projects for all enrolled in the class.
4. Arrange for each student to have sufficient working space and the equipment necessary for the job to be done.
5. Have all tools, equipment, and supplies on hand.
6. See that the shop is clean and that everything is in its proper place.
7. Be courteous, friendly, and patient.
8. Show interest in the students and answer questions clearly.
9. Provide an environment that will stimulate desirable work habits.

[1]Adapted from Misc. Pub. 2611, U.S. Office of Education, Washington, D.C.

Step 2. *Develop the students' interest in each job and supply basic information.*

In general, it is expected that students will have a genuine interest in the jobs that are to be undertaken by them. In case there is not a natural interest on the part of the students, the instructor, before attempting to teach the students how to do a job, should plan a method of arousing student interest. The instructor should also plan some procedure to follow in helping students to secure basic information pertaining to the job.

1. See that the students are at ease.
2. Ask questions which will arouse student interest in doing the job.
3. Discuss reasons why the job is important.
4. Have students, when possible, study references pertaining to the job or jobs to be done.
5. Discuss the various skills or techniques required to do the job.
6. Call upon individuals in the group to give briefly their experience in doing similar jobs.
7. Explain and show tools, equipment, and materials necessary in doing the job.
8. Explain procedures that will be followed in doing the job.
9. Take students on a field trip, if necessary, to acquaint them with the job being done.

Step 3. *Demonstrate jobs.*

The demonstration is one of the important procedures in teaching a shop class. It must be well done to be effective.

1. Be sure tools, equipment, and materials are available before starting a demonstration.
2. Give the demonstration with the class arranged so that each student can see and hear exactly what takes place.
3. Demonstrate each step slowly, using the proper safety precautions.
4. Call attention to each step by making comments and explanations and by questioning students. Encourage the students to think through the demonstration by asking questions. Call attention to safety precautions.
5. Encourage the students to ask questions to clarify any step or problem.
6. Ask the students to demonstrate various phases of the job.
7. Encourage the students, in some cases, to take notes or make sketches for future use and study.
8. Have the students examine the finished job for quality of work.
9. Test the students to see that they know how to proceed.

Step 4. *Secure student participation.*

Any demonstration or other instruction not followed by student participation is almost useless. Plans for student participation, therefore, must be carefully made.

1. Have students do the job or perform certain operations immediately following the demonstration.
2. Provide for student participation until desired skills and abilities are acquired by the different students.
3. Teach the students to think and reason for themselves, and show them how to find new information necessary for solving difficulties in doing the job.
4. Provide for the amount of repetitious training necessary for the students to develop desirable skills.

Step 5. *Teach while the students are at work.*

Learning is a continuous process. Students will not acquire all the information and skills they need during the demonstration or discussion period. They will need supplementary instruction. Much of this can be provided while the students are at work.

1. Ask students why they do the job in a certain way.
2. Give individual help but do not do the job for a student.
3. When the need arises, call the group together and redemonstrate any step or skill, or point out why certain mistakes are being made.
4. Recognize good quality work and call it to the attention of individuals and the group.
5. Have students evaluate their own work by comparing it with an accepted standard, and let them tell how they think the job could be improved.

Step 6. *Check individual performance.*

It is important for the instructor to be alert at all times in checking the performance of each member of the class. The instructor may do this by moving from student to student or from group to group while they are at work. While doing this the instructor should:

1. Inspect the work quality as the job is progressing.
2. Check to see that the proper tools are selected and used correctly.
3. Inspect the steps being followed by the individuals in the performance of skills.
4. Check safety measures being followed.
5. Record the proficiency of each individual.
6. Record jobs that are completed by each individual student or group of students.

Step 7. *Close the work period.*

The instructor must remember that other classes will be using the shop. It is very important, therefore, that the shop be left clean and in order.

1. Have students clean and put away tools.
2. Check tools to see that they are all in place, and lock the cabinets or tool room.
3. Have students mark and put in a safe place the materials with which they are working.
4. Give students definite responsibility in cleaning the shop and in leaving everything in order.
5. Call students together to review progress made during the period and to plan for the following period.

Step 8. *Review accomplishments of class period.*

Immediately after each work period, the instructor should review for his/her own use the things that have been accomplished and the procedures which were followed in carrying out the instruction. This review should help in planning for the further development and improvement of the instruction.

1. Was every student fully occupied with worthwhile activities throughout the period?
2. Was the quality of each student's work sufficiently high?
3. Was each student interested in the job and did he/she take pride in it?
4. Did each student use the tools correctly and in a professional manner?
5. Did each student keep the tools in good working condition?
6. Were all students properly dressed for the type of work done?
7. Did each student clean and return the tools to the proper place?
8. Were there any violations of safety precautions?
9. Was the instructor properly dressed for the work to be done?

Conducting the First Meeting of a Course—Considerable planning must be done for the first meeting of a course and every effort made to impress the enrollees with the practicality of the instruction to be offered. The first meeting may well be considered the "spark plug" for future meetings. The instructor should let the adults know that the instruction is going to be built around their problems. There are a number of things that an instructor should do at the first class meeting:

1. Be on hand to greet the enrollees as they arrive; see that the facilities are the best that can be secured locally.
2. Do everything possible to make the group comfortable and to make the members feel at home. Mingle among the enrollees and converse with them before the time for the meeting to start.
3. Have appropriate materials on display, such as farm and agribusiness machines which have been repaired and painted by high school or young adult groups, farm and agribusiness machinery to be repaired, equipment to be used, labor-saving devices constructed, and pictures of activities of former adult students.

4. Open the meeting with appropriate remarks or a story. Make a statement concerning the aims and purposes of the instruction. *Be sincere and frank.* Admit not knowing all the answers.
5. Determine present status and goals of enrollees that relate to the content of the course.
6. Decide with the group members the problem areas and activities which will best meet their needs, and list these on the chalkboard.
7. Decide on the sequence in which the problem areas or activities will be studied.
8. Decide on the place, time, and frequency of meetings.
9. Discuss an important problem. Get the members of the class participating in the discussion as much as possible—*get them interested.*
10. Present a well selected demonstration related to the problem being discussed.
11. See that the enrollees leave the meeting talking among themselves and making statements such as: *"That is just what we need," "I am not going to miss a meeting," "That is what we should have had when I was in school,"* or *"Why have they not offered such courses before?"* These are the kinds of statements they will make if the meeting is properly conducted.

Conducting the Last Meeting of a Course—The last session of a course, like the first meeting, should be especially impressive. The members of the course should leave the meeting feeling proud that they completed the course. They should have a greater respect for the local school because of having had the opportunity to participate in a practical training program. They should feel better acquainted with the school administrators and their fellow agricultural workers as a result of their associations in the course. Although this is the final meeting for their course, they should realize that similar courses will be offered in the future.

Some of the kinds of activities which may be included in this meeting are:

1. Completion of problems and activities in the course.
2. Short entertainment, which may include some special feature such as educational sound films and slides of projects completed in the course.
3. An exhibit of the activities completed, such as agriculture machines repaired and painted and labor-saving devices constructed.
4. The taking of pictures of projects and of the members enrolled in the course.
5. Summarization by the instructor, with the help of the class members, of their accomplishments in the course and the instructor's asking if they would like to have another course either in the immediate future or the next year.
6. Serving of light refreshments or perhaps a dinner.

This meeting may be used as an open house and the public invited to attend. Enrollees take pride in showing some of the results of their training.

USING TEACHING MATERIALS

The use of teaching materials is also discussed in Chapters 36 and 37.

Using Field Trips and Tours—It is often desirable to take a class to appropriate places, such as farm machinery dealers' display rooms and repair shops, local farms, packing plants, food preservation centers, and marketing centers. Arrangements for visits to such places should be made in advance of the trips.

Definite objectives for a trip should be developed by a class. A discussion should be held at the place visited, if possible, and another discussion should be held when the class returns to the classroom.

Using Duplicated Materials—An instructor can often save considerable time by having duplicated materials pertaining to the problem or skill being studied ready to pass out to the class members. Care should be taken to see that the information is concise, clear, and useful to the adults. Extra copies of these materials may be saved, and each enrollee may be given a set bound in a manila folder at the final meeting.

Seeing That Enrollees Have Notes—Since most adults do not like to take many notes during a class period, it is desirable for an instructor to have the secretary of the group or an FFA member take notes on the discussion, listing the main conclusions regarding the different problems discussed and the approved practices recommended by the group for adoption. These notes may then be duplicated and briefly discussed at the next meeting of the course. The enrollees should be encouraged to keep these materials for future reference in a manila folder which may also be supplied to them.

INDIVIDUAL INSTRUCTION

Providing Follow-up of Class Instruction—An effective follow-up program on the farm or job is one of the most essential parts of systematic instruction. Individual instruction to assist adults in applying the knowledge and skills obtained in a course is a necessary part of successful teaching. An accepted principle of education is that we learn by doing. Some say, *"Without practice there is no learning."* Following are the essentials for individual instruction on the farm or in the agribusiness job:

1. Make frequent and effective instructional visits to the farms or agribusiness jobs of members of a course at crucial periods in the adoption of approved practices.
2. Continue the instruction in a course until an effective degree of learning has been attained. Make sure the enrollees can and do apply the training given, such as fertilizing their lawns, maintaining and properly operating their machinery, feeding balanced rations, and producing and conserving their food.
3. Suggest additional content areas in which education should be obtained.
4. Keep accurate records of approved practices completed.

Checking Approved Practices—The approved practices recommended for adoption by the members of a course may be summarized and listed on a check sheet. The check sheet illustrated in Form 8.2 is a desirable type to use. Before the class meetings of a course are completed, each enrollee may be given a list of this kind and asked to check the practices he/she now uses and the additional ones that will be adopted.

A copy of the check sheet as completed by each student may be made so that the enrollee may also have a copy. The teacher of agriculture may review this list with the enrollee during each visit to the adult student's home or job and record the approved practices completed. If a check sheet of approved practices is used in this way, the teacher of agriculture will, at the close of the year, have a complete report from each enrollee covering his/her accomplishments in the use of the approved practices discussed in class.

Form 8.2. Partial Check Sheet of Approved Practices for Agricultural Business Employees

Approved Practices Recommended for Adoption by the Group	Present Practice	Practice Planned	Practice Completed
1. Keep up-to-date inventory of:			
a. supplies			
b. repair parts			
2. Inform prospective customers of services available:			
a.			
b.			
c.			
3. Provide suggestion box for:			
a. employees			
b. customers			
4. Keep customers informed of:			
a. pricing policies			
b. credit policies			
c.			

CHAPTER

9

How to Teach Persons with Special Needs

INTRODUCTION

The early history of education in agriculture illustrates the concern for the disadvantaged and the handicapped. Programs in public schools were established because agricultural workers were considered to be disadvantaged in many ways. They were often socially isolated, economically harassed, and without adequate opportunities for formal schooling and cultural experiences. They often lacked many of the amenities of living such as electricity, running water, and indoor plumbing which persons living in the urban areas enjoyed.

These situations often created an environment in which the agricultural families and their individual members were highly motivated for materialistic improvement. They were often severely handicapped by lack of knowledge, poor communication ability, superstition, tradition, and environmentally produced debilitating attitudes.

The teachers of agriculture who were prepared and employed in the years immediately following the passage of the Smith-Hughes Act in 1917, which provided federal financial assistance for public school vocational education in agriculture, were well aware of the special needs of persons in agriculture. They were also highly motivated to reach and assist rural people in overcoming their disadvantages and meeting their special needs.

Society, with the assistance of public school vocational education in agriculture, was highly successful in upgrading the average education and amenities of living, such as transportation, electricity, communication, and so forth, of rural people. This process was so successful that soon rural living was the equivalent of urban living. And in recent years with urban pollution, crowding, crime, and transportation problems, rural living has more appeal for many persons than urban living.

As the "disadvantaged" status of rural living was alleviated, vocational education in agriculture changed. Teachers were placed under considerable pressure to produce changes in people. It was easier to obtain results with the more advantaged sector of the youth and adults in agriculture than it was to obtain similar results with those with special needs. Also, many contests were incorporated into the public school program in agriculture. These contests often encouraged teachers to focus much of their attention on the advantaged students instead of the disadvantaged so that they could win their share of the awards.

The final outcome was that disadvantaged and handicapped youth and hard to reach adults received less and less attention. This same process was occurring in the other fields of vocational and technical education.

Finally, Congress became aware of the process and of the needs of those who were disadvantaged and handicapped. In the Vocational Education Acts of 1968 and 1976, Congress mandated special attention to the disadvantaged and handicapped youth and adults who were not being served or who could not profit from the instruction in the regular classes. Special financial assistance in these acts was earmarked for providing relevant vocational and technical education for the disadvantaged and the handicapped.

From moral and financial viewpoints, teachers of agriculture and renewable natural resources must give attention to the special needs of the disadvantaged and the handicapped.

Importance—How important is education in production agriculture, agribusiness, and renewable natural resources for the disadvantaged and the handicapped? It is vital for the continuing smooth functioning of society; the agriculture industry needs the educated and dedicated services of all types of persons. Jobs in agriculture can effectively utilize the full spectrum of abilities of workers. Some jobs in agriculture and renewable natural resources require workers with few talents, and other jobs require workers with many very sophisticated talents. The advantaged, disadvantaged, and handicapped may all find a place to serve society effectively in agriculture, if they receive the proper education. The opportunity for placement in production agriculture, agribusiness, and renewable natural resources exists for the disadvantaged and the handicapped if the educators in agriculture are successful in devising educational programs that meet the unique needs of these persons.

Needs—Are there persons with special needs in rural and urban areas who need vocational and technical education for employment in production agriculture, agribusiness, and renewable natural resources? There is ample documentation that, even in the most prosperous rural areas, many persons may be identified who are disadvantaged or handicapped in one or more ways and need to be recruited into programs and provided special services by teachers of agriculture. In urban areas no one questions that there are vast numbers of disadvantaged and handicapped who need special attention in vocational and technical education. Many jobs in off-farm agriculturally oriented firms exist in urban areas. Teachers of agribusiness have many opportunities to recruit and educate the disadvantaged and the handicapped for these jobs which require many levels of ability and education.

The needs are apparent as soon as the educators in agriculture give them their attention, and when the needs are given attention they are so very apparent that they can no longer be ignored. Programs for the disadvantaged and the handicapped, persons with special needs, become mandatory.

DEFINITION OF SPECIAL NEEDS

Disadvantaged—Who are the disadvantaged? "Disadvantaged" is defined very broadly. They are the youth and adults who have special needs and cannot profit adequately in regular courses without special attention. They are the atypical. They are the persons who need special attention. They include primarily the:

1. Economically disadvantaged.
2. Socially and culturally deprived.
3. Academically disadvantaged.

They manifest many different characteristics and needs, and they require many types of special educational services.

Handicapped—Who are the handicapped? By definition, the term "handicapped" is often limited to persons with an emotional, mental, physical, or health disability. Often these disabilities create special education needs. They also may manifest themselves in attitudes and fears which are similar to the attitudes and fears of the disadvantaged. They are the persons with disabilities of such a nature that they cannot profit from the regular courses without special attention.

Identification—The problem of identifying persons with special needs is both easy and difficult. If teachers of agriculture start looking for persons with special needs whom they are serving or should be serving, they will locate several immediately. However, some persons with dire special needs are relatively invisible. For example, in very prosperous communities, the economically and socially disadvantaged have a way of becoming hidden. They live in out-of-the-way places, they remain inconspicuous, and they "put up a good front."

Research studies recently have located many economically disadvantaged families in prosperous rural communities where the teachers of agriculture, often with many years of tenure, have vowed that they had almost no economically disadvantaged in their communities. They are there, and they can be found if they are sought out in a systematic manner.

A systematic procedure is required. The following procedure is recommended for the identification of the economically and socially deprived:

1. Utilize the published tax roll of the community.
2. Ask local key individuals for their assistance.
3. Check welfare rolls.
4. Check school rolls for those receiving special assistance.
5. Find out who receives assistance from various aid agencies in the community.

MAINSTREAMING

Recent federal legislation relating to the education of the handicapped with emotional, mental, health, or physical disabilities requires schools receiving federal financial assistance to provide the handicapped access to vocational programs, including vocational education in agriculture. The legislation further requires that the handicapped be educated in the regular classes to the maximum extent possible. The regulations for the Rehabilitation Act of 1973 specifically state that a school shall educate each qualified handicapped person in its jurisdiction with persons who are not handicapped to the maximum extent appropriate to the needs of the handicapped person. A school shall place a handicapped person in the regular educational environment operated by the school unless it is demonstrated by the school that the education of the person in the regular environment with the use of supplementary aids and services cannot be achieved satisfactorily.

The comments regarding the regulations for P.L. 94-142 and P.L. 2497 in the August 23, 1977, Federal Register state, "It should be stressed that, where a handicapped child is so disruptive in a regular classroom that the education of other students is significantly impaired, the needs of the handicapped child cannot be met in that environment. Therefore, regular placement would not be appropriate to his or her needs."

The federal legislation insures that handicapped students be placed in the least restrictive environment in a school. This process is called *mainstreaming*. It means that teachers of agriculture will probably have handicapped students in their regular classes. However, they should have access to supportive aids and services in handling the handicapped students in their classes, such as the help of special education teachers who have had specialized training in educating the handicapped.

THE EDUCATIONAL PROBLEM

When a community has identified its persons with special needs who could profit from education for the production agriculture, agribusiness, and renewable natural resources world of work, what can or must be done? What special efforts need to be provided? What programs need to be developed? Part of the answer to these questions is dependent on the characteristics of the persons identified and to be served.

However, research has identified certain dimensions of the problem. Schools and other educational agencies have often attempted in the past to provide appropriate education in agriculture for the disadvantaged. Their efforts have often been rather unsuccessful. Many times the interest and attention of the disadvantaged families have not been obtained. The attitudes of families have a vast influence on the way individuals in a family behave and develop.

The findings of Project REDY (Rural Education for Disadvantaged Youth) indicated that "most existing and proposed vocational education programs for the disadvantaged focus primarily on the individual and fail to give adequate attention to the individual functioning as a family member. Thus, an important root of the problem of the disadvantaged is neglected."[1]

Previous research has indicated that the educational problem is as follows:

1. Failure to obtain the attention of disadvantaged families. The production agriculture, agribusiness, and renewable natural resource programs to serve the disadvantaged family must obtain and maintain the attention of the disadvantaged family members. Educators can do this by involving them in planning their own educational program. This is in contrast to providing a program for them and then either inviting them to participate or imposing the program upon them.
2. Failure to create readiness for learning. If the disadvantaged are to be reached effectively, agricultural programs must create learning readiness by involving family members in activities that include the analysis of the family's present situation and the development of realistic individual and family goals. An erroneous assumption is often made that disadvantaged youth and adults desire to change or are ready to change. Disadvantaged youth and adults are often more fearful of change than they are of continuing in their present capacity. The only program that can succeed is the program that starts where they are and develops readiness, instead of providing a program or imposing one on them.
3. Failure to recognize the importance of the family. For many disadvantaged, the family is especially important because it provides security against the frightening and undependable milieu of society. Educational programs for the world of work in agriculture should recognize the family as the basic educational unit. This procedure provides security to the individual and helps create readiness for participation in specialized efforts of a teacher of agriculture.
4. Failure of disadvantaged or handicapped persons to determine their problems, define their objectives, identify possible alternatives for solving their problems, select specific and detailed goals, and plan a program for obtaining their goals. Most disadvantaged adults and youth in or available for production agriculture, agribusiness, and renewable natural resource educational programs have not learned how to do these things. Therefore, the first educational undertaking by a teacher of agriculture must be directed toward developing abilities in the performance of these tasks. Often programs of agricultural education disregard this essential step in the educational process. It is an important step in all educational programs, but it is especially important when persons are working with the disadvantaged and the handicapped. When this step is not handled adequately, educational opportunities are offered, but the disadvantaged ignore or rebel against them because they are not ready for them.
5. Failure to involve lay citizens, at all economic and social levels, in providing the program. Lay citizens may be used in the development and identification of opportunities; the providing of psychological support to the disadvantaged; and the teaching of specialized production agriculture, agribusiness, and renewable natural resource skills and abilities needed by the disadvantaged. Professional agricultural educators, with their middle-class values and personal biases, often plan programs which do not reflect the needs of the disadvantaged.

Characteristics—In developing a program and in teaching the disadvantaged, teachers of agriculture need to take into consideration the characteristics of the disadvantaged and the handicapped. Their past experiences and inabilities have often produced one or more of the following characteristics:

---

[1]Phipps, Lloyd J., Hollie Thomas, and David Williams, *Development of Human Resources Through a Vocationally Oriented Education Program for Disadvantaged Families in Depressed Rural Areas*, Final Report USOE Project No. 5-0125, Vocational and Technical Education Department, University of Illinois, Urbana–Champaign, pp. 1–3.

1. Resentment toward authority.
2. Need to receive attention.
3. Fear of the new and unknown.
4. Undesirable attitudes.
5. Dependence on tradition.
6. Lack of ability to handle the fundamental tools of learning.
7. Lack of understanding of the world of work.
8. Prejudicial attitudes toward agriculture.
9. Lack of knowledge of job opportunities in production agriculture, agribusiness, and renewable natural resources.
10. Lack of social abilities.
11. High incidence of illness.
12. Poor physical condition.
13. Lack of ability to handle economic matters.
14. Poor nutritional habits.
15. Lack of motivation for education.
16. Undefined goals.
17. Unrealistic goals.

PROGRAM

Home Visitation—An essential ingredient of any program to serve persons with special needs is many home visits by the teacher of agriculture. These home visits are essential so that the teacher can develop understanding of the situation. Home visitation helps the teacher develop understanding of the feelings and attitudes of the persons with special needs. It creates understanding of how the disadvantaged and the handicapped got the way they are and helps the teacher to predict and influence future behavior. It provides the teacher with understanding and insights which cannot be obtained in any other way. Further, it helps develop effective rapport with the student and with the family, and, as was stated earlier, rapport with both is essential. Home visits help the teacher identify unique needs and motivations of persons with special needs. They permit a teacher to "tailor-make" a program for a special need student. Home visits are important for all students in an education program in agriculture. They are especially important for students with special needs. Also, more on-the-job visits are needed for students with special needs.

Family Approach—As was emphasized in the section on the educational problem, a family approach must be utilized in working effectively with persons with special needs. They are often dependent on their families, and their families have vast influences on their attitudes and motivations. When working with a person with special needs, a teacher must work as much as possible with the whole family. The family is in a position to undo in a brief period of time all the good work of the teacher.

Content—The specialized content and methods for persons with special needs should be based on their unique problems. However, in designing a program, the teacher should give attention to the following content because persons with special needs often require instruction in one or more of the following areas:

1. Coaching persons regarding use of fundamental tools of learning.
2. Understanding acceptable behavior.
3. Understanding the school's occupational program, especially in produc-

tion agriculture, agribusiness, renewable natural resources, and the career education program in agriculture.
   a. Understanding job requirements for youth and adults.
   b. Understanding the school's career guidance, placement for experience, placement, and follow-up programs.
4. Identifying educational and training agencies in the community and the state.
   a. Identifying post–high school institutions available.
   b. Gaining admission to post–high school programs.
   c. Financing further education.
   d. Setting goals for education.
5. Helping persons with special needs and their family members establish educational and occupational goals.
   a. Helping persons in job entry.
   b. Determining individual and family expenditures.
6. Helping youth or adults with community action programs.
   a. Participating in community action programs.
   b. . Understanding youth employment opportunities.
7. Analyzing individual and family expenditures and managing expenditures.
8. Establishing long-range individual and family financial goals.
   a. Establishing financial plans.
   b. Developing educational goals based on financial plans.
9. Developing individual and family financial plans.
   a. Understanding the importance of financial planning.
   b. Developing individual and family budgets.
10. Developing financial plans and using business, family, and individual records.
   a. Planning financial expenditures.
   b. Planning finances to meet educational goals.
   c. Supplementing individual and family income.
11. Adjusting resources to increase income.
   a. Determining resources.
   b. Keeping records.
12. Using credit wisely.
   a. Understanding the use of credit.
   b. Using credit to meet educational goals.
13. Utilizing community services.
   a. Understanding the value of community services.
   b. Identifying community services available.
   c. Using community services.
14. Obtaining realistic on-the-job experiences.
15. Obtaining skills and knowledge in production agriculture, agribusiness, and renewable natural resources necessary to handle on-the-job activities.
16. Obtaining skills and knowledge in agriculture necessary for a job.
17. Reviewing and revising goals.
   a. Establishing individual and family goals.
   b. Improving individual and family income.
   c. Improving financial management.
   d. Enhancing enjoyment of living.

Adult Education—The teacher should not overlook young and older adults with special needs when planning educational programs in agriculture. They are present in every community and must be served. A committee of young and older adults who have special needs and who want special instruction should be used to assist in identifying and recruiting others for instruction. The task of a teacher is to identify one or two adults with special needs and to gain their confidence. They can be utilized in getting other committee members.

Other than recruiting, the problems of developing a program and teaching adults with special needs are not much different from providing for youth with special needs. The problems and needs are similar. The teacher should remember that adults with special needs are similar to other adults. Care must be exercised to treat them as adults and not as children, regardless of the type of special need. All persons have special educational needs. It is just a matter of degree.

PART

Developing Agricultural Education Programs

CHAPTER

10

How to Use Advisory Councils and Plan Programs

The successful development of an effective program of agricultural education is facilitated by the use of advisory councils and committees and by the development of written policies. Suggested methods of obtaining and using (1) policies, (2) advisory councils and committees, and (3) written annual and long-time plans will be presented in this chapter.

ORGANIZING AND USING ADVISORY COUNCILS[1] AND COMMITTEES

A prerequisite for a good annual and long-time program for an agriculture department is having adequate policies for agricultural education. When a school does not have adequate written policies officially adopted by the board of education, an advisory council for the agriculture department may be used to determine the policies needed and to recommend these policies to the board for adoption. Since an advisory council is so important in the process of developing a good program of agricultural education in a school, the organization and use of advisory councils and committees will be discussed as the first step in developing annual and long-time programs.

Why Have a Council?—The Vocational Education Amendments of 1976 require that a federally funded program be served by a local advisory council. They state, "Each eligible recipient receiving assistance under this Act to operate vocational education programs shall establish a local advisory council to

---

[1]The term "citizens' committee" is preferred by many.

provide such agency with advice on current job needs and on the relevancy of courses being offered by such agency in meeting such needs. Such advisory councils shall be composed of members of the general public, especially of representatives of business, industry and labor."

A local advisory council should be provided for agricultural education, not because it is required for federal funding for vocational education in agriculture, but because it is essential for the effective operation of the education program in agriculture.

The advisory council has been found to be one of the most effective devices for implementing the principle that those affected by a program should have a part, directly or indirectly, in formulating the program. Every teacher can profit from an advisory council. Some of the values of an advisory council to a teacher of agriculture follow:

1. Council members understand the program and support it and the teacher in the community.
2. A council provides considered advice.
3. The advice received from a council usually represents the community.

Some ask why the values of a council cannot be secured by other means. It may be that some teachers can secure advice by other means, such as personal visits with individuals in the community. The advantages of an advisory council over visits with individuals in a community, however, are that a council makes possible more efficient use of time; it assures the obtaining of opinions that represent the community; and it provides for thoughtful, considered opinion. Teachers who go to individuals for advice tend to seek advice from their friends, and these persons are their friends probably because they think the same way they do. The result is that they receive the type of advice they want to receive. Individuals asked for advice are usually unwilling to give the time necessary to study the problems presented. The advice received is usually based on snap judgment or prejudice rather than considered judgment.

Uses of an Advisory Council—The primary functions of an advisory council are (1) the formulation and recommendation of adequate policies for agricultural education, (2) the evaluation of these policies as they are applied, and (3) the recommendation of needed revisions in existing policies. The study of policies is a continuing job for a council and is its most important job. Since the development of policies for an agriculture department is so important, policy making will be discussed in detail in the next section of this chapter. In that section the use of councils in policy making will also be discussed in more detail. Another function of an advisory council is helping to plan annual and long-time programs. Some of a council's activities involved in planning a program are:

1. Studying the community to determine needs.
2. Evaluating the present program of the department.
3. Studying the need for extending and broadening the department's program.
4. Developing the objectives for the department's program.
5. Considering ways of evaulating the objectives suggested.
6. Helping in publicizing the suggested program for the reaction of the community.
7. Determining national and state standards that should apply locally.

A council may also be used to consider ways and means of implementing the program it has helped to plan. Some of the activities involved in implementing annual and long-time programs are:

1. Considering the facilities needed to carry on the annual program and the facilities needed to develop the long-time program which has been planned.
2. Considering ways of improving the department's public relations.
3. Supporting and sponsoring courses for out-of-school young adults.
4. Supporting and sponsoring adult courses.
5. Advising regarding who should be enrolled in courses.
6. Advising regarding courses that might be taught and the most useful content for these courses.
7. Considering ways of improving supervised "learning-by-doing" programs.
8. Advising regarding programs of work of the FFA or other school-sponsored agricultural organizations.

An important use of an advisory council is in helping in the evaluation of a department's program of agricultural education. Some of a council's activities concerning evaluation are:

1. Giving opinions regarding results of specific aspects of the program.
2. Considering how the various outcomes of the program might be measured.
3. Considering sources of information regarding the results of various aspects of the program.
4. Assisting in planning devices, such as surveys and records, for evaluating results.
5. Assisting in planning an annual evaluation report.

What a Council Should Not Do—A council is advisory to the teachers, the administrators, and the board of education. A teacher should not use it as a pressure group. A council should have complete freedom in making recommendations, and the board should welcome these recommendations. A council and board should understand, however, that the board is free to reject recommendations of a council. When recommendations of a council are rejected, the council should not attempt to bring pressure on the board by rallying support in the community for its ideas. If a member or members feel so strongly about a recommendation that they are compelled to pursue the issue further, they should resign from the council. Councils that are adequately educated regarding their function do not become pressure groups.

Councils are advisory groups for an educational program, and they should not be used as action groups to sponsor noneducational activities, such as swine improvement associations, fire prevention districts, community fairs, and artificial insemination rings. A council may choose to recognize the need for such action groups and sponsor an educational program to help the community recognize this need. For example, a council might sponsor an adult course in swine production, and the participants might organize themselves into a swine improvement association for the duration of their educational program as a means of learning how to operate such an organization. The organization would be limited to members of the course, however, and if the swine improvement association served a purpose in the community, it might continue on its own momentum after the educational program was concluded, without the necessity of sponsorship by the agriculture department or the advisory council.

Studies of activities of advisory councils have located the following undesirable uses of advisory councils which councils themselves were wise enough to reject as being outside their field:

1. Obtaining funds for the junior livestock show at the county fair.
2. Organizing a soil testing service.
3. Reorganizing the school district.
4. Storing buses in a part of a proposed shop building.

How to Organize a Council—A teacher of agriculture desiring an advisory council should first discuss this wish with the school administrators. The administrators should then discuss the request for an advisory council for agriculture with the board of education.

After the board has approved an advisory council, it may then be asked to develop a statement of policy or a charter regarding the organization and operation of advisory groups. Such a statement or charter usually includes the following:

1. The recognition that advisory groups are a part of the machinery of the school.
2. The purposes of the council.
3. The duties of the council.
4. The channels of communication with the board of education.
5. The method of selecting and replacing council members.
6. The terms of council members.
7. The method of eliminating inactive members.
8. The officers and internal organization of the council.
9. The persons excluded from council membership.
10. The method of obtaining representation at council meetings by the board of education and the school administrators.
11. The relationships of the council to the administrators, teachers of agriculture, and other teachers.
12. The provision for councils in other areas of the school system.

A charter for advisory groups may prevent misunderstandings and promote the effective operation of such groups. A board of education can profitably devote two or more meetings in developing a charter for advisory groups. The charter may be worded so that other departments in the school may have councils under the same terms. For example, the advisory council for agriculture may be a subcommittee of the council for vocational education. And, the vocational education council may be a subcommittee of the advisory council for the whole school.

Often a teacher shows the administrators and the board a policy statement or charter which another school has adopted for its advisory groups. An excellent time to provide administrators and board members with a sample charter for an advisory council for agricultural education is when they are considering the teacher's request for the establishment of a council. A sample charter may orient the board members regarding the proposed advisory council, and the administrators and board will not feel they are approving a "pig-in-a-sack." The sample charter will also be of help to the board in developing its own charter for advisory groups. Following is a sample charter for an advisory council for agricultural education.[2]

---

[2]Adaptation of the charter presented in H. M. Hamlin's *Local Policies for Agricultural Education in the Public Schools*, College of Education, University of Illinois, Urbana–Champaign.

• • •

SAMPLE CHARTER

Status of Council

The Advisory Council for Agricultural Education shall exist only during the time it is authorized by the Board of Education. It shall be a subcommittee of the advisory council for vocational education and an integral part of the advisory council system for vocational education. Since the Board of Education is the legally constituted authority over the schools, it surrenders none of its authority or responsibility in establishing an advisory council for agricultural education.

The Advisory Council shall advise (1) the teachers of agriculture and other school personnel who are in any way associated with the agriculture program, (2) the school administrators, and (3) the Board of Education on matters which directly concern the school's Department of Agricultural Education. The school employees, the school administrators, and the Board of Education are free to accept or reject the advice of the Council. The Council and its affiliated committees will advocate their plans and ideas in the community only after receiving specific authorization from the Board of Education.

Purpose

The purpose of an advisory council is to help in improving the agricultural education of the people in the district. The Council may contribute to this purpose by:

1. Studying the agricultural education problems of the district that are the concern of lay persons or the concern of both lay persons and the professional personnel of the school and then reporting its findings to the proper person or group in the school.
2. Advising the Board of Education regarding official policies for agricultural education.
3. Evaluating the progress made toward accepted objectives.
4. Promoting communication between the public and the school officials and personnel concerned with agricultural education.
5. Facilitating the use of the agricultural education and human resources in the community to improve the school's agricultural education program.

Membership and Terms of Members

1. The Advisory Council for Agricultural Education shall include 12 members. The affiliated committees of the Council may include any number of persons.
2. A selection committee appointed by the Board shall recommend to the Board of Education the original members of the Council. Selection committees appointed by the Board will also be used to recommend to the Board of Education replacement members for the Council.
3. Selection committees will include seven or more members. More than one-half of the members of each selection committee shall be lay persons in the district who are interested in agricultural education and who are not members or employees of the Board of Education. Each selection committee shall include a member of the Board of Education, the Superintendent of Schools or a representative appointed by the Superintendent, and a teacher of agriculture in the district.

4. Selection committees, in preparing a slate of proposed members of the Advisory Council for Agricultural Education, shall:
   a. Consult with a large and representative part of the citizens of the district who are directly or indirectly concerned with or affected by the program of agricultural education in the schools, in order to secure their suggestions regarding persons who should be considered for membership on the Council.
   b. Classify the names suggested by the citizens consulted, taking into consideration the following attributes and situations:
      (1) The general ability of each person.
      (2) The ability of each person to work constructively with others.
      (3) Insight and interest in public school education in agriculture.
   c. Classify the names suggested as to the following so that the slate recommended by the selection committee to the Board of Education shall be as representative as possible of all the citizens of the district who are directly or indirectly affected by the agricultural education program in the public schools of the district:
      (1) Geographic distribution.
      (2) Age.
      (3) Association with the various organizations of agricultural workers.
      (4) Religion.
      (5) Farming status: landlord, tenant, laborer, size of farm, type of farm.
      (6) Type of off-farm agricultural occupation: agricultural business, agricultural industry.
      (7) Status of off-farm agricultural worker: employer or employee.
      (8) Sex.
      (9) Length of residence in the community.
      (10) Parental status.
      (11) Nationality group.
      (12) Amount of taxes paid.
      (13) Attitude toward the school and the Department of Agricultural Education.
      (14) Type of agricultural education interest: vocational, avocational, practical arts, consumer, citizenship, and so forth.

      All groups represented on the Council should be in proportion to the number of people in each group in the community.
   d. Resist recommending a person for membership on the Council as a representative or spokesperson for any particular organization or group in the district. The persons recommended for membership on the Council should collectively have contacts with most of the organizations and groups in the district so that the members of the Council will have firsthand communication with all groups in the community which are concerned with agricultural education in the schools. In general, persons who are officers or professional employees of any agricultural organization or institution shall not be recommended for membership on the Council. Members of the selection committees may be recommended as members of the Council.
   e. Recommend to the Board of Education the exact number of persons needed for the Advisory Council for Agricultural Education. If the names submitted are not satisfactory to the Board, the Board shall ask the selection committee for additional names.
5. Each of the original members of the Council will serve a one-year term. At the end of the first year, equal numbers of the original members will draw lots for terms of one, two, and three years so that a systematic rotation of members can be established. Replacement members shall serve three-year terms. Council members are not eligible for reelection until they have been off the Council for one year.
6. The Advisory Council for Agricultural Education is authorized to recommend to the Board of Education persons to fill unexpired terms when vacancies occur during the terms of members.
7. A representative of the Board of Education, appointed by the Board; the Superintendent of Schools or a representative; and the teacher or teachers of agriculture shall meet with the Advisory Council for Agricultural Education. They will serve as consultants to the Council.

Affiliated Committees

The Council is encouraged to establish affiliated committees as needed to assist with special projects in agricultural education. Affiliated committees, for example, may be needed to assist in organizing and conducting courses for adults. Each affiliated committee shall have a definite purpose or field in which to work. It shall continue until it has accomplished its purpose. Membership of affiliated committees may or may not include members of the Advisory Council for Agricultural Education. Affiliated committees shall periodically report their progress to the Council. A teacher of agriculture in the district shall meet with each affiliated committee as a consultant. The members of affiliated committees should be chosen primarily because of their ability to contribute to the purposes of the committees.

Relationships and Duties

1. The Council is expected to give an oral or written reaction to the Board regarding the proposals for school policies for agricultural education which the Board of Education has submitted to it.
2. The Council may recommend policies for agricultural education to the Board of Education. The Board of Education will inform the Council regarding its action relating to the policies recommended.
3. The Board of Education and the Advisory Council for Agricultural Education will meet together when meetings are desired by both groups.
4. The Council will send the minutes of its meetings to each member of the Board of Education.
5. The Advisory Council for Agricultural Education and its affiliated committees may request information and counsel from the Board of Education or any of its employees on problems related to the purposes and functions of these committees.
6. Any teacher of agriculture in the district may request the Council to appoint an affiliated committee to work on a special project or in a special field.
7. The Council and its affiliated committees shall not consider or discuss the employment, salary, dismissal, promotion, or transfer of any individual employee of the Board of Education. The Council and its affiliated committees may, however, consider and recommend policies regarding working conditions and the general uses of the time of the teachers of agriculture.
8. The Advisory Council for Agricultural Education and its affiliated committees are encouraged to promote interest and participation in the agricultural education program among the citizens of the district.
9. Each committee member is expected to provide two-way communication between the school and the citizens of the district.
10. The Advisory Council for Agricultural Education and its affiliated committees shall not release, independently of the school, publicity about the Council and its affiliated committees or the work of these groups. The Council or its affiliated committees, in releasing publicity, should follow the publicity procedure established by the school.
11. The Board of Education may release the recommendations of the Council before or after it has taken action on these recommendations.

Organization of the Council

1. The Advisory Council for Agricultural Education is authorized to establish its own bylaws regarding the frequency of its meetings, the conduct of its meetings, and the method to be employed in attacking its problems.
2. The school will provide a reasonable amount of clerical service for the Council.

Amendment of Charter

1. The charter of the Advisory Council for Agricultural Education shall be reviewed annually by the Council and by the Board of Education.
2. The Board of Education or the Council may originate recommendations for changes in the charter.
3. The Board of Education shall consult the Council about any changes it proposes.
4. Changes in the charter may be made by a majority vote of the members of the Board of Education.

• • •

Most of the precautions necessary in selecting members for a council and in establishing a council are contained in the sample charter which has just been given. Since teachers of agriculture are members of the selection committee for the council, they should reinforce some of the precautions in the charter by informing the selection committee that it is usually undesirable to select for council members all the so-called key agricultural workers, officer holders, or paper leaders in the community.

These terms usually refer to the persons in a community who hold many offices due to their family background, financial status, or age. If a council is composed of individuals of this type, it may be found that the council is ineffective because the members are so busy serving the community that they have little time left for council activities. Or it may be found that because of favored financial status, the members do not understand the problems of those less favored. It is even more serious to have a council composed of professional office holders, who have been before the public eye so long that they neither represent nor have a following in the community.

One way to prevent obtaining a council of "key agricultural workers," "office holders," or "paper leaders" is to ask the persons contacted for the nomination of persons whom they would desire to have represent them on the council. One easy way to obtain a council composed of "key agricultural workers," "office holders," and "paper leaders" is to bypass the procedure outlined in the sample charter for obtaining nominations and substitute for it the nominations of friends and acquaintances by the agriculture teacher, administrator, board of education, and professional agricultural and educational leaders.

Most professional people, such as county agents, county superintendents, soil conservation service personnel, and so forth, do not usually make good council members, and they should not ordinarily be members of a council. Due to their training and position they often do not fit into a council or represent the people of the community, which is the purpose of a council. They may be used as consultants to a council.

Notification of appointment to the council should come to the council members from the board of education. A date, place, and time for the first council meeting may be a part of the letter of notification of appointment. A statement of the board's policies regarding the new council should be enclosed in the letter of notification of appointment.

After a council is organized, nominations for replacements may be solicited from the council by the selection committee for replacements, but the council should not be the only source of nominations. If a council is allowed to become self-perpetuating, it will probably soon become unrepresentative of the community.

How to "Start Off" with a New Council—New council members need to be thoroughly informed regarding the local, state, and national policies and programs of agricultural education. They should also be informed in detail regarding the purpose of any advisory council. They should understand that they are not a pressure group for the local department of agriculture and that they are advisory to the teachers of agriculture, the school administrators, and the board of education, who are free to accept or reject their advice.

A teacher of agriculture should not act as the chairperson of a council. A chairperson and secretary may be obtained at the first meeting, but some believe that it is wise for the board or the committee that selected the council members to appoint a temporary chairperson and secretary and not have an official chairperson and secretary elected until the second or third meeting of the council. This period with temporary officers will give the council members a chance to become acquainted with their job and with one another. The interval usually insures a wise choice of permanent officers. Another task for the first meeting is to determine the time, date, and place of subsequent meetings.

The board's statement of policies regarding the operation of the council should be discussed item by item. Special attention may have to be given to a discussion of the value of holding 11 or 12 monthly meetings a year and of keeping minutes of council meetings, which are circulated among members and others concerned. A system for determining the length of term of each council member is a necessary item of business during one of the meetings during the first year of a council's existence. Usually a chance drawing from a hat for term length is a satisfactory procedure.

A council needs to recognize, develop, understand, and observe some moral obligations or rules of propriety. A council needs to understand that it is advisory only unless other responsibilities are specifically delegated to it by the board. A council for the agriculture department is advisory only regarding the area of agricultural education. A council as a whole is delegated to advise school officials, but individual members have no more authority than they do as citizens. Recommendations of the council go to the board or to someone designated by the board, and not to the public. A council has a moral obligation not to engage in public controversy with the board of education or with school personnel. A council should resist any attempts by a board to secure a "yes" group for endorsing its policies.

Council members who cannot attend meetings regularly, participate in advisory council activities, and respect the rules of propriety for a council should resign. Council members should withhold their final judgment when the council is considering any issue until a thorough study by the group has been completed. Council members are obligated to maintain their contacts with as many other citizens as possible and to obtain their viewpoints regarding issues being discussed by the council. In these discussions with citizens, they may not be privileged to reveal the discussions of the council.

Within the framework of a board's statement of policy, a council should develop its own rules of operation, such as:

1. The time and length of meetings.
2. The use of committees of the council.
3. The method of notifying members of meetings.
4. The method of calling special meetings.
5. The method of developing agenda for meetings.

Following is a sample set of bylaws for an advisory council for agricultural education:

● ● ●

SAMPLE BYLAWS

Meetings

1. The Council shall meet__________of each month.
2. Special meetings may be called by the chairperson.
3. Written notices of the agenda of all meetings will be prepared and mailed to all Council members.
4. The executive committee will prepare the agenda for each meeting.
5. The meetings shall not continue for more than two hours unless so voted by the Council members present.
6. Parliamentary procedure will not be used in meetings unless it is necessary to transmit a decision to someone else. The discussion procedure will be used in meetings for the purpose of arriving at a consensus of opinion.
7. Minutes of each meeting will be sent to the members by the secretary.

Officers and Their Duties

1. The officers shall be: a chairperson, a vice-chairperson, and a secretary. These three officers shall be considered members of the executive committee.
2. The officers shall be elected annually by a majority vote of the Council members at the September meeting of the Council.
3. The chairperson of the Council shall be elected from members who have served on the existing Council for at least one year. Duties shall be:
   a. To preside at all Council meetings.
   b. To serve as chairperson of the executive committee.
   c. To appoint special committees which may include persons other than Council members.
4. The vice-chairperson shall perform the duties of the chairperson during the chairperson's absence.
5. The duties of the secretary shall be:
   a. To keep attendance records of Council members.
   b. To keep a record of discussions, recommendations, motions passed, and committee appointments.
   c. To maintain a permanent record file of all Council activities.
   d. To distribute minutes of the Council meetings and copies of other Council documents to Council members, Board of Education members, school administrators, teachers of agriculture, and others who may be concerned.
6. The duties of the executive committee shall be:
   a. To prepare agenda for as many Council meetings in advance as possible.
   b. To call special meetings as needed.

Loss of Membership in the Council

The Council will recommend to the Board of Education the replacement of members who fail to attend three consecutive meetings without reasons satisfactory to the Council.

Limitations and Responsibilities

1. The Council and its affiliated committees will not recommend candidates for the Board of Education.
2. Council members and affiliated committee members are expected to withhold final judgment regarding a problem until they have had an opportunity to study carefully all aspects of the problem and until they have had an opportunity to discuss the problem at a Council or committee meeting.
3. Council and affiliated committee members will not report outside of meetings opinions discussed and decisions reached by individual members.
4. Individual members of the Council or its affiliated committees have no more authority than they do as citizens. To avoid confusion regarding whether Council members or committee members are speaking as citizens or as members of the Council or committee, they should exercise their rights as citizens with extreme caution.

Consultants

The Council and its affiliated committees will use consultants as needed.

• • •

What to Do the First Year—A teacher should encourage the council, early in its life, to make some real decisions and to carry them out successfully. During the first year of the life of a council, meetings of the following type may be held:

1. A meeting or meetings to familiarize council members with programs of agricultural education in other communities.
2. A meeting to familiarize council members with the legal and administrative framework of agricultural education and the history of agricultural education.
3. Meetings to discuss the role of the agriculture department in the community, with questions such as these: What is our agriculture department for? How good is it? How many people is it reaching with systematic instruction? What territory should it serve? How many people and what people within that territory should it serve? How should it serve them?
4. Meetings to discuss the community agricultural situation, the principal needs of the people of the community for agricultural education, and the efficiency of the agricultural workers in the community. The teachers may make a list of the things they want to know about the community and spend an evening having the council members indicate their opinion of the situation. For example: What percentage of the land has been tested for acidity? What are the employment needs in off-farm agricultural occupations? What off-farm agricultural services are needed?
5. Meetings to plan the adult program for the year—one meeting may deal with young adults, another with courses for older farmers and off-farm adults in jobs requiring knowledge and skills in agriculture. If adult programs are started, time will have to be devoted to them later in council meetings.
6. A meeting to consider prospective agricultural opportunities in the community and the guidance which should be given high school students and young adults regarding their choice of occupations.
7. A meeting with the FFA chapter.

8. A meeting with the FFA executive committee.
9. A trip to the homes or places of work of representative high school students to observe their occupational experience programs in agriculture.
10. A meeting to discuss students' supervised occupational experience programs.
11. A meeting with representatives of farm organizations: agricultural extension, the soil conservation district, Farm Credit Administration, Rural Electrification Administration, and other public agencies serving agriculture.
12. A meeting on buildings and facilities for the agriculture department, especially if material improvement is needed.
13. Meetings devoted to particular projects, such as environmental quality control.
14. Meetings to consider whether national and state standards for vocational education in agriculture are applicable locally and how those applicable may be implemented.
15. An annual meeting devoted to evaluation of the work of the department.
16. An annual meeting for planning the program for the coming year.
17. An annual social meeting for members and families.
18. An annual meeting with the board of education.
19. An annual meeting to evaluate the work of the council during the year.
20. A meeting with school officials and other teachers in the school system to discuss problems of mutual interest and to correlate the program of agricultural education with other programs in the school.
21. A meeting with the advisory council for vocational education.
22. Meetings to analyze and revise policies and formulate new policies for recommendation to the board of education.[3]

POLICY MAKING

Advisory councils for agricultural education are almost a prerequisite in most schools for the development of sound and effective policies for agricultural education. Written official policies are also almost a prerequisite for a good annual and long-time program of agricultural education in a school.

One of the difficulties in program planning is the vague or different ideas existing in a community regarding the functions and policies of agricultural education. This difficulty is lessened in importance when a school adopts a written policy statement regarding its agriculture department. A policy statement provides the framework for an effective agricultural education program. A plan may then be developed within this framework.

Written official policies produce many benefits that are directly or indirectly related to a good program of agricultural education in a school. A statement of policy is valuable for informing new board members of the program. It also may serve the same purpose for new superintendents, principals, other teachers, and new or additional teachers of agriculture. A policy statement helps prevent misunderstandings and confusion because it indicates objectives, responsibilities, and divisions of authority. A written statement of official policies helps those interested in agricultural education understand and appreciate what their local school's department of agriculture is trying to do. Policies promote continuity and consistency in the program of a department,

[3]List adapted from H. M. Hamlin's *Using Advisory Councils in Agricultural Education*, Bul. 63, Bureau of Educational Research, College of Education, University of Illinois, Urbana–Champaign, pp. 50–51.

even when there is a change of teachers or school administrators. Official policies provide a teacher with protection against pressure groups, and they prevent misunderstandings between the teacher and the administrators of the school.

Many departments of agriculture in the public schools are operating under unwritten policies that have developed through tradition and through board action. Often these unwritten policies are outdated and no longer serve the needs of agricultural education. An attempt to develop official written policies forces all concerned with agricultural education in a district to analyze the existing procedures that may have been started during the primitive days of agricultural education to determine whether they fit the modern situation.

When procedures are analyzed to determine what policies they represent, some very primitive and ridiculous policies are often uncovered. For example, some schools, when their procedures are analyzed, seem to be operating under the policy that a school has no obligation for providing agricultural education to young and older adults or to present and prospective workers in off-farm jobs requiring knowledge and skills in agriculture, or that a teacher of agriculture is expected to provide on-the-job instruction as an overload. Unwritten and often unrecognized policies such as these are preventing agricultural education from becoming as valuable as it might become and from serving all whom it is supposed to serve. Thus, unwritten policies based on tradition or on snap judgments of administrators or boards of education are preventing districts from obtaining the type of agricultural education they desire.

In most communities that do not have written official policies that are basically sound, the morale of the teachers of agriculture would improve if such policies were developed. Policies give teachers a framework in which to work. They promote the sharing of responsibility with those with whom responsibility should be shared. They help teachers avoid difficulties. For example, in one instance a teacher of agriculture, teaching in a school without written policies, established the regulation that 20 enrollees would be the maximum number permitted to enroll in an adult course. One of the adults in the district who was not able to enroll in the course because of this limit on enrollment told the board about the policy. The board stated that it had no such policy and forced the teacher to reverse the policy and enroll the adult in the course. This is an example of a teacher making a policy without authority. After this situation occurred, the board recognized its need for written policies and later upheld the judgment of the teacher by adopting a policy limiting enrollment in certain types of adult courses to a maximum of 20 enrollees.

What Are Policies?—Before proceeding further, "policies" should be defined. Policies adopted by school boards are a form of legislation, and they should conform to the standards of well written legislation. Policies are not rules and regulations to determine the procedure for accomplishing a specific task. Instead, policies are general principles of operation. A policy is designed to be applicable over a considerable period of time, while a rule or regulation may apply to only one situation or for a short period of time. Our National Constitution is a good example of a set of policies. The Constitution of the United States has withstood the test of time with very few amendments. Many state constitutions that have tried to outline procedures in detail have quickly become out of date and have been replaced. Sound policies establish the framework for agricultural education and allow considerable freedom for the school administrators and the teachers of agriculture to design methods for accomplishing and fulfilling these policies.

Who Makes Policies?—It is the legal responsibility of a board of education to establish policies. It cannot legally give this responsibility to anyone else. A board may and probably should seek help from others in formulating policies for the school, however.

Steps in Policy Making—Many schools will never obtain adequate policies for agricultural education if the boards of education must initiate the formulation of the policies needed. Many schools have obtained sound policies for agricultural education by having the advisory councils formulate and recommend policies to their boards of education. Often a charter for an advisory council contains a statement granting the council permission to formulate and recommend policies to the school board. If this statement is not present in the charter for a council, the council should request permission to formulate and recommend policies.

The steps a council and the teachers of agriculture in a school may take in formulating policies for agricultural education might be as follows:

1. Determine federal policies for vocational and non-vocational education in agriculture.
2. Determine state policies for agricultural education and for vocational education in agriculture.
3. Determine existing policies that may be found in board minutes.
4. Analyze existing procedures to determine unwritten policies.
5. Determine the areas policies should cover and the questions policies should answer.
6. Divide the council into committees to work on policies for certain areas of the agricultural education program.
7. Have each committee of the council formulate written policies for its area.
8. Have each committee submit its written policies for approval, revision, or rejection by the entire council.
9. Submit the policies formulated by the council to the board of education for adoption, revision, or rejection.

Often joint meetings of a board of education and a council are held at the time the policies formulated by the council are submitted to the board. In this way the council may indicate the thinking behind the various policies suggested. Often a board of education submits the recommended policies of the council to the public in the district before it reacts to them.

Since policy formulation is a long and arduous task, many councils do not wait until they have a complete set of policies for agricultural education before submitting proposed policies to their boards of education for their reactions. A council, for example, may submit policies for adult education first and later follow with policies for other areas, such as the FFA, the agriculture mechanics program, and the young adult program.

When a council is engaged in formulating policies for agricultural education in its community, the teachers of agriculture have an important role to play. Teachers of agriculture have had considerable education regarding what is good agricultural education. They should be in a position to give a council considerable help in the formulation of policies. This does not mean that they should tell the council what policies are needed, but they should be ready at all times to help council members and the council as a whole to consider the effects of the policies they are proposing. They should be able to help a council recognize all the different areas that policies should cover and all the different questions that policies should answer. In some cases it may be necessary for them to suggest policies which the council has overlooked.

It is usually not wise for a teacher to give a council copies of policies formulated by other councils in other schools before the members as individuals and as a group have had an opportunity to do a considerable amount of thinking about the policies that are needed. If sample policies from other schools are presented to a council before the members have had an opportunity to think in some detail about the policies they should have, the council may be stampeded into accepting these policies without thinking through their implications. There is also the tendency for councils to take the easy way out by just recommending the policies which some other school has adopted. The recommendation of policies without the thinking through of their implications and the adoption of policies by a board of education before the members understand what they mean often produces few results. When members of a community have *not* gone through the rigorous process of developing policies which they understand, they often forget to use their policies when the opportunity to use them arises.

Boards of education, councils, administrators, and teachers have been known to establish policies or procedures contrary to written official policies because they forgot they had policies that covered the situation. When this occurs, it is an indication that those concerned did not understand the policies that were adopted previously. The areas which school policies should cover and the questions which school policies should answer have not been definitely determined, but the policies for agricultural education should probably at least answer the following questions:

1. What is agricultural education? What are the purposes of the agricultural education program in the school system?
2. What groups in the community should the agriculture department serve?
3. What geographic territory does the agriculture department serve?
4. What kind of educational services in agriculture will be provided?
5. What are the relationships of the school's department of agriculture to the remainder of the school?
6. How will a program for agricultural education be planned, and who will participate in the planning?
7. How will the various parts of a program of agricultural education be financed?
8. How will advisory groups be organized and used in the management of the department of agricultural education?
9. How are the educational outcomes of agricultural education to be determined, and who will determine them?
10. What are the admission and retention requirements for students in the various agricultural education courses?
11. What are the minimum and maximum sizes of classes in agriculture?
12. What reports regarding agricultural education will be made to the board of education and to the community?
13. How many staff members and how much staff time will be provided for the agricultural education program?

14. How will staff time be used in agricultural education?
15. How will the facilities of the schools in the district be used for agricultural education?
16. What provisions will be made for the on-farm or on-job instruction of high school students, young adult students, and older adult students enrolled in agriculture?
17. What provisions will there be for group instruction away from the school?
18. What provisions are there for the protection of the instructors from liability for accidents?
19. What are the regulations under which school-sponsored agricultural organizations must operate?
20. What are the relationships that shall exist between the agriculture department and other agricultural education and agricultural organizations outside the school?
21. What is to be the nature of the program for older adults?
22. What is to be the nature of the program for young adults?
23. What is to be the nature of the high school program?
24. How will equal education and avoidance of bias and stereotyping by sex, race, and handicaps of students be accomplished?

Ideally a school should have policies which apply school-wide. When a school has school-wide policies, these usually answer many of the questions that have just been presented, and the special policies needed for agricultural education are greatly reduced. For example, a school should have school-wide policies for the dissemination of publicity about the school. If such policies are present, special policies for the release of publicity about the agriculture department would probably not be needed.

Examples of Policies—Following are a few selected examples of policies that have been adopted by boards of education for their agricultural education programs. These policies are not necessarily ideal, but they do represent the type of policies that boards of education do establish.

1. Adult education in agriculture is to be provided. When possible, state and federal funds will be used. In some courses, such as welding, there shall be an enrollment fee to cover the consumable supplies used.
2. The program in agricultural education is to be an educational program. The department has no responsibility for performing services for farmers or other agricultural workers.
3. The instruction provided for adults is to be organized and systematic. The courses are to consist of a series of meetings on related topics. The content dealt with in the different meetings is to be unified, interacting, or interdependent. The various meetings of a course are to be designed to contribute to the same predetermined objectives. Understanding of the instruction provided at a meeting of an adult course will be based to a considerable extent on the instruction received at previous meetings.
4. The regular teachers of agriculture will be employed full-time for agricultural education on a 12-month basis, with no more than 1 month of vacation.
5. Qualified special teachers may be employed to teach part-time in the adult courses when the regular teachers of agriculture, because of the limits of time or because of the special training needed, cannot teach the courses. These special teachers are to be employed by the board of education.
6. Mileage expenses will be allowed to teachers for on-job instruction. On-job instruction is to be considered a part of the teaching load of the agriculture teachers.
7. The board of education will carry insurance to protect the teachers of agriculture against liability for accidents.
8. Drinking by any person, when associating with the school, is prohibited.

9. Persons not eligible for enrollment in courses reimbursed with state and federal funds may be offered courses in which they are eligible to enroll if they request them or if the need for such courses is apparent.
10. Field trips of an educational nature may be planned and conducted by the instructors during school time if advance approval is obtained from the administrators of the school.
11. Field trips that will contribute to the educational progress of the students are to be recognized as worthy and sometimes necessary.
12. The school will provide transportation for field trips of high school groups.
13. The FFA is to be self-sustaining financially, and the funds of the organization are to be handled with the regular school activity funds.
14. School organizations shall not seek donations. Gifts for worthy projects may be accepted, if the persons or organizations making the gifts are not solicited and if the gifts are approved in advance by the board of education.
15. Young and older adult enrollees in courses may form organizations. Their constitutions or purposes must be approved by the board of education. Membership in an organization shall be limited to the members in good standing in the courses.
16. Enrollees in adult courses shall be definitely enrolled far enough in advance of the meetings of the courses so that plans for the courses can be made and so that the instructor can gain a firsthand knowledge of the problems of those enrolled.
17. A minimum and a maximum enrollment for each adult course is to be determined in advance by the teacher of agriculture responsible for the course, with the advice of the general council or the special committee for the course.
18. The advisory council for agricultural education is to assist the teachers of agriculture in planning a long-time program of adult education. This program is to indicate the purposes to be served, the manner of evaluating the program and its outcomes, the courses to be offered, the centers and times at which the courses are to be offered, and the general arrangements necessary to carry out the program.

NATIONAL AND STATE STANDARDS FOR VOCATIONAL EDUCATION IN AGRICULTURE

In the development of policies and a program for a local department of production agriculture and agribusiness, ideas may be generated by a review of the recommended national and state standards for quality agricultural education programs. These standards were developed by a large group of the leading vocational education in agriculture professionals in the country. They were validated in the states by teachers, teacher educators, and supervisors. They provide suggestions for "benchmarks" for both policies and program ingredients. The local advisory council for agriculture can profit by reviewing them when advising regarding policies or programs. The school administration needs to be aware of the standards that apply locally.

The complete list of standards is too long to include in this book. Teachers may obtain a copy of the complete list of standards from their state supervisor of agriculture at the state department of education.

Following is the table of contents for the national and state standards:

Standards Common to All Programs

Instructional Program
Supervised Occupational Experience
Leadership Development

Student Recruitment, Enrollment, and Counseling
Public Relations
Facilities and Equipment
Staffing
Administration and Supervision
Finance
Placement
Evaluation

Standards Specific to Production Agriculture

Instructional Program
Supervised Occupational Experience
Staffing
Administration and Supervision

Standards Specific to Agricultural Supplies and Services

Instructional Program
Supervised Occupational Experience
Leadership Development
Student Recruitment, Enrollment, and Counseling
Facilities and Equipment
Staffing
Administration and Supervision

Standards Specific to Agricultural Mechanics

Supervised Occupational Experience
Facilities and Equipment
Staffing

Standards Specific to Agricultural Products

Instructional Program
Supervised Occupational Experience
Leadership Development
Student Recruitment and Enrollment
Facilities and Equipment
Staffing

Standards Specific to Ornamental Horticulture

Instructional Program
Leadership Development
Facilities and Equipment
Staffing

Standards Specific to Agricultural (Natural) Resources

Instructional Program
Supervised Occupational Experience
Facilities and Equipment

Standards Specific to Forestry

Facilities and Equipment
Staffing

Standards Specific to Adult Education in Agricultural Occupations

Instructional Program
Young Farmer Educational Association
Development
Planning and Conducting the Instructional Program
Administration
Evaluation

Standards are available for both programs in rural areas and programs in metropolitan areas.

Following are a few *examples* of standards taken from the total list of standards. These *sample* standards were selected at random to illustrate the kinds of standards being recommended.

1. The instructional program contains the necessary balance of class time, laboratory work, field trips, and occupational experience to prepare students adequately for employment or advanced educational programs.
2. The instructional program is reviewed and modified in light of local, state, and federal manpower data.
3. Supervision of students engaged in cooperative occupational experience programs is accomplished by both the instructor and the cooperating employer.
4. All secondary vocational education in agriculture students participate in the FFA.
5. Students enrolled in a specialized program of vocational education in agriculture have completed a one- or two-year basic vocational education in agriculture program.
6. The classrooms, shop, and laboratories are adequate for the number of students enrolled. The equipment replicates that found in the occupations for which training is provided.
7. The instructor(s) must possess the personal, technical, professional, and occupational competencies necessary to prepare students for entry level employment or for advanced educational programs.
8. The vocational education in agriculture program is an integral part of the local district plan for vocational education.
9. The instructional program is supported by an annual board-approved budget that considers program needs and the number of students enrolled.
10. The instructor(s), in cooperation with the school counselor(s), will assist in the placement and follow-up of students.
11. The instructor(s), local administrator(s), and appropriate state education staff member(s) meet at regular intervals to examine and evaluate formally the vocational education in agriculture program.

PLANNING A PROGRAM

A policy statement by a board of education outlines the framework for agricultural education in a community. A written annual and long-time plan is also needed to fill in the details within the framework established by a policy statement.

Why Have a Plan?—The primary function of a teacher of agriculture is to provide a program which will best meet, with the help of other teachers of agriculture, the educational needs in agriculture of all the people living in a school area. A teacher needs to allot time so that it will be used most effectively in developing the program. A teacher may be called upon by various organizations to assist with community activities, all of which might be desirable, but it may be too time-consuming to help with all of them. A written plan prepared with the guidance of others in the community will help protect a teacher from inroads on the time available for teaching and conducting a comprehensive agricultural education program.

Following are some of the advantages that usually result from long-time planning in a department of agriculture:[4]

1. All factors affecting community welfare are given careful consideration. The community is studied thoroughly, and each activity making demands upon a teacher's time is weighed on the basis of its advantages to the community as a whole.

---

[4]List adapted from F. W. Armstrong's "Long-Time Planning in Departments of Vocational Agriculture," *Agricultural Education Magazine*, Vol. 18, No. 11, p. 205.

2. The job of the teaching staff is defined. Each teacher knows what the community is working toward.
3. Efforts can be concentrated on the important things that need to be done. The energies of the teaching staff are conserved for the big jobs, and unproductive tangents are avoided.
4. There is continuity to the program. A long-time plan ensures that important objectives will not be abandoned before they are achieved. Emphasis in the department is not shifted from year to year without good reason.
5. It is easier to obtain needed supplies and equipment.
6. Since the plan is in writing and is easily understood, misunderstandings are prevented and greater cooperation is obtained from the people living in the community, from the organizations working in the community, and from others.
7. A long-time plan places a department on a more businesslike basis.
8. A long-time plan permits easier evaluation of a department's accomplishments.
9. When a teacher of agriculture leaves a school, the successor can become oriented more easily if a long-time plan is left in the school.
10. When a long-time plan has been prepared with the assistance of an advisory committee and other community leaders, the teacher is not required to defend the program against all comers, as is so often the case otherwise. The program of the department becomes a true community program with full community support.

Who Should Participate in Planning?—All who are affected by a plan should participate directly or indirectly in its preparation. Teachers of agriculture should not attempt by themselves to plan the programs of agricultural education in their schools or communities. Bringing in persons from outside the community who are capable of representing state, national, and world needs and who have a knowledge of other programs of agricultural education is a desirable practice. These individuals may be used to review plans and to suggest additions and deletions.

Those most affected by a plan should be brought into the planning early. They would probably be the administrators, persons enrolled in agriculture courses at all levels, parents, and other teachers. Different levels of planning can be done best by various groups. Overall planning can best be initiated by a representative body, such as an advisory council.

Using an advisory council to assist in the development of a program of agricultural education is recognized as being essential in most communities. A council can assist teachers in determining community needs, securing cooperative relationships, and deciding on the educational program which should be developed to best meet the needs of all the people living in the school area. The support of a council can be of untold value to teachers of agriculture.

Since all in a community are directly or indirectly affected by a plan, such a plan should be published for critical review by the community before it is finally adopted. Major changes in the plan which are proposed should also be published before adoption. The long-time plan and the new yearly plan should probably be published each year.

What to Include in a Plan—A plan should indicate the needs of the community for agricultural education. Objectives should be established, and procedures for reaching these objectives should be determined. Methods of evaluating results should be stated. This may necessitate the evaluation of the present status of agricultural education in the community and the establishment of standards for measuring progress.

Detailed plans should be developed for the various phases of the program of agricultural education, such as the elementary school program, the high school program, the program for the handicapped, and the adult programs.

For the *elementary school program*, procedures and plans should be established for:

1. Promoting career awareness and instruction regarding careers in agricultural occupations.
2. Promoting occupational exploration activities and units of instruction in agriculture.
3. Providing consultant services to elementary school teachers.
4. Providing resource materials to elementary school teachers relating to careers in agricultural occupations.

For the *high school program*, procedures and plans should be established for:

1. Guidance, recruitment, and selection of students.
2. Number and sequence of courses for farming and for off-farm occupations requiring agricultural knowledge.
3. FFA and subsidiaries.
4. Supervised occupational experience programs.
5. Individual instruction on the job.
6. Follow-up.
7. Placement.
8. Publicity.
9. Use of advisory committees and council.
10. Tours and field trips.
11. Provisions for serving students with special needs.

For the *adult programs*, procedures and plans should be established for:

1. Use of advisory committees and council.
2. Courses and sequences of courses.
3. Recruitment and selection of members.
4. School-sponsored organizations.
5. Individual instruction on the job and in the home.
6. Supervised occupational experience programs.
7. Recreation.
8. Placement.
9. Tours and field trips.

Other procedures and plans should be developed regarding:

1. Visual aids.
2. Guidance and counseling.
3. Records and reports.
4. Instructional materials and facilities.
5. Use of school land.
6. Administration of the department.
7. School, community, and professional duties.
8. Fairs and contests.
9. The summer program.
10. The schedule of teachers' time.
11. The calendar of activities.
12. Public relations.

Most public school departments of agriculture have developed plans and procedures for many of the items listed. These may be incorporated into a total program plan. After the first program is developed, revisions are fairly easy. Course outlines and detailed plans, within the framework of the overall plan, can be developed by those most concerned. Objectives, procedures, and evaluation devices are part of all detailed plans. Plans should be checked to see that the programs adopted are based on needs and serve the groups which should be served, such as young and older adults, as well as high school students.

Planning a Program to Serve All Groups—In planning a program of agricultural education in a community, a teacher of agriculture must give attention to all groups that should be served. All needs of all groups must be considered together, or the program may become top-heavy in one or more areas. Some schools have overemphasized their vocational agriculture for farming courses or their high school programs and have neglected others, such as the adult and off-farm agriculture programs. Another undesirable result of not considering all groups that should be served is the accretion during the year of educational activities for neglected groups with the result that the teachers soon become overworked. If the education and progress of adults, high school students, and others advance together, the total results from a program of agricultural education will probably be greater over a period of years than they would be if the program were allowed to slight the education of one or more groups that should be served by an agricultural education department.

DETERMINING NEEDS

Secure Basic Community Data—In determining the objectives and the activities to include in the long-time plan for the agricultural education program in a community, it is important that the community be studied thoroughly. Securing basic data and interpreting them effectively are essential in developing a sound and well balanced educational program in agriculture. The following is a list of some of the sources of basic data in agriculture:

1. United States Farm Census (secure from the Department of Commerce, Bureau of the Census, Washington, D.C.).
2. The local advisory council.
3. The agricultural college.
4. Prospective students and parents.
5. Farmers, off-farm agricultural workers, agricultural businesspersons, the county agent, and other interested persons.
6. Aerial maps of individual farms.
7. Soil conservation offices.
8. Production Marketing Administration offices.
9. The county agricultural council.
10. County land-use committees.
11. County soil survey maps.
12. The township assessor.
13. The county clerk.

These basic data should reveal the following information regarding a community:

1. The more important farm enterprises and agriculturally oriented businesses in the community.
2. The equipment on farms and in agricultural businesses.
3. The home conveniences on farms and in homes of off-farm agricultural workers.
4. The number of home shops.
5. The approved practices needed.
6. The sizes of farms and the types of farming.
7. The sizes and types of off-farm agricultural businesses.
8. The percentage of landowners, managers, and tenants.
9. The names of agricultural organizations in the community.
10. The social and economic problems related to agriculture and rural life.
11. The farm enterprises and the off-farm agricultural businesses which may become important in the community in the future.
12. The trends in agriculture in the community.
13. The improvements needed in the community.
14. The nationalities represented in the community.
15. The efficiency of farms and off-farm agricultural businesses.
16. The miscellaneous data the instructor believes valuable.

Data should be obtained to reveal the following about agriculturally oriented businesses and jobs or occupations requiring knowledge and skills in agriculture:

1. Number, names, locations, and functions of agriculturally oriented businesses in the community.
2. Job titles of workers who need knowledge and skills in agriculture.
3. Activities of workers in jobs requiring knowledge and skills in agriculture.
4. Specific knowledge and skills needed by workers in certain off-farm jobs.
5. Employment opportunities and working conditions in off-farm jobs requiring knowledge and skills in agriculture.

Summarize and Interpret Basic Data—After the basic data have been collected, they must be summarized and interpreted. A survey may show that very few off-farm agricultural businesses are in a community. This may mean that more agricultural businesses are needed, or it may mean that the community is not suited to their needs. The farmers may not be practicing hog lot sanitation, but this may be the very thing that they should be doing. The data may show that although there is very little need for vocational education in agriculture for farming, there is much need for vocational education in agriculture for off-farm agriculturally oriented jobs. For these reasons, a teacher must exercise care in interpreting community data. A teacher should ask the advisory council to assist in interpreting the data and to make recommendations for the activities to be included in a long-time plan.

DEVELOPING OBJECTIVES

After basic data have been collected, summarized, and interpreted, the teachers of agriculture, the advisory council members, and others are ready to develop objectives for an annual and long-time program of agricultural education. If the objectives are to be desirable in our present culture, they should meet the following criteria:

1. The objectives are compatible with democratic values.
2. The objectives are based on basic human needs and on the needs of our culture.

3. The objectives are based on the agricultural needs of the nation and the community.
4. The objectives are not contradictory.
5. The objectives are stated in terms of changed behavior of people.
6. The objectives are capable of attainment.
7. The objectives are stated clearly so that there is no doubt as to what the department hopes to accomplish.
8. The objectives are specific enough to enable the teachers and the community to determine when they have been accomplished.
9. The objectives are comprehensive and challenging to the teachers and the community.
10. The objectives include all phases and types of agricultural education.

Those who are developing objectives for a community program of agricultural education should analyze the needs of the community in terms of the objectives of agricultural education and of general education.

A partial list of objectives for agriculture and general education may be found in Chapter 1. The written objectives developed by teachers and a council should be checked against the criteria characterizing desirable objectives and then presented to the entire community for revisions and ratification.

The persons developing objectives should make a distinction between *agricultural* and *educational* objectives and between *education* and *service*. We are concerned with education and educational objectives. Educational objectives pertain to the development of desirable changes in people. Agricultural objectives pertain to the development of desirable changes in agriculture. Success in the accomplishment of an educational objective may result in a desirable change in agriculture. However, success in the accomplishment of an agricultural objective may not result in a desirable change in people. For example, if the agricultural objective to increase the use of limestone is adopted, it may be possible to obtain this increase through subsidies, gifts, and sales campaigns with little change in knowledge, attitude, and understanding on the part of the people. When the campaign for increasing the use of limestone is over, limestone use may be discontinued. But if an educational objective is adopted, for example, to increase people's ability and improve their attitudes regarding the use of limestone, the objective would imply an educational program to effect relatively permanent changes in people regarding their knowledge, attitudes, skills, and understandings pertaining to the use of limestone. This educational program would probably bring about an increase in the use of limestone, but it would also result in an educational change in the people of the community. We must be certain that our objectives are educational and not just agricultural.

Another pitfall which advisory councils and communities sometimes encounter in developing objectives is the adoption of objectives or ways and means for accomplishing objectives that create a service program instead of an educational program. The first task in guiding a community toward a program of agricultural education, instead of an agricultural service program, is the development of an understanding of the difference between educational objectives and service objectives. A service program is concerned only with getting a job done. An educational program is concerned with developing the abilities of individuals to do a job themselves. An agriculture department is a part of a school. Schools are established for education and not for service. An agriculture department cannot afford to dissipate its energy on service activities.

Develop Objectives for a Community Program of Agricultural Education—In developing objectives for a program of agricultural education, the persons involved should review existing lists of objectives for agricultural education and general education, accepting or revising them to meet present and local conditions. Understanding of state and national objectives for education in agriculture and for general education is necessary for the intelligent development of community objectives. In a written program, the state and national lists of objectives, as revised, should be given. Then a more detailed list of objectives for the community should be given.

Determine Year to Accomplish Each Objective—Some of the objectives will pertain to current problems which need immediate attention, and these should be achieved the first year. Others will be less urgent and may be delayed until the following year or later years. All objectives in a long-time plan should be listed and ways and means of accomplishing the objectives for the current year developed. Each year, ways and means of accomplishing the objectives need to be developed and the necessary changes made in the long-time plan. Some of the objectives may cover a period of several years, while others may be of shorter duration.

Evaluate Accomplishments—At the close of each school year, the teachers and the advisory council should evaluate the accomplishments in terms of the objectives for the year. In other words, an appraisal should be made of the long-time plan to see how it is working. On the basis of this evaluation, ways and means for the improvement of the program should be developed by the teachers and the advisory council. Some objectives may need to be revised or

Form 10.1. Long-Time Objectives for Agricultural Education

School____________________ Date________________ 19 ____

Objectives	Ways and Means of Accomplishing Objectives	Accomplishments	Year to Be Accomplished				
			19____	19____	19____	19____	19____

eliminated, while others may need to be added. A long-time plan may be divided into three columns: one for listing the objectives, one for ways and means of accomplishing the objectives, and one for accomplishments. The year in which an objective should be accomplished may also be indicated. (See Form 10.1.)

PLANNING AN EFFECTIVE SUMMER PROGRAM

Teachers of vocational agriculture are often employed for 12 months per year because of the need for year-round instruction. Teachers of nonvocational agriculture are also often employed year round. The summer program is an important phase of a program in agricultural education, especially for vocational education in agriculture. It offers many opportunities for instructors to do an effective job of supervision and teaching on the job. Every teacher, with the help of others. should develop a list of the activities planned for the summer and allot time for each. A copy of this list should be given to the advisory council, the school board, the superintendent, the state supervisor, and those who have helped to develop the summer plans.

The summer plans may be partially developed during the school term as the different enterprises, major units, and problems are studied. For example, when the swine enterprise is being studied and the job of vaccinating swine is discussed, the instructor may plan visits to the different members of the class to aid them in vaccinating. Follow-up class meetings for young and adult farmers and for adults in agriculturally oriented businesses or jobs may be developed in the same way. As these activities are planned, a calendar of summer activities may be developed.

Form 10.2, "Time Allotment for Summer Activities," is an example of one way of recording summer plans.

Summer Activities—It is true that the activities in various communities will differ; nevertheless, there are many duties that apply to every community. Some of those listed here will need to be included every summer, while others may be included but once. It is not expected that instructors can carry out all the activities suggested, but the list should be helpful in selecting summer activities. Many of the duties continue throughout the summer and for this reason no attempt has been made to distribute them by months. Each instructor will need to work out a calendar for summer activities. Following is a partial list of summer duties of an agricultural teacher:

1. Conduct class meetings for young, out-of-school adults.
2. Conduct class meetings for adult farmers and other adults in agricultural jobs.
3. Conduct follow-up class meetings, tours, field trips, and demonstrations for high school students, young farmers, adult farmers, and other adults in agricultural jobs.
4. Attend young farmer association meetings.
5. Hold FFA chapter meetings.
6. Provide individual instruction regarding supervised occupational experience programs of high school students, young farmers, adult farmers, and other adults in agricultural jobs.
7. Visit prospective students.
8. Organize and supervise prevocational programs for prospective high school students.
9. Attend the annual state conference of teachers of agriculture.
10. Follow up on former students.
11. Arrange for exhibits of supervised occupational products at local fairs.
12. Plan a picnic for all present and prospective students of agriculture.
13. Become acquainted with persons interested in agricultural education.
14. Attend FFA leadership meetings.
15. Cooperate with local organizations.

16. Make monthly reports to the superintendent and the school board showing accomplishments.
17. Send reports to the state board for vocational education.
18. Make community surveys.
19. Prepare a spot map indicating location of high school students, young and older adult students, and other prospective students.
20. Develop or revise course of study outlines for the following year.
21. Plan definite field trips and laboratory activities for the school year.
22. Develop plans for instruction in agriculture mechanics.
23. Take pictures of supervised occupational experience and FFA activities.
24. Collect visual aids for instructional purposes.

Form 10.2. Time Allotment for Summer Activities

Activity	Approximate Number of Days to Be Spent				
	May	June	July	Aug.	Total
I. "Learning-by-Doing" Programs					
Individual Instruction					
Tours					
II. Adult Education					
Class Meetings					
Individual Instruction					
III. Community Work					
Demonstrations					
Service (educational)					
Fairs					
IV. New Students					
V. School-sponsored organizations					
VI. Self-improvement					
Summer School					
Agriculture Teachers' Conference					
Other					
VII. Rooms and Equipment					
VIII. Planning Next Year's Program					
IX. Records and Reports					
X. Public Relations					
XI. Other Activities					
XII. Vacation (Notify supervisors of dates you expect to leave and return)					
TOTALS					

Remarks (further details or explanations):

School ______________________ Instructor ______________________

25. Prepare requests for equipment, books, bulletins, and other necessary supplies not already ordered.
26. File new bulletins.
27. Write articles for the local and state newspapers.
28. Prepare for the school administration the annual report containing a summary of activities and accomplishments.
29. Give the local newspapers a summary of the accomplishments of the department for the year.
30. Develop professionally through home reading, summer school, and conferences for teachers.
31. Arrange classroom and shop equipment before school opens.
32. Complete records and inventories if the teacher is leaving the department.

Summer Vacation—Instructors should plan in advance when to take their vacation, so as to arrange for the more important summer activities to come at the time they are on the job. The summer vacation should ordinarily come at a time when teachers can be of the least service to the students and the community. As a general rule, this can easily be determined. If some teachers plan to attend summer school, they will have to take their vacation at that particular time. When possible, it is desirable for teachers to return home week-ends during summer school to visit their students. Some institutions arrange for all classes to be held from Monday through Thursday to make it possible for those within driving distance to spend Friday and Saturday visiting the homes and jobs of their students. This is especially important for teachers who attend summer school for more than three weeks.

Publicity—It is important that the teachers of agriculture in a community keep the public informed of the activities of the department during the summer months. Following are some of the ways this may be done:

1. Taking and exhibiting pictures of activities.
2. Writing articles for local and state newspapers.
3. Making and showing 2″ x 2″ slides.
4. Conducting tours of supervised occupational experience programs.
5. Giving talks.
6. Keeping the superintendent informed.

A comprehensive publicity program should be developed on a year-round basis in order to keep the public properly informed. This program is discussed further in Chapter 11.

Evaluation—At the close of the summer months, teachers, with the help of others, should make an evaluation of achievements in terms of the objectives formulated for the summer program.

CHAPTER

11

How to Develop a Desirable Public Relations Program

Enlisting the aid of the public in developing an agricultural education program and keeping the public informed of its progress and accomplishments are the principal components of a program of public relations. The proposed program, progress reports, and the annual evaluation report should be published or otherwise widely distributed. Comments and suggestions regarding these reports should be solicited and considered in the revision of the program. Members of the public cannot be expected to cooperate to the fullest extent unless they have a clear understanding of the aims and purposes and the possible achievements of the agricultural education program.

Objectives of Public Relations—A desirable public relations program in agricultural education should attempt to:

1. Develop understandings of the objectives of the program in vocational agriculture for farming and for off-farm occupations requiring knowledge and skills in agriculture.
2. Develop understandings of the objectives of the non-vocational phases of the school's program of agricultural education.
3. Inform the public of the achievements of the program.
4. Create good will and desirable relationships.
5. Obtain the cooperation and support of the public, including all agricultural organizations and other agencies interested in agricultural education.
6. Interest students in enrolling in high school and adult courses in agriculture.
7. Develop a comprehensive program of agricultural education.
8. Create a feeling of need for the program of agricultural education.

Responsibility of Teachers—Teachers of agriculture must accept responsibility for heading the public relations programs of their departments. They should, however, enlist the aid of others, such as advisory council members, students, and administrators.

RELATIONSHIPS WITH SPECIFIC GROUPS

A department of agriculture in a public school and the teachers in a department must maintain desirable relationships with the general public. This means working with many specific groups as well as the public in general. Following is a partial list of groups that must be worked with successfully:

1. Parents and students.
2. Farmers enrolled in adult courses.
3. Young farmers enrolled in courses.
4. Adults enrolled in courses for off-farm agriculturally oriented jobs and in non-vocational agriculture courses.
5. Agricultural organizations.
6. Cooperatives.
7. Agricultural agencies and businesses working with farmers.
8. The agricultural extension service.
9. Local voluntary organizations.
10. Local organizations of teachers.
11. The state vocational association.
12. State educational organizations.
13. Local school administrators, the school board, and the teaching staff.
14. Prospective high school, young farmer, adult farmer, and other adult students in agricultural jobs.
15. The state teacher education service.
16. The state department of education.
17. Other groups contributing to the promotion and progress of the local program in agriculture.

Parents and Students—There is no substitute for the home visit in developing desirable relationships with parents and students. Desirable relationships can best be developed through broad supervised occupational experience programs in agriculture. Group meetings of parents, sons, and daughters are desirable in developing basic understanding and relationships.

Agricultural Organizations—There are a number of agricultural organizations, such as the Nursery Association, Farm Equipment Dealers Association, farmer organizations, marketing associations, and cooperatives, with which teachers of agriculture should work. Teachers can afford to attend and participate in some of their meetings. Representatives of agricultural organizations should be invited to participate in the activities of the schools' departments of agriculture.

Agricultural Agencies—Agencies such as the Production Credit Association, the Farm and Home Administration, and the U.S. Employment Service can contribute to the development and progress of a program of agricultural education. Teachers should contact these agencies and solicit their cooperation.

Agricultural Extension Service—There are many ways in which teachers of agriculture, county agricultural agents, and the state extension service staff may cooperate. Some of the things agriculture teachers may do are as follows:

1. Work with the county agent in developing a community program of agricultural education.
2. Become familiar with the state policies for teachers of agriculture and for extension workers.
3. Cooperate with the county agent in developing activities for which the teachers are responsible, and solicit the cooperation of the extension agent in developing the agricultural education program.

Voluntary Organizations—Most towns and cities have one or more voluntary organizations, such as the chamber of commerce, Rotary, and Lions, which can be of considerable help to teachers of agriculture in promoting agricultural education activities. Teachers should participate in some of their meetings and activities. They must cooperate if they expect the club members to cooperate with them.

Relationships with Farmers and Off-Farm Agricultural Workers—Teachers must develop a comprehensive educational program for farmers and off-farm workers who need agricultural education, win their confidence and good will, and solicit their cooperation. An effective educational program based on individual interests and needs should result in desirable relationships.

Relationships with the School—Teachers are hired by a local school board; consequently, it is imperative that they develop friendly relations with the superintendent, principal, school board members, school trustees, and school faculty. They should:

1. Consider themselves members of the school system the same as other teachers.
2. Be friendly with all staff members.
3. Adhere to all school rules and regulations unless excused by the superintendent.
4. Participate in staff functions.
5. Cooperate in all school activities and offer their services when needed.
6. Accept their share of school responsibilities.
7. Cooperate with all teachers and solicit their cooperation.

Teachers of agriculture must be loyal to the superintendent, the principal, and other school officials at all times.

Teachers' Organizations—Many schools have one or more professional or social organizations of teachers. Teachers of agriculture are working toward objectives which are similar to the objectives other teachers believe to be important. Participation with other teachers in state and national organizations assists teachers of agriculture in reaching their objectives and paves the way for effective cooperation with other teachers. Teachers cannot attain maximum results in their programs unless they have the cooperation of other teachers, nor can they attain maximum enjoyment from their work.

HOW TO INFORM THE PUBLIC

There are a number of desirable ways and means of informing the public, some of which are as follows:

1. Appropriate news items for local papers. *Be sure to mention that the ac-*

tivities are sponsored by the agricultural education department and are administered by the public school.

2. Appropriate news stories for state publications, such as daily papers, agricultural magazines, and releases from the state agency for vocational education. *Be sure to include glossy prints of action pictures.*
3. Radio talks, local and state.
4. Pictures, *denoting action*, of activities in the instructional program, including FFA activities. *Be sure to take plenty of good pictures which tell a story.*
5. Talks before civic clubs, agricultural organizations, church groups, and public meetings.
6. Posters made up of pictures of activities, exhibited in appropriate places.
7. Personal visits.
8. Telephone conversations.
9. Letters, post cards, and the like.
10. Open houses.
11. Exhibits of achievements resulting from instruction: products produced in individual agriculture experience programs, agriculture machines repaired, labor-saving devices constructed, food processed, and the like. *Be sure to use placards about an exhibit to inform the public of items such as efficiency factors of costs, sizes, and amounts.*
12. Slide shows. Make a series of 2″ x 2″ slides of activities of the department and show them before agricultural organizations, civic clubs, parent-teacher meetings, and the like.
13. Tours. Invite school officials, representatives of agricultural organizations, civic club members, and agricultural workers to attend.
14. Demonstration teams.

There is little danger of too much emphasis on a desirable public relations program designed to educate the public regarding agricultural education and the opportunities it provides. Too many teachers do not emphasize it enough. However, a publicity program designed to deceive the public or enhance the prestige or ego of the teacher may be very dangerous.

Exhibits—Teachers are often expected to provide exhibits. These may include window displays, assembly displays, booths at fairs and institutes, and floats. Often requests or opportunities for such exhibits provide little advance notice. Time for preparing these exhibits is usually limited. If teachers and students are to produce acceptable exhibits, it is desirable to have minimum supplies on hand. The following supplies are recommended:

1. Background paper of various colors.
2. "Paste-on" letters of various sizes.
3. Stencils.
4. Crystal flakes of various colors.
5. Spotlights.
6. Small electric motors.
7. China pencils and felt-tip pens.
8. Speed ball pens and India ink.
9. Poster paint of various colors, and brushes.
10. A small spray gun.
11. Some 8″ x 10″ glossy prints and 2″ x 2″ slides.
12. A case for exhibiting 2″ x 2″ slides.
13. Cardboard and sign cloth.

One principle to remember is that people learn from exhibits through what they see. Very few take time to read printed material. Keep the reading material to a minimum. Actual working models probably make the most effective exhibits. For further details on preparing exhibits, see Chapter 37, "How to Prepare and Use Visual Aids."

Writing for Adults—Much of the written material prepared for and sent or otherwise distributed to farmers and off-farm agricultural workers is too difficult for them to read. The material is written at the college level. McGraw[1] found that, on the average, the reading level of adult students was one year below the number of years of schooling completed. We should probably be writing our materials for farmers and off-farm agricultural workers at the sixth grade level.

Written material may be made more readable by:

1. Using words familiar to farmers and off-farm agricultural workers.
2. Avoiding technical terms.
3. Using short sentences.
4. Using personal pronouns, such as *I* and *you*, whenever possible.
5. Using illustrations, pictorial and written.
6. Avoiding use of prefixes and suffixes.

In writing to or for off-farm agricultural workers and farmers, authors should consider the psychological approach for the message they wish to convey. Often authors and writers of letters approach their subject logically. A busy adult does not or will not take time to read such a document. The first sentence of any communication should meet a psychological need. Principles of newspaper writing may be of considerable value in writing for farmers and off-farm agricultural workers. The "meat" of the message should be in the first few sentences.

---

[1]McGraw, Edgar Leon, "A Measure of the Reading Ability of Veteran Farm Trainees in Alabama," Master's Thesis, Alabama Polytechnic Institute (now Auburn University), 52 pp.

PART

Organizing and Planning a High School Program

CHAPTER

12

How to Organize Education in Agriculture

AGRICULTURE CURRICULUM

Importance of a Well Planned Curriculum—A carefully worked out agriculture curriculum is essential if students are to receive the full benefit of a cultural and vocational education. The curriculum for the students enrolled in the agriculture courses should be outlined so that the students and parents will know what subjects are necessary for its completion. Often parents and students have only a vague idea of what subjects are essential in the different high school curriculums.

Vocational Agriculture Courses to Include in the Curriculum—In determining the vocational education in agriculture subjects to include in the curriculum, the local superintendent and the agriculture teachers should consult their state supervisor of agricultural education. The state agency for vocational education in every state has the privilege of working out plans for the administration of the program which seems best adapted to that particular state. Most states have samples of curriculums for vocational education in agriculture to aid superintendents and agriculture instructors. State administrators should be familiar enough with their state to devise plans which are adapted to the conditions. The plans, however, should be flexible enough to be adaptable to the varying agricultural occupations in the different communities of the state.

Most state administrators have recommended for several years that high school course content be integrated around the supervised occupational experience programs of the students.

Agriculture I, II, III, and IV as titles for the courses in vocational education in agriculture have not proved entirely satisfactory. For high school students and parents, school administrators, guidance personnel, and other teachers, they are not very descriptive or meaningful titles. Most other courses in high schools have descriptive titles, and the public expects the same type of course titles in agriculture.

Agriculture has changed rapidly and has become specialized. Vocationally oriented high school students are often interested and involved only in certain phases of agriculture. The objectives of vocational education in agriculture have broadened to include more than education for farming. The result has been the continuing acceptance of the soundness of organizing content around the supervised occupational experience programs of the students, coupled with an attempt to give courses more descriptive titles. There also seems to be a desirable trend toward the offering of more agriculture courses at the high school level to meet the increasing diverse needs of the students.

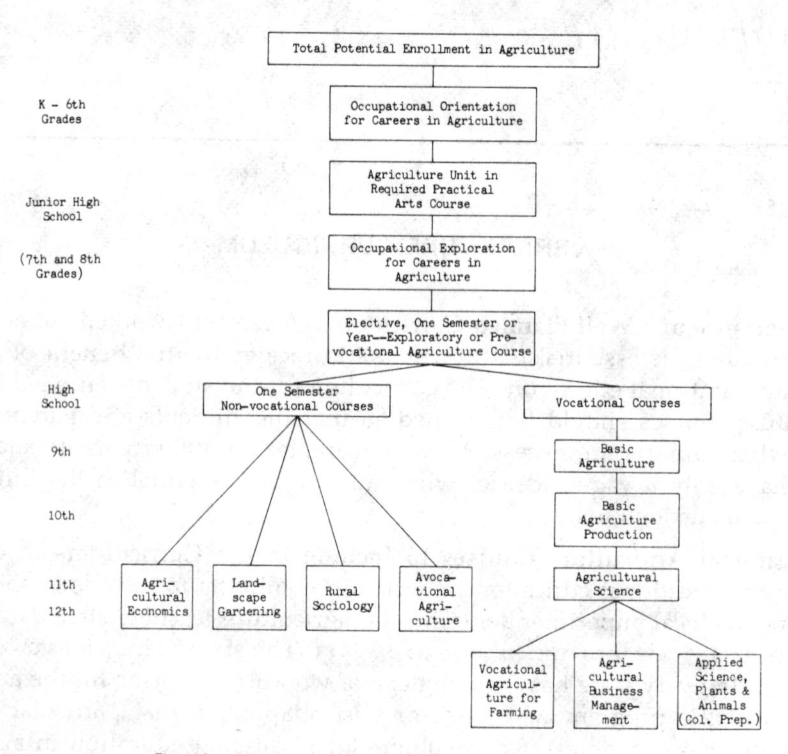

Fig. 12.1. Multiple-track agricultural education program.

Some of the descriptive titles given vocational courses in agriculture are:

1. Basic Agriculture.
2. Advanced Vocational Agriculture.
3. Agricultural Techniques.
4. Agricultural Business.
5. Agricultural Occupations.
6. Agricultural Science.
7. Agriculture for Part-Time Farmers.

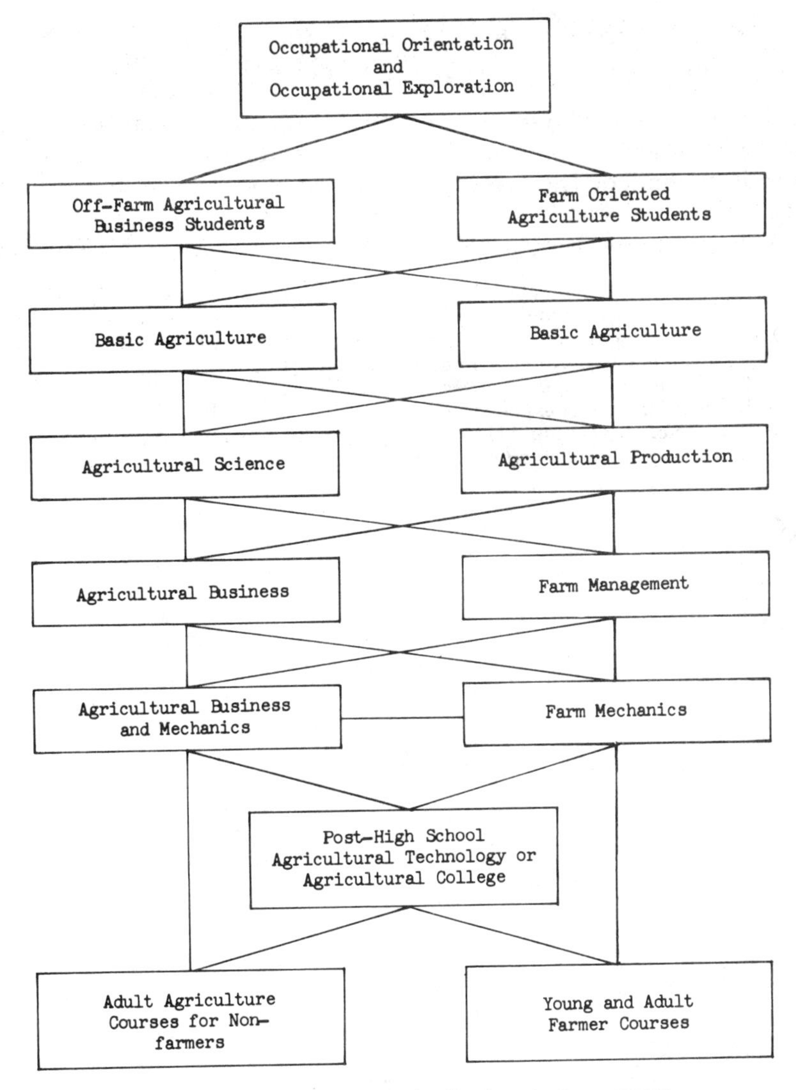

Fig. 12.2. Two-track vocational education in agriculture program.

8. Commercial Agriculture.
9. Farm or Ranch Business Management.
10. Advanced Agriculture Mechanics.

In geographical areas with specialized types of agriculture, courses such as ornamental horticulture, nursery management, rural recreation management, agricultural processing, and fruit business management probably should be offered. The descriptive titles listed include courses for vocational education in agriculture for farming and vocational education in agriculture for off-farm occupations requiring knowledge and skills in agriculture.

In schools with limited teacher time for agricultural education, the offering of more vocational courses in agriculture with descriptive titles necessitates the development of some rotation system for offering the courses. The possibility of making some courses one-semester courses should not be overlooked.

Number of Years of Vocational Agriculture to Include in the Curriculum—A four-year program for high school students is the one most frequently recommended. The reasons for this recommendation are as follows:

1. Teachers of vocational agriculture are in contact with students throughout high school.
2. The supervised occupational experience programs are continued throughout the four years in high school, and students more nearly approach establishment in farming or in off-farm jobs requiring knowledge and skills in agriculture than they do when fewer years of instruction are included.
3. Better work in advanced courses is possible as a student becomes older and has had a variety of experiences.
4. A four-year program in vocational education in agriculture stimulates students to enroll in high school and to remain in school.

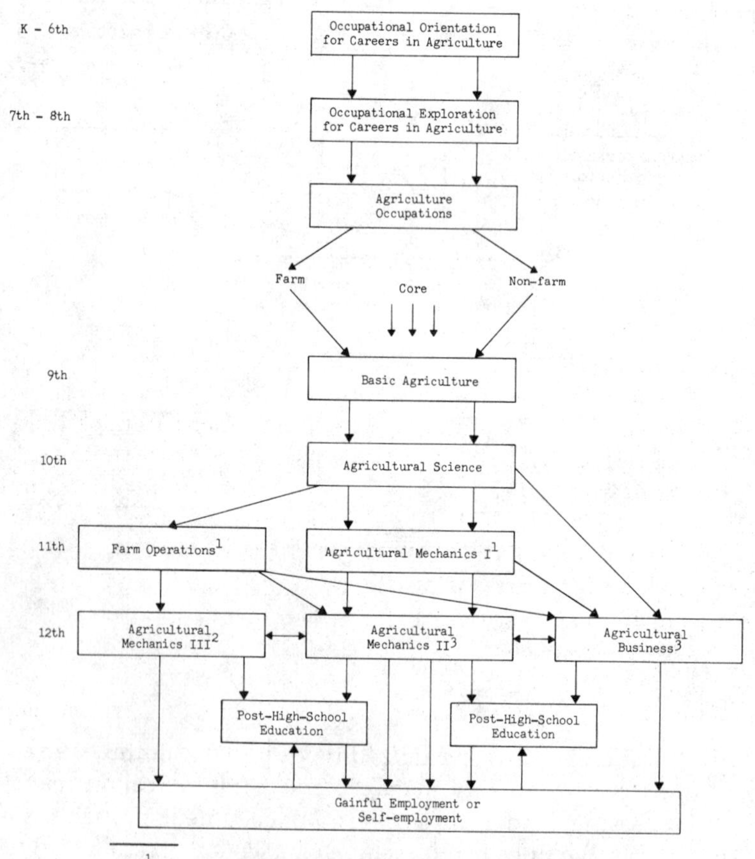

[1]Student has choice of either one or both courses in 11th year.

[2]Student whose schedule permits may choose a double period in Agricultural Mechanics.

[3]Student has choice of either one or both courses in 12th year.

Fig. 12.3. Core vocational agriculture program, with specialized courses for farming and off-farm occupations requiring knowledge and skills in agriculture.

Recent emphasis in most states is being placed on extending instruction in agriculture downward to the junior high schools, middle schools, and elementary schools. Occupational awareness and orientation information are provided at the elementary school level for careers in agriculture. Occupational exploration is provided at the seventh and eighth grade levels for careers in agriculture.[1]

Non-vocational Agriculture Courses to Include in the Curriculum—The agriculture courses to offer at the high school level in addition to the vocational courses for farming and those for off-farm jobs requiring knowledge and skills in agriculture will vary depending on the location and size of the school.

It is difficult to conceive of a school without a need for some agriculture courses in addition to the vocational courses. In order to meet varying needs, a number of courses, both one and two semesters in length, might be offered on a rotation basis. Following are some of the courses that have been offered successfully:

1. Suburban Agriculture or Suburban Living.
2. Economics of Agriculture.
3. Agriculture Policy and Programs.
4. Agricultural Arts.
5. Practical Arts Agriculture.
6. Agricultural Occupations and Professions.
7. Agriculture for Everyone.
8. Consumer Agriculture.
9. Avocational Agriculture.
10. Agriculture in Our Lives.

MAKING OUT SCHEDULES

Importance—The development of daily schedules in a high school requires considerable time and effort on the part of the administrators. A teacher of agriculture can aid the local superintendent very much in planning the schedule for the agriculture classes. In some departments the instructors teach two high school classes in agriculture, and the rest of their time is devoted to out-of-school groups. Under this plan it is desirable to have the high school instruction in the morning, with the afternoon free for agricultural education for young and older adults. This plan has proved popular in those states where it has been used, and it warrants consideration for use in other states.

Three or four high school classes should be the maximum teaching load so that some time will be available for out-of-school groups. The latter part of a school day should be free of high school classes for teachers of agriculture. This time should be used for directing the students' supervised experience programs and for providing training for adult groups.

In many departments, there is a need for two or more teachers of agriculture. In those situations where two or more teachers of agriculture are employed, it is usually best for the teachers to teach high school classes in agriculture less than full time and to devote the remainder of their time to out-of-school groups.

---

[1]For additional information regarding exploratory or prevocational courses, see Chapter 6.

Combining Shop and Other Agriculture Subjects—In vocational education in agriculture for farming courses, teachers may simplify their schedules by teaching at least part of the agriculture mechanics in combination with the other agriculture subjects. This is the plan which is followed in most states.

Most superintendents, instructors, and students prefer to have the agriculture mechanics instruction in beginning courses, and especially in vocational education for farming courses, combined with the other vocational agriculture subjects for the following reasons:

1. It permits the instructor to integrate and correlate the classroom instruction and the agriculture mechanics activities.
2. It relieves the monotony of classroom instruction day after day.
3. It aids superintendents in arranging schedules. It frequently happens that when the classroom work is given separately from the shop instruction, all students cannot register in both because of conflicts with required subjects.
4. When the agriculture mechanics and other agricultural activities are combined, every student secures training in all phases of the program in vocational agriculture—namely, agriculture shop, classroom, supervised occupational experience, and FFA.
5. The agriculture mechanics is taught by the same person who teaches the other agricultural work. This is to be desired.

In most departments, agriculture mechanics is taught by teachers of vocational agriculture. There are, however, a few situations where agriculture mechanics is taught by shop teachers. The desirable plan is for a qualified agriculture instructor to teach all phases of agriculture, including agriculture mechanics. This promotes the integration of the instruction in agriculture, and agriculture mechanics should be an integral phase of vocational education in agriculture.

Combining Agricultural Classes—Often it is impossible to teach all the agriculture subjects each year; therefore, some provision is necessary for combining students. The most common procedure is to group the freshmen and sophomores into one class and the juniors and seniors into another class.

Meeting Time Requirements—The local procedure for meeting time requirements must be in accordance with the state plan and must have the approval of the state agency for vocational education.

STUDENT REGISTRATION

Whom to Register—An appropriate course should be available to meet the needs and interests of all high school students. Some instruction in agriculture should be a required part of the general education of students at the high school level. Most of the instruction provided should be elective, however.

All students who desire to engage in the production phases of agriculture and who are able to conduct appropriate supervised agriculture production programs have a right to enroll in at least the beginning vocational courses for farming. In fact, many of them may be encouraged to enroll. If their interest continues, they may be encouraged to enroll in advanced vocational courses in farming, especially if this interest is manifested in their supervised occupational experience programs. If their interest shifts to the agricultural professions, to the technical occupations in agricultural business, or to the off-farm agriculturally oriented jobs, they should be permitted and encouraged to shift their enrollment to the appropriate vocational agriculture courses for the off-farm agriculturally oriented occupations.

If a student is interested in agriculture but is not interested in supervised occupational experiences or in a vocation in agriculture, he/she should be permitted and encouraged to enroll in an appropriate non-vocational course in agriculture. Teachers of agriculture need to serve as guidance counselors in enrolling high school students in the agriculture courses most appropriate for them.

Typical Agriculture Courses Not for Misfits—The typical courses in agriculture are not intended for students who have difficulties in earning their credits in other subjects; in other words, agriculture should not be a "dumping" place for misfits. However, there may be students who, because of their interest in agriculture, do much better work in agriculture than they do in other subjects. Quality of work is just as essential in agriculture as it is in other subjects. Agricultural educators, however, cannot ignore their responsibility for educating misfits, potential dropouts, and the handicapped.

Guidance Essential—Considerable time is required in guiding students into or out of agriculture. Teachers of agriculture should contact each prospective student in advance of the time of enrollment, in order to help the student and the parents decide whether enrollment in agriculture would be a wise choice. The criteria previously mentioned should be considered.

CHAPTER

13

How to Develop Courses of Study

Detailed course planning is based on the general principles of developing a program of agriculture, as presented in Chapter 10, and on the general principles of teaching, as presented in Chapter 4. These chapters should be reviewed before an instructor attempts to develop a course of study for high school students. A course plan is a detailed presentation of the overall program of the department, and its development should be based on the general principles of effective instruction.

LEVELS OF INSTRUCTION

Agricultural subject matter for production agricultural occupations and for off-farm agricultural occupations may be divided into four levels. They are:

1. Operational.
2. Skilled.
3. Technical.
4. Professional.

Most occupations have workers at all four levels. For example, at the operational level a worker could operate a machine. At the skilled level the worker would be able to operate and repair the machine. At the technical level the worker could build the machine, and at the professional level the worker would design the machine.

The operational level has been neglected, except in the instruction of the handicapped and the disadvantaged, in most courses of study in vocational agriculture. The operational level and the skilled level need to be emphasized in secondary programs of vocational agriculture.

ANTICIPATING WHAT TO TEACH

When effective procedures are followed, it is possible for teachers to anticipate the needs of the students and the needs of the community fairly accurately and in this way make the necessary preliminary plans for the course content. Later the students should be given an opportunity to participate in the selection of suitable materials. Teachers, as a result of their experiences in planning, should be able to do effective planning with the students.

Preliminary planning prevents instruction from degenerating into a hit-and-miss affair. Preliminary planning of a course of study, however, is not a process of autocratically determining what is to be taught. It is rather an attempt to use what is known to anticipate what will need to be taught so that the teachers may prepare for teaching and be in a better position to help students select the abilities they need. In trying to anticipate what will need to be taught, teachers should consider the factors in the following paragraphs.

Consider Objectives—A course of study should contribute to the objectives of the department, which in turn should contribute to the overall objectives of general education, vocational education, and agricultural education.

Determine Needs—Methods of determining community, state, and na-

(Photo from Robert W. Walker, Pennsylvania)

Fig. 13.1. In planning the curriculum for vocational education in agriculture, teachers need to consider all kinds of on-farm and off-farm agriculture, such as commercial flower arranging.

tional needs and interpreting the basic data collected are discussed in Chapter 10. If teachers have the information suggested in that chapter, they should be in a position to choose desirable teaching content.

Determine Important Farm Enterprises and Agricultural Business Units— The summary of the basic data pertaining to the community should reveal the more important farm enterprises and off-farm agricultural jobs in the community. Some of the enterprises and off-farm agricultural jobs will be considered major, and instruction about them may be continued through all the courses. These enterprises and jobs should be placed at the top of the list of problem areas to be included in the instructional program.

Determine Problems—The surveys made in a community, the observations of the teacher, and the conferences with members of the advisory council and other key persons should indicate many problems related to agriculture which should be included in the course of instruction. These problems should be properly summarized.

Anticipate Supervised Occupational Experience Programs of Students— Since the supervised occupational experience programs of the students are usually based on the farm enterprises and agricultural businesses which appear most frequently in the community, it should be possible for teachers to anticipate with a fair degree of accuracy the activities that will probably be included in these programs. This will be especially true if the teachers have visited the homes of the students and have developed desirable relationships with the families. The distribution of past activities by classes is often a good criterion for predicting supervised occupational experience programs for the immediate future. The anticipation of problems that will probably develop from the supervised occupational experience programs should be used as the core of the instructional program.

Anticipate FFA Activities—If an FFA program of work has been developed, it should be reviewed, and those activities which involve training may be sorted out and included in the course content. If a program of work has not been developed, previous programs may be reviewed and possible activities listed. There are many activities in the FFA program of work which have implications for desirable instruction:

1. Developing public speakers.
2. Developing demonstration teams.
3. Selecting suitable samples of crops for show and sale.
4. Selecting suitable animals for show and sale.
5. Determining procedures to follow in conducting group projects or activities, such as sheep dipping, orchard management, and home improvement.
6. Buying cooperatively.
7. Treating seed.
8. Mixing feed.
9. Developing teams in parliamentary procedure.
10. Sponsoring community improvement campaigns.

Anticipate Needs in Agriculture Mechanics—Teachers should keep in mind the agriculture mechanics activities which will be needed in the students' supervised occupational experience programs. These activities should be included as a part of the courses of instruction. The degree of difficulty of projects in agriculture mechanics should become greater each year as the instruction proceeds and students' abilities develop.

Consider Experiences Needed by Students—If teachers make a thorough study of their communities, their students, and their students' homes, they should be able to list a number of experiences in agriculture needed by the students. These experiences should be provided in the courses.

Consider Approved Practices Needed—As a result of the studies made in a community, teachers should know of a number of approved practices which should be taught. Some of these may be taught during the current year, while others may be delayed and taught later in the instructional program.

Consider Student Orientation Needed—There will be a need at the beginning of the year for a period of orientation for all students enrolling in agriculture for the first time. This period may be divided into four areas or units of instruction:

1. Getting acquainted with agricultural education.
2. Exploring career opportunities in agricultural occupations.
3. Selecting comprehensive supervised occupational experience programs.
4. Becoming effective members of FFA.

The instruction in these units should be very helpful in developing student understandings, in selecting desirable programs of supervised occupational experiences, in building a strong FFA program, and in developing suitable course materials. Approximately 6 to 12 weeks may be used to cover these four units of instruction.

Provide for a Unit on Supervised Occupational Experiences—In each course there will be a need for a unit covering activities such as the following:

1. Evaluating present supervised occupational experience programs and determining how to improve them.
2. Determining the outlook for various enterprises, activities, and employment opportunities.
3. Budgeting to determine probable outcomes of activities.
4. Making financial and business arrangements.
5. Selecting new projects and supplementary practices.
6. Writing essential preliminary plans for new activities.
7. Revising objectives.

Most of the instruction should be based on the supervised occupational experience programs, but it is also desirable to have a special unit on supervised occupational experience programs early in the school year for revising the individual programs. These revisions will indicate needed instruction regarding new activities which have been added. Many of these activities may be studied in the classroom, with each student working individually or with groups of students having the same problems. Some of the problems will be common to the class and may be discussed by the entire class, with students adapting the conclusions to their particular situations.

Form 13.1. Developing Courses of Study in Agriculture (Survey of Off-Farm Agriculturally Oriented Businesses and Jobs)

Types of Off-Farm Jobs Available Which Require Agricultural Knowledge	Number of Workers Employed	Number of Job Opportunities	Primary Function of Workers	Primary Agricultural Knowledge and Skills Needed	Experience Required	Job Opportunity Trend	Financial Rewards

Form 13.2. Developing Courses of Study in Agriculture[1]
(Survey of Farming Enterprises)

Enterprise	Percentage of Total Farm Income Provided	Number of Farms with This Enterprise	Number of FFA Farms with This Enterprise	Number of Former Students Engaged (Placed)	Number of Students Interested	Number of Projects in Enterprise	Adaptability to Area	Trend	Opportunity for Placement	Percentage of Time Allotted

[1]Obtained from S. S. Sutherland, California.

Form 13.3. ______________________________ **Group Production Project in Vocational Agriculture**

(Name)

School ____________ Agriculture ____________ Year ________

(Name of Course)

Names of Students Unless Entire Class Is Included	Scope: Size of Agricultural Business	Location	Jobs to Be Done	Financial Arrangement

Form 13.4. Approved Practices Which Need Special Emphasis

Enterprise or Unit ______________________ Agriculture ______________
(Name of Course)

School ______________________ Date ______________

Approved Practice	Year to Be Started			
	19___	19___	19___	19___

Form 13.5. Projects in Agriculture Mechanics to Be Constructed or Repaired (Includes Home Shops and Home Conveniences)

School ______________________ Agriculture ______________ Year ________
(Name of Course)

Name of Project	Needed by	Date Needed

COURSE ORGANIZATION FOR VOCATIONAL EDUCATION IN AGRICULTURE

Types of Course Organization—At the present time there are at least three general plans of course organization followed in agricultural education. These plans are as follows:

1. *The traditional plan* of course organization in which each course is devoted to a different phase of instruction. For example, a course may be devoted to crops and soils, another to livestock, a third to management, and a fourth to marketing.
2. *The cross-sectional plan* of course organization in which the problems in an area of instruction are distributed throughout two or more years of instruction. A large amount of individualized instruction may be used in this plan of organization.
3. *A modified cross-sectional plan* of course organization in which certain phases of instruction, such as introduction to agriculture, advanced agriculture, agricultural science, or agricultural business management, receive central emphasis in each course.

The first plan for basic courses has been replaced in many schools with a plan similar to either the Number 2 or the Number 3 plan. There appear to be three basic premises of major significance to the theory of the cross-sectional plan. These are as follows:

1. Flexibility in meeting the needs and interests of students in developing and carrying out their supervised occupational experience programs and other activities in agricultural education is met by the cross-sectional plan.
2. The cross-sectional plan makes possible the distribution of content according to the developing level of understanding and ability of the students.
3. It permits the organization of content on a problem basis. Problems of agriculture often encompass more than one of the traditional areas of instruction (soils, plants, animals, agriculture mechanics, farm management, agriculture distribution, agricultural supplies, ornamental horticulture, forestry, natural resources, and agriculture leadership).

If the instruction is based on the supervised occupational experience programs of students, cross-sectioning of course material develops naturally.

The long-time supervised occupational experience programs of students preparing to farm will include the major farm enterprises in the community, and these enterprises will be continued in their programs from year to year. This means that these students will be needing instruction on some problems related to these enterprises each year throughout high school. For example, in a long-time dairy project, a student will have new problems each year for which instruction will be needed. After students leave high school, they will continue to have new problems in connection with major enterprises; consequently, they will need additional instruction as young farmers.

A similar situation exists for students preparing for an off-farm agricultural occupation and working part-time in the occupation under the supervision of the teacher of agriculture and the employer. The content of the class instruction should relate to and be influenced by the problems encountered in the part-time job.

Since the students' supervised occupational experience programs are basic to effective instruction, a cross-sectional plan of instruction in some form should be followed for most effective results in meeting the needs of the students.

Cross-sectional Plan Not a Do-as-You-Please Process—*The cross-sectional plan must not be considered by teachers and students as a do-as-you-please process.* Careful, systematic planning is necessary in using the cross-sectional plan. It should not be a plan whereby students are permitted to study anything whenever they want to. The problem areas for instruction must grow out of the supervised occupational experience programs and be effectively taught just prior to the time the students will need to know about them. Basing instruction on the needs of students does not necessitate an undue amount of individual instruction. Many problems will be common to a group of students or to the entire class and, consequently, can be taught as such under a proper course organization.

Course Plans—The following course plans, without details, illustrate the major units included each year and the time allocated to each unit in a partially cross-sectioned organization.

• • •

A FOUR-YEAR PROGRAM OF COURSE OFFERINGS IN VOCATIONAL AGRICULTURE[1]

Ninth Grade—Basic Agriculture

Units	*Number of Days*
I. Orientation, FFA	15
II. Study of Agricultural Occupations in the Community	20
III. Supervised Occupational Experience Programs	27
IV. Animal Science and Career Opportunities	40
V. Agriculture Mechanics and Career Opportunities	35
VI. Soils and Crops and Career Opportunities	40
VII. Summer Program	3
	180 days

Tenth Grade—Basic Agricultural Science

Units	*Number of Days*
I. Supervised Occupational Experience Programs	14
II. FFA	18
III. Agricultural Economics and Career Exploration	25
IV. Animal Science and Career Exploration	40
V. Soils and Crops and Career Exploration	40
VI. Agriculture Mechanics and Career Exploration	40
VII. Summer Program	3
	180 days

[1]The first two years of this four-year program might serve as core courses for students preparing to farm and for students preparing for off-farm jobs requiring knowledge and skills in agriculture. If enrollment is large, more optional courses would be offered.

Eleventh Grade—Optional Courses

Agricultural Operations

Units	Number of Days
I. Supervised Occupational Experience Programs	19
II. FFA	18
III. Agricultural Techniques and Operations	70
IV. Advanced Agriculture Mechanics	70
V. Summer Program	3
	180 days

Ornamental Horticulture

Units	Number of Days
I. Status of Development of Industry	5
II. FFA	20
III. Supervised Occupational Experience Programs	20
IV. Greenhouses and Related Structures	30
V. Propagating Horticulture Plants	50
VI. Growing Horticulture Plants	50
VII. Summer Program	5
	180 days

Twelfth Grade—Optional Courses

Production Management

Units	Number of Days
I. Supervised Occupational Experience Programs	25
II. FFA	12
III. Managing Agricultural Machinery and Agriculture Mechanics Program	30
IV. Managing Soils and Crops Program	30
V. Managing Animal Production Program	30
VI. Marketing	30
VII. Business Management	20
VIII. Summer Program	3
	180 days

Advanced Ornamental Horticulture

Units	Number of Days
I. Supervised Occupational Experience Programs	25
II. FFA	12
III. Vocabulary and Identification of Ornamentals	10
IV. Nursery Plant Production	25
V. Vegetable and Fruit Production	30
VI. Landscaping	25
VII. Turf and Land Development	20
VIII. Garden Center Operations	30
	3
	180 days

Agricultural Business Operations

Units	Number of Days
I. Supervised Occupational Experience Programs	25
II. FFA	12
III. Agricultural Supply Operations	30
IV. Agricultural Processing Operations	30
V. Agriculture Mechanics Sales and Agricultural Repair Operations	30
VI. Agricultural Business Service Operations	30
VII. Conservation and Rural Recreation Operations	20
VIII. Summer Program	3
	180 days

• • •

Under the *modified cross-sectional plan*, a central emphasis is given to some phase or phases of agriculture in each course.

Steps in Organizing Course Content—Before courses of study are organized, objectives for each course should be formulated. These objectives should be based on the overall objectives of the department. The teacher should, with the help of others, write a statement of the objectives and goals to be attained. Specific and clearly stated objectives in behavioral terms are essential for intelligent selection and organization of suitable course materials. In formulating objectives and goals, the teacher must keep the development of student abilities or behaviors foremost in mind. The course materials must be properly selected to provide for the development of abilities essential to success in agricultural occupations. Objectives should be formulated by the teacher and later developed or discarded through teacher-student planning. A form similar to that used for the FFA program of work is desirable for recording appropriate objectives for the instruction. A form such as Form 13.6 may be used.

Form 13.6. Annual Objectives in Vocational Education in Agriculture

Agriculture ______________________ Year ________
(Name of Course)

Objectives	Ways and Means of Accomplishing	Accomplishments

After a teacher has determined the needs of the students, decided on the plan of course organization to use, and formulated behavioral objectives for the instruction, he/she is ready to organize the course content. The first step is to prepare a list of the units of instruction to be included, with the time allotment for each unit for each course to be offered. This list of units should be based on the major agricultural occupations in the community and the ones included in the supervised occupational experience programs. The amount of time to allot to units of instruction will depend on their importance in the community and on the extent to which they are included in the supervised occupational experience programs. Problem areas in the major units of instruction should be distributed over a period of years, as needed by the students.

Each instructor will need to determine the amount of time to allot to each unit of instruction each year, based on student and community needs. The following example is merely suggestive of time allotments for the first year of instruction.

• • •

BASIC AGRICULTURE (CROSS-SECTION ORGANIZATION)

Enterprise	*Number of Days*
1. Orientation (getting acquainted with vocational agriculture education)	5
2. Supervised occupational experience programs	30
3. FFA	10
4. Off-farm agricultural occupations	15
5. Crops and soils	32
6. Livestock	30
7. Agriculture mechanics	40
8. Miscellaneous (fairs, holidays, exams, etc.)	18
Total	180 days

• • •

The time distribution is essential, since it gives the instructor a guide to follow in working out teaching plans. Often, when units of instruction are not allotted certain amounts of time, the year draws to a close and certain units have not been sufficiently covered. Time allotment, however, must be thought of merely as a guide to follow and not as something that cannot be changed. Plans must be flexible to allow for any changes that may need to be made. Some students may use considerably more time for individualized instruction on the units included in their supervised occupational experience programs than the instructor has allotted for the year. Problems may arise which need attention but which were not anticipated by the instructor.

After a teacher has decided what units of instruction should be included in the course of study, the problem areas involved in these units need to be identified. The teacher must exercise considerable care in selecting the problem areas to make sure they are those which will be needed by the students in their supervised occupational experience programs. It is also important to divide problem areas so that they will not be too broad in scope. Many teachers are of the opinion that in most instances it is not desirable to spend more than a week on one problem area since students may tire before it is completed. For example, a problem area on controlling diseases and parasites is too broad in scope in most instances for effective instruction. It is better to divide this problem area into one on controlling diseases and one on controlling parasites. It is also possible to divide enterprises into sections requiring too little class time. Teachers agree that most divisions should require a time allotment of more than one day.

Some units of instruction may include more problem areas than can be covered in the time available; consequently, those of least importance must be eliminated. It is more desirable to cover the more important problem areas well than to deal with a large number superficially. An example of dividing an enterprise into problem areas is illustrated in the following breakdown for swine:

Problem areas:

1. Deciding whether swine production is profitable.
2. Selecting foundation stock.
3. Providing housing and equipment.
4. Feeding sows or gilts before farrowing.
5. Managing a sow or gilt during the farrowing period.
6. Caring for sows and litters until weaning.
7. Feeding market pigs.
8. Controlling diseases.
9. Keeping records.
10. Marketing.

Some of the problem areas might be taught for the first time or at a different level in the advanced courses of vocational education in agriculture. At least some of the problem areas would be taught in more detail in the advanced courses. Also, other problem areas may be added to meet student needs.

After the units of instruction have been divided into problem areas, the next step is to decide on the course, and time period in that course, to teach each problem area, and the number of days to devote to each. In the *cross-sectional plan*, a problem area is taught in the course and at the time in that course when the students have the most need for help with that particular area. The plan must be kept flexible to meet individual needs.

Form 13.7 indicates a way of recording a problem area breakdown by months.

After problem areas are arranged by courses and time periods in the courses, the next step is to make monthly layouts of problem areas, that is, to list the problem areas to be taught in each of the nine school months, using a separate sheet for every month. In this way the teacher will know what problem areas should be taught each month in each course offered. Two or three days should be left open each month in each course for unanticipated problems. A teacher must think of the monthly layout as a flexible list which should be changed when necessary to meet student needs. In arranging the problem areas to be taught, the teacher should consider the order of teaching, that is, which problem areas should be taught at the beginning of the month and which near the close of the month (see Form 13.8).

On Form 13.8, a teacher may record not only the anticipated problem areas to be taught in the approximate order of teaching but also the anticipated problems for each problem area.

Form 13.7. One-Year Teaching Plan ________

Problem Areas to Be Included in the ______________________________ Unit

School ____________________ Agriculture ____________________ Year______
(Name of Course)

Problem Areas to Be Discussed	Periods to Devote to Each Problem Area										
	Sept.	Oct.	Nov.	Dec.	Jan.	Feb.	Mar.	Apr.	May	June	Summer

Form 13.8. Suggested Monthly Layout

School ____________________ Instructor ____________________

Course ____

Month of ____________________ 19______

	Problem Areas and Problems to Be Discussed
1	
2	
3	
4	
5	
6	
7	
8	

Forms to Use—There are a number of forms helpful to teachers in laying out course materials. The forms illustrated in this chapter have been successfully used by teachers of agriculture under the supervision of the author. They provide an organized guide to teachers in dividing units of instruction into problem areas and in scheduling these problem areas by months in courses.

These forms help teachers visualize when the instruction should be offered and how much time should be devoted to each area. Their use lessens the danger of some problem areas being allotted too much time, others being omitted, and perhaps some being included that should not be. Also, they enable a teacher to see what has been taught in any year and what is planned for other years. In this way overlapping and repetition of instruction are avoided.

Evaluating a Course of Study—The primary aim in organizing a course of study is to ensure that the supervised occupational experience programs and other necessary activities become of central importance in the instruction. This aim may be evaluated by applying the following criteria to the course of study planned:

1. Units of instruction, activities, and problems represented in individual supervised occupational experience programs are included in the course of study.
2. The unit of organization, such as the topic or the problem, is in terms of activities.
3. Each unit of the course is taught at the time of the year in which it will give greatest assistance to the student in carrying out his/her supervised occupational experience program.
4. The course of study provides for training which will help students to participate more effectively in FFA activities.
5. The course of study develops psychologically instead of logically. (Consideration should be given to the way students approach a problem area instead of the logical way it would be approached in a textbook.)
6. Content is of primary importance for the age level of the students.
7. Content is educationally sound.

Summary of Steps—Following is a summary of the steps in organizing a course of study:

1. Make a list of the units to be included in courses to be offered. Determine other essential units to include in the program, such as acquainting students with agricultural education, supervised occupational experience programs, FFA activities, and off-farm agricultural occupations.
2. Determine the number of days to allot to each unit.
3. Divide these units into problem areas to be taught.
4. Estimate the number of days to devote to each problem area.
5. Decide on the course and the period of time (month) to teach each problem area, keeping in mind the seasonal order of teaching.
6. Prepare a monthly layout of problem areas.

COURSE ORGANIZATION FOR SPECIALIZED VOCATIONAL AGRICULTURE COURSES

The general principles and steps to be followed in organizing specialized courses, such as courses for ornamental horticulture workers and for workers in off-farm jobs requiring agricultural education, are similar to the general principles and steps for organizing the more typical agriculture courses.

Following is an example of a senior-level course for students preparing for jobs in off-farm agriculturally oriented businesses.

• • •

TITLE OF COURSE: AGRICULTURAL BUSINESS

Objectives

1. To develop an awareness of the variety of agriculturally oriented businesses.
2. To develop an understanding of the functions of agricultural businesses.
3. To develop the understanding and technique required in agricultural businesses.
4. To develop an understanding of specific jobs and skills required in various agricultural business occupations.
5. To develop an understanding of training, education, and knowledge needed for various agricultural occupations.
6. To develop an understanding of agricultural businesses and their relationship to government and the national economy.

Units

1. Types of Agricultural Businesses.
2. Functions of Agricultural Businesses.
3. Economics of Agricultural Businesses.
4. Opportunities in Agricultural Businesses.
5. Knowledge and Skills Required for Different Types of Agricultural Businesses.
6. Clusters of Job Titles for Agricultural Businesses.
7. Competencies Other Than Agricultural Competencies Needed in Agricultural Businesses.
8. Advanced Education Needed for Agricultural Businesses.
9. Study of Specific Agricultural Knowledge and Skills Needed in Many Agricultural Businesses (Soils, Nutrition, Agriculture Mechanics, Quality Control, and Processing).
10. Government Regulations Affecting Agricultural Businesses.
11. Marketing of Agricultural Products.

• • •

ORGANIZATION OF CONTENT IN NON-VOCATIONAL COURSES

The process of planning content of agriculture courses such as "Suburban Agriculture," "Agriculture Around the Home," "Practical Arts Agriculture," and "Agriculture for Everyone" is similar to the process of planning vocational courses, but there are certain differences.

In anticipating what to teach in a course without vocational objectives, the first step is to define what changes the course is designed to produce in the behavior of the enrollees.

The second step is to determine the interests and needs of the enrollees. As with vocational education in agriculture, a study of the community may produce many hints regarding the needs of the enrollees. Interests of the prospective enrollees may often be determined to a considerable extent through personal individual conferences with these persons.

The third step is to determine the experiences prospective enrollees have had with agricultural businesses and with farming. Such experiences will often provide clues regarding needs, interests, attitudes, and understandings of prospective enrollees. As with vocational courses, an important step is anticipating the agricultural experiences that can be provided the enrollees during the course. In anticipating the possible agricultural experiences that may be provided, the teacher should not overlook agriculture mechanics activities, especially in practical arts agriculture courses.

In planning the content of any course, the teacher should include time for instruction to orient the enrollees regarding the purpose of the course, the experiences which may be provided, and the procedures that will be followed. Time should also be provided for teacher-student planning of the content of the course. In most agriculture courses, unless they are 100 per cent academic, it is possible for the enrollees to develop supervised occupational experience programs.

TEACHER-STUDENT PLANNING OF COURSE MATERIALS

The preliminary planning of a course should aid a teacher in guiding the students in selecting appropriate course materials. Chapter 4, "What Is Good Teaching?" and Chapter 7, "How to Teach Effectively," discuss in detail successful procedures for teacher-student planning of course materials. These chapters should be reviewed before such planning of course materials is attempted.

In addition to the day-by-day planning of a course, the teacher should also enlist the aid of the students in the overall planning of the course. After the students have selected the activities to be included in their supervised occupational experience programs, a course of study may be developed with the students. The following steps in teacher-student course building are suggested:

1. Develop with the students a list of units that will need to be included in the course of study because the activities are represented in the students' supervised occupational experience programs or their FFA program of work.
2. Discuss with the students the units that are represented in their supervised occupational experience programs to such an extent that they could be taught to the whole class. Using the same criterion, develop two other lists of units—one for individual instruction and one for small-group instruction.
3. Discuss with the students the units represented in their supervised occupational experience programs in which they will have the most immediate and pressing problems.
4. Discuss with the students other units which should be included in the course of study.
5. Explain to the students the meaning of a problem area, and with their help divide the units selected for immediate attention into problem areas.
6. Arrange, with the help of the students, the problem areas for each unit in seasonal order. Estimate the desired number of class periods for each.
7. Select for immediate attention the problem area in which problems are most pressing.

Teacher-student planning of course materials is a continuous process. It is not something done at the beginning of the year and then forgotten. If the preceding steps are followed at the beginning of a course, the students will develop insights into what the course will contain and how the content is determined, and they will be prepared for future teacher-student planning as the course develops.

A teacher may facilitate teacher-student planning of course materials by having the students decide on what month and on what approximate date they will need to do jobs in their occupational experience programs. Students may make individual calendars of their activities. Some modification of these activities and dates will probably have to be made as the instruction proceeds. Form 13.9 indicates how students may plan their activities by months, with approximate dates.

Form 13.9. Calendar of Activities for My Supervised Occupational Experience Program, 19 ______

Month	Approximate Date	Activity (Selling chemicals, treating grain, working in garden center, etc.)

After the students have planned their supervised occupational experience programs for the year, their FFA program of work, and their calendar of activities for their supervised occupational experience programs and have assisted in planning their course, the teacher is in a position to revise the preliminary course plans to more nearly meet the needs of the students. If the teacher has done a good job of preliminary planning of course materials, only minor changes should be necessary.

PART

Supervised Occupational Experience Programs

CHAPTER

14

What Are Supervised Occupational Experience Programs in Agriculture?

An important part of all courses in agriculture is the supervised occupational experience programs of the students. *Supervised occupational experience programs in agriculture consist of all the practical agriculture activities of educational value conducted by students outside class or on school-released time for which systematic instruction and supervision are provided by their teachers, parents, employers, or others.* Supervised occupational experience programs of students make the instruction in an agriculture course practical and meaningful to the students. They have great motivational value.

In vocational courses in agriculture, supervised occupational experience programs are essential. In vocational courses for farming, this directed or supervised practice in agriculture has been called supervised farming. In vocational courses for off-farm occupations requiring knowledge and skills in agriculture, supervised placement in occupations for observation or experience is often provided, and teachers encourage, on school land laboratories and at students' homes, the development of practical agriculture experience projects that are appropriate to the objectives of the courses.

In vocational courses for farming, the supervised occupational experience programs may become primarily supervised farming programs. In all other agriculture courses, the enrollees are usually encouraged to conduct supervised farming programs if they have the opportunity. For example, high school students enrolled in a vocational course such as ornamental horticulture or in a vocational course for certain off-farm agricultural occupations are encouraged to work part-time in the occupations they are preparing to enter. In addition, the students are urged to broaden their practical experience in agriculture by conducting appropriate programs involving plants and animals if land and other facilities are available.

Since occupational experience programs of various types and scopes are encouraged for enrollees in vocational agriculture courses, considerable attention is given in Chapters 12, 13, 14, 15, and 16 to supervised programs. A supervised occupational experience program is an integral and essential part of vocational education in agriculture, *not an appendage*. Each student should be instructed regarding the vast importance and many advantages of this program. It should be made clear that it is not a penalty for being enrolled in vocational education in agriculture.

When the National Vocational Act was passed in 1917, there were some misconceptions concerning the comprehensiveness of a broad program in supervised practice. At that time the directed or supervised practice in agriculture was interpreted in various ways, the term "home project" being *frequently used since many students carried but one project*.

Most administrators and teachers soon realized, however, that the instruction in vocational education in agriculture must be carried to the doing level to be effective. If the instruction in agriculture is to be carried to the doing level, students need to have more than one or two projects a year. Because of this recognized need, new types of activities have been developed during recent years to help students conduct broader supervised occupational experience programs.

The "project" during recent years has become recognized as a *unit* in an individual's occupational experience program. The terms "home projects" and "supervised practice" used formerly are now replaced with the more comprehensive term "supervised occupational experience."

Activities Included—The term "supervised occupational experience program" is used to encompass both experience programs for persons preparing for farming and experience programs for persons preparing for off-farm occupations requiring knowledge and skills in agriculture. A supervised occupational experience program would usually involve several of the following activities, depending on the occupational objectives of the student:

1. Exploratory experiences.
2. Placement in agriculturally oriented businesses and jobs.
   a. On school-released time.
   b. After school, during school vacations, and in the summer.
   c. Without pay.
   d. With trainee pay.
3. Occupational experiences in school facilities.
   a. On school-released time.
   b. After school, during school vacations, and in the summer.
   c. On school land.
   d. In school laboratories.
   e. In school shops.
   f. In school forests, arboretums, ponds, conservation areas, greenhouses, and so forth.
4. Farming programs.
   a. Production projects on the farm.
      (1) Crops.
      (2) Livestock.

b. Improvement projects on the farm.
c. Supplementary farm practices.
d. Placement on the farm.

Why Have Occupational Experience Programs?—Persons engaged in agricultural education are cognizant of the need for providing education in agriculture which will give the students opportunities for learning through experiences in real-life activities adapted to particular interests and needs. They also realize that in order for the instruction to be vocational in nature it must be carried to the *doing stage*. Students need to conduct supervised occupational experience programs in order to have opportunities to apply the knowledge and skills they acquire in the classroom.

The values of supervised occupational experience programs are many. A supervised occupational experience program in agriculture:

1. Provides an opportunity for the development of the abilities needed for proficiency in agriculture.
2. Provides an avenue to satisfactory, progressive establishment in farming or other occupations requiring knowledge and skills in agriculture.
3. Provides opportunities to earn, save, and use money.
4. Provides a desirable type of motivation and develops students' interest in agriculture.
5. Develops students' originality, pride of ownership, initiative, self-confidence, and managerial ability.
6. Provides opportunities for contributing to desirable family living.
7. Develops desirable habits, understandings, appreciations, ideals, abilities, and attitudes through challenging true-to-life situations.
8. Provides opportunities for students to plan work, make budgets, use financial agreements, review information, form judgments, evaluate activities, make decisions, solve problems, put plans into action, and keep accurate records.
9. Provides an opportunity to grow into farming or another occupation requiring knowledge and skills in agriculture.
10. Provides an opportunity for contributing to the improvement of the home.
11. Develops desirable relationships with parents or employers.
12. Contributes to community improvement.
13. Contributes to desirable relationships among the school, the home, and the community.
14. Develops teacher-parent-student understanding and cooperative relationships.
15. Develops opportunities for functionalized instruction based on individual needs, interests, and abilities of students, thus making the supervised occupational experience program the core of the instructional program.
16. Provides a basis for evaluating the effectiveness of the instruction in agriculture.
17. Develops abilities in cooperation.

Relationship to Establishment in an Occupation—Comprehensive occupational experience programs involving a number of activities may and should lead toward progressive establishment in farming or other occupations requiring knowledge and skills in agriculture. Through a program of supervised occupational experiences, students have an opportunity to accumulate cash savings and other capital assets. It is the responsibility of teachers of agriculture to motivate students to develop their programs to the extent that they will be challenging to them and will assist them in becoming established in an occupation.

Importance of Supervised Occupational Experience Summarized—From the foregoing discussion it is apparent that supervised occupational experience programs are a very important phase of the program in production agriculture, agribusiness, and renewable natural resources. Every effort should be made by instructors to promote these programs. They are exceedingly beneficial to high school students, as well as to a community. Having good occupational experience programs is one of the best ways of giving agricultural education and teachers of agriculture favorable publicity and of making agriculture courses a permanent part of a community's secondary school educational program. Supervised occupational experience programs are attractive, interesting, and educational to students, parents, and others. On the other hand, if teachers do not do an effective job with supervised occupational experience programs, there may be much unfavorable criticism of the program of vocational education in agriculture.

Relationship of Supervised Occupational Experience to Instruction—The supervised occupational experience programs should be used as a basis for the instruction. If this is done, the programs must be comprehensive and provide many experiences. If the individual programs are not comprehensive, there is danger that the courses may become academic in nature and devoted to information or subject matter which will not be used. Students are interested in developing needed skills and abilities which will help them in solving true-to-life problems which they will encounter in the immediate future in connection with their occupational experience programs. Since the occupational experience programs frequently include a cross-section of the agriculture in a local community, the instruction will need to be organized on a cross-sectional basis. This is necessary so that students may learn the best way to perform the needed jobs in their occupational experience program a short time before they have to do them.

The instruction in vocational agriculture should be closely related to students' occupational experience programs in order to provide opportunities to:

1. Develop needed abilities in performing the jobs in connection with the program.
2. Study and evaluate materials so that students will know what approved practices to adopt.
3. Construct or repair equipment needed.
4. Develop students' interest in vocational education in agriculture.
5. Prepare complete plans for carrying each activity to completion.
6. Solve the problems encountered in the program.
7. Make the instruction vocational by carrying it to the *doing stage*.

Course building is discussed in detail in Chapter 13.

EXPLORATORY EXPERIENCES

An important ingredient of supervised occupational experience programs for all students studying agriculture, regardless of their career goals, is *exploratory experiences*. An exploratory experience is a study-visit with workers in production agriculture, ornamental horticulture, forestry, conservation, agricultural services, agricultural processing, agriculture mechanics, or professional agriculture. The purpose of exploratory experiences is to get a feel for the work involved in the various jobs in agriculture, to understand the working conditions, and to get acquainted with the life style of the workers in the different jobs. Exploratory experiences are helpful to students in making career decisions, and they have many intangible values in preparing students for any occupation.

SUPERVISED FARMING PROGRAM

The supervised occupational experience program for students preparing for farming is often entitled a "supervised farming program." The following is a discussion of ways and means of organizing desirable supervised farming programs. Students who are preparing for off-farm agricultural occupations may engage in supervised farming program activities in addition to their part-time employment in the occupation for which they are preparing.

Activities Included—A good farming program should include a series of related activities. The following classifications serve to distinguish the component parts in a student's farming program, namely: *production projects, improvement projects, supplementary farm practices,* and *placement for farm experience.*[1]

Production Projects—A production project is a business venture for experience and profit involving the production of a crop or some type of livestock. The minimum length of a production project is a full production cycle. Often a production project is carried on through two or more production cycles or as a continuation project.

A production project is owned in full or in part by, and managed by, the student. If the student owns the project in full, he/she should receive the net income after all expenses are paid. If it is a partnership setup, the student should receive his/her full share of the profits or losses. In other words, a project should be carried on in a businesslike manner.

Production projects are a fundamental part of a student's schoolwork, supervised by the instructor and parents and carried to completion by the student. They involve careful study, planning, recording, execution, summarization, and evaluation. They may contribute to establishment in farming or an off-farm agricultural occupation.

Production projects provide an opportunity to find out how efficiently a unit of animals or crops can be produced, and how much profit can be made from the undertaking. They may be classified as major projects, minor projects, or contributory projects.

A *continuation project* is a production project planned to continue over a period of years. For example, a student may start with a gilt the first year and raise a litter of pigs. The second year two or more gilts may be kept for producing litters. The third and fourth years several gilts may be kept. In this way

[1]The definitions pertaining to these activities are largely taken from *Directing Vocational Agriculture Day-School Students in Developing Their Farming Programs,* Voc. Bul. 225, U.S. Office of Education, Washington, D.C., pp. 7–14.

Table 14.1. A Continuation Swine Project[1]

Year	Kind	Scope	Net Labor Income or Loss
Freshman	Registered Berkshires	5 sows	
		1 boar	
		39 pigs	
	Feeder hogs	16 head	
	Feeder hogs	11 head	
Sophomore	Berkshires	5 sows	
		1 boar	
		70 pigs	
	Feeder hogs	32 head	
	Feeder hogs	35 head	
Junior	Berkshires	11 sows	
		1 boar	
		32 pigs	
	Feeder hogs	108 head	
Senior	Berkshires	20 sows	
		3 boars	
	Feeder hogs	35 head	
			Total

[1]Continuation swine project of Verne Hoffman, Acampo, California. Verne also conducted projects in sheep and dairy.

the swine enterprise is well established in the supervised farming program, and the student has learned a great deal through experience. A number of projects of this type should be encouraged.

Improvement Projects—An improvement project is an undertaking involving a series of related activities which usually cover a relatively long period of time. It is designed to improve (1) the efficiency of a farm enterprise, either crop or livestock; (2) the whole farm business; (3) the appearance or real estate value of the farm; or (4) the comfort and convenience of the farm family. Ownership remains with the family, and an improvement project usually provides no direct income to a student. A student's financial benefits are indirect. An improvement project often results in more income to the farm family, which makes it possible for the parents to give the student more financial assistance than would otherwise be possible. Often the opportunities which improvement projects provide for contributing to the welfare of the family are a major reason for interest in these projects.

Since improvement projects do not involve ownership, they should not be used to replace production projects. They should, however, be included in a program because they provide opportunities for a more comprehensive occupational experience program.

It is sometimes difficult for beginning students to differentiate between production and improvement projects, since both include a number of jobs and approved practices which may be very similar. The main thing to remember is that a production project involves some definite ownership and an improvement project is owned by the whole family. Students should be stimulated to use a large number of approved practices in production projects and in improvement projects.

Some Examples of Improvement Projects—There are many kinds of improvement projects. A few of the more common ones are illustrated in this chapter. It must be remembered that an improvement project is composed of a series of related activities or jobs, not just one job, and that many of these activities may be similar to those in a production project. In fact, a number of the following improvement projects would become production projects if the student had some ownership in them. Some examples of improvement projects follow:

1. *Swine herd improvement* involving a series of activities such as selecting and using a purebred boar; flushing the sow at breeding time; feeding a balanced ration during the gestation period; adopting a system of sanitation; caring for the sow properly at farrowing time; weighing the pigs at birth and at 56 days of age; feeding a balanced ration for fattening; providing suitable houses, pens, and equipment, including labor-saving devices; keeping records; and marketing at a desirable time.
2. *Home grounds improvement* involving activities such as removing unattractive objects, seeding the yard, fertilizing plants, planting shrubs, pruning shrubs, setting out trees, pruning trees, mowing the lawn, and fencing.
3. *Home improvement* involving activities such as repairing window screens, repairing porches, constructing walks, repairing windows, painting the house, installing a septic tank, installing a water system, installing a lighting system, and constructing cabinets.
4. *Home garden improvement* involving activities such as budgeting needs of the family; planning the garden; preparing the seedbed; selecting seed; fertilizing the soil; planting seed; cultivating the soil; and harvesting, storing, and processing the crops.
5. *Establishing a home shop* through activities such as providing space, constructing suitable homemade equipment, securing tools and equipment, storing tools, repairing tools, remodeling or building a shop, and arranging the equipment.
6. *Keeping accounts* involving activities such as taking inventories, keeping a record of expenses and receipts, and summarizing and interpreting accounts.
7. *Establishing family living or live-at-home projects.* There are numerous projects which contribute to family living. Some of these may be developed on a cooperative basis between a brother and sister and in some instances with other members of the family. Some examples of such improvement projects are (1) planning, producing, and processing food for the family; (2) butchering, preparing, and preserving the family meat supply; (3) developing a home library; and (4) improving the home by installing conveniences, refinishing furniture, constructing cabinets, painting, and papering.

Supplementary Farm Practices—*A supplementary farm practice is a job undertaken for experience or for the development of a skill, and it is in addition to the practices included in a student's production or improvement projects.* Supplementary farm practices are sometimes designated as "supplementary farm jobs." A supplementary farm practice or job consists of a single job, such as culling hens; feeding a balanced ration; caponizing; treating seed; inoculating seed; treating horses for bots; testing soil for acidity; selecting proven sires; selecting adapted seed; or constructing equipment such as a sheep feed rack, workbench, poultry feeder, tool cabinet, hay feeder, breeding crate, or feed cart. Jobs of this type provide for the development of ability to carry out numerous specific approved practices which would not otherwise be included in a student's supervised occupational experience program; consequently, a student should be encouraged to put into effect a large number of desirable supplementary farm practices, which ordinarily require only a short time to complete.

Supplementary farm practices should be selected because they provide:

1. Experiences an individual needs.
2. Experiences not already acquired.
3. Experiences which are not acquired by pick-up methods but which require systematic instruction and participation.
4. Experiences that will be frequently used.
5. Experiences that are not included in the production or improvement projects.
6. Experiences with approved practices which have been tried, tested, and accepted as having superior merit by the agricultural experiment station and/or farmers of a community.
7. Experiences with approved practices agreed upon as a result of the *instruction* in agriculture.

Placement for Farm Experience—Placement for farm experience refers to locating a student on a farm for experience. It is intended primarily for:

1. Students not living on farms but interested in securing farm experience and developing farming programs.
2. Students whose home-farm facilities provide inadequate opportunities for farming programs.

Such placement may be a desirable supervised occupational experience for many students preparing for off-farm jobs requiring knowledge and skills in agriculture.

Before placing a student on a farm for experience, an instructor should make sure that suitable facilities and opportunities are available there for the student. Cooperative relationships should be established between the employer, the parents, and the student. There should be a definite understanding regarding wages, nature of work, training, and opportunities for developing a comprehensive program in supervised farming.

Group Projects—It is sometimes desirable to have a group of students conduct a project to supplement the members' individual occupational experience programs. Such a project should not be thought of as a substitute for the individual programs of students but rather as a means of providing additional opportunities for experience. Such projects may be conducted by small groups, by one or more classes in agriculture, or by the local FFA chapter. When an entire class conducts the undertaking, it is usually spoken of as a "class project." It is known as an "FFA project" when conducted by an FFA chapter.

Some Advantages of Group Projects—Some of the advantages of group projects are as follows:

1. They may provide many additional learning opportunities.
2. They motivate interest because of the large number of true-to-life problems involved that must be solved.

Table 14.2. Long-Time Supervised Farming Program[1]

Production Project	Classification	In School				Out of School		
		1st Year	2nd Year	3rd Year	4th Year	1st Year	2nd Year	3rd Year
Cotton	Major	3 acres	6 acres	4 acres	10 acres	10 acres		
Beef, breeding	Major	7 head	7 head	7 head	14 head	17 head		
Beef, feeding	Minor	2 steers	3 steers	3 steers	6 steers	5 steers		
Swine, feeding	Minor	2 barrows			2 barrows			
Wheat	Minor			10 acres	6 acres	5 acres		
Peanuts	Minor				2 acres			
Broom corn	Minor				10 acres	8 acres		
Corn	Contributory	6 acres	10 acres	6 acres	8 acres	20 acres		
Barley	Contributory		5 acres	12 acres	15 acres	20 acres		
Oats	Contributory	8 acres	10 acres	15 acres	20 acres	20 acres		
Lespedeza	Contributory	4 acres		5 acres	6 acres			
Cane	Contributory		4 acres	6 acres	8 acres			
Sweet clover	Contributory		8 acres		8 acres	10 acres		
Hegari	Contributory		8 acres	8 acres	10 acres	10 acres		
Soybeans	Contributory				10 acres			
Improvement projects		Seeded a lawn.	Planted shrubs.	Terraced 50 acres. Fenced 160 acres.	Fenced 160 acres. Constructed concrete walks.	Terraced 100 acres. Painted the house.		
Supplementary farm practices		Docked sheep. Sheared sheep. Treated wheat for smut.	Castrated pigs. Vaccinated hogs.	Butchered hogs. Culled poultry.	Trimmed horses' hoofs. Adjusted mower, proper lead, and register of sickle bar.	Pruned trees. Fitted sheep for show. Treated poultry for lice.		

[1]This program of a student in the southeastern plains area shows a stable growth in a diversified farming program well suited to his section. (U.S. Office of Education, Voc. Div. Bul. 225.)

3. They furnish many problems which may become a part of the instructional program for a group or perhaps an entire class.
4. They furnish opportunities for obtaining desirable breeding stock for a community, and they stimulate community interest.
5. They may help the students become established in agricultural occupations.
6. They furnish a type of demonstration project for a community which often results in the adoption of a number of approved practices by farmers in the community.
7. They provide many opportunities for teachers to carry on effective instruction outside the classroom.
8. They may sometimes be used by a local FFA chapter as a means of raising money.
9. They provide many opportunities for developing leadership and cooperative activities among the members of a group.
10. They provide an opportunity for students to learn to work with others.

SUPERVISED AGRICULTURAL EXPERIENCES FOR OFF-FARM AGRICULTURALLY ORIENTED JOBS

Farming programs of the traditional types described in the preceding section of this chapter may not be suitable and are definitely inadequate for students preparing for occupations in ornamental horticulture, in agriculturally oriented businesses or jobs, or in agricultural service or regulatory jobs. If students are in a position to conduct farming programs, these provide excellent supervised occupational experience for them regardless of their vocational objectives in the complex field of agriculture. However, if they are preparing for jobs in the ornamental horticulture field, for example, they should also have supervised experiences in this area. If they are preparing for other off-

(Photo from Jasper Lee, Mississippi)

Fig. 14.1. Students being placed in agricultural businesses for supervised occupational experience need to be taught skills such as the use of cash registers.

farm jobs requiring knowledge and skills in agriculture, they should also have meaningful observational, participatory, and work experiences in these jobs. These experiences should provide them opportunities to utilize their knowledge and skills in agriculture.

Unfortunately, many students in vocational agriculture who are preparing for off-farm jobs requiring knowledge and skills in agriculture do not have opportunities for self-initiated occupational experience programs. These students should be provided by the school with opportunities to obtain appropriate experiences with plants, animals, soils, agriculture mechanics, agriculture distribution, agriculture management, agriculture leadership, and so forth. A school can do this by providing opportunities for:

1. Placement for farm experience.
2. Participatory experiences in school-owned greenhouses.
3. Participatory experiences on school-owned land or other public lands.
4. Participatory experiences in the school's agriculture mechanics shops.
5. Participatory experiences in the school's arboretum and nursery.
6. Participatory experiences in the school's animal science laboratories.
7. Observational experiences in agriculturally oriented businesses.
8. Placement for supervised occupational experience in agriculturally oriented businesses.
9. Participatory experiences with farm organizations, agricultural cooperatives, and agricultural regulatory and service agencies.

TEACHERS' RESPONSIBILITY

Teachers Must Visit Homes and Jobs—The importance of visiting the homes of students cannot be overemphasized. Many supervised occupational experience programs have been successful because of the large number of home and job visits by teachers. Others have been of little value because teachers, and in some instances administrations, did not have an appreciation and vision of the needs for adequate supervision at home and on the job. *There is a need for teachers to make many more home and on-the-job visits than have been made in the past.* In many schools, more time should be earmarked for visits to the homes and jobs by teachers.

Responsibility Rests upon Teachers—It is easy for teachers to criticize the students, the parents, the school, or the community for the failure of supervised occupational experience programs. In reality, the burden of responsibility rests upon the teachers. Teachers who believe in occupational experience programs and appreciate their importance can, in most cases, motivate very satisfactory programs. To a large degree, the responsibility for the success or failure of the supervised occupational experience programs in a community depends on the teacher. Naturally, teachers cannot always insure a financial profit, but in most cases they can insure educational profits. There are a few rules which, if followed, will tend to produce superior programs of supervised occupational experiences. Instructors:

1. Must be in sympathy with the program of supervised occupational experience.
2. Must encourage high standards for the program.
3. Must encourage modern, up-to-date, and economical approved practices and complete, accurate records.

4. Must visit each program frequently and give helpful assistance to the student, the parents, and the employer.
5. Should try to develop the interest and pride of the students in doing jobs which will result in desirable educational and financial returns.
6. Should encourage the vocational students to have programs which will aid them in becoming established in farming or in agriculturally oriented jobs.
7. Should base the classroom instruction on the programs of the students and give the students an opportunity to study, discuss, and decide on the best possible approved practices to follow in conducting their programs.
8. Must develop cooperative teacher-parent-student relationships.
9. Must guide the students in developing well balanced, comprehensive programs.

Tell me the kind of supervised occupational experience programs your students have, and I will tell you the kind of teacher of agriculture you are.

CHAPTER

15

How to Develop Supervised Occupational Experience Programs in Agriculture

---

The preferred term for the supervised occupational experience programs for the enrollees in vocational agriculture courses for farming is "farming programs." The term "farming program" is less inclusive than the term "occupational experience program." *Farming program* refers to on-farm supervised agriculture experience.

All enrollees in vocational agriculture courses for farming have farming programs. Enrollees in vocational agriculture courses for off-farm occupations requiring knowledge and skills in agriculture often conduct farming programs as a portion of their supervised occupational experience programs. However, the high school enrollees preparing for off-farm occupations requiring knowledge and skills in agriculture typically are placed on school-released or non–school-released time for part-time employment in a job. The job in which a student is placed is selected because of its appropriateness for the occupational objectives of the student. Such placement is often entitled a *cooperative education program.*[1] This term implies a cooperative arrangement between a school and an employer for the purpose of providing occupational experiences of educational value. Enrollees in agriculture courses with non-vocational objectives also often conduct farming programs, frequently on a small scale, utilizing the facilities of the land laboratory of the school or other facilities. The principles of developing farming programs and other types of supervised occupational experiences are similar.

---

[1]It is called "cooperative education" because it requires a cooperative arrangement between the school and the business involved.

DEVELOPING UNDERSTANDINGS

Cooperation of All Persons Involved Essential—It is important to assure an understanding of the aims and purposes of supervised occupational experience programs with all persons concerned in the development of these programs. This is especially urgent in departments where unsatisfactory experience programs have been conducted due to a lack of teacher-parent-student-employer understanding and to inadequate supervision by the instructor. The development of these understandings may be undertaken before the instructor launches the classroom instruction on supervised occupational experience programs. The following persons should be visited and their cooperation solicited:

1. The local superintendent, principal, and school board members.
2. The parents or guardians.
3. The students.
4. Other persons, such as employers and prospective employers.

The Local Administration—An instructor should consult the local superintendent, principal, and directors of vocational education and discuss with them the objectives of the supervised occupational experience program.

The teacher should make sure that the administrators understand the primary aim of vocational education in agriculture, *to educate for proficiency in farming and for proficiency in other occupations requiring knowledge and skills in agriculture*. The necessity of providing opportunities for students enrolled to develop satisfactory occupational experience programs and the relationship of the instruction to the occupational experience programs should be explained.

Instructors must develop in their administrators understandings of occupational experience programs so that these officials will realize that some of the most effective teaching in agriculture is done outside the four walls of a classroom and that much of the instruction should be given where a job is being done. The following techniques have been used successfully by teachers in the developing of understandings by school administrators:

1. Invite the administrators to go on field tours to observe supervised occupational experience programs.
2. Invite administrators to attend parent-student-employer get-togethers and to participate in the programs.
3. Prepare a monthly report of visits made to supervise occupational experience programs for the administrators and board members to review.
4. Take pictures of activities and show them to administrators, board members, and the public.
5. Prepare news items illustrated with pictures for the local paper and see that all administrators receive copies.
6. Invite administrators to attend classes, including the agriculture mechanics classes.
7. Invite administrators to attend FFA meetings.

Instructors should also explain the need for adequate supervision of the occupational experience programs and show the desirability of having sufficient time allocated for effective supervision.

Cooperation of Parents—The parents or guardians of students must have the program carefully explained to them in such a way that they will understand the objectives and the educational value of the program to their sons and daughters, to them as parents, and to the community as a whole. It is only natural for parents to want their children to receive the best possible training, to learn through experience, and to have the opportunity to develop a program which will assist in becoming established in a suitable occupation. Most parents are glad to cooperate with instructors who have an interest in their sons' and daughters' welfare.

If parents understand the objectives of a supervised occupational experience program, they will:

1. Add their encouragement to that of the instructor.
2. Provide opportunities for the student to develop a comprehensive program.
3. Permit the student to adopt and put into effect a large number of approved practices.
4. Provide opportunities for the student to learn through experience.
5. Back the instructor in guiding the student to develop and maintain a sound, well balanced program.
6. Assist the instructor in motivating the student to develop desirable work habits.
7. Assist the instructor in supervising the student's program.
8. Permit the student to have the money earned.
9. Encourage the student to keep complete and accurate records.

The most satisfactory supervised occupational experience programs are developed as a result of proper instructor-parent-employer relationships. The securing and maintenance of desirable relationships and understandings are the duty of every instructor of agriculture.

Cooperation of Employers—An increasing percentage of the supervised occupational experience programs in agriculture involve employers. Often these

(Photo from Robert W. Walker, Pennsylvania)

Fig. 15.1. Instruction related to ornamental horticulture is receiving increased attention, especially in urban areas. Teachers need to work closely with persons in the industry.

employers are in off-farm agricultural businesses. As with parents, it cannot be assumed that employers providing students with supervised occupational experiences understand the program. The teacher needs, individually and in group meetings, to explain the following to the employers recruited to provide supervised occupational experiences in agriculture:

1. Purposes and philosophy of supervised occupational experience programs.
2. Relationships of the program to classroom activities.
3. Relationships among the student, employer, and teacher-coordinator.
4. Duties of the employer.
5. Duties of the teacher-coordinator.
6. Responsibilities of the student.
7. The legal situation.
8. Necessity for training plans.
9. Necessity for a supervised occupational experience written agreement between the student and the employer.
10. Procedures for handling grievances.

The complete understanding and cooperation of employers is essential to the success of a supervised occupational experience program.

How to Develop Cooperative Relationships—*Cooperative relationships among an instructor, the parents, the employers, and the students have a very important bearing upon the effectiveness of the instruction. They are basic to all teaching and must be secured. An instructor cannot depend solely on the students to explain the program to parents and employers. Too frequently, the students themselves do not understand the objectives of supervised occupational experience programs. They may give the parents and employers an erroneous idea of such programs.*

Some of the ways of developing desirable cooperative relationships with parents and employers are through:

1. Visits to the homes and agricultural business firms.
2. Tours of supervised agriculture experience programs.
3. Group meetings with parents and employers.
4. Parent-student-employer banquets or other get-togethers.
5. A series of newspaper articles.
6. A series of circular letters.
7. The use of slides, filmstrips, and movies of students' programs.
8. The activities of the FFA members, including newsletters sponsored by the local chapter.
9. Attendance of parents and employers at FFA chapter meetings.
10. The development of understandings by students regarding supervised occupational experiences so that they may intelligently discuss their programs with their parents and employers.
11. The development of desirable prevocational projects.

Visits to the Home—This is one of the best methods of developing desirable relationships. It gives an instructor an opportunity to see and understand a student's home situation and to form judgments on the kind of occupational experience program possible. *Any conference to talk over a student's interests and needs and the possibilities for the development of a desirable supervised occupational experience program which will aid the student in becoming established in some occupation requiring knowledge and skills in agriculture should include the father, mother, and son or daughter. There is no substitute for such a conference.* There may be times when it is desirable to have a conference with just the parents. The first home visit should be made prior to the student's enrollment in agriculture or soon afterwards.

There are also opportunities for an instructor to discuss a student's program with the parents by inviting them into the school, by visiting them when they come to the shopping center, or by visiting with them after church. Such conferences, however, should not be used as complete substitutes for home visits.

Conferences with Employers—Teachers should conduct conferences with employers who provide students with supervised occupational experience at these times: before the student starts, during supervision visits, and when the students terminate their programs. Group conferences as well as individual conferences should be provided. For the content of such conferences, review the section in this chapter on cooperation of employers.

Tours of Supervised Occupational Experience Programs—A tour of supervised occupational experience programs is especially desirable for parents and employers who have not previously been acquainted with vocational education in agriculture. *Tours must be well planned, and the programs visited should be those of students who have good supervised occupational experience programs.* Otherwise, the tours may do more harm than good. In established departments, a tour may be made before school opens in the fall to give the parents of beginning students an opportunity to observe the programs and develop understandings regarding supervised occupational experiences before their sons and daughters enroll in agriculture.

Group Meetings with Parents and Employers—Teachers often invite parents and employers to attend group meetings to discuss the program in agricultural education and to observe the work being done by the students. The first group meeting with parents and employers may be used to discuss the objectives of agricultural education and of the supervised occupational experience programs.

Such meetings are very important for many reasons. They may be used to:

1. Develop understandings, attitudes, ideals, and appreciations regarding supervised occupational experiences.
2. Develop good will and cooperation.
3. Obtain parents' cooperation in motivating students to develop comprehensive programs based on individual interests, needs, and abilities.
4. Establish in the minds of parents the opportunities they have for improving family living conditions through occupational experience programs.
5. Develop parents' and employers' confidence in the instructor.
6. Procure valuable suggestions from the employers and parents for ways and means of improving the occupational experience programs and other activities in agriculture courses.
7. Create understanding as to why a student should keep complete and accurate records, pay all expenses, and receive the profits on a sound business basis.
8. Radiate the interest of some parents and employers to other parents and employers.

Such meetings should not be used to replace home visits, individual conferences, and on-the-job visits, but rather to supplement them. They save time by permitting the presentation of the program to a group of parents and employers and the procurement of group recommendations.

Teachers have found that it is necessary to organize meetings of parents and employers very carefully. Suggestions regarding what should be considered at a meeting may be obtained from the advisory council and from the agriculture students. The following types of activities at such meetings have been used successfully to educate parents and employers regarding agricultural education, supervised occupational experiences, and FFA.

1. Showing motion pictures concerning agricultural education, supervised occupational experiences, or FFA.
2. Having former students discuss their growth into agricultural occupations through vocational education in agriculture.
3. Showing color slides of occupational experience programs of former and present students.
4. Discussing with parents the purposes of occupational education and the place of supervised occupational experience programs in agriculture courses.
5. Discussing with parents and employers the meaning of the term "supervised occupational experiences."
6. Discussing with parents and employers the type of activities included in a supervised occupational experience program.
7. Discussing with parents and employers the question, "What is a good occupational experience program?"
8. Having one or two students discuss the FFA program of work.
9. Discussing with parents and employers the purpose of FFA activities in agricultural education.

DEVELOPING STUDENT UNDERSTANDINGS

Importance of Student Understandings—The students, as well as the parents and the employers, must understand the fundamental principles regarding supervised occupational experience programs. The importance of different activities must be discussed and a realization of their values established in the minds of the students. Students cannot be expected to cooperate or be enthusiastic about a program they do not understand.

Motivation of Students Essential—It is important that an instructor use a variety of methods of increasing interest in supervised occupational experience activities. Such methods include the following:

1. Visiting outstanding programs of other students.
2. Showing pictures, slides, and films of desirable occupational experience program activities.
3. Reviewing desirable records kept by former students.
4. Reviewing individuals' occupational experience opportunities.
5. Basing instruction on individual problems growing out of the supervised occupational experience programs.
6. Visiting homes and jobs of students.
7. Budgeting to determine possible profits. (Students like to earn money. Show them they can do it through occupational experience programs.)
8. Providing a special visiting day for eighth grade graduates.
9. Visiting rural elementary schools and explaining the program to the teachers and students.
10. Developing group projects.
11. Providing participation in FFA activities relating to occupational experience programs.

Classroom Instruction—Soon after school opens in the fall, an instructor should conduct a series of discussions and field trips pertaining to supervised occupational experiences. A sufficient amount of time should be used to develop proper understandings, attitudes, and ideals regarding comprehensive programs of supervised occupational experiences. *The unit of instruction on this important phase should be taught early in the school year. Discussions should be on problems such as, "What is meant by 'supervised occupational experiences'?" and "Why should I have an occupational experience program?"*

DEVELOPING LANDLORD AND EMPLOYER UNDERSTANDINGS

Landlord Understandings—Often a student's parents live on a farm and work for a farmer or rent land on a share basis. They also may have the livestock on a share basis. In such cases the parents and the student have to obtain the cooperation of the landlord if a comprehensive program of supervised farming is to be developed. Lack of understanding and cooperation of landlords often results in students having very narrow farming programs which afford insufficient opportunity for the development of needed abilities.

An instructor should realize the responsibility of meeting with landlords, parents, and students to explain the program of supervised occupational experiences. The instructor should point out how to develop a program which will be of mutual benefit to all concerned.

When landlords understand the aims and purposes of the different kinds of activities in the farming program—how students adopt approved practices as a result of organized instruction and how these activities are supervised by the teacher of agriculture—they will usually be willing to cooperate.

Employer Understandings—Before a student is placed in an agriculturally oriented business for experience, the teacher of vocational agriculture should interview the employer for the following purposes:

1. To discuss the objectives of vocational education in agriculture and the reasons why the student needs the experience.
2. To find out what the working conditions will be.
3. To find out what will be expected of the student and the nature of the work to be done.
4. To secure the full cooperation of the employer.
5. To see whether suitable opportunities and facilities are available for developing the needed abilities.
6. To work out a plan that will provide for effective training and for the development of the abilities needed by the student.
7. To discuss the safety precautions which should be followed.
8. To discuss the amount of wages.
9. To point out the need for the student to develop abilities through the use of approved practices.
10. To discuss and, if possible, demonstrate to the employer procedures to use in training on the job.

The teacher should also interview the student's parents (or guardian) and arrange for a conference with the employer, the parents, and the student, to make sure that all understand the arrangements. This should be done before the student is placed in the business. After the student is placed, the instruction should be followed up by the teacher since this is a definite part of the educational program in agriculture. The teacher should continue to give the employer some instruction pertaining to his/her responsibilities and in other ways provide any additional aid necessary.

DEVELOPING COMMUNITY RELATIONSHIPS

Importance of Community Understanding—One of the essential duties of a teacher of agriculture is to inform the community concerning the objectives and activities of the supervised occupational experience program. This is necessary in establishing desirable community relationships and in procuring the support of the community in promoting and developing an agricultural education program. A school cannot expect its patrons to support a program they do not understand.

Developing Understandings—One of the best ways to develop community understandings is to demonstrate the effectiveness of the program through the activities of the department. If sound programs of supervised occupational experiences are developed, there will be little difficulty in developing community realization of the importance of supervised occupational experiences.

LAUNCHING SUPERVISED OCCUPATIONAL EXPERIENCE PROGRAMS IN AGRICULTURE

Scope of Supervised Occupational Experience Programs—It is often said that supervised occupational experience programs are indicative of the effectiveness of the teacher of agriculture. This is true, for if the instructor has weak, poorly developed supervised programs, a vast amount of academic subject matter which is not carried to the "doing level" will have to be taught and the instruction will become nonfunctional and ineffective.

Instructors should encourage the students to set high their supervised occupational experience standards. A supervised occupational experience program should be of sufficient scope and should be conducted in such a way as to make it practical, interesting, challenging, and educational. It should afford opportunities for growth and for a good financial profit. If instructors stimulate students to carry out satisfactory occupational experience programs of sufficient size and quality, they will have very little difficulty in developing an effective program of agricultural education.

Often teachers feel that they must not encourage high standards for supervised occupational experience programs because they are afraid that it will decrease the enrollment in their departments and cause parental antagonism. This is a very foolish, yet common, mistake. Parents send their sons and daughters to school to learn, and they appreciate having instructors who encourage programs that are practical and of real educational value.

Essentials in Launching Programs—The discussion of the following questions is usually considered essential to the successful launching of occupational experience programs:

1. What are supervised occupational experience programs?
2. What are the purposes of supervised occupational experiences?

3. How many students "grow into" occupations requiring knowledge and skills in agriculture through supervised occupational experience programs?
4. What kinds of projects and activities constitute occupational experience programs?
5. What is a comprehensive program of supervised occupational experiences?
6. What should be considered in selecting a job to obtain occupational experiences?
7. What should be considered in selecting production projects, improvement projects, and supplementary practices?
8. What types of agreements should the students arrange?
9. How should experiences be financed?

It is important that instructors visit the homes of prospective students before school opens. During these visits the preliminary selection of a number of activities for the supervised occupational experience programs may be made. The instructors should record the preliminary selections and discuss them further with the students after they enroll in agriculture.

In guiding students in their selection of supervised occupational experience activities, the FFA members may be very helpful. A local chapter ordinarily has a committee designated as the Committee on Supervised Occupational Experiences.

Provide for Improvement Projects—Improvement projects provide many opportunities for motivating students to learn through experience. Following are a few procedures often used to create and maintain interest in improvement projects:

1. Arrange a field trip to plan possible improvement projects.
2. Have a student with a good improvement project tell about the project.
3. Secure the interest of parents during home visits.
4. Encourage the establishment of goals for improvement projects and the development of ways and means of charting progress toward these goals.
5. Use simple records and discuss frequently with class members what the records being kept tell them.
6. Provide publicity for improvement projects underway.
7. Hold meetings of parents and students to discuss improvement projects.

Include Agriculture Mechanics Activities—Instructors must be cognizant of the need for many agriculture mechanics activities in the supervised occupational experience programs. During recent years, farming and other agriculturally oriented businesses have become highly mechanized; consequently, there is a need for increased emphasis on many activities in agriculture mechanics.

Review Records of Former Programs—The students should analyze the records of the supervised occupational experience programs of former students. These records should have been accurately kept and summarized for the school files. They are exceedingly valuable in helping beginning students in their selection of desirable practices to follow.

Select Occupational Experience Programs Early—It is important that, immediately following the opening of school, the beginning students be given instruction which will develop an understanding of the objectives of supervised occupational experiences. Following this basic instruction, the students should start planning programs. *Soon after school opens, placement for experience jobs, production projects, improvement projects, and supplementary practices* *and activities should be selected.* Additional activities should be added as individual needs and opportunities develop. The early selection of occupational experience programs is necessary if the instruction in the classroom is to be based on the students' programs.

The students who have had one year or more of agriculture should analyze their programs soon after school opens to determine which of their activities they should continue. They also need to decide what additional activities should be added to their occupational experience programs.

BUDGETS, FINANCES, AND AGREEMENTS

Budgets—Before students make a final selection of projects or activities to include in their occupational experience programs, they should carefully estimate the receipts and expenses to determine the probable outcomes. A project is a business venture for profit and should be conducted as such. Some of the reasons for a budget are:

1. It provides an opportunity to anticipate and plan for the money needed for expenses.
2. It provides an opportunity to anticipate the possibility of profit in an undertaking.
3. It may result in a number of problems for classroom or individual instruction.
4. It is useful in securing credit and in developing business agreements.
5. It gives students and parents some knowledge as to the costs involved. (The students may not be able to finance their activities.)

Many teachers believe budget making kills interest. When it does decrease interest, the teaching procedures used need to be scrutinized. Planning and anticipating possibilities of profit or loss are normal interests of students. Budget making is a difficult job, however, and immature students need help in developing their budgets. They usually need assistance in developing the arithmetical skills required and help in locating information needed.

The type of budget shown in Form 15.1 is a desirable one to use. It provides for estimated and actual receipts and expenses.

Financing an Occupational Experience Program—A student's supervised occupational experience program is a business undertaking planned for profit. It must be planned on a sound financial basis.

Form 15.1. A Desirable Type of Project Budget Form

Item	Estimated		Actual	
	Amount	Value	Amount	Value
1. *Operating and miscellaneous expenses:*				
2. *Overhead expenses:*				
3. *Receipts and miscellaneous credits:*				

After a student has carefully prepared a budget showing the estimated expenses and receipts, the budget should be checked by the teacher. A meeting should then be arranged for the teacher, parents, and son or daughter to discuss the methods of financing the program. If the parents cannot finance the program, their cooperation should be solicited in making arrangements for financing from some other source. Care must be taken, however, to see that the money borrowed will be for a desirable investment and that the student has a very good chance of making a profit from the undertaking.

Numerous methods have been successfully used for financing agriculture occupational programs. Following is a list of some of these successful procedures:

1. Securing funds from parents.
2. Securing loans from local bankers. When this is done, someone other than the teacher should sign the note with the student. Teachers who have financed projects have on some occasions been accused of receiving some of the profits. On other occasions the teachers have had to absorb financial losses.
3. Securing funds from finance corporations.
4. Securing loans through the local FFA chapter. The chapter may have a revolving fund for this purpose.
5. Securing funds from local service clubs.
6. Securing funds from friends.

A student should study the possible methods of securing finances and compare the merits of each before deciding where to borrow money. All loans should be protected by collateral and insurance. Some FFA chapters have developed their own cooperative insurance associations. When money is borrowed, it is essential that a sound repayment plan has been formulated. *It is always important in borrowing money to have a written contract.*

Business Agreements—The businesslike procedure to follow in any type of undertaking is to protect the venture by a written agreement. Some of the purposes of a written agreement are:

1. To have all parties know what the agreement includes and what is expected of each party. (The agreement must be well prepared so that it is easily understood and so that it covers all the items which should be included.)
2. To have a record of the agreement in case of death of one of the parties.
3. To avoid misunderstandings which may result if only a verbal agreement is made.
4. To have a record of the agreement in case of a dispute between parties.
5. To develop desirable abilities for conducting business procedures.
6. To develop agreements which will be fair to all parties concerned.
7. To show the division of responsibility.
8. To help insure a successful program.

It may require considerable diplomacy to secure an agreement between parents and the son or daughter or between an employer and a student, but a tactful instructor should be able to develop a realization of the desirability of such an agreement. Some adults, if approached on the signing of an agreement before complete rapport has been attained, may be resentful and perhaps look with suspicion at the procedure. The value of a written agreement probably depends on how well the teacher has developed proper relationships and how thoroughly the agriculture occupational program is understood by all concerned. If a teacher has developed desirable cooperative relationships with employers and parents, there should be no difficulty in developing written agreements. Written agreements are desirable, and they should be encouraged.

All agreements should be in writing to avoid any misunderstanding. Agreements should include items such as the following:

1. When to begin the agriculture occupational program.
2. What activities are included.
3. What the parent or the employer agrees to do.
4. What the student agrees to do.
5. What the teacher agrees to do.
6. The signatures of all concerned.

SUMMARY OF CLASSROOM INSTRUCTIONAL PROCEDURES ON SELECTING OCCUPATIONAL EXPERIENCE PROGRAMS

Immediately following the opening of school, some basic related instruction should be offered to orient beginning students concerning agricultural education and to develop a thorough understanding of supervised occupational experiences.

Teachers can save themselves much time and trouble by using all the class time needed to discuss and develop understandings regarding occupational experience programs. The students should clearly understand that the instruction offered in their vocational education in agriculture courses will be based largely on their occupational experience programs. All students also need to understand that a single project or activity is only one unit of a comprehensive program. Students cannot make much progress in agriculture if their occupational experience programs consist of short-term, unrelated activities that are selected to meet statutory requirements and are terminated soon after they are started. A continuously growing occupational experience program is necessary for satisfactory results.

Instruction Prior to Early Selection of Projects—The following activities and problems are usually included in the course of study for first-year students during the first few weeks of school:

1. Acquainting students with one another and with the school facilities.
2. Developing an understanding of the objectives of agricultural education, with special emphasis on supervised occupational experience programs.
   a. What is agricultural education?
   b. What is the relationship of vocational education in agriculture to the FFA?
   c. What are the objectives of vocational education in agriculture?
   d. Why should I study agriculture?
   e. What activities are included in supervised occupational experience programs? (Cover placement in off-farm jobs for experience, production projects, improvement projects, supplementary farm practices, and group projects.)
   f. What is a good occupational experience program? (Go on a tour of programs and invite parents and employers to go along. Hold group meetings of parents and employers. Stress the importance of long-time plan-

ning. Place examples of good long-time programs on the chalkboard or pass out mimeographed plans from students' notebooks.)

g. Why should I have a good occupational experience program? (Stress the opportunity to make money, learning by doing, and home improvement.)
h. Why should I make a survey of my home situation?
i. What facilities do I have available at home?
j. What major projects and activities should I select?
k. What improvement projects should I select? (Explain that every student should do something to improve the home, increase its real estate value, and contribute to family living.)
l. What supplementary practices should I learn how to do this year?
m. What off-farm agricultural activities should I include in my program?
n. How may FFA activities contribute to supervised occupational experience programs?

Some instruction pertaining to the selection of suitable occupational experience activities should also be offered for the students who have been enrolled previously. They will need to evaluate their occupational experience programs and their plans for the year's activities. They may need to make a few changes in their present plans.

Instruction in Selecting Activities for Supervised Agriculture Programs— After the students have surveyed their situations and have developed an understanding of supervised occupational experience programs as previously suggested, they should be ready to select experience activities. The following instructional procedures are suggested:

1. Have students talk with their parents regarding the activities that will be most desirable for them to include in their experience programs this year and in the years following. *The teacher should be diligently visiting the homes and jobs of the students each afternoon after duties at the school are completed and on Saturdays to assist the students, employers, and parents in choosing the activities the students should include in their programs.* These visits are necessary to supplement the visits made during the summer months. The teacher must not fail to visit the homes. *The first few weeks is a crucial time in developing parent-student-employer understandings and cooperative relationships. These relationships are essential in developing comprehensive supervised occupational experience programs and a course of instruction based on these programs.*
2. Have students list the placement for experience jobs and production projects it will be possible for them to have.
3. Divide the students into groups having the same placement for experience jobs or production projects.
   a. Have each group budget estimated expenses and receipts to determine the probable profits.
   b. Have each group report on findings and compare profits.
   c. Review records of supervised occupational experience programs of former students.
4. Have each student evaluate the previous discussions and make a final selection of desired experiences. (The student should record these in a notebook or record book after they have been approved by the teacher and the parents.)
5. Have each student prepare a list of improvement projects planned. (After the projects are approved by the teacher and the parents, list them on a long-time plan sheet.)
6. Discuss with students the possibilities for group projects, and list any which are needed to provide experiences for certain class members who do not have an opportunity for such experiences at home or on a job. (Some may be sponsored by the FFA chapter.)
7. Have each student prepare a list of the agriculture mechanics activities to

be included in the program. Have each individual decide on any equipment needed in connection with the program.

8. Have students preparing for off-farm occupations requiring knowledge and skills in agriculture plan appropriate participatory experiences.

Since the development of comprehensive programs in supervised occupational experiences is a continuous process, it is not to be expected that all activities in a student's program will be selected soon after school opens, but as many as possible should be selected so that the related instruction may be planned.

DEVELOPING SUPERVISED OCCUPATIONAL EXPERIENCE PROGRAMS[2]

Deciding on Objectives and Goals—After the occupational experience programs are selected, some additional time should be spent in classroom discussions pertaining to the objectives the students hope to accomplish in their programs. In other words, students need to know where they are going and how they expect to get there. After objectives are formulated, the students should develop *plans of action* for accomplishing them. The objectives formulated will depend on the abilities needed.

The students should also determine production goals for their production projects. These may be stated in terms of the amount of feed required to produce a quart of milk or a pound of wool, the weight of a lamb at five months, and the like. Class discussions should be held on the meaning and importance of standards and goals. Students should study and decide on efficiency standards for their supervised occupational experience programs.

Standards should stimulate considerable interest in the problems studied in class. At the end of the year the students should analyze their records in relation to efficiency standards and try to determine why they obtained the results they did.

Using Approved Practices—Farmers and adults in agriculturally oriented businesses are realizing more and more the importance of using standard approved practices in their operations. Likewise, teachers of agriculture are cognizant of the need for students to use approved practices in their programs. These practices should grow out of the instruction. The term "approved practices" refers to those practices which have been tested and are accepted as being of superior merit. Students will need to adopt many approved practices in order to accomplish their goals.

The importance of using approved practices in production or in an off-farm agricultural occupation cannot be overemphasized. Teaching students to do a job correctly is an important part of their instruction in agriculture.

If students decide to follow a poor practice, it is the instructor's responsibility to show the students by means of experimental and local data that they should not follow it. The instructor should help them select a desirable prac-

[2]The supervised farming programs for young farmers and adult farmers are discussed in Chapter 8, "How to Teach Young and Older Adults."

tice. This does not mean that an instructor is to be dictatorial and require them to carry out methods they do not believe are worthwhile, but it does mean that an instructor should, by effective teaching methods, motivate students to use the best procedures.

Writing Plans for an Occupational Experience Program—A plan becomes the blueprint indicating exactly what the student intends to do. There should be an overall written plan indicating the exploratory experiences, placement for experience jobs, production and improvement projects, and supplementary practices for each year in a long-time program. This plan should include the student's objectives for the current year and for the future. A more detailed plan should also be written for each activity.

Following are some of the reasons why plans should be in writing:

1. To ascertain whether the students have made a thorough study of what is planned and have arrived at sound, practical conclusions.
2. To make sure that the use of standard approved practices is planned.
3. To discover whether the students know how to perform the jobs planned.
4. To give the instructor and the parents or employer an opportunity to approve the plan before it is put into operation.
5. To prevent any misunderstanding regarding how the projects or activities are to be conducted.

What to Include in a Plan—A plan should contain the name of the activity, the size, the objectives, the goals, the method of financing, and the information regarding all jobs or decisions that will be necessary in carrying the activity to a satisfactory completion. A plan should tell the *what, when, why, how,* and *where.* It must be *specific, clear,* and *complete.* The writing of a plan should require considerable reflective thought regarding essential steps in the execution of an activity or project.

Most jobs or decisions related to an activity should be discussed in class, and plans should be made for doing them. While there are no set patterns for written plans which may be used throughout the country, there are certain items which should probably be covered in any plan. Following is a list of these items:

1. Name of project or activity.
2. Kind of project or activity.
3. Scope or size.
4. Objectives (includes reasons for choosing).
5. Goals to be attained.
6. Budget of expenses and probable returns.
7. Financing.
8. Agreement (may be on a separate sheet of paper).
9. Location of project or activity.
10. Time to begin project or activity.
11. Tools, equipment, and buildings needed (where to get the equipment, what rent to pay, etc.).
12. Records to keep and use to be made of them.
13. Use of money made from project or activity.
14. Plans for future.
15. Detailed plans on how to complete each job. (The activity should be divided into jobs and detailed plans written on each one, with specific information on how each is to be performed. These detailed plans should develop from and be one of the results of the instructional program throughout the year.)

When to Write Preliminary Plans—As soon as each activity is selected, the student should write preliminary plans. Plans should be checked by the instructor before being copied in the notebook or record book.

Detailed plans for performing the different jobs, however, should not be written until the students have studied the jobs and discussed them in class or received individualized instruction. Each job should be studied to the extent possible just prior to the time it is performed. The students should then evaluate the different possible practices to use and select standard approved practices which will be best for them to adopt and use.

Instruction on Writing Plans—Some instruction on the writing of plans is desirable, especially for beginning students. It may include the following activities:

1. Discuss with the class questions such as: *Why write plans? Why does a contractor need a blueprint? Why do you need a blueprint? Will a plan help you to avoid mistakes? What is a good long-time plan? What is a good plan for an individual student project?* Show good plans. Have a former student who has a good plan tell the class about it.
2. Discuss with the class desirable objectives and their validation for occupational experience programs.
3. Discuss with the class how to formulate suitable efficiency standards.
4. Decide with the class what to include in a long-time plan.
5. Decide with the class what to include in plans for each activity.
6. Decide with the class what agreements should be written. (The teacher may need to visit parents or employers again.) Show some desirable types of agreements.
7. Have students, individually or by groups with the same activities planned, write preliminary plans.
8. Have the students give their preliminary plans to the teacher to review and approve. After the plans have been approved by the teacher, the students may copy their plans into their notebooks or record books.

KEEPING AND USING RECORDS

Importance—In the past, some teachers of agriculture have considered the keeping of records to be of little importance. Record keeping often has not been properly stressed; objectives for keeping records have not been developed; and little emphasis has been placed on student motivation. The result often has been inaccurate, poorly kept records. If more consideration were given to the keeping and the intelligent use of complete and accurate records, there would be less difficulty in getting adults to keep records after they are graduated from high school. Records should be accurate, up-to-date, and legible. Some of the reasons for keeping records are so that students can:

1. Know the results obtained in their occupational experience programs.
2. Compare their results with standards and goals achieved by other members of their class.
3. Evaluate their results and set new efficiency goals.
4. Discover weaknesses in individual programs and determine what practices should be changed to improve efficiency.
5. Develop interest and improve the individual occupational experience programs.
6. Develop desirable habits, ideals, attitudes, and appreciations regarding records.

Form 15.2. Supervised Occupational Experience Plans for Individual Projects

(Name of Activity or Project) (Scope) (Year)

Objectives:	Goals:

Jobs or Decisions	Date to Perform	Detailed and Specific Information on How Each Job Is to Be Done (Budget may also be set up in this space.)	Necessary Changes or Additions

7. Have furnished to them many desirable problems for classroom and individual instruction. (These problems may grow out of the analysis of the project records.)
8. Be motivated to use approved practices to meet their goals.
9. Develop desirable abilities in agriculture.
10. Determine costs of production.

Keeping Records of Job Experiences—For experiences obtained during job placement, the students need to keep records of the following:

1. Experiences planned and experiences obtained.
2. Duration of each experience.
3. Hours worked.
4. Earnings.
5. Supervision and instruction received, and from whom.
6. Skills learned.
7. Abilities developed.
8. Problems encountered.
9. Expenditures related to the job.
10. Safety record.

Keeping Records of Production Projects—Separate records should be kept for each project. These should be simple and should be only those which are useful in a student's occupational experience program. The following is typical of records kept on production projects:

1. Survey results.
2. Budget estimates.
3. Business agreements.
4. Project plans (long-time and individual).
5. Sales or receipt records.
6. Expense record.
7. Production record.
8. Labor record.
9. Opening and closing inventories.
10. Financial summary.
11. Breeding record.
12. Loss record.
13. Diary.
14. Project story.
15. Record of teacher visitations.

There is considerable variation among the record books used in the different states. Some of the states have record books which provide space for most of the items mentioned; others provide for only a part of these. Some states have developed record books which provide space for the records of several individual projects and for the summary of the total occupational experience program.

All expenditures in connection with a production project should be figured. All inventories should be properly recorded and the correct costs or market values figured. If anything, such as feed or seed, is donated to a student, its local value should be figured. Whether or not rent is actually paid, it should be figured according to the prevalent rates in the community. The same is true for interest on the investment. All costs must be included if records are to be meaningful.

Keeping Records on Improvement Projects—The kind of records to keep will depend on the type of improvement project and the approved practices included. The use of approved practices is essential, and a record of these practices should be kept. Any records which will be useful in evaluating results, in developing functional course materials, and in conducting similar projects in the future should be maintained. Form 15.3 illustrates one method of keeping records on improvement projects.

Form 15.3. Improvement Projects

Use this form to plan and record results of one of your improvement projects. The scope of the project should be broad enough to include the planning and development of many skills. It should involve responsibilities over a period of time.

______________________________ (Kind of Improvement) ______________ (Year)

Plans		Checking Results	
Size planned ______________		Actual size ______________	
Things to improve		Actual improvements	
1.		1.	
2.		2.	
3.		3.	
4.		4.	
Estimated costs:		Actual costs:	
Hours student labor	____	Hours student labor	____
Hours other labor (not hired)	____	Hours other labor (not hired)	____
Hired labor	$____	Hired labor	$____
Supplies		Supplies	
1.	$____	1.	$____
2.	____	2.	____
3.	____	3.	____
4.	____	4.	____
5.	____	5.	____
Equipment rental	____	Equipment rental	____
Total costs	$____	Total costs	$____
Expected results		Actual results	
1.		1.	
2.		2.	
3.		3.	
4.		4.	
5.		5.	
Date to start ______________		Date started ______________	
Date to close ______________		Date closed ______________	

PROPOSED CHANGES FOR NEXT YEAR (list)

Keeping Records of Supplementary Practices—Each student should keep a list of supplementary practices performed which are not a part of production and improvement projects and which were experienced as a result of the instruction in agriculture. A separate page in a record book or notebook may be used for keeping a record of these practices. Form 15.4 illustrates one method of recording supplementary practices.

Form 15.4. Record of Supplementary Practices

	Check When Completed					
			Year Completed			
Agriculture Skills and Practices	In Class	On Farm or Job	1	2	3	4

How to Obtain Accurate Records—The following suggestions for obtaining accurate and up-to-date records have proved very satisfactory:

1. Discuss with the class the importance of good records and the necessity of records being complete and accurate if they are to be of any value.
2. Visit the students' homes and places of employment and secure the cooperation of the parents and employers.
3. Discuss with the students the records they think they should keep on their occupational experience programs, and why. After they have determined the types of records they need, present the official record books to them. Ask the members of the class if these books do not provide forms for the types of records they think they should keep.
4. Teach the students how to do the different jobs in record keeping just prior to or at the time they will be recording these records. Teach these jobs in seasonal order.
5. Provide drill in record keeping so that the students may develop the ability to perform easily the mechanics of record keeping.
6. Have the students keep their record books at school during the school term. A diary or day book may be kept at home or on the job.

a. Have the students fill in the record books once a week during class time. (Some instructors may prefer to have this done every two weeks.)
b. Set aside a definite day in each week when the students are to bring to school their diaries or day books, which they at other times keep at home.
    (1) During supervised study periods, ask all students to record in their books any records they may have.
    (2) Carefully supervise each student.
c. Keep the books in a cabinet in the classroom which is readily accessible to the teacher, superintendent, or supervisor.
d. In the summer, have students keep records in a diary or day book.

7. Have students close the records for the year under the supervision of the instructor.
8. Have the students make summaries of records and proper analyses of them during and at the completion of each project.

Using Records Effectively—A teacher of agriculture has many opportunities for making use of the occupational experience program records kept. If the records are complete and accurately kept, they afford some of the most valuable data attainable for use in the instruction in agriculture.

In the following list, there are a number of suggestions on how to use records effectively:

1. Summarize, analyze, and evaluate records to determine weaknesses in individual programs and group projects. This evaluation will likely indicate the need for additional approved practices, which will involve a number of problems to be included in the course of study.
2. Have students analyze their records and compare their achievements with those of other members of their class and with farmers and off-farm agricultural workers in the community.
3. Analyze agreements used and work out ways and means of improving these agreements.
4. Analyze and evaluate methods of financing and develop improved methods.
5. Use the records in the instruction at appropriate times.

Form 15.5 is an example of a form that may be useful in helping students use and analyze their records for production projects. A similar form may be developed for all types of production and improvement projects.

Students may be helped in visualizing their results through bar graphs or "scattergraphs" showing their results in relation to those of others.

Forms similar to Form 15.5 are of little value unless they are interpreted. A teacher may use the following questions in leading class discussions to interpret results being obtained in the production projects:

1. How much did it cost you to produce whatever you were producing?
2. How did your cost of production compare with what you could have bought the product for on the open market (producer's cost)?
3. How did your cost of production compare with that of the more efficient producers in your community?
4. How did your cost of production compare with that of other students in the department having the same kind of project?
5. If your cost of production was higher than that of similar projects, what were the reasons for this?
6. If your costs were lower than the average of those of the classmates having the same kind of project, how did you keep your costs down?
7. How could you have managed your project so as to reduce the cost of production?
8. What was your average yield?

Form 15.5. Individual Efficiency and Summary Record Sheet[1]

Name of Student ______________________ Year in School ________

Item	Class Goals	Individual Goals	Class Accom-plishments	Individual Accom-plishments
1. Average number of animals				
2. Lbs. beef per cow				
3. Lbs. milk per cow				
4. Height and weight of heifer at 6 mos.				
5. Height and weight of heifer at 12 mos.				
6. Height and weight of heifer at 18 mos.				
7. Lbs. feed to produce 100 lbs. milk				
8. Lbs. feed to raise a heifer to 12 mos.				
9. Returns per $100 feed fed				
10. Cost of producing 100 lbs. milk				
11. Hours of labor per cow				
12. Hours of labor per heifer				
13. Labor and management earnings				

[1]Prepared by Bob Howey, teacher of vocational agriculture, Illinois.

9. How did your yield compare with that of the more efficient producers in your community?
10. How did your yield compare with the yield that others carrying the same kind of project received? How did it compare with the average in the community?
11. What did you do that helped to make your yield higher or lower?
12. What things that you had no control over affected your yield?
13. What could you have done to increase the yield?
14. Would it have paid you to have done it? Why?
15. How did the quality of your product compare with that of products of the more efficient producers in your community?
16. Was the quality of your product as good as, better than, or not as good as, that of others?
17. What did you do that increased or decreased the quality of what you produced?
18. What things that you had no control over affected the quality of your product?
19. Are you sure that you kept accurate records of all expenses and receipts?
20. Why is it important that records be accurate?
21. How much did you get for each unit of production?
22. Was the price you received higher or lower per unit than that received by the more efficient producers in your community?
23. Was the price you received higher or lower than the average for the group having the same kind of project?
24. How do you account for this difference?
25. What improved practices would have helped you make a better financial return from your project?

CHAPTER

16

How to Conduct Off-Farm Supervised Occupational Experience Programs

INTRODUCTION

This chapter concerns the procedures involved in the conduct of vocational education in agriculture instruction designed to prepare students for gainful employment in jobs, other than in production agriculture, that require considerable knowledge and skill in plant and animal science and related agriculture mechanics. An attempt has been made throughout the book to integrate information regarding educating for off-farm agricultural occupations. Also, special sections of other chapters have been devoted to certain aspects of these programs. The content of these special sections is not repeated in this chapter. The reader interested in the conduct of off-farm agricultural occupations programs should, in addition to reading this chapter, see the special sections in the other chapters.

IMPORTANCE AND OPPORTUNITIES

The Vocational Education Act of 1963 and the Amendments of 1976 broadened the objectives of vocational education in agriculture. They made possible the providing of educational programs in agriculture for all jobs requiring knowledge and skills in agriculture and were a mandate for schools and teachers of agriculture to offer such programs.

Automation in agriculture, and in all other occupational areas, is rapidly changing manpower needs. Automation decreases the needs for workers in certain areas while it increases the needs for workers in other areas. It also creates new kinds of jobs. Such has been the case in agriculture. Automation has decreased the number of farmers, ranchers, and other production agriculture workers needed. At the same time it has increased the need for technical- and semi-technical-level workers in the off-farm industries servicing production agriculture. A large percentage of these technical- and semi-technical-level workers need basic vocational education in the plant and animal sciences and in related agriculture mechanics.

Automation has also created or increased job opportunities in businesses and industries that do not service production agriculture, for persons with vocational education in plant and animal science and in the related agriculture mechanics. If departments of vocational education in agriculture are to do the job society expects them to do, they must provide effective programs to prepare workers for gainful employment in (1) off-farm agriculturally oriented businesses and industries and in (2) non-agricultural businesses and industries that employ persons who must have knowledge and skill in plant and animal science and in the related agriculture mechanics. A department of vocational education in agriculture that provides education only in production agriculture has but a limited, partial program and probably cannot survive in a modern school.

Opportunities and needs exist in almost all communities for the vocational education of persons for employment in off-farm jobs requiring knowledge and skills in agriculture. Most teachers studying the opportunities for placement of students in their communities in off-farm jobs requiring considerable knowledge and skill in applied or vocational plant and animal science are surprised at the extent of the opportunities.

The U.S. Office of Education has listed, among others, the following objectives for vocational education in agriculture:

1. To develop agricultural competencies needed by individuals engaged in, or preparing to engage in, agricultural occupations other than production agriculture.
2. To develop an understanding and appreciation of career opportunities in agriculture and of the preparation needed to enter and progress in agricultural occupations.
3. To develop the ability to secure satisfactory placement and to advance in an agricultural occupation through a program of continuing education.
4. To aid in developing those abilities in human relations required for success in agricultural occupations.

Agricultural occupations programs of various types and dimensions are needed to meet these objectives.

DETERMINING LOCAL OPPORTUNITIES

Essential to programs designed to prepare individuals for gainful employment in jobs requiring knowledge and skill in plant and animal science and related agriculture mechanics are opportunities for supervised experiences in these jobs. All communities have types of employment in which students may receive supervised on-the-job experiences. Often teachers are unaware of the opportunities that exist. The first task of a teacher preparing to conduct an off-farm agricultural occupations program is to study the local jobs requiring employees with knowledge and skill in applied plant and animal science and in agriculture mechanics.

The teacher of agriculture undertaking such a study should attempt to identify all local businesses employing persons who meet these qualifications. The classified section of the telephone directory will provide many clues. The teacher should then visit the businesses that may have such employees.

A survey schedule similar to Form 16.1 may be used to identify the businesses that employ workers who need technical or vocational education in agriculture. If job titles are found that appear to require workers with the knowledge and skills usually gained from education in agriculture, Form 16.2 may be used to obtain more information about these job titles. The information obtained from the use of Form 16.2 is useful in curriculum development in programs designed to prepare individuals for gainful employment in nonproduction plant and animal science related occupations.

Form 16.1. Agricultural Occupations Survey[1]

Date ____________

1. Name of company or business ____

____

2. Address ____

3. Persons to contact:

______________________________________ Telephone ____________
(name and position)

______________________________________ Telephone ____________
(name and position)

4. Functions of company or business:

_____Manufacturing
_____Purchasing
_____Servicing
_____Constructing
_____Retailing
_____Warehousing
_____Processing
_____Wholesaling
_____Contracting
_____Other (Specify) ____________

5. List of products or services involved in items checked in No. 4:

____
____
____
____

6. _____Percentage of business agriculturally oriented

7. _____Total number of workers (owners and employees)

8. Job titles and number of workers in each:

[1]Adapted from a schedule used in a study by Lloyd J. Phipps, A. H. Krebs, Paul Hemp, J. R. Warmbrod, and Gerald Fuller, *Technical Education in and for Rural Areas*, Agricultural Education Division, University of Illinois, Urbana–Champaign, 64 pp.

Form 16.2. Information for Planning Programs for Off-Farm Agricultural Occupations[1]

1. Name and address of firm ______________________
2. Job title ______________________
3. Alternative titles ______________________
4. Activities and duties of persons with this job title:

a. *Working with people outside firm:*

___Meeting farm people
___Meeting nonfarm people
___Selling
___Advising, consulting, and diagnosing
___Estimating costs
___Buying
___Other (Specify)

Clarification Comments

____

b. *Working with personnel in firm:*

___Handling workers (boss)
___Inducting new personnel
___Training others
___Appraising work of others
___Supervising others
___Other (Specify) ______________________

Clarification Comments

____

c. *Working with production, products, materials, or service:*

___Designing
___Making and building
___Sketching and drawing
___Mixing
___Assembling
___Inspecting
___Testing
___Calculating costs
___Conducting research
___Using technical and service manuals, parts lists
___Developing techniques for production or service
___Planning production or service
___Other (Specify) ______________________

Clarification Comments

____

d. *Working with firm's or customer's equipment, tools (hand or power), supplies, and instruments:*

___Constructing
___Designing
___Repairing
___Operating
___Assembling
___Calibrating
___Remodeling
___Adjusting
___Maintaining
___Inspecting, testing, trouble-shooting
___Installing
___Selecting
___Other (Specify) ______________________

Clarification Comments (List items of equipment, etc.)

____

____

e. *Working with business problems:*

___Policy making
___Planning
___Promoting
___Handling money
___Keeping records and accounts
___Writing articles, copy, etc.
___Making speeches
___Filing
___Inventorying
___Making technical reports
___Reading technical reports
___Decision making
___Other (Specify) ______________________

Clarification Comments

____

____

(Continued)

Form 16.2 (Continued)

5. Areas with which workers must be familiar to do job:
   ____Soils
   ____Soil and water management
   ____Crops
   ____Horticulture
   ____Floriculture
   ____Livestock
   ____Poultry
   ____Dairy
   ____Feeds
   ____Animal nutrition
   ____Animal diseases
   ____Plant diseases
   ____Tractors and other power units
   ____Electricity
   ____Farm mechanization
   ____Shop work
   ____Carpentry
   ____Farm buildings
   ____Farm conveniences
   ____Agricultural economics
   ____Agricultural and rural life in general
   ____Agricultural chemicals
   ____Insect and pest control
   ____Forestry
   ____Food processing
   ____Rural recreation
   ____Credit
   ____Insurance
   ____Taxes
   ____Accounting
   ____Business principles
   ____Office procedures
   ____Sales skills
   ____Chemistry
   ____Physics
   ____Advanced mathematics
   ____Foreign language
   ____Research procedures
   ____Electronics
   ____Mechanics
   ____Sound and light
   ____Hydraulics
   ____Metallurgy
   ____Heat
   ____Architecture
   ____Other (Specify) ________________

   Clarification Comments

   ____

   ____

6. Prerequisites of job:
   ____Work experience required prior to acceptance of job
   ____On-job training

   Clarification Comments

   ____

   ____

7. ____Are there specific policy limitations on ages for employment? If so, what?

   ____

   ____

   ____

8. Employment opportunities:
   ____Total number of different persons with this job title employed in past five years.
   ____Anticipated additional persons with job title needed in five years due to growth.
   ____Number of additional people with job title needed in next 12 months due to growth or turnover.

[1]Adapted from a schedule used in a study by Lloyd J. Phipps, A. H. Krebs, Paul Hemp, J. R. Warmbrod, and Gerald Fuller, *Technical Education in and for Rural Areas*, Agricultural Education Division, University of Illinois, Urbana–Champaign, 64 pp.

TYPES OF PROGRAMS

Organization—The core of an agricultural occupations program is the placement-employment experiences of the students. Two patterns are usually followed in the organization of placement-employment programs. A desirable pattern, especially in rural communities, is to place students in jobs for pay after school, on week-ends, and during the summer. This placement-employment pattern resembles the experience program pattern followed in the conduct of supervised farming programs.

The program's flexibility gives it several advantages. The students may be employed during the periods of the year when employers need them. They do not need to have school-released time for their placement-employment experiences. The scheduling of other courses by the students is thereby facilitated. Parents and school officials often prefer this pattern of organization because the students are in the school buildings the same hours as the students in non-vocational courses.

The second pattern of organization utilizes school-released time for the placement-employment experiences, usually 2 to 3 hours a day for a total of 10 to 15 hours a week. This works well in urban areas. Businesses and schools in these areas are often familiar with the placement-employment (cooperative) programs in industrial education, office education, and distributive education.

Both patterns of organization can be made to work. The pattern adopted should be the one better adapted to the community and school in which the program is to be conducted. The advantages and disadvantages of each should be studied and analyzed before the pattern to be used is selected.

Class instruction must accompany and be integrated with placement-employment programs. Appropriate class instruction may be provided if separate courses are established for individuals preparing for employment in the nonproduction sector of agriculture. If the number of students who are preparing for such employment is not sufficient to justify separate courses, they may be enrolled in existing vocational education in agriculture courses. This is not an ideal arrangement, however, and separate courses should be established as soon as the enrollment makes it feasible to do so.

Cooperative Education—The placement-employment experience program using school-released time is often called the "cooperative education program." This terminology was developed in other vocational subject areas such as distributive education and industrial education and has been adopted in agricultural education in some schools. It is termed "cooperative education" because it provides for the cooperative efforts of the school and the businesses in the education of the students. Businesses provide on-the-job training and the school provides the related vocational class instruction and part of the on-the-job supervision.

SELECTING AND PLACING STUDENTS

Only students who have a reasonable chance for success should be selected for placement-employment in agriculturally oriented jobs in a community. However, vocational education in agriculture also has a responsibility to prepare for employment students who have special needs. These students may receive their placement-employment experiences in a school-sponsored "sheltered workshop" until they are capable of handling placement-employment experience in a business in the community.

Proper selecting and placing of students in placement-employment programs in agriculturally oriented businesses in the community or in school-sponsored "sheltered workshops" are important to the success of agricultural occupational programs.

To insure proper placement and desirable relationships, Form 16.3 or a similar form may be used.

Form 16.3. Employment Agreement for the Supervised Occupational Work Experience of a Student of Vocational Horticulture

To insure a permanent basis of understanding and to promote better working relations, this agreement is established on ________________ ________________, 19 ____.

The work will start on ________________, 19 ____, and will terminate on or about ________________, 19 ____ (subject to further agreement for continued work).

Person in industry responsible for on-the-job experiences and education:

____

The usual working hours will be as follows:

When attending school ________________________

When not attending school ________________________

Provision for overtime ________________________

Provision for time off ________________________

Liability insurance coverage ________________________

Compensation will be at the following rate(s) ________________________

And will be paid (when?) ________________________

THE EMPLOYER AGREES

To provide the student with opportunities to learn how to do well as many jobs as possible, with particular reference to those contained in the on-the-job experience program.

To coach the student in desirable work procedures and in desirable ways of handling problems.

To make an honest appraisal of the student's performance on the job at the end of specific periods agreed upon.

To give the instructor time for short conferences regarding the progress of the student.

To avoid subjecting the student to unnecessary or unusual hazards.

To notify the parents and the school immediately in case of accident, sickness, or any other serious problem which arises.

To permit the trainee to conduct a productive enterprise in the industry whenever conditions are favorable and the proposition has the approval of the instructor and parents.

To permit the instructor to take whatever time necessary for supervisory visits to the industry.

THE STUDENT AGREES

To notify the employer at once when it is necessary to be absent from work for justifiable cause.

To do a good day's work according to age and ability.

To keep the employer's interest in mind, being punctual, dependable, and loyal.

To follow instructions, avoid unsafe acts, and be alert to unsafe conditions.

To be courteous and considerate of the employer and others.

To keep records of work experiences and to make reports as required by the school.

THE INSTRUCTOR, ON BEHALF OF THE SCHOOL, AGREES

To visit the student on the job at frequent intervals for the purposes of instruction and of insuring that the student gets the most out of his experience.

(Continued)

Form 16.3 (Continued)

To show discretion in the time and circumstances of these visits, especially during emergency periods when the work is pressing.

THE PARENTS AGREE

To assist in promoting the value of the student's experience by cooperating with the employer and the instructor.

To satisfy themselves in regard to the work conditions made available to the student.

ALL PARTIES AGREE

That the initial 10 working days be regarded as a trial period to allow the student time to adjust and prove himself/herself.

That in the event of difficulties in the interpretation of the terms of this agreement, the school shall be the mediator and its decision will be final.

This agreement may be terminated for cause at any time by either party after due notice, but not without first consulting the school.

Student ______________________	Employer ______________________
Address ______________________	Address ______________________
Telephone No. ______________________	Telephone No. ______________________
APPROVED	*APPROVED FOR THE SCHOOL*
Parent ______________________	Instructor ______________________
Address ______________________	Home Telephone No. ______________________
Telephone No. ______________________	Director ______________________
	School Telephone No. ______________________

SELECTING AND ORGANIZING COURSE CONTENT

Pilot studies in the conduct of programs for off-farm agricultural occupations have indicated that teachers of agriculture become enthusiastic regarding the general vocational education knowledge and skills students in placement-employment programs need. As a result they often neglect to provide adequately the plant and animal science and related mechanics skills and knowledge the students require. Content such as employee-employer relationships, sales skills, and so forth is important, but the students will not be successful unless they are also taught the plant and animal science and related mechanics abilities they must have to perform their jobs. Businesspersons can and will teach sales skills, telephone techniques, and so forth, but they usually depend heavily on the teacher of agriculture to teach the agricultural content.

A teacher of agriculture with students in placement-employment programs, therefore, should analyze the plant and animal science and related mechanics knowledge and skills the students need, and he/she should provide these in appropriate units of instruction. In addition to agricultural subject matter content, the teacher will need to teach other core or general vocational education content units.

Professor Paul Hemp has listed the following problem areas that are related to placement-employment programs:

1. Determining job titles and their requirements in agriculturally oriented businesses.
2. Determining employee responsibilities in agriculturally oriented businesses.
3. Determining employer responsibilities in agriculturally oriented businesses.
4. Knowing the agricultural products and services.
5. Selling agricultural products and services.
6. Developing good customer relationships in agriculturally oriented businesses.
7. Purchasing agricultural products for resale.
8. Pricing agricultural products and services.
9. Promoting agricultural products and services.
10. Transporting and storing agricultural products.
11. Keeping agricultural business records and taking inventories.
12. Preventing accidents and handling emergencies in agriculturally oriented businesses.
13. Improving agricultural businesses.

LEGAL REGULATIONS

Teachers of agriculture in charge of placement-employment programs need to familiarize themselves with federal and state legal regulations that apply to the employment of student-learners. They should obtain from the U.S. Department of Labor copies of publications describing the provisions of the Fair Labor Standards Act as it applies to child labor and student-learners. The Fair Labor Standards Act and state labor legislative acts regulate the employment of youth, limit the length of the work week, establish the minimum wages paid, and determine employment duties in hazardous occupations.

Teachers of agriculture also need to understand the workmen's compensation, social security, and liability regulations that apply to students in placement-employment programs. If unions are involved, teachers of agriculture should understand labor laws and local union policies.

The basic minimum age for employment as a learner in a nonhazardous occupation is 16. Certain occupations are declared hazardous by the Secretary of Labor, and students usually may not be employed in one of these until they are 18 years of age. However, in certain instances and under specified conditions, persons under 18 years of age may be employed in hazardous occupations. For these details, teachers of agriculture should consult the bulletins relating to student-learners published by the U.S. Department of Labor.

Employers may protect themselves from unintentional violation of the minimum age provisions for employment by requiring that students employed supply them with Age or Employment Certificates. The employers should keep these certificates on file.

Students are not permitted by law to be occupied more than a total of 40 hours a week in school and in work. Student-learners must be paid the minimum wage unless the employers obtain student-learner employment permits. If employers have such permits, they may pay 75 per cent of the minimum hourly rate.

ON-JOB SUPERVISION

It is advisable for teachers of students placed for occupational experience to visit the students periodically on the job to facilitate and promote the learning activities of the students.

In multiple-teacher departments, however, the policies of some schools do not permit this arrangement. For economic efficiency, in some schools one teacher is assigned responsibilities for all on-the-job supervision. When this occurs, the classroom teachers do not have an opportunity to supervise their students in the occupational experience program. This is unfortunate and is not educationally defensible. However, the practice does exist. Where it exists, a close continuous working relationship must be maintained between the classroom teachers and the teachers providing the on-the-job supervision.

SUMMARY

Following is a chronological procedure for developing an off-farm supervised occupational experience program:[1]

1. Survey agricultural businesses in the community by using Forms 16.1 and 16.2.
2. Have students apply for placement-employment.
3. Interview students applying for placement-employment.
4. Identify agricultural businesses which could be used as on-job experience stations.
5. Determine willingness of selected agriculturally oriented businesses to accept students in placement-employment.
6. Outline tentative experience programs for students in placement-employment.
7. Review tentative on-job experience programs and related classroom instruction with agricultural employers.
8. Arrange for students to be interviewed for placement-employment jobs.
9. Develop and sign an on-job experience agreement for each student in placement-employment.
10. Supervise students on the job frequently.

[1]Adapted from a step-by-step procedure for establishing and planning placement-employment programs which was developed by Prof. Paul Hemp, Agricultural Education Division, University of Illinois, Urbana–Champaign.

CHAPTER

17

How to Supervise Occupational Experience Programs in Agriculture

Importance—Adequate supervision is essential in the selecting, planning, and conducting of supervised occupational experience programs. Too frequently instructors believe that parents, employers, and students know what is to be done and how to do it and that only a minimum number of home and on-job visits is necessary. The result of this attitude is narrow and poorly developed programs. The better teachers of agriculture are cognizant of the need for many effective home and on-job visits.

The primary purpose of home and on-job visits is to provide individual instruction, but visits to the homes and jobs of students also give teachers an opportunity to develop face-to-face relationships with parents and employers. A teacher learns firsthand regarding a student's status in the family group and on the job. With this knowledge teachers know better how to handle each student in class, in the FFA, around school, and during individual counseling. During home and on-job visits, teachers may check on the effectiveness of their teaching. They usually become acquainted during home and on-job visits with the agricultural or guidance problems that should be studied in the classroom.

Individual instruction on home visits or on visits to businesses or farms where students are obtaining participatory experiences requires considerable teacher time, but the results obtained justify the time required. Industries and businesses recognize the value of individual instruction in training their employees. They do not question the high cost of this type of instruction because they recognize its effectiveness. A person learns as an individual. Learning by a person may be fostered in a group or in a class, but an ability is seldom completely developed through group or class instruction. When adults have problems, they usually insist on individual instruction regarding the solution of their problems. We have organized classes in agriculture for convenience in teaching, but instruction in class groups can never be entirely satisfactory.

An instructor has opportunities to engage in the following activities during individual instruction visits:

1. Observe the home situation or the job situation.
2. Meet members of the family or the employer in order to become acquainted.
3. Find out the interests of the family members or the employer and seek cooperation in developing a comprehensive occupational experience program for the student.
4. Observe the home and job environment. This often is very helpful to a teacher in providing effective supervision.
5. Discuss with the student, the parents, and the employer the activities which might be included in the student's supervised occupational experience program.
6. Determine the approved practices needed.
7. Teach by discussing with the student any problem being encountered, by testing the student's understanding of the practices being used, and by developing the abilities of the student in the performance of skills which have not previously been learned.
8. Check to see whether the plans are being followed and whether they are satisfactory.
9. Check the diary and records of the student for completeness and accuracy.
10. Encourage the use of approved practices.
11. Discuss with the student and the parents the possibilities for expanding the program during the succeeding months and years.
12. Assist in evaluating progress to date.
13. Counsel the student regarding his/her all-around development and plans for the future.

When to Begin Visits—The first visit to a prospective student should be made early in the summer. Some teachers visit prospective students who are still in elementary school.

Time and Frequency of Home and Job Visits—The better teachers of agriculture plan to visit their students several times during the year. These visits are made at crucial times in students' occupational experience programs. Many consider six visits a year for each student a minimum number of visits.

Form 17.1 illustrates one method of recording crucial times in the occupational experience programs.

The following visitation schedule is suggested:

1. Visit prospective students early in the summer before they enter school in the fall. Explain the program in agriculture, stressing the FFA activities and the objectives of supervised occupational experiences.
2. During the first two months of school, visit all the students to assist them in the final selection of activities for their occupational experience programs for the year, keeping in mind long-time planning.
3. Soon after a student starts one or more activities, visit him/her at home and on the job.
4. Visit students during the school year at crucial times when they need help in learning skills or in solving problems.

During the summer, students should be visited once a month and more frequently if possible. The scope of the agricultural education program will

Form 17.1. Approximate Time of Performing Essential Jobs in the Supervised Occupational Experience Programs

(May be summarized from students' calendars of activities)

Name	September				October
	First Week	Second Week	Third Week	Fourth Week	First Week
Mary Jones		Cull hens. Make feeder.	Mix feed.	Test milk. Grade eggs.	Start work in machinery dealer's parts department.
Frank Peters					
James Long					

influence the number of visits which can be made. Teachers having high school, young farmer, adult farmer, and adult agriculture courses for off-farm workers will probably have a large total enrollment, making careful planning of visits necessary.

In some instances, school administrators have not realized the necessity of teachers of agriculture visiting the homes and jobs of their students. A teacher may often alleviate this situation by explaining to the superintendent, principal, and vocational director the reasons why adequate supervision is necessary and by turning in a monthly report indicating the date each student was visited, the purpose of each visit, and the number of miles traveled.

Form 17.2 is one type of visitation report.

Form 17.2. Visitation Report of the Teacher of Agriculture

Date	Place Visited	Purpose of Visit	Miles Traveled

A teacher should usually plan to visit a number of homes, farms, or business firms on each trip. This is especially true for Saturday and summer visits, when the entire day may be spent visiting. A definite circuit of visits may be developed in advance. The number of homes and agricultural businesses that can be visited in a day depends on many factors, such as distance traveled and individual needs of the students visited. It is often possible, however, to visit from four to six homes or businesses a day when adequate previous planning has been made. Maps showing the locations of the homes and on-job locations of students have proved very helpful to teachers in planning circuit trips.

Many administrators provide their instructors with more time for visits by relieving them of (1) study hall duties, (2) responsibility for teaching classes other than agriculture, and (3) school duties during the latter periods of the school day.

Teachers may provide themselves with more time for visits by budgeting their time carefully, by not accepting too many community responsibilities, and by delegating certain responsibilities to others, such as the FFA members.

The need for visits may be decreased by use of the following techniques:

1. Teaching in the classroom regarding problems which develop in the students' occupational experience programs.
2. Teaching in a way that will stimulate interest, thought, understanding, self-reliance, and initiative. A teacher's objective should be to teach in a way that will make the students increasingly able to solve their own problems and increasingly independent of him/her.
3. Conducting group visits. During the school year a day may be set aside occasionally for visitation of supervised occupational experience programs.
4. Holding individual conferences away from the home or job.
5. Conducting tours in which the parents, sons and daughters, employers, civic club members, and other interested persons participate.
6. Aiding each student in the complete preparation of occupational experience program plans, with specific information on how to perform each job.

Notifying Students—There has been some difference of opinion regarding whether a student should be notified of a proposed visit by the instructor. The trend, however, is toward notifying persons of proposed visits.

When notified of a proposed visit, all those concerned can arrange for an effective visit. The notification will prevent persons from feeling that the teacher is trying to catch them doing something wrong. Necessary equipment and supplies may be secured if the development of a skill is planned, and the parents or employer and the student have time to decide in advance the questions they wish to ask the teacher during his/her visit.

Visitation Procedures—While making a supervisory visit, there are a number of things which the teacher may do, some of which follow:

1. Meet with the student, and if possible the parents or employer, to observe the projects or activities in the student's occupational experience program.
2. Be alert for opportunities for teaching. A teacher may observe some practices being used which are not recognized as approved practices. In such instances, questions may be raised, such as "Where did you learn that method?" "Does it give good results?" "Is it an approved practice?" and "Do you think it should be changed?" Individual instruction also provides many opportunities for demonstrations.
3. Review the diary and records of the student. Records are not an end in themselves. Their only justification is their use in evaluating results. Records become meaningful when they are analyzed.
4. Discuss changes which may need to be made in the student's plans.
5. Discuss problems encountered.
6. Observe and discuss improvement projects and supplementary practices.
7. Discuss specific activities in which the student might engage for additional experiences.
8. Visit with the members of the family or employer and discuss immediate agricultural problems.

9. Visit with the employer and discuss the problems involved in working with the student.
10. Leave a memorandum regarding the improvement of the students' occupational experience program which was developed cooperatively by the student, parents or employer, and teacher.
11. Observe agricultural enterprises of the parents or employer and give helpful suggestions.

Form 17.3 is convenient for recording recommendations made. Form 17.4 offers a convenient method of keeping records regarding the progress of each student's occupational experience program.

Form 17.3. Instructor's Recommendations Made at the Time of a Visit

Date	Name	Instructor's Recommendations	Student's Reactions

Form 17.4. A Suggested Visitation Record of the Supervised Occupational Experience Program

Name ______________________________ Date__________

Persons contacted ______________________________

Participatory Experiences in Off-Farm Agriculturally Oriented Jobs

Type of Experience	Scope	Opportunities It Provided to Use Knowledge and Skills in Agriculture
1.		
2.		
3.		
4.		
5.		

(Continued)

Form 17.4 (Continued)

Participatory Experiences in On-Farm Jobs

Production Projects					Improvement Projects				
Name	Scope	Condition			Name	Scope	Condition		
		A	B	C			A	B	C
1.					1.				
2.					2.				
3.					3.				
4.					4.				
5.					5.				

Supplementary Practices Completed Since Last Visit

Name	Scope	Quality			Name	Scope	Quality		
		A	B	C			A	B	C
1.					5.				
2.					6.				
3.					7.				
4.					8.				

Approved Practices Completed Since Last Visit

1.	5.
2.	6.
3.	7.
4.	8.

Exploratory Experiences Completed Since Last Visit

Type	Time Required	Comments
1.		
2.		
3.		
4.		

PART

FFA

CHAPTER

18

What Is the FFA and How Is It Organized?

INTRODUCTION

The FFA is the national organization of, by, and for youth studying vocational education in agriculture in public secondary schools under the provisions of the National Vocational Acts. It is an integral part of the program of vocational education in agriculture. *"The foundation upon which the FFA organization is built includes leadership and character development, sportsmanship, cooperation, service, thrift, scholarship, improved agriculture, organized recreation, citizenship, and patriotism."*[1] There is no secrecy in the activities of the organization. The FFA is an intra-curricular activity for vocational education in agriculture.

Origin—For many years previous to the FFA movement, vocational agriculture clubs existed in many parts of the United States.

The movement received its first definite recognition as a state organization in Virginia. Professor Henry C. Groseclose of Virginia, while confined to a hospital in 1926, wrote the constitution and bylaws of the Future Farmers of Virginia (FFV). This constitution and these bylaws, with the accompanying ceremonies, attracted national attention. Leaders of vocational education in agriculture in other states soon realized that such an organization was exceedingly worthwhile. Within two years after the FFV was founded, six states in the southern region of the country had similar organizations. A national organization meeting was held in November 1928 at Kansas City, Missouri. At

[1]*Official Manual for FFA,* Alexandria, Virginia: FFA Supply Service.

this meeting national officers were elected and the National Constitution and Bylaws adopted.[2]

Importance—The FFA is one of the most outstanding national organizations in America. It is now recognized as the largest high school agricultural youth organization in the world. It has grown from an active national membership of 16,217 in the fiscal year 1928–1929 to more than 500,000, with more than 8,000 active, chartered chapters.

Aims and Purposes—The National Association of FFA has definite aims and purposes. The primary aim of the organization is the development of agricultural leadership, cooperation, and citizenship. The specific purposes for which this organization was formed are:[3]

1. To develop competent, aggressive agriculture leadership.
2. To create and nurture a love of agriculture.
3. To strengthen the confidence of young people in themselves and their work.
4. To create more interest in the intelligent choice of agricultural occupations.
5. To encourage members in the development of occupational experience programs and in establishment in agriculture careers.
6. To encourage members to improve the home and its surroundings.
7. To encourage participation in worthy undertakings for the improvement of agriculture.
8. To develop character, train members for useful citizenship, and foster patriotism.
9. To participate in cooperative efforts.
10. To encourage and practice thrift.
11. To encourage improvement in scholarship.
12. To provide and encourage the development of organized recreational activities.

Every state association of the FFA has definite aims and purposes. Likewise, each chapter within a state has certain goals of attainment for its members.

The FFA Motto—The following motto reflects the true vocational education spirit and the sincerity of purpose of the FFA:

"Learning to Do,
Doing to Learn,
Earning to Live,
Living to Serve."

This is one of the finest mottoes that could have been chosen for such an important national organization of youth. Most of the *essentials* of an education are embodied in the motto.

The FFA Colors—The official colors of the organization are *national blue* and *corn gold*. These colors should be used in connection with all meetings and in the equipment and paraphernalia used. The corn yellow color is used on a background of medium blue.

---

[2]*Ibid.*

[3]*Ibid.* (paraphrased).

Why Young People Belong to the FFA—The organization provides numerous opportunities for young people to do what they like to do. Young people enjoy doing something worthwhile, excelling in their work and play, being appreciated, being in responsible positions, learning how to help themselves, having opportunities to participate in activities, and obtaining recognition through outstanding service and achievement.

In numerous surveys, parents have indicated that membership in the FFA:

1. Develops young people socially.
2. Develops responsible citizenship.
3. Gives young people a feeling of belonging in a school.
4. Develops abilities of expression.
5. Develops, through the degree program, a feeling of accomplishment.
6. Develops leadership ability and the ability to follow good leadership.
7. Teaches thrift.
8. Develops abilities to work with others.
9. Dignifies work.
10. Promotes vocational accomplishments.
11. Develops, through community service, awareness of responsibility to others.
12. Strengthens the confidence of young people in themselves and in their work.
13. Creates more interest in the intelligent choice of an agricultural occupation.
14. Creates abilities for the improvement of agriculture.
15. Develops character.
16. Encourages scholarship.
17. Develops recreational abilities.

ORGANIZATION OF THE FFA

National Headquarters—The national adviser of the FFA is located in the U.S. Office of Education, Washington, D.C. The national headquarters are located at the National FFA Center, Alexandria, Virginia. The national conventions are held annually in Kansas City, Missouri, at the time of the American Royal Livestock Show.

National Officers—There are six student officers and three adult officers:

Student Officers:
- President
- First Vice-President
- Second Vice-President
- Third Vice-President
- Fourth Vice-President
- Secretary

Adult Officers:
- Adviser
- Executive Secretary
- Treasurer

The student officers are elected annually at the National FFA Convention.

National Board of Directors—The governing body of the FFA is a national board of directors composed of (1) the chief of the Agricultural Education Service, Office of Education, who shall act as chairperson, (2) four staff members in the Agricultural Education Service, Office of Education, and (3) four state supervisors of agricultural education. The Board of Directors exercises the powers granted in Public Law 740. See the Appendix for a copy of P.L. 740.

National Dues—The FFA is a self-supporting organization. It is operated nationally on nominal membership dues, which include a subscription to *The National FFA* magazine.

State and Local Organizations—The FFA operates under the rules and regulations set forth in the national constitution and bylaws of the FFA. The organization is composed of chartered state associations. The state associations are composed of local chapters. Collegiate chapters may be organized, chartered, and operated under the jurisdiction of the state association concerned.

Local chapters are organized by the students in the local departments of vocational agriculture who meet and elect officers. After a chapter has elected officers, a constitution is written and adopted, and a program of work is planned by the members. The local chapter adviser may then apply to the state adviser for a charter.

More than one chapter may be chartered in a school when deemed appropriate by the executive committee of the state association. Active chapters of the FFA for students enrolled in public secondary programs shall be chartered only in such schools where recognized systematic instruction in vocational education for agricultural occupations is offered under the provisions of the National Vocational Education Acts. Schools with large enrollments or multiple programs may establish mini-chapters as subdivisions of the regular chapter. When mini-chapters are used as subdivisions of the regular or parent chapter, they shall be coordinated by the officers and advisers of the parent chapter.

State Officers—The officers of a state association consist of a president, vice-presidents, secretary, treasurer, reporter, and adviser. The state supervisor of agricultural education assumes the responsibility of the state adviser. Other officers and a state advisory council may be elected if desired. The student officers are elected annually by a majority vote of the delegates in attendance at a state convention.

Membership—There are four kinds of membership in the organization:

1. *Active membership.* Any student who is regularly enrolled in vocational education in agriculture is entitled to become an active member of any chartered FFA chapter. To retain membership during high school, the member must be enrolled in at least one vocational education in agriculture course during the school year and/or follow a planned course of study for an agricultural occupation which includes a supervised occupational experience program the object of which is establishment in an agricultural occupation. Members may retain their active membership until November 3, following the fourth National FFA Convention after graduating from high school. No individual, however, may retain active membership beyond his/her 23rd birthday.
2. *Alumni membership.* Membership shall be open to former active FFA and NFA (Negro Farmers of America) members, collegiate or honorary FFA and NFA members, present and former professional agricultural educators, parents of FFA members, and others interested in and supporting the FFA.
3. *Collegiate membership.* Collegiate membership may include students en-

rolled in agriculture courses and former active members who are enrolled in a two- or four-year institution having a collegiate chapter.

4. *Honorary membership.* Farmers, school superintendents, principals, board of education members, chapter advisers, teachers, staff members in agricultural education, businesspersons, and others who are helping to advance vocational education in agriculture may be elected to honorary membership.

Degrees of Membership—There are four degrees of active membership, based upon achievement, namely: *Greenhand, Chapter Farmer, State Farmer,* and *American Farmer.* Advancement to each of these degrees is based on individual accomplishments with respect to agriculture activities, earnings, investments, leadership, and scholarship as set forth for each degree in the FFA's national constitution. The first two grades of membership are conferred by the local chapters; the State Farmer degree is conferred by the state associations, and the American Farmer degree is conferred by the national FFA organization. Every member should be encouraged to wear the insignia which represents the degree he/she holds.

Fig. 18.1. Official chapter degree pin, actual size. Greenhands wear a bronze pin and Chapter Members a silver-plated pin.[1]

Fig. 18.2. Official State Farmer degree key, actual size.[1]

Fig. 18.3. Official American Farmer degree key, actual size.[1]

Fig. 18.4. Official Collegiate Chapter and adviser pin or button, actual size.[1]

[1]Cuts of insignia furnished by the L. G. Balfour Co.

State Meetings—Most state associations have at least one meeting every year. Each chapter in a state may have delegates at this meeting. Officers are elected, programs of work are outlined, and State Farmers and honorary members are elected. Recreation of various types is usually provided. Agricultural contests and award programs are often held in connection with the meetings.

National Convention—As stated previously, the national conventions of the FFA are held annually in Kansas City, Missouri. Some of the activities at the national meetings are to outline an annual program of work, to discuss old and new business, to grant American Farmer degrees, to announce awards, to elect officers, and to honor adults. Time is devoted to the awarding of contest prizes, to a public speaking contest, and to planned educational tours related to agriculture. After attending one of the national conventions, one cannot help realizing the vast importance of this organization, the splendid work it is doing, and the inspiration it provides youth.

THE FFA FOUNDATION, INCORPORATED

Origin—The FFA Foundation was incorporated under the laws of the District of Columbia on March 29, 1944. The original certificate of incorporation, bylaws, and proposed foundation awards were revised and adopted by the Board of Trustees of the FFA Foundation at a special meeting in Kansas City, Missouri, on October 7, 1944.

Purposes—Through the years since the beginning of the national organization of the FFA, many individuals, corporations, business concerns, and associations have become enthusiastic supporters of the organization. These supporters have provided prizes and awards for members of the FFA who have demonstrated outstanding abilities in the various vocational education in agriculture activities. Because of the increasing number of parties desiring to cooperate, the FFA Foundation was incorporated.

As stated in Article IV of its certificate of incorporation, "the objects and purposes of the FFA Foundation, Incorporated, are to receive, maintain and hold, by bequest, devise, gift, or otherwise, either absolutely or in trust, for any of its purposes, any property, real or personal, funds or fund, without limitations as to amount or value; to convey such property and to invest and re-invest any principal; and to deal with and expend the income and/or principal of the Corporation for such educational activities and in such manner as in the judgment of the Board of Trustees will stimulate and promote the best interests of students and former students of vocational education in agriculture on a local, state or national basis."

The purposes of the Foundation are as follows:

> "The corporation is organized for the overall purpose of furthering education and development of FFA members with emphasis in all segments of the industry of agriculture in America at the national, state and local levels.
>
> "Specific purposes, without limiting the scope of the foregoing, include the following:
>
> "(a) To promote and stimulate interest in agriculture leadership and careers for youth in agriculture;

"(b) To promote and develop interest on the part of the general public in agricultural education, including the activites of the FFA;

"(c) To provide funds for awards, scholarships, or other recognition as authorized by the National FFA Board of Directors and Board of National FFA Officers to deserving FFA members who have achieved distinction on a national, state or local basis and to administer, direct or supervise the granting of such recognition;

"(d) To publish an annual report of the activities of the corporation, including a statement of receipts and expenditures, and to prepare and issue such other publications as may from time to time be approved by authority of the Board of Trustees.

"(e) To provide or support conference and other educational facilities for the use of FFA members, teachers and such other persons and groups as may from time to time be approved by authority of the Board of Trustees."[4]

Following is a statement of the policies adopted by the Board of Trustees of the FFA Foundation:[5]

"1. Sound public relations demand that all property, real or personal, and all funds accepted by the foundation by bequest, devise, gift, or otherwise from any organization, corporation, business concern, or individual shall be used as directed by the Foundation.

"2. The affairs of the corporation shall be managed by a board of directors, known as a Board of Trustees, consisting of members selected as follows:
   a. Three persons chosen by the Governing Council of the Sponsoring Committee of the corporation established in Article X of these Bylaws.
   b. Two persons who shall be teachers of agriculture chosen at the annual national meeting of the National Vocational Agricultural Teachers Association.
   c. Two persons who shall be teacher educators in agriculture chosen at the annual national meeting of the American Association of Teacher Educators in Agriculture.
   d. Two persons who shall hold the office of executive secretary or its equivalent at the State level of the FFA, chosen at the annual national meeting of the National Association of Supervisors of Agricultural Education.
   e. Four persons who shall be the State supervisors of agricultural education (or equivalent) currently serving as directors of the FFA.
   f. Two persons who shall be members of the staff of the United States Office of Education in the Department of Health, Education and Welfare, having responsibilities in agricultural education, chosen by the Board of Directors of the FFA.
   g. The National Advisor, the National Executive Secretary, and the National Treasurer of the FFA, all ex officio with vote.
   h. The National President of the FFA who shall serve as an ex officio member of this Board, without vote.

"3. The foundation reserves the right at any time to reject contributions from any donor or potential donor.

"4. Foundation donors will be provided with copies of the annual report of the foundation containing statements of the achievements of persons or groups receiving funds and statements of cooperation extended by the donors, together with just and proper recognition of such cooperation.

"5. The foundation will not knowingly duplicate national awards for the same types of activities to persons or groups who have received similar awards from other sources.

"6. Donors may publicize their relationship to the foundation by preparing news and feature stories about the objectives, activities, and accomplishments of the foundation for publication and broadcasting. Such releases

---

[4]*The Future Farmers of America Foundation, Incorporated.* Revised Articles of Incorporation.
[5]*Ibid.*

may contain statements of the cooperation and support given to the foundation by the donor. They are not to be used to indicate that the foundation or any individual student of vocational agriculture or member of an FFA chapter endorses the products manufactured, distributed, sold, or advertised by the sponsors.

"7. Donors may use the emblem of the foundation, during the period of their cooperation with the foundation, in educational bulletins and charts published by the donors, in paid advertising, news releases, motion pictures, slides, filmstrips, and exhibits, but with the understanding that the manner in which it is used will not indicate that the foundation, any individual student of vocational agriculture, or any FFA member or chapter endorses the products manufactured, distributed, sold, or advertised by the donors. A statement must also be included to indicate that an organization, business concern, or individual is a donor to the foundation. Glossy print photos of the foundation emblem from which cuts can be made may be secured from the office of the national secretary."

The following types of projects or activities are representative examples of those which are now or may later be sponsored by the FFA Foundation, Incorporated:

1. Agricultural proficiency awards.
2. Public speaking awards.
3. National chapter awards.
4. National chapter safety awards.
5. "Build Our American Communities" awards.
6. National judging contest awards.
7. Establishment in agriculture awards.
8. Star Farmer and Star Agribusiness of America awards.

For more details regarding the FFA Foundation, Incorporated, see the Certificate of Incorporation and the Bylaws.

FFA SUPPLY SERVICE

Since 1948 the national FFA organization has operated a supply service handling official FFA merchandise which is sold to local chapters and to FFA members. The address of the National FFA Supply Service is P.O. Box 15159, Alexandria, Virginia 22309. The supply service is located on the former grounds of the National FFA Camp which is south of Alexandria, Virginia.

The FFA Supply Service is owned by the FFA, and its operation is directed by the national Board of Directors of the FFA. Each year a catalogue of supplies is printed and distributed to all FFA chapters.

THE NATIONAL FUTURE FARMER MAGAZINE

The National Future Farmer magazine is owned and published by the FFA. The first issue was printed in October 1952. The address of the magazine is:

The National Future Farmer
P.O. Box 15130
Alexandria, Virginia 22309

It is the goal of the national organization of the FFA to have every FFA member a reader of the magazine.

THE OFFICIAL FFA CALENDAR

The official FFA calendar is published by *The National Future Farmer* magazine. In the interest of good public relations, the national organization desires to furnish quality calendars depicting FFA activities. For additional information concerning official FFA calendars, write *The National Future Farmer*, P.O. Box 15130, Alexandria, Virginia 22309.

THE NATIONAL FFA ALUMNI ASSOCIATION

The FFA Alumni Association was organized in 1971. The national organization consists of chartered state associations and local affiliates. It is an organization of former active, collegiate, and honorary FFA and NFA members, and present and former vocational education in agriculture educators.

The purposes of the FFA Alumni Association are:

1. To support and promote the FFA organization, FFA activities, and vocational education in agriculture on local, state, and national levels.
2. To provide a "tie" to the FFA that will assist FFA and agricultural education personnel to involve former FFA members in worthy activities.
3. To promote greater knowledge of the agricultural industry and to support education in agriculture.
4. To cooperate with the National FFA Board of Directors, the National FFA Foundation Board of Trustees, and the National FFA Foundation Sponsoring Committee.
5. To promote and maintain an appreciation of the American free enterprise system.
6. To promote the personal development aspects of the FFA.

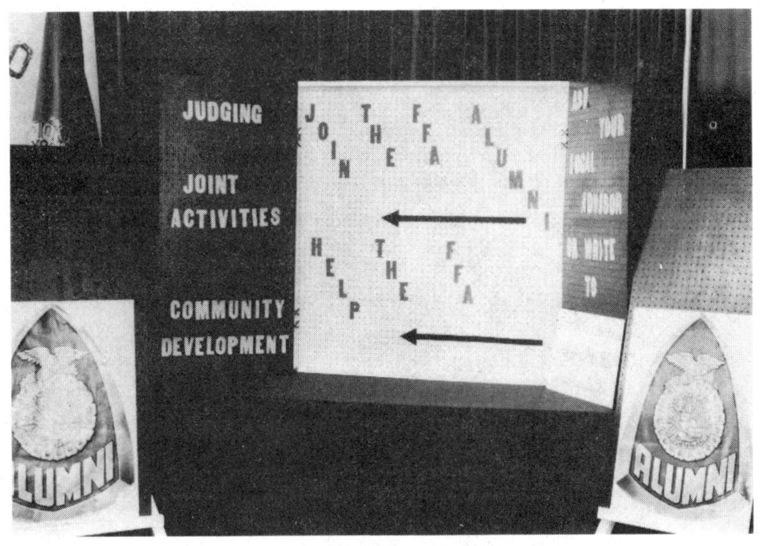

(Photo from H. W. Gadda, South Dakota)

Fig. 18.5. The FFA Alumni group may make a significant contribution to the vocational education in agriculture program in a local community.

CHAPTER

19

How to Organize and Develop FFA Chapters

ORGANIZING A LOCAL FFA CHAPTER

Why Have a Local Chapter?—The activities of the FFA organization provide many opportunities for educating youth which would be difficult to provide in other ways, if not impossible. The FFA gives students opportunities to compete for local, state, and national honors. Its program develops interests, desirable attitudes, and understandings. Every department of vocational education in agriculture should have a local chapter of the FFA.

Characteristics of a Good Chapter—Strong, effective FFA chapters have several definite characteristics. These characteristics, as listed in the *Official Manual for FFA*, are:[1]

1. Interested members.
2. Capable officers and leaders.
3. A challenging program of work.
4. Adequate financing.
5. Distributed responsibility shared by all members.
6. Proper equipment and records.
7. A knowledge of the FFA on the part of *every* member.

How to Organize a Chapter—In organizing a local chapter, a teacher may profitably engage in many of the following activities:

1. Secure a copy of the official FFA manual and become familiar with it.
2. Ask the state adviser for full information regarding the steps that should be followed, and secure copies of forms needed.

[1]*Official Manual for FFA*, Alexandria, Virginia: FFA Supply Service.

3. Inform the school authorities and the advisory council of the aims and purposes of the organization.
4. Discuss the organization with the students enrolled for vocational education in agriculture and also with their parents.
5. Discuss with the students enrolled for vocational education in agriculture the origin, purposes, degrees, dues, insignia, relation to vocational education in agriculture, and values of the FFA.
6. Take the students to visit other chapters.
7. Show pictures of FFA activities and tell of accomplishments of other chapters.
8. Show a sample program of work from an outstanding chapter.
9. Discuss the advantages of the FFA and what it takes to have a good chapter.
10. See that a committee is appointed to bring in a report on whether a chapter should be organized. When a chapter is organized, it should be because the students want it—not just to please the teacher.
11. Call a meeting of parents to discuss with them the purposes, activities, and values of the FFA.
12. Call a meeting of students and have them vote on whether to apply for a charter.

THE OPERATION OF A LOCAL CHAPTER

Officers—The officers of a local chapter consist of a president, vice-president, secretary, treasurer, reporter, sentinel, and adviser. A local teacher of vocational agriculture assumes the responsibilities of local adviser. The officers are elected either annually or semiannually at a regular chapter meeting.

Some Characteristics of Chapter Officers—It is very important to have well qualified officers, since the success or failure of a chapter often depends on its officers. The following are characteristics which all officers should possess:

1. Ability to conduct meetings by following parliamentary procedure.
2. Willingness to memorize the opening and closing ceremonies for meetings.
3. Ability to work with others effectively.
4. Ability to motivate all members to participate in the activities of the organization.
5. Willingness to become familiar with the chapter constitution and bylaws and the annual program of work.
6. Willingness to perform duties adequately.
7. Ability to delegate responsibility.
8. Willingness to "give and take."
9. Willingness to meet frequently and to plan agenda for meetings.
10. Faith and vision in the program.
11. Erect posture.
12. A clear voice.
13. Neat appearance.
14. Good judgment.

Methods of Nominating Officers—It often happens that the most popular students in a school are elected as officers, although they may not be the best qualified persons for the positions. A local adviser should provide careful guidance that will help the members of the chapter select the best persons for officers. This is one of the most important duties of a local adviser.

Several procedures are used by chapters in nominating officers. Most chapters precede the nominations by a thorough discussion of the necessary characteristics of successful officers. Many chapters have the executive committee consider all members and nominate a slate of officers. Some chapters require a prospective officer to petition for a nomination. Most petition forms require a number of signatures of FFA members, the parents' signatures, a statement of the applicant's qualifications, and a statement from the applicant regarding why he/she wants an officer's job and how the applicant will behave as an officer. Some petition forms require the signatures of a youth's parents to a statement that they will assist if the student is elected. Whatever method is used to secure the nomination of officers, it should require the members of a chapter to consider carefully how they may select the best individuals as their officers.

Duties of a Local Adviser—The key to the success of a local chapter is the local adviser. Following are some of the characteristics of a good chapter adviser:[2]

1. Ability to lead youth.
2. Faith in youth and in the program of the FFA.
3. Willingness to work.
4. Ability to delegate responsibility.
5. Ability to develop interest and enthusiasm in the activities of the chapter.
6. Resourcefulness and creative ability.
7. Ability to motivate chapter members to keep accurate and complete records of all chapter activities.
8. Ability to motivate youth to develop a desirable publicity program.
9. Ability to motivate the chapter members to secure and maintain complete chapter equipment and paraphernalia.
10. Ability to motivate members to strive for higher membership degrees.
11. Ability to motivate the chapter to secure and maintain an adequate chapter library.
12. Ability to motivate the holding of regular meetings which are carried on in a businesslike manner.
13. Ability to train chapter officers.
14. Willingness to keep informed on all new FFA developments and to inform the members of these developments.
15. Willingness to assist the members in developing an effective program of activities and in carrying it to completion.
16. Willingness to see that sound financial procedures are used and that the funds of the FFA are properly safeguarded.
17. Knowledge of the constitution, of parliamentary procedure, and of ceremonies.
18. Ability to prevent horseplay at all times, especially in initiations.
19. Ability to show no partiality.
20. Willingness to confer with officers, individually and in groups.
21. Ability to stimulate officers and members to do their own thinking.
22. Willingness to act as an ex officio member of all committees.
23. Ability to inform members of FFA awards and to assist members in applying for awards.
24. Willingness to set an example for members.
25. Willingness to be present at all chapter meetings.
26. Ability to assist members in developing outstanding comprehensive occupational experience programs.
27. Ability to interest members in retaining their membership after graduation.
28. Ability to motivate former FFA members to participate in adult agricultural education activities and to accept responsibilities of leadership in adult organizations.

[2]Some of these duties are adaptations of those listed in the *Official Manual for FFA,* Alexandria, Virginia: FFA Supply Service.

29. Willingness to see that all acts of the local chapter are in accordance with the constitutions and bylaws of the national organization, the state association, and the local chapter.
30. Ability to integrate chapter activities with an instructional program.
31. Willingness to help promote state and district activities.
32. Willingness to cooperate with other chapter advisers.

Local Constitution—Each chapter prepares its constitution and bylaws. The local constitution and bylaws, however, must not be in conflict with the national and state constitutions and bylaws.

Program of Work—Each local chapter develops a program of work for each year, listing activities, committees responsible, goals, and ways and means. At the end of the year, a list of the accomplishments is recorded. The activities in a program of work are discussed in Chapters 20 and 21.

Local Dues—The dues each member pays must be sufficient to cover the national dues, the state dues, and the local assessment, if any. Each state association decides the amount of its dues. Dues should be kept relatively low so that worthy persons are not prohibited from becoming members because they cannot afford the dues charged. Ways and means other than membership dues may be used in securing funds to finance the activities of a chapter. Financing is discussed in Chapter 20.

TRAINING FFA OFFICERS

The Local Adviser's Responsibility—Since the effectiveness of a chapter is dependent to a large degree on its officers, it is imperative that the officers be properly trained. It is the responsibility of the local adviser to assist in instigating ways and means of developing officers. Good chapter morale and desirable conduct by the members are encouraged when the officers memorize their parts for all ceremonies, when the rules of parliamentary procedure are followed in all meetings, when the officers speak clearly and distinctly, and when responsibility is delegated to the members. The instructors who set outstanding examples of good leadership for the officers to follow usually have good FFA chapters.

The Parents' Responsibility—Intelligent parents can do a great deal to encourage and otherwise help FFA members become good officers. They can permit attendance of meetings after school, at night, in camps, at state conventions, at leadership conferences, and elsewhere to learn ways of developing desirable FFA programs. An adviser should discuss with the parents of officers, either individually or in a group, how they can help the students develop into effective officers.

The Officers' Responsibility—An adviser should encourage the newly elected officers to be open-minded and willing to learn; otherwise, little may be accomplished in developing them as effective officers. They must be willing to put in many extra hours and to persevere during difficult times. They must accept their duties with vigor and determination.

Training by Old Officers—The FFA members who have served as officers usually have learned many effective ways of doing a good job. They probably have discovered a number of weaknesses in their chapter which should be corrected. These officers should be able to give the new officers many helpful suggestions. If new officers are elected in the spring, the old officers will have an opportunity to train the new officers.

Use of Assistant Officers—Some advisers have found it desirable to have assistant officers. Assistant officers are understudies to the officers. They are usually appointed from the sophomore and junior classes by the executive committee and the adviser. They assist the officers and in this way learn a great deal about the duties of officers, and they have some opportunity to demonstrate their ability as officers. Serving as assistant officers increases the interest of these understudies and gives more members an active part in the chapter activities. These members often become the officers in the chapter the following year.

Some chapters have mini-chapters which are subsidiaries of the local FFA chapter. They have their own officers. These officers, if successful, will probably be FFA officers before their school careers are finished.

Leadership Training Conferences—Leadership training conferences have become very popular in a number of states. The purpose of district, state, or national conferences is the development of desirable qualities of leadership. Persons who have had outstanding experiences may assist in conducting discussion on specific topics such as program planning, parliamentary procedure, duties of officers, objectives of the FFA, qualities of leadership, and other chapter activities.

Leadership training is generally included in state FFA leadership center programs. In fact, most programs are planned around leadership training and recreation. For example, in a Missouri leadership center, the members were divided into five groups, and one of the following topics was discussed by each group:

1. The responsibilities of FFA officers.
2. Organizing FFA activities for a five- or six-school area.
3. The scope and history of the FFA.
4. The use of parliamentary procedure in your chapter.
5. Sources of programs for chapter meetings.

Training conferences are often conducted for a small area in a state, with 3 to 10 schools meeting together in a centrally located school. An entire chapter may attend a training conference of this type. The theme of these conferences is often the developing of FFA programs of work. Several schools may have their members give demonstrations on desirable activities, such as parliamentary procedure. These demonstrations are frequently followed by small-group meetings to discuss topics such as program planning and duties of officers.

In some area training conferences, each local chapter goes through the ceremony of opening a meeting to demonstrate its ability in this activity. The demonstrations are observed very carefully to see whether the ceremony in the FFA manual is followed properly. The manner in which the members present their parts and their general posture during a presentation are also noted. The president is given a motion or other point of business to see whether he/she knows how to handle it properly. Officers are questioned to see whether they know their duties and responsibilities and understand how to execute them. The secretary may be asked to go to the chalkboard and write a sentence from the FFA creed. This indicates the ability to write legibly. The secretary may also be asked to read a portion from the FFA manual to demonstrate the ability to read effectively.

Chapter Training Conferences—A local FFA adviser may provide the chapter members with leadership conferences. There many discussions are held on how to improve the chapter through better meetings, a more comprehensive program, better qualified officers, more complete and accurate records, and a better publicity program. Fun and work are mixed in desirable proportions to develop a very worthwhile conference.

Meeting Ceremony and Parliamentary Procedure—Some states or districts in a state sponsor contests in which the officers from a chapter compete with the officers from other chapters in conducting a chapter meeting. The officers of a chapter are given a topic and asked to demonstrate their skill in opening, conducting, and closing a meeting. This usually covers a period of from 10 to 15 minutes. Three judges are usually provided who question the officers at the close of the demonstrations. At the close of the contest, a rating of the chapter officers participating is made. Such a contest offers many desirable opportunities for effective training of officers in the use of parliamentary procedure. They must know what to do, when to do it, and how to do it.

Providing Manuals for All Members—Every member should have an official FFA manual, be encouraged to study it, and know what it contains.

Having a Good Chapter Library—An adequate chapter libary is desirable. A chapter library might contain a collection of good books which are not easily available elsewhere. Members may also share their own books through a chapter library. Most chapter libraries contain good collections of FFA reference books. Members can develop understandings regarding the FFA through reading about the accomplishments of other individuals and chapters. FFA publications, manuals, and proceedings of the national conventions should be available in an FFA library.

Cooperation Between Chapters—Joint meetings may be held by two neighboring chapters. Often a chapter has another chapter perform the ceremonies for raising members to advanced degrees. These joint activities develop interest and leadership abilities among the members participating.

Having Officers Attend Conventions—The officers in a chapter should be given the opportunity to attend state, regional, and, when possible, national meetings of the FFA. These meetings provide opportunities to obtain many worthwhile experiences and to observe ways of conducting meetings effectively. They give the officers better appreciation and understanding of the aims, purposes, and scope of the FFA. Officers come home with new vigor and with determination to improve their chapter, and they stimulate the other chapter members by relating their experiences at the convention.

Using School Time for Leadership Training—Can the use of school time for FFA leadership training be justified? Certainly. Since the FFA is an integral part of vocational education in agriculture, the use of school time, in which organized training essential to success in agricultural leadership and family living is involved, cannot be questioned. It is in keeping with accepted practice to use a part of class time in vocational education in agriculture for FFA chapter planning and leadership training.

CONDUCTING MEETINGS

Importance of Well Conducted Meetings—Chapter meetings must be properly conducted for best results. The members of a chapter appreciate the vast importance of the FFA organization more and have a greater respect for it when the meetings are conducted in a businesslike manner. In all meetings, the ritual should be followed, with officers having their parts memorized so that they may repeat them in a sincere and effective manner. The meetings should be made as impressive as possible. This is especially true when members are initiated into the different degrees.

Frequency of Meetings—Just how often to hold the meetings of a chapter is a local problem which must be decided by the members and the adviser. Meetings are usually held at least once or twice each month throughout the calendar year. Many chapters hold meetings every two weeks.

Ways of Creating Interest—One of the best ways of creating interest is to involve each member. Responsibility should be delegated to all members. Meetings should be started and closed on time and conducted in a businesslike fashion. Members should be there for a purpose; they should have something to do and do it. The room should be properly arranged.

Location of Meetings—Where facilities permit, it is desirable to have a special room for FFA meetings. If a building for agriculture is provided, it may include a room for FFA activities. Provision for a room used exclusively by the FFA, however, is impossible in most schools. The agriculture classroom may be used if it is large enough to accommodate the group. Whatever room is used should be made appropriate for each meeting by using and locating properly all equipment and paraphernalia.

1 American flag
1 FFA felt banner (size 3′ x 6′)
1 official FFA flag (optional)
1 plow (miniature)
1 ear of yellow corn
1 picture of Thomas Jefferson
1 bust of George Washington
1 owl (artificial)
1 rising sun emblem or picture
1 gavel and block
1 secretary's book
1 treasurer's book
1 scrapbook
1 copy of charter (framed)
1 copy of purposes (framed)
1 copy of creed (framed)
1 copy of profanity order (framed)
1 shield for sentinel station
7 or more official FFA manuals
1 *FFA at 50* (history)

These items of FFA paraphernalia should be used in connection with all FFA chapter meetings. Copies of the FFA manual should be available for all members, and officers should have their own personal copies.

Room Arrangement—A chapter's meeting room should be neatly arranged, with all paraphernalia in its proper place. The following symbols should be placed at the officers' stations as indicated in Figure 19.1.

Rising Sun	President
Plow	Vice-President
Ear of Corn	Secretary
Bust of Washington	Treasurer
American Flag	Reporter
Owl	Adviser
Shield of Friendship	Sentinel

The sentinel should sit by the door.[3]

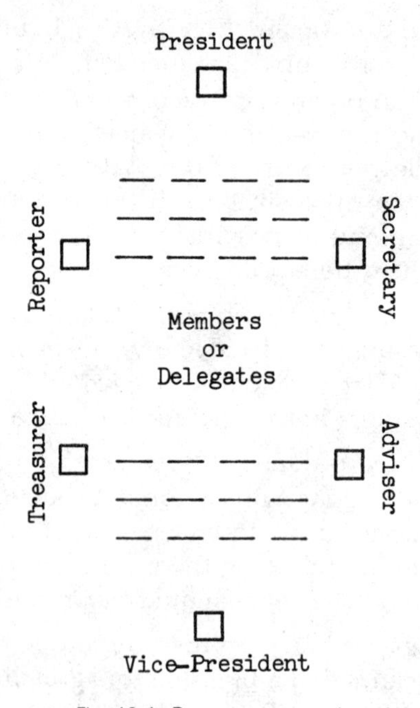

Fig. 19.1. Room arrangement.

Officer Stations—The meetings are more impressive when officer stations with tables or pedestals are used. Either tables or pedestals can be made by an agriculture mechanics class and painted blue and yellow (as similar as possible to the FFA colors). The pedestals are cheaper to construct than folding type tables, but pedestals are less attractive and convenient than tables. The type of folding table illustrated in Figure 19.2 is attractive and satisfactory. It will last for many years, and the cost is relatively low.

Chapter Meetings—All chapter meetings should be planned well in advance of the time they will be held. The agenda of each meeting should be posted where all members can see it. All members should know what business is to be brought before each meeting. All meetings should start and close on time and progress with vigor, not allowing a dull moment for any member.

Members should know how to use the basic principles of parliamentary procedure when they are needed. Discussions in FFA meetings may lead to a

[3]*Official Manual for FFA,* Alexandria, Virginia: FFA Supply Service, p. 57.

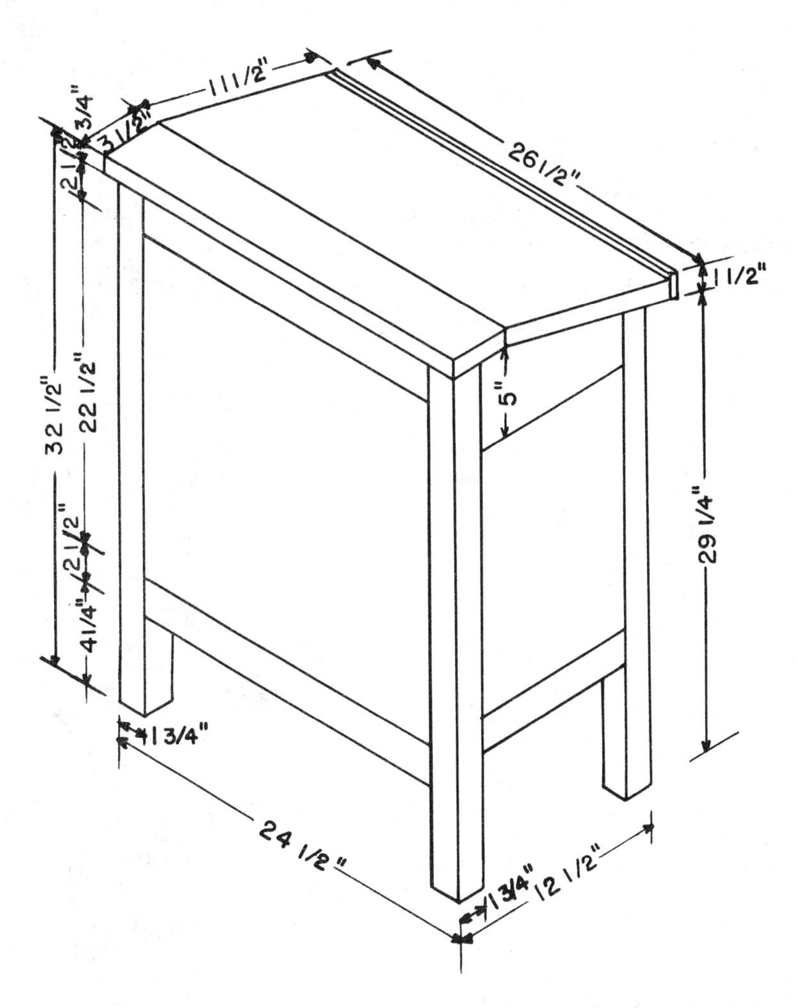

Fig. 19.2. FFA folding table for officer stations. The ends are hinged to the front legs and fold in under the top. The 11½" top board is hinged to the 3½" top piece and folds down over the legs. Such tables require very little space when folded. They have been successfully used by a number of chapters.

consensus, making the use of elaborate parliamentary procedure unnecessary. Unnecessary use of parliamentary procedure may hinder group processes instead of aiding progress.

FFA members usually learn through participation in their FFA chapters how to use essential parliamentary procedure, but they also need to learn that parliamentary procedure is not used in meetings to confuse others, in order to prevent the will of a group from prevailing, or in order to obtain special advantages. If FFA members use parliamentary procedure in their meetings to confuse, block progress, or obtain special privileges, their FFA chapter will not progress in carrying out its program. Misuse or overuse of parliamentary procedure may cause a chapter to disintegrate or become inactive, and it often causes disagreements in a school among FFA members or groups in the FFA.

Order of Business—The following order of business is suggested in the FFA manual:[4]

1. Opening ceremony.
   (This includes the call to order and the roll call.)
2. Minutes of the previous meeting.
   (To be read by the secretary and approved or amended by the group assembled.)
3. Orders of the day.
   (Not used at regular meetings unless called for from the floor. In such an instance, a statement of the order of business determined for the meeting is made by the secretary at the request of the president.)
4. Officer reports.
   (This includes any or all chapter officers who have reports to make at the meeting.)
5. Report on chapter program of work.
   (At this point the chairpersons of the various sections of the program are called upon to report plans and progress.)
6. Special features.
   (This includes speakers, special music, etc.)
7. Unfinished business.
8. Committee reports.
   a. Standing.
   b. Special.
9. New business.
10. Degree and installation ceremonies.
    (Used only when new members are initiated, Greenhands are raised to the Chapter Farmer degree, or officers are installed.)
11. Closing ceremony.
12. Entertainment, recreation, refreshments.
    (This part of the meeting should be turned over to a committee or committees, which take charge immediately after the closing ceremony.)

Chapter Records—Complete and accurate records should be kept of the activities of a chapter. A definite place in a filing cabinet may be designated for all chapter records. Records such as the following are usually kept:

1. The annual program of work.
2. Budgets, receipts, and expenditures.
3. An inventory of equipment.
4. Annual reports.
5. Attendance records.
6. Minutes of meetings.
7. Committee reports.
8. A list of all members.
9. Names of officers.
10. Chapter prizes and awards.
11. A record of achievements of individuals.

A scrapbook including pictures of FFA activities may be kept. The official treasurer's book and the official secretary's book should be used.

---

[4]*Ibid.*

CHAPTER

20

How to Develop an FFA Program of Activities

DEVELOPING A PROGRAM OF ACTIVITIES

What Is a Program of Activities?—An FFA program of activities consists of an outline of activities, covering approximately one year, based on the interests, needs, and desires of the chapter members. A chart is often used for recording activities in the program. This chart includes space for a list of the activities, for the names of committee members responsible for each activity, for the goals to be achieved, for the ways and means of achieving the goals listed, and for the accomplishments. Programs of activities are developed annually.

Why Have a Program of Activities?—Effective planning and outlining of objectives are essential in any kind of endeavor. They are especially important in teen-age groups. A well developed program of activities based on the interests and needs of the members and the organization as a whole usually results in a very worthy list of accomplishments. The opposite is usually true when a program of activities is inadequately developed. A comprehensive program stimulates interest, provides many opportunities for worthwhile experiences, helps to develop an effective educational program for agricultural purposes, and develops community interest and understanding. A well planned program is absolutely essential to successful chapter operation.

When to Develop a Program—In an established chapter, the planning of a program of activities for the coming year often begins in the spring before school is out. Sometimes a chapter has leadership conference meetings during the summer months when considerable program planning is done. After school opens in the fall, additional planning is done to round out a broad program of worthy activities for the current year.

Basic Criteria in Selecting Activities—The activities to include in a program should be based on the needs of individual members, the chapter, the school, and the community as a whole. Much thought and study should be given to the selection of the activities. A local adviser must provide considerable guidance in helping the members decide on the activities to include in an annual program. A chapter's first program of activities is usually not very elaborate. Each year the program should expand, developing into a comprehensive program.

Following are some criteria to consider in selecting an activity for an FFA program of activities:

1. Does it have sufficient educational value?
2. Will it contribute to the development of leadership?
3. Will it provide cooperative participation for a majority of the members?
4. Is it challenging to the members?
5. Is it physically possible this year?
6. Will it stimulate and motivate interest?
7. Will it promote the FFA and agricultural education in the community?
8. Will it contribute to an effective educational program for agricultural occupations?
9. Will it be a good financial risk?
10. Will it afford an opportunity for satisfactory profit?
11. Will sufficient funds be available to operate it?
12. Will it provide an opportunity to render suitable community service?
13. Is there sufficient need to justify it?
14. Will it contribute to the development of comprehensive supervised occupational experience programs?
15. Will it develop pride in doing?
16. Will it contribute to the development of success in farming or other occupations requiring knowledge and skills in agriculture?
17. Will it contribute to the improvement of agriculture in the community?

Building a Program—There are a number of procedures that may be used by a chapter in developing an effective program of activities based on the thinking of a majority of the members:

1. Appoint a program of activities committee with subcommittees for each of the sections or divisions to be included in the program. The program of activities committee usually consists of the chairpersons of the subcommittees.
2. Give every member a job by seeing to it that each one is serving on a committee and, insofar as possible, the committee of his/her choice.
3. Review last year's program of work.
4. Review the programs of activities from winning chapters in the state and from other states if available.
5. Review the state program of activities and the national program of activities.
6. Review the official FFA manual.
7. Decide with the group as a whole regarding the desirability of continuing certain activities and of adding others.
8. Have the committees work individually, with each committee deciding on what activities it desires to recommend for its division.
9. Have the committees report their findings and recommendations at a chapter meeting.
10. Have the committees rework their suggestions as recommended by the chapter as a whole.

11. When the chapter has approved the activities to include, check with the school authorities for their approval.
12. Then adopt the program and appoint permanent committees for the year.

Often a chapter continues as permanent committees, the committees that prepared the program of activities, because if a committee's members suggested an activity, they would be the logical ones to sponsor the activity. A chapter may find it desirable to have all members of each program of activities committee from one agriculture class. This makes the use of class time for committee meetings possible. Some schools have no activity period, and unless this procedure is followed, the committees have no time to meet. This procedure results in having all members of a committee with approximately identical amounts of experience in the FFA, but this disadvantage is probably not as serious as having no time for a committee to meet.

Form to Use for a Program of Activities—The method of organizing a program of activities used by many of the more successful chapters is illustrated in Form 20.1.

Form 20.1. An FFA Program of Activities Record form

Area	Committee Members	Activity	Goal	Ways and Means	Accomplishments	Comments
Supervised occupational experience.	B. Stone (Ch.) S. Ruch D. Smith E. Downs	Assisting members in developing a comprehensive supervised occupational experience program.	100% of members with comprehensive occupational experience programs.	Assist in carrying out a parent-student-employer meeting to develop an understanding of comprehensive occupational experience programs.		

Some chapters have omitted the activity column in the form for their programs of activities. This makes a program of activities hard to understand because the activities are then often listed in the column for goals. The result is a mixture of activities and goals with no clear distinction between them. Activities are often listed with no accompanying goals, and goals are listed that relate to no definite activity. It seems that a column for listing activities is essential.

The goals listed in an FFA program of activities should be educational, performance oriented, and measurable goals that are related to life goals. The FFA is not an end in itself, but a means of achieving the educational objectives of general education and of agricultural education.

FFA programs of activities often show evidence of a failure to think clearly. Goals are frequently listed as ways and means. Statements are often indefinite. Often there is no distinction made between the duties of a teacher and the duties of an FFA chapter. Errors such as these may be prevented if the advisers and members become conscious of them.

Indefinite statements that can be neither executed nor measured can be prevented if the adviser will ask each committee to develop definite ways of carrying out and measuring results of each activity it suggests.

Sections of a Program of Activities—The major divisions usually included in a program of activities are:

1. Supervised occupational experience in agriculture.
2. Cooperation.
3. Community service.
4. Leadership.
5. Earnings and savings.
6. Conduct of meetings.
7. Scholarship.
8. Recreation.
9. FFA publicity and information.
10. Participation in state and national activities.

POSSIBLE ACTIVITIES UNDER EACH SECTION OF A PROGRAM OF ACTIVITIES

Supervised Occupational Experience—In the supervised occupational experience section, provision should be made for the motivation of comprehensive programs. Following are some of the activities which are commonly included:

1. Assisting members in securing desirable exploratory experiences.
2. Assisting members in securing part-time jobs for occupational experience.
3. Assisting members in securing production projects of desirable scope.
4. Assisting members in securing improvement projects and supplementary practices.
5. Providing a loan fund for members.
6. Conducting tours.
7. Developing understandings of parents and employers.
8. Offering suitable rewards for outstanding achievements.
9. Assisting members in developing home libraries.

Cooperative Activities—The most effective way to learn cooperation is to practice it. Cooperative activities should be an important part of every FFA chapter's activities. There are many ways in which FFA members may participate in cooperative activities in real-life situations. Following are some of the cooperative activities that FFA chapters list in their programs of work:

1. Buying and selling cooperatively.
2. Mixing feeds and fertilizers.
3. Incubating and brooding chicks.
4. Building agricultural and chapter equipment.
5. Conducting group projects.
6. Organizing a mutual insurance company.
7. Organizing a livestock improvement subsidiary.
8. Organizing a crop improvement subsidiary.
9. Holding shows and sales of products.
10. Advertising products cooperatively.
11. Operating a garden center.

Community Service—All FFA members should be encouraged to render as much community service as their time, ability, and facilities will permit. Community services of educational value to the members participating are preferred. Following are some of the community services which are being offered by FFA members:

1. Providing a "Build Our American Communities" program.
2. Beautifying the school and home grounds.
3. Sponsoring first aid classes.
4. Preparing first aid demonstration teams.
5. Sponsoring fairs.
6. Removing pollution from roadsides.
7. Conserving natural resources.
8. Conducting driver safety campaigns.
9. Helping needy families.
10. Eliminating insect breeding places.
11. Making agricultural surveys.
12. Providing an FFA safety program.
13. Improving parks in the community.
14. Conducting a natural resources conservation day.
15. Constructing labor-saving devices.

Leadership Activities—Advisers should strive to allow students full responsibility in as many activities as possible. Following are some of the leadership activities in which members in FFA chapters participate:

1. Acting as chairpersons of committees.
2. Speaking before groups.
3. Conducting debates.
4. Sponsoring demonstration teams.
5. Entering the state chapter contest.
6. Attending meetings of various kinds.
7. Conducting contests, such as in parliamentary procedure and public speaking.
8. Participating in leadership training conferences.
9. Broadcasting over the radio.
10. Contacting eighth grade students.
11. Conducting meetings.
12. Publishing a chapter newsletter.
13. Sending delegates to district and state leadership training conferences.
14. Visiting other chapter meetings.

Earnings and Savings—Most chapter members use their earnings to further develop their supervised occupational experience programs. Following are some of the earnings and savings activities commonly outlined in a program of activities:

1. Preparing a chapter budget.
2. Increasing chapter investments.
3. Increasing chapter earnings.
4. Assisting members in making sound investments in land and equipment.
5. Establishing and maintaining a chapter account.
6. Keeping accurate and complete records.
7. Assisting members in establishing financial goals.

Conduct of Meetings—Careful plans in a program of activities should be developed for conducting meetings effectively. Following are some of the activities regarding conduct of meetings that are often present in the programs of activities of the better chapters:

1. Providing suitable facilities, including a chapter room and equipment.
2. Providing a definite schedule for meetings through the 12 months.
3. Providing desirable programs in connection with meetings.
4. Using a standard set of paraphernalia at all meetings and having the room properly arranged.
5. Providing officer stations with pedestals or folding tables.
6. Providing suitable refreshments.
7. Training officers.
8. Conducting meetings in a businesslike way.
9. Making all ceremonies and initiations impressive.

Scholarship—Every chapter should encourage its members to do commendable school work. Following are some of the scholarship activities included in the better chapter programs:

1. Honoring members with most improved scholarship.
2. Teaching members how to study.
3. Assisting members in trying for school honors.
4. Having older members help new members.
5. Providing an FFA library.
6. Inviting former members to discuss the importance of scholarship.

Charting grades of members and maintaining an honor roll are commonly included as scholarship activities. These activities are questionable because they may have as much negative as positive value. Some students do not have the inherent capacity to earn grades that will place their names on an honor roll. If grades become too important, these students usually give up, quit school, or develop some form of maladjustment. Cases could be cited of students starting to stutter after an honor roll was established in a classroom. Scholarship activities in an FFA program of work should emphasize positive approaches to better scholarship, such as teaching members how to study.

Recreation—In any program of activities, it is important to have wholesome recreation as well as work. This is well taken care of in most FFA programs of activities through activities such as the following:

1. Holding joint meetings with other clubs and participating in sleighing parties, skating parties, wiener roasts, dancing parties, and hayrack rides.
2. Organizing a quartet.
3. Taking camping trips.
4. Going on tours.
5. Attending state camps.
6. Sponsoring parent-member "fun feeds" and banquets.
7. Sponsoring a community picnic.
8. Providing games in connection with chapter meetings and noon hours.

Recreational activities sponsored by an FFA chapter should supplement and not compete with school or community recreational activities. If a school's extramural program provides adequate opportunities for participation on athletic teams, the FFA should concentrate its energies on other types of recreational activities instead of organizing additional athletic teams. The recreational activities of FFA should attempt to broaden the recreational interests of its members along lines they can follow in their own communities after they graduate from school. Undue emphasis on team sports, for example, creates interests that cannot be followed after school years because of a lack of facilities or team members and increasing age. Emphasis on team sports is usually adequately handled by other departments in a school. Interschool competition of FFA athletic teams is probably not justified because the schools' teams provide enough of this type of activity. FFA athletic teams provide participation opportunities for only a few FFA members, and they create a competitive attitude between chapters when a cooperative attitude should be encouraged. An athletic team takes too much of the time of a teacher of agriculture on an activity that is not agricultural education and not what a teacher of agriculture is being employed to teach. There are other school employees hired to sponsor athletic teams.

FFA Publicity and Information—FFA chapters devote time to publicity and informational programs, and these activities need to be planned. Some of the activities often included are as follows:

1. Providing programs for various civic organizations and school assemblies.
2. Utilizing local newspapers, radio, and TV.
3. Purchasing and maintaining multimedia equipment.
4. Encouraging proper wearing of official FFA clothing.
5. Providing educational exhibits concerning production agriculture, agribusiness, and renewable natural resources, and concerning FFA.
6. Erecting and maintaining FFA welcome signs on roadsides.
7. Sponsoring a parent-employer-member FFA banquet.
8. Assisting in the conduct of elementary and junior high school occupational orientation programs related to production agriculture, agribusiness, and renewable natural resources.

Participation in State and National Activities—At the time the FFA program of activities is planned, plans need to be made regarding the participation of FFA members and the chapter in state and national activities. Following are a few of the activities often included in a program of activities:

1. Providing chapter delegates at the state FFA convention.
2. Preparing delegates and members for participation in the state FFA convention.
3. Providing ways and means for attendance of each state award winner at the state FFA convention.
4. Promoting National FFA Week.
5. Informing members about, and promoting participation in, the National FFA Foundation award program.
6. Participating in the national chapter award program.
7. Informing members about, and promoting participation in, judging activities.

FFA activity programs cannot help but develop in members abilities and attitudes which will remain with them throughout life.

FINANCING CHAPTER ACTIVITIES

Each chapter should prepare a yearly budget of receipts and expenses. The amount of money needed to operate a chapter depends largely on its program of activities. The promotion, development, and carrying out of activities should be carefully studied in developing a budget of the amount of funds needed for these purposes. Some activities will take considerable working capital, while others will take very little, if any. The *pay as you go plan* is recommended.

Form 20.2 presents a budget prepared by a Gold Emblem chapter in the Illinois Chapter Contest.

A number of methods of financing chapter activities have been successfully used. Chapter members should consider carefully the concomitant results of their proposed money-making activities. Since the FFA is based on agriculture and has educational purposes, it is logical to assume that a chapter should earn its finances through agricultural activities that will have some agricultural education value. A chapter can find ample agricultural activities from which it may earn money without engaging in non-agricultural activities.

Another reason for avoiding the excessive use of non-agricultural activities, such as managing food concessions at games, is that other school clubs which have few ways of earning money like to control these methods of financing their organizations. Better school relationships may be fostered if FFA does not compete excessively for these sources of finances.

Money-making activities that may compete with existing businesses usually should be avoided. FFA has many opportunities to earn money and should not resort to begging for money by asking for donations. Selling advertisements in an FFA paper or yearbook is considered begging by some.

Following is a list of criteria found to be sound in evaluating proposed money-making activities for an FFA chapter. An activity should:

1. Render a service to the community.
2. Be related to agriculture.
3. Not compete with local concerns.
4. Not be done on school time.
5. Be educational.
6. Be acceptable to the community and to the school.
7. Provide for sufficient profit to pay for the labor expended.
8. Provide for participation by all members.

Following is a partial list of worthwhile money-making methods frequently used by FFA chapters:

1. Constructing concrete hog troughs.
2. Painting rural mailboxes.
3. Feeding livestock.
4. Growing crops.
5. Preparing exhibits or demonstrations for fairs.
6. Poisoning vermin.
7. Growing plants in hot beds and cold frames.
8. Growing flowers.
9. Growing ornamental plants.
10. Rendering lawn service.
11. Raising broilers.
12. Producing young trees for transplanting.
13. Mixing minerals.
14. Treating seed.
15. Spraying crops.
16. Pruning trees.
17. Landscaping.
18. Constructing farm equipment.
19. Repairing farm equipment.
20. Sharpening and repairing hand tools.

Form 20.2. FFA Budget

Item	Estimated Expenses	Actual Expenses
Expenses		
Stationery and stamps	$ 2.50	
Cement, sand, and gravel	40.00	
Stunt festival	45.00	
FFA banner	20.00	
All-school FFA carnival	50.00	
U.S. flag	4.00	
National dues	112.50	
State dues	75.00	
Paint for community service project	15.00	
Spray chemicals	75.00	
Prizes for members' accomplishments	40.00	
Parties	15.00	
Stand at local fair	50.00	
Parent, employer, and member banquet	100.00	
Seed corn for corn plot	140.00	
Funds to increase FFA library	10.00	
Delegates' convention expenses	15.00	
Miscellaneous	10.00	
Total	$ 819.00	

Item	Estimated Receipts	Actual Receipts
Receipts		
Concrete hog troughs	$ 150.00	
Stunt festival	65.00	
All-school FFA carnival	75.00	
National dues collected	112.50	
State dues collected	75.00	
Local dues collected	5.00	
Community service project	15.00	
Spraying	150.00	
Sale of corn raised on FFA plot	600.00	
Receipts from stand at local fair	105.00	
Total	$1,352.50	

SUMMARY

	Estimated	Actual
Receipts	$1,352.50	
Expenses	819.00	
Balance	$ 533.50	

21. Dipping sheep.
22. Controlling cattle grubs.
23. Spraying trees.
24. Controlling bots.
25. Collecting service fees on purebred sires.
26. Creating FFA cooperatives—local and state.
27. Organizing mutual insurance companies.
28. Selling milkweed pods.
29. Renting hog slaughtering equipment.
30. Butchering hogs.
31. Fee fishing.

ACTIVITIES AND CHARACTERISTICS OF WINNING CHAPTERS

The programs of activities of chapters that win in the National FFA Chapter Contest reveal worthwhile activities and characteristics. Some of the characteristics of these chapters are listed with the hope that they will be helpful to local chapter advisers and members in developing and achieving outstanding FFA programs:

1. Outstanding cooperation among members was apparent.
2. Outstanding leadership was provided by the local advisers.
3. Comprehensive programs of work, with definite activities, goals, and means of accomplishment, were developed.
4. Broad, well balanced supervised occupational experience programs were developed.
5. All members participated in the activities of their chapters.
6. Long-time supervised occupational experience programs were developed.
7. Numerous committees were used to develop and carry out the programs of activities.
8. Many cooperative activities were developed, such as buying feed, livestock, seed, and fertilizer; rendering service to farmers and agriculturally oriented businesses; beautifying homes; conducting group livestock projects and crop projects; establishing loan funds; holding shows and sales of products; and conducting camps and tours.
9. Members were encouraged to be thrifty and to invest their labor earnings in farming or in agriculturally oriented businesses.
10. The chapters' reports of accomplishments were neat, complete, accurate, and attractively bound.
11. The most common frequency of meetings of chapter members was twice per month during the school year and a total of three or four times during the summer months.
12. Many chapter members were awarded State Farmer degrees, and some were awarded American Farmer degrees.
13. The election of local members to state offices was common.
14. The officers of the chapters were active in district leadership training schools.
15. The members were well represented in district, regional, and state contests.
16. The cooperative programs were closely allied with community service. Many services, such as controlling bots and dipping sheep, were sponsored and conducted.
17. Correct parliamentary procedure was used in all meetings.
18. The FFA was recognized as an integral part of vocational education in agriculture.
19. Several members in each chapter participated in public speaking, parliamentary procedure, and demonstration contests.
20. Many opportunities for developing leadership were provided, such as through public speaking and parliamentary procedure.

(Photo from W. J. Kortesmaki, Minnesota)

Fig. 20.1. A children's barnyard sponsored by the FFA at a fair. An FFA chapter renders a vital community service when it promotes agricultural education for everyone.

21. Many recreational activities were engaged in during the year.
22. Cooperative purchase of equipment was common.
23. Many pictures of activities were taken.
24. Strong publicity programs were usually developed.
25. Numerous types of awards were established for outstanding achievements.
26. Home libraries and school FFA libraries were usually established.
27. Members usually owned copies of the official FFA manual.
28. Sound methods of financing chapter activities were used.
29. All official chapter equipment was owned by the chapters.
30. Ceremonies for opening and closing meetings were memorized by officers.
31. Official secretary's and treasurer's books were used by chapters.
32. Meetings were planned in advance, and agenda were posted on tackboards.
33. FFA banquets were held.
34. Dues were collected early in the year, and state and national dues were sent to the state office.
35. Delegates were sent to state and national conventions.
36. The members were tested on their knowledge of the FFA by written tests.
37. Some chapters organized mutual insurance companies.
38. Livestock and crop improvement subsidiaries were organized.
39. Many efficiency standards of production were used.
40. Budgets of expenses and receipts were prepared.
41. Balanced occupational experience programs were stressed.
42. Leadership training was provided for all members.
43. FFA cooperatives were developed.
44. Chapters usually kept their programs of work displayed on wall charts in their classrooms.
45. Chapter program activities emphasized safety.
46. Chapters were actively involved in the "Build Our American Communities" program.
47. Chapters were actively involved in the "Food for America" program.

CHAPTER

21

How to Carry Out FFA Activities

CONDUCTING FFA DEMONSTRATIONS

Importance—FFA demonstrations may be of considerable educational value to the youth who participate in the demonstrations and to the audiences who observe the demonstrations. An FFA demonstration team will also promote desirable public relations.

Planning and participating in a demonstration may help students to develop many fundamental understandings in agriculture. A demonstration provides students with many opportunities for developing desirable abilities in public speaking and leadership.

Many people enjoy local talent more than they enjoy any other kind of entertainment. Demonstrations, however, should be educational as well as entertaining. Demonstration teams may perform at FFA programs, school programs, fairs, community meetings, and state contests.

Suggestions for FFA Demonstrations—A demonstration may be given by one or more persons, but probably the most common number is two. Teachers often permit as many as five members to appear in a demonstration. When so many persons are used, generally two or three of them have little to do. When two members give a demonstration, one may demonstrate while the other explains. Interchanging jobs from time to time keeps both in action. The following procedures for planning and conducting a demonstration are suggested:

1. Demonstrations should be adapted to the community. If possible, choose something to demonstrate that the members on the team have put into practice in connection with their supervised occupational experience programs.

2. Have the introduction to the demonstration include the FFA members' names, the name of the FFA chapter sponsoring the demonstration, and the name and purpose of the demonstration.
3. Give everyone in the FFA an opportunity to try out for the demonstration team.
4. Select members with good speaking voices.
5. If possible, select two members of about the same size.
6. Have participants plan the demonstration.
7. Have the team use illustrative materials, such as pictures, charts, and models, in the demonstration.
8. Insist that each participant on the demonstration team be neatly and properly dressed for the occasion.
9. Have the participants on the demonstration team dress alike.
10. Use a large, neatly made sign, at least 3′ by 6′ in size, which gives the name of the demonstration and the name of the local FFA chapter. Have a member of the demonstration team place this banner facing the audience just before the demonstration.
11. Encourage the participants to speak plainly and distinctly and to talk to their audience.
12. Encourage teamwork and neatness.
13. Have the team present practical information in an understandable manner by the use of models (living, if possible) and charts. If possible, the team should perform all operations pertaining to a demonstration.
14. In a demonstration contest, permit a team to use the full amount of time allotted but no more.
15. Insofar as possible, have the participants keep all models and charts out of sight when the demonstration begins and present them as the demonstration proceeds. This creates interest.
16. Be sure the team gives the audience or judges a chance to ask questions after the demonstration has been given.
17. Teach the participants to repeat the questions asked by the audience or judges before they attempt to answer them.

CONDUCTING FFA PARENT, EMPLOYER, AND MEMBER BANQUETS

Banquets for FFA members, parents, and employers have been popular for a long time. There are many reasons why instructors should endeavor to promote parent, employer, and member banquets. Some of the values of a banquet follow:

1. It promotes a closer fellowship and comradeship between parents, employers, and FFA members.
2. It helps the parents and employers understand the agriculture program and the FFA.
3. It brings the parents and employers in agricultural business into closer contact with their school.
4. It provides a friendly, educational, and social meeting for the people whose cooperation is needed in making the FFA and the agriculture program a success.
5. It offers a splendid opportunity for the discussion of community work.
6. It provides valuable training in leadership and cooperation for the FFA members.
7. It affords a fine opportunity for exhibiting the work of the students in the department.
8. It offers an opportunity for explaining the objectives of the FFA and the accomplishments of the local chapter.
9. It provides an opportunity to give recognition to outstanding members and to persons in the community who have contributed to the promotion and success of the chapter.

10. It gives the members an opportunity to entertain their parents and their employers.

A banquet should be sponsored by a chapter as an FFA activity. The students enrolled in a school's home economics department may be asked to cooperate by serving the banquet.

Planning and Organizing—If a banquet is to be a success, it must be properly planned and organized. The planning should begin well in advance of the date of the banquet. Every detail of the banquet should be anticipated.

In promoting plans for an FFA banquet, an adviser should engage in the following activities:

1. Explaining the banquet, stressing its importance, to the superintendent and the principal and asking their permission to hold a banquet if the members include it in their program of activities.
2. Acting as an ex officio member of the executive committee when it selects members for the banquet committees.
3. Urging parents and employers of FFA members to be present at the banquet.

Whom to Invite—All people who are vitally interested in the school and the department sponsoring the banquet should be invited. The following partial list is suggested:

1. All active FFA members, collegiate FFA members, and FFA Alumni members.
2. Parents of the members.
3. Employers of FFA members obtaining occupational experiences in their agricultural businesses.
4. The superintendent, principal, and director of vocational education.
5. School board members or school trustees.
6. The county or regional superintendent.
7. Members of the advisory council and committees for the department.
8. Certain local businesspersons, photographers, editors, and bankers.
9. The county agent, other agriculturalists, and neighboring FFA advisers.
10. Prospective students and FFA alumni.
11. Honorary FFA members.
12. The state supervisor, the state director, and a teacher educator.
13. Other teachers in the high school.
14. Other persons living in the community who have shown special interest in the chapter and who have contributed to its success.
15. Persons to be awarded honorary membership.

The invitation committee should be sure to extend special invitations to the mothers. They will appreciate it and will become boosters of the chapter and the department. Often it is a mother's influence that keeps an FFA member in school.

Where to Hold a Banquet—Whenever possible it is advisable to hold a banquet in the school. Even though some outside organization serves the banquet for an FFA chapter, it is best to hold the banquet at the school. In some instances this may not be possible, especially if a church group prepares and serves the meal. When a chapter holds its banquet in the school, it is possible to exhibit the work of the FFA members in the vocational agriculture classroom and the shop.

FFA banquets are often held in home economics rooms, school cafeterias, agriculture rooms, or gymnasiums. The choice of a room should depend on the size of the room and its nearness to the kitchen where the food is prepared. The room used for a banquet should easily accommodate the number of persons at the banquet, but it is best not to have a room that is too large.

How to Arrange a Banquet Room—Regardless of the room that is used, it should be neatly and attractively arranged and decorated. A few good pictures and charts illustrating FFA activities should be placed on the walls. Care should be exercised to concentrate the seating of the people so that they all may hear the program. Insofar as possible, the members should be seated between their parents and near their employers. The toastmaster and any speakers must be seated in a place where they can be easily seen and heard. All FFA equipment and paraphernalia should be in its proper location. The officers and adviser should take their places at their stations when it is time for the program to begin.

Place cards should be provided by the reception committee, and each guest or parent should be assisted by one of the FFA members in finding the place assigned. The FFA member should know in advance where the guest or parent is to be seated.

When to Hold a Banquet—A banquet may be held at any time during the school year. If a banquet is to be essentially an achievement function, it should probably be held within the period from the middle of the school year to early spring. If its function is to acquaint the parents with the objectives and the activities of the local FFA chapter, it should probably be held before the middle of the school year. If it is held after the middle of the school year, there should be a parents' and employers' meeting in the fall to explain supervised occupational experience concepts and the FFA.

The evening is the most convenient time of day to hold an FFA banquet because parents and other adults are generally busy during the daytime. Whatever hour is set for starting a banquet, it should be adhered to so that the dinner may be served on time. No banquet should last more than three hours. A banquet shorter than three hours is preferred.

Necessary Committees—The number and kind of committees necessary for planning and conducting a banquet will vary with the type of banquet held. In general, the following committees will be necessary:

1. An invitation committee.
2. A decorating and arranging committee to see that the room is made attractive, that the tables are arranged correctly, and that the place cards are properly located.
3. A foods committee to secure the food.
4. A finance committee.
5. A program committee to arrange for the program and to provide for small folders containing the program and the menu.
6. A dish-washing committee, if necessary.
7. A clean-up committee.
8. A reception committee.

It is desirable to have a reception committee to welcome the parents, employers, and other guests at the door, to assist them with their wraps, and to usher them to the banquet room. Name cards may be provided for all persons.

They help people become acquainted. A reception committee should use every opportunity to introduce the persons present and to help them feel at home before the banquet begins. The FFA Supply Service has many banquet supplies which may be used effectively.

Some of the types of meal services used at banquets are:

1. Formal service of food in courses.
2. Informal or family service in which food is placed on the tables and passed.
3. Buffet or cafeteria service.

Financing a Banquet—Adults like plenty of good, common, wholesome food. Following are some of the ways that have been used to finance FFA banquets:

1. Chapter funds are used.
2. A school cafeteria meal is provided.
3. A potluck meal is served.
4. Mothers are asked to prepare certain foods at home and donate them.
5. Products are donated by members, and food is prepared at school.
6. A charge is made to supplement costs of items not donated.
7. Cooperative production projects are used to furnish part of the food.

Program—Considerable time is required to plan a program. The members should understand that the program is theirs and that they should plan and conduct it. An adviser should be inconspicuous at a banquet. The adviser, of course, will need to be present for the opening and closing ceremonies, and should assist in welcoming the parents and other guests.

Often the best programs for banquets are those presented from beginning to end by the members. The use of outside speakers, other than state FFA officers, at banquets is being discontinued in many schools. If a banquet is to be presented by the members, the adviser will need to spend considerable time in coaching them on what to do and how to do it. When introducing parents and employers, a member should stand and speak clearly. The toastmaster may need considerable coaching on how to conduct the meeting effectively. The members who are to appear on the program should be coached to speak clearly and distinctly so that everyone can hear them. They may present their speeches before the chapter members in advance of the banquet. Such talks offer many opportunities for developing leadership, and their preparation during school time can be justified.

The member who introduces the guests, administrators, board of education members, and other teachers should know well in advance the persons to be introduced and the order in which they are to be introduced. The member should practice these introductions in advance and should learn to pronounce all names correctly.

Following are some of the activities included in the more desirable FFA banquet programs:

1. Organ or other instrumental music during the meal.
2. Opening and closing FFA ceremonies, with the officers at their stations.
3. Introduction of administrators, school board members, and trustees.
4. Introduction of parents, employers, or representatives of FFA Foundation sponsors, and other guests.

5. Talks by several FFA members on topics such as objectives of the FFA, their occupational experience programs, or FFA degrees.
6. Reports by FFA members on topics such as community services, FFA group projects, FFA co-ops, achievements of the chapter, or the FFA program of work.
7. Musical numbers by FFA members or other high school students.
8. Group singing (limited amount).
9. Recognition of all who have helped make the banquet a success.

A program should be educational, entertaining, informal, and well balanced.

Final Duties—Pictures of the banquet should be taken. Pictures are prized more highly by those sponsoring a banquet than anything else that could be given as a remembrance. A photographer might be included as a guest at the banquet.

All equipment should be properly cleaned after a banquet, and all borrowed or rented articles should be returned. All those helping to make a banquet a success should be given credit and thanks. A news article describing the banquet should be placed in the local papers.

MISCELLANEOUS ACTIVITIES

Environmental Control Subsidiary—A rather popular type of subsidiary to the FFA in some areas is an environmental quality club. Following is one plan for such a subsidiary.

• • •

FFA SOIL SAVERS

Set up as a subsidiary to the ________________ Chapter of the FFA in the belief that:

1. No problem in America is more fundamentally important than the proper use and preservation of our soils.
2. The FFA should and must have a vital part in solving this problem.
3. Such a subsidiary as the Soil Savers can strengthen and make more successful the parent chapter.

ORGANIZATION

1. Only active members of the ________________ FFA Chapter may become active members of the ________________ ________________ FFA Soil Savers.
2. Membership grades and privileges shall be based upon achievement and shall be awarded by vote of the membership following a recommendation by the chapter adviser. Degrees of advancement shall be:
   a. Soil Saver.
   b. Skilled Soil Saver.
   c. Expert Soil Saver.
   d. Master Soil Saver.

To become a Soil Saver, the requirements shall be:
(1) To have been initiated as a Greenhand in the FFA.
(2) To have presented before a class in vocational agriculture or during a meeting of the FFA a creditable five-minute talk on some phase of soil conservation.
(3) To have earned at least 20 points from the official point scale.

To become a Skilled Soil Saver, the requirements shall be:
(1) To have been a Soil Saver.

(2) To have set up and completed an approved soil conservation program upon at least one acre, on the home farm, on some other farm, or on public land.
(3) To have earned at least 100 points from the official point scale by carrying out at least three of the practices.

To become an Expert Soil Saver, the requirements shall be:
(1) To have been a Skilled Soil Saver.
(2) To have had in approved operation for at least one year a program of soil conservation upon at least 20 acres. (Note: this does not require ownership or financial control by the member, but should not have the adviser's approval unless it represents real responsibility and performance by the member.)
(3) To have earned at least 500 points from the official point scale by carrying out at least 10 of the practices.

To become a Master Soil Saver, the requirements shall be:
(1) To have been an Expert Soil Saver.
(2) To have an approved soil conservation plan covering the entire home farm or another farm, or on public lands approved by the adviser.
(3) To have had this plan in approved operation for at least one year.
(4) To have earned at least 1,000 points by carrying out at least 15 of the approved practices listed.

3. Awards emblematic of the various degrees shall be in the form of colored brassards or sweater emblems and may be awarded to members at any time they shall have become qualified to receive them, following certification and recommendation by the chapter adviser and approval by a majority vote of the members. Additional awards may well be set up with the aid of soil conservation districts, county bankers' associations, farm machinery companies, or farmers' organizations. All such awards shall be approved by the chapter adviser and by a majority vote of members.
4. Officers, to be elected annually, shall be a president, a vice-president, and a secretary-treasurer.
5. Meetings shall be held at least quarterly and may be part of the regular meetings of the chapter. The members should endeavor to present at least one program a year for the FFA. Programs may also be presented for other interested organizations.

• • •

It should be remembered that the plan presented is just one plan. A subsidiary club to the FFA should be controlled by the local chapter of the FFA, and regulations should be adjusted to local conditions.

Constitution for FFA Cooperatives—An FFA cooperative should be conducted on a businesslike basis. This usually necessitates a constitution. Following is one example of a constitution for a cooperative which may serve as a source of ideas.

• • •

ENVIRONMENTAL QUALITY

CONSTITUTION OF AN FFA ENVIRONMENTAL QUALITY ASSOCIATION

ARTICLE I—Name:

The name of this organization shall be "The ______________________ ______________________ FFA Environmental Quality Association."

ARTICLE II—Object:

To provide an opportunity for members of the FFA to obtain environmental quality experience and to obtain experience in a business requiring knowledge and skills in agriculture.

ARTICLE III—Membership:

Any FFA member or former FFA member may become a member of the association upon the purchase of shares of stock.

ARTICLE IV—Amount of a Share:

The amount of a share will be governed by the capital worth of the association and by the number of shares issued.

ARTICLE V—Voting:

Each member shall be entitled to one vote, regardless of the number of shares owned.

ARTICLE VI—Officers:

1. President.
2. Vice-President.
3. Secretary.
4. Treasurer.

ARTICLE VII—Duties of Officers:

1. President.
   a. Preside at meetings.
   b. Vote only in case of a tie.
   c. Appoint necessary committees.
2. Vice-President.
   a. Preside over meetings in absence of the president.
   b. Assist in preparing committee reports.
3. Secretary.
   a. Keep an accurate record of all meetings.
   b. Carry out all necessary correspondence.
   c. Prepare advertising material.
   d. Prepare items of business before each meeting.
   e. Make all necessary reports.
4. Treasurer.
   a. Keep accurate account of receipts and expenses.
   b. Pay all bills.
   c. Secure written receipts.
   d. Give a treasurer's report at each meeting.
   e. Open an account with the School Activity Fund and keep all funds in same.

ARTICLE VIII—Election of Officers:

Officers shall be elected annually in September.

ARTICLE IX—Meetings:

Meetings shall be held every two months at a place appointed by the association.

ARTICLE X—Purchasing Equipment:

Equipment and supplies will be purchased by a committee appointed by the president. The agriculture teacher shall serve on this committee. The association shall vote funds necessary for this purpose.

ARTICLE XI—Auditing the Books:

The president shall appoint a committee to audit the books. A teacher or some outsider shall be on this committee.

ARTICLE XII—Amending the Constitution:

All officers and two-thirds (⅔) of the other members have to be present. There has to be a two-thirds (⅔) vote on all amendments.

ARTICLE XIII—Rules and Bylaws:

Rules and bylaws can be established by a two-thirds (⅔) vote of the members.

• • •

Tours—Various kinds of tours are sponsored by FFA chapters. They may be for purchasing supplies, for supervising occupational experience programs of FFA members, or for visiting some business, such as a feed dealer. Tours should be for specific agricultural education purposes. Some teachers have taken students for extended vacation tours covering many hundreds or thousands of miles. The purpose of these trips is primarily recreational. Such trips or tours are of questionable value. They place a great burden on teachers in case of mishaps. A community may also wonder if there are not more worthwhile activities that a teacher could be doing than traveling over the country on a pleasure trip. For high school students there is usually plenty to see of educational value relatively close to home without traveling over several states.

Most tours should not require more than one day. The transportation for an FFA tour may be furnished by a school bus or by cars. From the standpoint of safety, cars are the least desirable. The teacher should take out a blanket insurance policy covering the group and secure the consent of all parents before leaving on a tour. Parents should also sign waivers in case an accident occurs.

Leadership Conferences—Leadership training and recreation make a desirable combination for an effective camp program. State camps usually are conducted for a period of from three to seven days for a specific group. The total length of the camping season in state camps which different groups of students may attend varies from two weeks to three months, depending on the need. Some camps operate stores for miscellaneous supplies for the campers, including items such as T-shirts and FFA manuals. Some states own their camp sites; other states have used the camps of the Park Service and the Soil Conservation and Forestry Service. A camp is usually maintained by the agency owning the site, by a caretaker paid from state camp funds, or by a local agriculture teacher.

The following recreational activities are often included in camping programs:

Swimming
String bands
Water carnivals
Boat trips
Volleyball
Treasure hunts
Glee clubs
Group singing
Field events
Ping-pong
Table games
Baseball
Boxing
Fishing
Boating
Minstrels
Mock trials
Tetherball
Rope tying
Archery
Box hockey
Softball
Wrestling
Hikes
Tennis
Stunts
Magic
Badminton
Charades
Tap dancing
Stones
Horseshoes

The educational programs often include the following activities:

Nature study
Leadership training
First aid
Tours and hikes
Speakers
Health
Citizenship
Career exploration
Career development
Movies
Conservation
Discussions
Radio broadcasts
Dramatics

CONTESTS AND AWARDS

Contests and awards are means of motivating FFA members to carry out their chapter's program of work and to develop their individual abilities. There are a number of contests which FFA members may enter. Some of these are national in scope, while others are on the state or district level. Contests which measure practical agricultural abilities essential to success may be desirable if they are properly conducted. They are usually justified if they relate directly to the instruction for agricultural occupations.

A contest is not properly conducted if its awards are such that they motivate the overdevelopment of certain abilities. When a contest puts too much emphasis on first place, some teachers may put in more time than is justified in preparing a team or an individual for the contest. Awards based on definite standards of ability are to be preferred. When an individual or a team reaches this standard of ability, the award should be given.

Evaluating Contests and Awards—FFA chapters and members should be encouraged by their chapter advisers to evaluate a contest or an award carefully. The help of a department's advisory council may be solicited in evaluating contests in which a chapter and its members wish to participate.

Each contest in which participation is anticipated should be evaluated to determine whether it develops desirable or undesirable attitudes or interests. A good contest should reward abilities and not be a guessing contest. Some livestock and grain judging contests have been criticized as guessing contests. Awards and contests should be checked to see whether they reward and motivate the most desirable abilities. Concomitant abilities encouraged by an award or contest should be given careful consideration. If students are motivated to outsmart the judge in showing their livestock, the undesirability of the concomitant ability developed may more than offset the value of the ability the award or contest is promoting. Some say that certain livestock shows can be criticized on this basis.

All awards and contests should be checked to see whether they have become ends instead of means. Some awards and contests may degenerate until they become ends in themselves. An award or a contest is not justified if its only value is creating interest among the participants and capturing the attention of the public. A contest should not highlight the winning team or individual to the extent that some teachers, administrators, and portions of the public will assume that the winning of the contest is a principal criterion of the success of an agricultural education program.

Awards and contests do have values when they are carefully selected and conducted and when teachers use sound judgment in the amount of time used in preparing a team or an individual for a contest. Contests and awards may provide opportunities for:

1. Participation in group enterprises.
2. Improvement in community cooperation.
3. High-grade entertainment and recreation.
4. Promoting and motivating the program of agricultural education.
5. Increasing interest in, and knowledge of, plants and animals and off-farm agricultural businesses.
6. Learning facts.
7. Thinking.
8. Building interests and attitudes.
9. Developing skills.
10. Developing ability to solve problems. This involves the ability to formulate tentative hypotheses, to make decisions, and to evaluate these decisions and report results.
11. Developing ability in self-evaluation.

Developing Interest in Awards and Contests—If a proper approach is made, interest may be developed in any contest or award which has been judged worthy of consideration as part of the instructional program for career exploration and development in production agriculture, agribusiness, and renewable natural resources. Teachers should:

1. Allow class time for explaining and discussing contests.
2. Consider in class the values of contests.
3. Determine in class the objectives of the students in participating in the contests.
4. Permit students to determine a procedure for making awards in a local contest that will provide recognition to a large part of the group that participates.
5. Provide many moderate awards so that a reasonable percentage of the participants may receive recognition.
6. Set aside class time to plan means of preparing for participation in a contest.

In developing interest in contests or award programs, teachers should utilize these successful teaching procedures:

1. Proceed from the simple to the difficult.
2. Provide opportunities to learn by doing.
3. Master each step thoroughly before proceeding to the next step.
4. Review by integrating what has been taught previously into what is currently being taught.
5. Eliminate content that is not used or is not useable.
6. Check results so that students may determine their progress.

NATIONAL AWARDS

FFA Foundation Contests and Awards[1]—The following contests and awards are sponsored by the FFA Foundation:

> "The FFA Foundation divides its awards program into five categories: (1) Establishment in Agriculture, (2) Agricultural Proficiency, (3) Contests, (4) Awards for Chapters, and (5) State Awards for Improving Agriculture and Leadership. Details of the program, including rules and regulations and the number and amounts of the awards, are contained in program bulletins which are printed periodically by the Foundation and distributed to FFA chapters, state officials, and sponsors."

Membership Awards

Establishment in Agriculture awards are associated with membership degrees in the organization, starting with medals provided at the local level for Star Greenhand (first year member) and Star Chapter Farmer. Each state association may elect 2 per cent of its membership annually to the State degree, based on achievement in agriculture and leadership. The most outstanding of these receives the Foundation's award for Star State Farmer or Star Agribusiness of America.

The American Farmer degree is awarded only by the national organization

---

[1]*Information and Statement of Policies*, The FFA Foundation, Incorporated, in cooperation with the Agricultural Education Branch, Division of Vocational and Technical Education, U.S. Office of Education, Washington, D.C., 1962, pp. 15–18.

(Photo from H. W. Gadda, South Dakota)

Fig. 21.1. American Farmer award ceremony at the National FFA Convention.

and is limited to about one member in a thousand. Four of these new American Farmer degree awardees are selected to receive regional Star Farmer of America awards and four are selected to receive regional Star Agribusiness of America awards. A Star Farmer of America awardee and a Star Agribusiness of America awardee are selected from the respective regional winners.

Agricultural Proficiency Awards

Awards for individual achievement in specific agricultural fields are provided in the following areas:

1. Agricultural electrification.
2. Agricultural processing.
3. Agricultural sales and/or service.
4. Agriculture mechanics.
5. Beef production.
6. Crop production.
7. Dairy production.
8. Diversified livestock production.
9. Fish and wildlife management.
10. Floriculture.
11. Forest management.
12. Fruit and/or vegetable production.
13. Home improvement.
14. Horse proficiency.
15. Nursery operations.
16. Outdoor recreation.
17. Placement in agricultural production.
18. Poultry production.
19. Sheep production.
20. Soil and water management.
21. Swine production.
22. Turf and livestock management.

Medals are provided for local chapter winners, with certificates or plaques, along with cash awards, provided on the state, regional, and national levels.

Star Awards

Each year, degree recipients who are outstanding at the chapter, state, and national levels are selected as star award winners. They receive star award plaques and medals presented by the National FFA Foundation.

Following is a list of the star awards:

1. Star Greenhand.
2. Star Chapter Farmer.
3. Star Chapter Agribusinessperson.
4. Star State Farmer.
5. Star State Agribusinessperson.
6. Star Farmer of America.
7. Star Agribusinessperson of America.

CHAPTER AWARDS

National Chapter Award

A set of standards has been developed for rating local chapters. The state associations recognize applying chapters meeting the standards as *Superior Chapters*. Superior Chapters applying for recognition at the national level, and recommended by their state associations, are grouped as bronze, silver, or gold award winners.

National Safety Award Program

The National Safety Award program recognizes chapters for making their communities safer places to live and work. Awards are given at the state and national levels for outstanding safety projects.

Build Our American Communities

The Build Our American Communities (BOAC) program recognizes chapters for outstanding performance in making their communities better places to live and work. Awards are available at all levels.

Food for America

Food for America is a chapter activity program, but it is not an award program. It consists of a combination of public relations and leadership development experiences for members, designed to emphasize the importance of farming and agribusiness. The value of the program is the teaching experience gained by FFA members and the improved image created for agriculture by the FFA.

NATIONAL CONTESTS

Public Speaking

Contests are conducted in local chapters, with the winners advancing through district or area eliminations to the state association contests. State champions are eligible to compete in four regional contests. The regional champions meet at the National FFA Convention, where the national winners are selected.

Prepared Public Speaking

In the prepared public speaking contest each participant writes and delivers before a panel of judges a five-minute speech. At the end of the speech, a speaker may be questioned for five minutes by the judges, who base their decisions on the written manuscript, the delivery of the speech, and the answers to the questions.

Extemporaneous Public Speaking

The extemporaneous public speaking contest requires the participants to deliver speeches on one of three agricultural topics presented to them. They have 30 minutes to prepare for the speeches. The judges may question each speaker for five minutes following the presentation. The speakers are judged on the information presented, their delivery, and their answers to questions.

Arousing Interest in Public Speaking—Following are some suggestions for teachers regarding ways of arousing the interest of students in public speaking:

1. Be sure all ninth graders have an opportunity to observe the district public speaking contest.
2. Invite a winner in the district public speaking contest to present a speech at a local FFA banquet.
3. Give recognition to a local public speaking contest by providing:
   a. Class time early in the school year to explain and discuss the public speaking contest.
   b. Class time to consider the values of public speaking and the ways in which the contest contributes to these values.
4. Provide opportunities for all students to give short reports in class. Reports may be increased in length as the students gain ability to appear before a group.
5. Have each class develop standards for evaluating short reports.
6. Provide class time to evaluate progress in public speaking.
7. Provide class time to organize a class public speaking contest and a local FFA public speaking contest.
8. Hold a class contest.
9. Allow students to select the winners of their class contest.
10. Hold a local FFA contest. Use judges from outside the local FFA.
11. Provide an opportunity for the winner of the local FFA contest to appear before other groups.
12. Assist with the agricultural content of speeches.
13. Provide opportunities for students to receive help in English from the English teacher and in speech from the speech teacher.
14. Record winning speeches.
15. Provide opportunities to record all speeches.

Following are some words of advice for teachers regarding FFA members who are prospective prepared public speakers:

1. Be sure each participant selects a topic dealing with current agricultural problems or issues.
2. Be sure the participant selects a topic in which he/she is vitally interested.
3. Have the participant review the literature to determine whether sufficient information is available before making a final selection.
4. Be sure the participant avoids topics too difficult for his/her ability.
5. Have the participant select a name for the speech that attracts attention and reflects the content of the speech.
6. Have the participant practice giving the speech:
   a. Before a full-length mirror.

b. In an auditorium with a public address system.
c. Before every available group.

7. Observe personal appearance and mannerisms.
8. Have the participant suggest a plan of action in the speech.

Students of vocational education in agriculture often need some suggestions regarding topics for public speaking. The following topics for public speaking are examples of some that have been used.[2]

1. Crop Insurance.
2. The Young Adult in an Off-Farm Agricultural Business.
3. Why Be in the Field of Agriculture?
4. Selling Agricultural Supplies.
5. Operating an Off-Farm Agricultural Business.
6. Managing a Parts Department for a Farm Machinery Dealer.
7. Improving Range Bulls.
8. Conservation of Water.
9. Housing Farm Machinery.
10. Using Proper Headgates.
11. Culture in Agriculture.
12. Saving Is Good Spending.
13. Inflation in Agriculture.
14. Improving Dairy Pastures.
15. Producing More with Less.
16. Eliminating the Border Cow.
17. Environmental Quality.
18. The Horse and Recreation.
19. The Problem of Soil Erosion.
20. Looking Ahead in Agriculture.
21. The Challenge of Agricultural Leadership.
22. The Rural Community Improvement Club.
23. The Standardization of Agricultural Products.
24. The Restoration of Agricultural Stability.
25. Cooperative Marketing.
26. Education, the Solution to Our Food Problem.
27. Technological Developments in Agriculture.
28. Conservation of Our Natural Resources.
29. The New Era in American Agriculture.
30. Labor Efficiency and Agriculture.
31. Eliminating the Property Tax.
32. Chemical Warfare on Insects.
33. Federal Grading of Products.
34. Methods and Machinery.
35. The Future of Cooperatives.
36. Rural Community Planning.
37. Reducing Fire Hazards.

A speech should be based on a contestant's own efforts. Training in both composition and delivery is usually limited to the facilities of the school from which a contestant comes, but facts and working data may be secured from any source. Three competent and impartial persons should be selected to judge a contest. One of the three judges, when possible, should be a teacher of speech. At least one judge should have an agricultural background. Each judge should formulate and ask questions and score the answers.

Prior to a contest involving more than one school, the judges should be furnished with typewritten copies of the contestants' speeches, which they

[2]*Utah Spotlight*, Utah State University, Logan, Utah.

will read and grade on content and composition, recording their judgment on score sheets, which should also be provided. The judges of a contest should seat themselves in different sections of the room in which the contest is held and score each contestant, using the score sheet provided.

Contestants should draw for places on the program. The program chairperson should then announce the subject. Applause should be withheld until all contestants have spoken. A timekeeper should be designated who will record the time used by each contestant in delivering the speech, noting overtime, if any, for which deductions may be made. After each speech, the judges should ask questions to determine the speaker's understanding of the topic. When all contestants have finished speaking, the chairperson of the judges should assemble the sheets from all the judges and the timekeeper. Totals should then be compiled, computations made, and a final decision regarding the winners rendered by the judges.

A scoreboard for judging a public speaking contest may be as follows:

Organization	20%
Presentation	40%
Evidence of information	20%
Practicality	20%

The FFA Executive Secretary in a state will supply the chapter advisers with the current scorecard in use.

Judging Contests—At the national level nine contests are conducted. These contests test knowledge and skills in some of the instructional areas in vocational education in agriculture. The contests are in the following areas:

1. Agriculture mechanics.
2. Dairy cattle.
3. Farm business management.
4. Floriculture.
5. Livestock.
6. Meats.
7. Milk quality and dairy food.
8. Nursery and landscape.
9. Poultry.

LOCAL AND STATE CONTESTS

Parliamentary Procedure Contests—Ability in parliamentary procedure is recognized as essential for FFA members. Some states have tried to promote this ability by sponsoring parliamentary procedure contests. Other states have encouraged the teaching of parliamentary procedure, but they do not have parliamentary procedure contests, for they feel that these would overemphasize this aspect of training. Some also feel that a parliamentary procedure contest produces a type of knowledge and ability in parliamentary procedure that is not conducive to the smooth conduct of business at meetings. The value of a parliamentary procedure contest is still a moot question. Its value probably depends on the way the contest is conducted.

Nearly everyone agrees, however, that all students in agriculture should receive some instruction regarding parliamentary procedure because:

1. Group meetings of adults and FFA indicate a general lack of ability in parliamentary procedure.
2. Parliamentary procedure is complicated.
3. Students need a knowledge of parliamentary procedure while in school and later in life.
4. Parliamentary procedure is not taught by any other department in many schools.
5. Students enjoy learning parliamentary procedure.

In teaching parliamentary procedure and in preparing teams for parliamentary procedure contests, teachers have developed many methods. One plan will be described. One class session is allowed for an explanation of the simple rules of parliamentary procedure. A second class session is devoted to a discussion of the value and objectives of learning about parliamentary procedure and to a review and practice of the elementary aspects of parliamentary procedure. A third class session is devoted to the teaching of the duties of the chairperson and secretary and to the practice of parliamentary procedure. A fourth class session is devoted to parliamentary practice. Other practice sessions are held during conference periods for those wishing to become members of the parliamentary procedure team.

Following are some other ideas regarding methods of teaching parliamentary procedure:

1. Allow three minutes at the beginning of each class period for a few weeks for practicing the elementary processes of parliamentary procedure.
2. Practice parliamentary procedure each day until a mistake is observed. Allow the person observing a mistake to select the chairperson for the practice on the following day.
3. Hold a local contest with the FHA (Future Homemakers of America) or some other club.
4. Present parliamentary problems to a class and have the class members answer the problems in writing.
5. Limit the teaching about parliamentary procedure and the parliamentary contest to the 8 or 12 more fundamental parliamentary skills.
6. Allow students to preside over class sessions or a part of the class sessions as a means of developing ability in parliamentary procedure.
7. Stress parliamentary procedure in mini-FFA and other subsidiary FFA organizations.
8. Provide special practice in parliamentary procedure for FFA officers.

Notice that in several of the suggestions regarding the teaching of parliamentary procedure, a maximum amount of time is suggested. It is easy for a class and its teacher to become enthusiastic regarding parliamentary procedure and to spend an undue amount of time on it.

Tractor Rodeos—Some local chapters and districts have sponsored tractor rodeos. Following are the events often used in a tractor rodeo:

1. Hook up to a plow.
2. Belt line-up to a hammer mill.
3. Park wagon. Back a four-wheel trailer into a narrow shed.
4. Pull implement through a gate that is shorter than the implement.
5. Pull and then back a two-wheel trailer around five barrels.
6. Attach a power take-off.
7. Back a two-wheel manure spreader into a narrow shed 15′ long.
8. Perform daily inspection, servicing, and starting of a tractor.
9. Take a written examination on farm tractor safety and service.

Events are judged on the basis of time, skill, operation, and safety. A scorecard is developed for each event.

Other Contests—Following are some of the other contests sponsored in one or more states:

1. Supervised occupational experience program.
2. Environmental quality.
3. Floriculture.
4. Crop production.
5. Agribusiness.
6. Livestock management.
7. Agricultural processing.
8. Community and home beautification.
9. Agricultural testing for quality control.
10. Outdoor recreation.
11. Seed processing.
12. Grading of agricultural products.
13. Demonstrations.
14. Forestry management.
15. Community development.
16. Weed identification.
17. Panel or booth exhibit.
18. Meat identification and processing.
19. Turf management.
20. Fish management.
21. Sale of agricultural services.

In summary, the following general principles regarding contests should be observed:

1. Contests should be thought of as means and not ends.
2. They should be evaluated as means of working toward desired educational objectives.
3. The time devoted to preparing for contests should be determined by the effectiveness of the contests in developing desired educational abilities.

SUMMARY

The success of an FFA program of work depends to a large degree on the cooperation of the members. It also depends on the guidance provided by the adviser. A great deal also depends on an efficient set of officers.

Use Committees—As in building a program of activities, there will be a need for committees for carrying out the program of activities. Every member should have a job and assume responsibility for performing it.

Hold Regularly Scheduled Meetings—A regular schedule of business meetings, perhaps twice per month, is necessary.

Keep a Record of Accomplishments—A chart of the activities included in a program of work should be posted in the classroom. As the activities are accomplished, they may be recorded in the column on the chart for accomplishments. These accomplishments may be reviewed and discussed in chapter meetings.

PART

Providing an Agriculture Mechanics Program

CHAPTER

22

How to Organize an Agriculture Mechanics Program[1]

MEANING, AIMS, AND PURPOSES

Meaning of Agriculture Mechanics—Agriculture mechanics involves the development of the mechanical abilities of students in performing agriculture shop activities; in operating, maintaining, repairing, and adjusting farm machinery; in constructing and maintaining farm buildings; in installing, operating, and maintaining farm electrical systems; in processing farm products; and in performing the mechanical activities in soil and water management programs. The terms "agriculture mechanics" and "agriculture shop" have often been used interchangeably in the past. The latest interpretation, however, is that "agriculture mechanics" is a more inclusive term than "agriculture shop." The instruction in agriculture shop is now considered one of the phases of instruction in an agriculture mechanics program.

What Does Agriculture Mechanics Include?—An agriculture mechanics program includes all the mechanical activities that a progressive farmer or off-farm agricultural worker should perform with the kinds of tools and equipment accessible. Recommendations on what should be included in the agriculture mechanics program have been made by committees on agriculture teacher education of the American Society of Agricultural Engineers, in collaboration with an advisory group of agricultural education specialists. These committees recommended six areas of instruction, namely:

1. Agriculture shop work.

[1]For a discussion of how to equip and arrange an agriculture mechanics shop and related facilities, see Part X, Chapter 34.

2. Agriculture power and machinery.
3. Agriculture buildings and conveniences.
4. Soil and water management.
5. Rural electrification.
6. Processing agricultural products.

These six areas of instruction have been carefully examined, and the following outline, which is very similar to the suggestions made by these committees, has been prepared:

Agriculture Shop Work

Woodwork and Carpentry

1. Providing and equipping a home shop.
2. Classifying, selecting, and caring for lumber.
3. Selecting and using nails, screws, bolts, and hinges.
4. Classifying, using, and caring for woodworking tools.
5. Fitting shop tools.
6. Figuring bills of material.
7. Sketching and reading blueprints.
8. Cutting rafters.
9. Carrying out woodworking and agriculture carpentry projects.

Painting and Glazing

1. Painting.
2. Glazing.

Rope Work

1. Selecting and caring for rope.
2. Using and handling rope.
3. Splicing rope.
4. Tying knots.

Harness Work

1. Repairing and caring for harness.

Sheet Metal Work

1. Selecting and using soldering equipment.
2. Soldering.

Forge Work

1. Preparing for forge work.
2. Working hot and cold metal.

Welding

1. Welding by the oxyacetylene process.
2. Welding with an electric welder.

Agriculture Power and Machinery

Transmission of Power

1. Selecting, using, and repairing belts.
2. Installing line shafts, pulleys, and belts.

Farm Motors

1. Understanding fundamental principles of engines.
2. Maintaining fuel, cooling, and ignition systems.
3. Maintaining farm motors.

Trucks and Tractors

1. Selecting, using, and caring for farm trucks.
2. Selecting, using, and caring for tractors.

Farm Machinery

1. Selecting farm machinery.
2. Using and maintaining farm machinery.
3. Constructing labor-saving equipment.

Agriculture Buildings and Conveniences

Concrete Work

1. Understanding the uses and composition of concrete.
2. Estimating quantities and proportions of concrete mixtures.
3. Mixing, pouring, and curing concrete.

Farm Buildings

1. Constructing, remodeling, and repairing farm buildings.

Farm Home Conveniences

1. Selecting and using plumbing equipment.
2. Installing and repairing plumbing fixtures.
3. Establishing farm water supply systems.
4. Establishing farm sewage disposal systems.
5. Heating farm homes.

Rural Electrification

1. Understanding electrical sources, terms, and materials.
2. Wiring a farmstead and maintaining equipment.

Soil and Water Management

1. Terracing to control soil erosion.
2. Using contour farming and strip cropping practices.
3. Providing farm drainage and irrigation.

Processing Agricultural Products

1. Refrigerating.
2. Preserving.
3. Modifying.

A New Emphasis on Agriculture Mechanics—Many departments of agricultural education in the public schools offer instruction in only the agriculture shop phases of agriculture mechanics. Inadequate teacher education in the other five areas of agriculture mechanics instruction, tradition, inadequate size of the agriculture mechanics shop, inadequate equipment, and the offering of agriculture mechanics instruction only to high school students are a few of the reasons for the narrowness of the agriculture mechanics programs in many schools. Most prospective teachers of agriculture mechanics are now receiving a broader training, and many established teachers are being provided with opportunities for professional improvement in the area of agriculture mechanics. The schools' agriculture mechanics shops are being opened in increasing numbers to young and older adults desiring instruction in agriculture mechanics. Many new agriculture mechanics shops of much greater size have been constructed. The result is that an increasing number of schools are now offering complete programs of agriculture mechanics. A school offering only agriculture shop work is becoming more and more difficult to locate. Students now demand that phases of agriculture mechanics such as arc welding, gas welding, farm machinery repair, maintenance and adjustment, soil and water management, and the mechanical phases of food processing be included as part of their instruction in agriculture mechanics.

Local, state, and national administrators are becoming more cognizant of the need for instruction in agriculture mechanics. This will mean larger and better agriculture shops in the future and more comprehensive programs for high school students and for young and older adults.

Importance of Agriculture Mechanics Instruction—The instruction in agriculture mechanics is an integral part of the program in agricultural education. It provides for the development of mechanical abilities essential for success in agricultural occupations and in family living. The students' supervised occupational experience programs offer many opportunities for desirable agriculture mechanics activities. The time usually allotted to agriculture mechanics varies from 25 to 40 per cent of the total time devoted to courses in agriculture, depending on local needs.

A few of the advantages of agriculture mechanics instruction may be listed as follows:

1. It provides training in the skills that are necessary to do the needed mechanical jobs in agriculture.
2. It gives students an opportunity to use their hands.
3. It helps students, after the job is done, to realize that they have accomplished something.
4. It stimulates the interest of students because they especially like this phase of instruction in agriculture.
5. It adds variety to a program in agriculture.
6. It makes farmers and off-farm agricultural workers realize that the instruction in agriculture is not merely theory but of real practical value when agriculture mechanics is a part of that instruction.
7. It shows immediate results.
8. It affords an opportunity to advertise the work of a department.

Objectives of Agriculture Mechanics Instruction—A comprehensive program in agriculture mechanics provides for agriculture mechanics instruction in high school courses, in post-secondary courses, and in courses for young and older adults. The primary objective of agriculture mechanics instruction is the development of the abilities necessary to perform the mechanical activities to be done in agriculture with the tools and equipment accessible. Some of the contributory objectives are:

1. To develop student interests, attitudes, habits, ideals, and understandings in agriculture mechanics activities.
2. To develop abilities required to construct or repair suitable equipment essential for supervised occupational experience programs.
3. To develop students' confidence in their ability to perform needed jobs.
4. To create a desire, and to develop the abilities required, to do quality work.
5. To develop students' interests in having desirable home shops.

6. To develop abilities in the selection, maintenance, and safe use of tools and equipment.
7. To develop judgment abilities.
8. To develop abilities in using tools and equipment effectively.
9. To develop abilities in creative thinking.

Character Building Through Agriculture Mechanics—There are numerous opportunities for character building through the instruction in agriculture mechanics. Agriculture mechanics provides opportunities to develop habits of industry, carefulness, orderliness, and accuracy. These habits are developed if agriculture mechanics is taught correctly. However, if not taught correctly, it may provide a fertile field for growth of undesirable habits such as carelessness, wastefulness, shiftlessness, untidiness, and deceit.

If instructors are to promote desirable habits, they must lead by having their work well planned, by being careful and accurate in their work, and by taking pride in keeping tools in place, benches in order, and floors clean.

DEVELOPING SUITABLE COURSE MATERIALS[2]

Base Course Content on Needs—In deciding what to teach in agriculture mechanics, a teacher must give first consideration to the interests, needs, and abilities of the students. The primary objective of the instruction should be the development of effective abilities in agriculture mechanics for present and prospective farmers and for off-farm agricultural workers. This means that the students must receive the type of training which will prepare them to perform the agriculture mechanics jobs they will need to do as progressive farmers or off-farm agricultural workers with the kinds of tools and equipment they will have accessible.

For example, if a teacher examined the supervised occupational experience programs of the sophomore students and found that most of them were planning corn production projects and that the rest of the students in the group could have corn improvement projects or be involved in supplementary jobs relating to corn production, the teacher could anticipate the necessity of teaching about corn production during the year. One of the problem areas in corn production which would probably be included would be increasing corn production yields. An approved practice in getting maximum corn production yields is the obtaining of an adequate population of corn plants per acre. Thus, the teacher could anticipate the probable necessity of teaching, at least to many of the students, how to adjust corn planters to obtain the correct plant population per acre. When classroom instruction is based on the supervised occupational experience programs of the students, the agriculture mechanics instruction can become, or be a natural outgrowth of, the classroom instruction.

Secure Basic Data—Available data, such as census reports and departmental records, should be studied. If available data regarding agriculture me-

---

[2]Developing course content is also discussed in Chapter 12, "How to Organize Education in Agriculture"; Chapter 13, "How to Develop Courses of Study"; Chapter 29, "How to Organize a Program for Young Adults"; and Chapter 31, "How to Organize Adult Courses in Agriculture."

chanics are lacking, a survey may be necessary. A survey of the farms and agricultural businesses in the community is usually advisable. This survey should reveal information such as the following:

1. Basic information about the farms and agricultural businesses, including sizes and types of operations.
2. Kinds of machinery used on the farms and in the off-farm agricultural businesses.
3. Mechanical activities of farmers and off-farm agricultural workers.
4. Tools and equipment in home shops and shops of agricultural businesses.
5. Kinds of construction or repair projects done on farms and in agricultural businesses.
6. Home conveniences on the farms.
7. Labor-saving devices being used.

The summary of such a study should focus attention on a number of activities in agriculture mechanics for which training is needed.

Instruction for High School Students, Post-secondary Students, and Adults—A comprehensive program in agriculture mechanics includes instruction in high school, post-secondary, and adult courses. There are so many abilities required in agriculture mechanics that it is impossible to develop all of them adequately in the high school classes. The instruction in agriculture mechanics needs to be a continuous process. This means that suitable and adequate instruction should be provided for all three groups of agriculture students. Some of the abilities in agriculture mechanics may be more effectively and efficiently developed after a student graduates from high school.

Maintenance, Repair, and Adjustment—Maintenance, repair, and adjustment of agricultural machinery and maintenance and repair of farm buildings

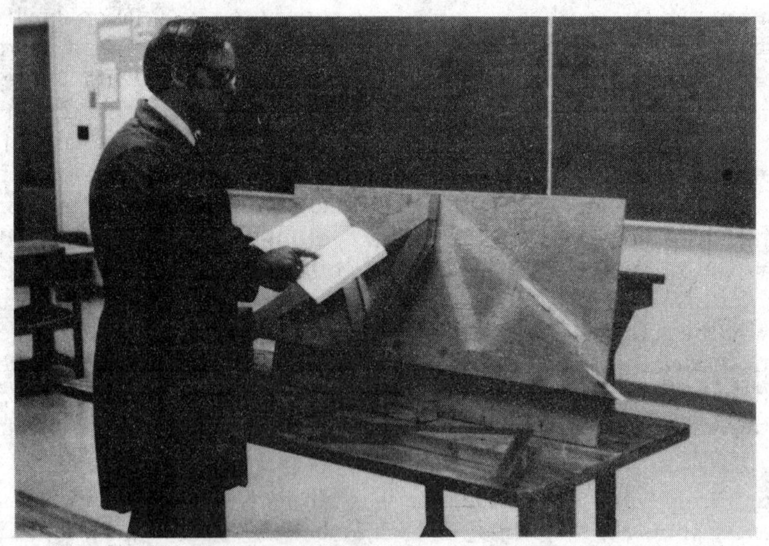

(Photo from Jasper Lee, Mississippi)

Fig. 22.1. The use of appropriate visual aids is important in teaching vocational education in agriculture. In this photograph Glen C. Shinn, of Mississippi, is preparing a visual aid for agriculture mechanics.

are often neglected in agriculture mechanics curriculums in favor of shop activities and the construction of buildings and new pieces of equipment.

Most of the agriculture mechanics activities of farmers and others in agriculturally oriented businesses concern the maintenance, repair, and adjustment of agricultural machinery. The repair and maintenance of farm buildings are often of more importance than is the construction of new buildings. An appreciation of the economy involved in the proper maintenance of agricultural machinery and buildings is vital to the efficient operation of a farm. Some studies show that most agricultural machinery is more or less out of adjustment. Teaching the proper adjustment of agricultural machinery may save a community many thousands of dollars each year.

If farmers or workers in agriculturally oriented businesses are to work with agricultural machinery, they must know how to make minor repairs. They need to know how to take a machine apart, remove broken parts, replace worn or broken parts, put the machine back together, and properly adjust it.

Undesirable Content—Often abilities are developed in agriculture mechanics courses which do not belong in agriculture mechanics—for example, teaching regarding the operation of metal lathes and of jointers commonly used in industrial shops and teaching regarding the construction and finishing of furniture, which is commonly taught in industrial arts courses. Content for agriculture mechanics should contribute to students' proficiency in agriculture. Since the mechanical abilities necessary for agricultural work are so numerous that all cannot be taught anyway, any content of doubtful value should be eliminated from the courses in agriculture.

The agriculture mechanics program is an educational program and not a factory for the manufacture of products. When a shop activity produces something in volume, the activity soon loses its value as a part of an educational program and becomes merely a work program. Some agriculture mechanics programs drift into mass production as a money-making activity. It may be all right to construct one feeder for sale. If more than one is produced, the project is probably rapidly approaching the point of diminishing educational returns.

Securing Shop Projects—With high school students it is sometimes difficult to obtain projects of the type required for a valid agriculture mechanics program. This may be the reason why some agriculture mechanics programs degenerate into shop programs.

If desirable rapport is established between a teacher, the parents, and agribusinesses and if good work is done in a school shop, parents and agribusinesses will usually allow the students to undertake construction projects and bring agricultural machinery to the shop for repair, maintenance, and adjustment.

A few of the ways teachers may motivate valid agriculture mechanics jobs and projects in the school's agriculture mechanics shop are as follows:

1. Visit the students, their parents, and their employers, and plan with them worthwhile jobs and projects which may be done in the shop.
2. Plan agriculture mechanics activities as a natural continuation of the classroom instruction.
3. Allow local newspapers to carry articles concerning the agriculture mechanics program.

4. Exhibit agriculture mechanics projects at county fairs, school fairs, and adult classes.
5. Stencil the department's name on each finished product.

After the students have decided on the activities to include in their supervised occupational experience programs, they should prepare a list of the shop projects needed in developing their programs, such as repairing, maintaining, and adjusting agricultural machinery and constructing hog houses, feeders, breeding crates, brooder houses, and trailers. They should also prepare a list of the improvement projects which they will complete during the year, such as installing drinking cups in a dairy barn or installing a water system in a home. The students should then list the supplementary practices involving agriculture mechanics activities which they plan to include in their supervised occupational experience programs. Students working in off-farm agricultural businesses should list the agriculture mechanics activities in which they will engage. Additions should be made to these lists as the need for agriculture mechanics activities becomes apparent as a result of the class instruction.

There may also be a need for numerous FFA or young farmer association activities involving projects in agriculture mechanics. For example, a portable sheep dipping tank may be needed for a program in dipping sheep. Equipment such as hog houses, feeders, waterers, and electric pig brooders may be needed for a group project in swine production. A portable sprayer may be needed for use in an orchard project.

Factors to Consider in Determining the Content of a Course—In outlining a course in agriculture mechanics, teachers should consider the following questions:

1. How long will the class period be?
2. How many periods each week will be devoted to agriculture mechanics?
3. How many years will be devoted to agriculture mechanics?
4. What are the needs of the students and the community?
5. What shop facilities are available?
6. What are the qualifications of the instructor?
7. What instruction will be offered young and older adult workers?

ANTICIPATING COURSE CONTENT

Planning the Instruction—In developing the course content in agriculture mechanics, teachers should do a great deal of planning previous to the time of the opening of school in the fall. After school opens, there should be considerable teacher-student planning of the instruction. In this way the students will have a part in deciding what agriculture mechanics activities should be included in their courses.

Deciding on Areas of Instruction—After teachers have made a thorough study of the students' needs, the areas of instruction in agriculture mechanics that should be taught need to be anticipated. The areas and phases of instruction to include in an anticipated program in agriculture mechanics should also be based on the facilities available, the qualifications of each teacher, the amount of time devoted to agriculture mechanics, and the abilities of the students.

Deciding on Units to Teach and Allotting Time—After the units in an agriculture course have been anticipated, teachers may begin looking ahead to the agriculture mechanics problem areas that will develop from these units. After the agriculture mechanics problem areas that may develop from the classroom instruction have been anticipated, teachers are ready to consider the allotment of time to each. They are also ready to determine the best time of year for teaching the various agriculture mechanics problem areas. For forms that may be used to facilitate course planning, see Chapter 13.

Planning a Four-Year Curriculum in Agriculture Mechanics—When agriculture mechanics activities are planned as an integral part of a comprehensive instructional program, it is often difficult to visualize the total program in agriculture mechanics. Many teachers summarize the problem areas which they anticipate, as a means of helping themselves visualize the agriculture mechanics program. Anticipated problem areas may be summarized or listed under certain broad headings, such as welding, metal projects, sheet metal work, agriculture power, agriculture machinery, agriculture carpentry, agriculture buildings, agriculture conveniences, fencing, electricity, soil and water management, and food processing. Form 22.2 illustrates such a summary for a four-year plan, with the approximate or tentative time allotment for each major area. This time allotment is based on the assumption that only 25 to 40 per cent of the total class time available for agriculture in a high school program should be devoted to agriculture mechanics instruction.

Form 22.3 illustrates a possible allocation of time by years for the summary units in Form 22.2. In interpreting Forms 22.2 and 22.3, the reader should remember that each of these forms presents a summary of the agriculture mechanics problem areas for a program of agricultural education at the high school level. Form 22.4 illustrates detailed planning for one of the major areas in agriculture mechanics.

After the teachers have anticipated the problem areas that will develop from the students' occupational experience programs and the classroom instruction, and after these problem areas have been summarized under the major phases of agriculture mechanics, the head of the department is ready to plan the calendar for the use of the school's agriculture shop.

Forms 22.1 to 22.4 are based on the assumption that agriculture mechanics is taught as an integral portion of other courses in agriculture. Agriculture

Form 22.1. A Suggested Form to Use in Recording a Calendar of Activities

Unit	Number of Days				
	First Year	Second Year	Third Year	Fourth Year	Total
Examples					
Woodwork and farm carpentry	20	15	10	10	55
Oxyacetylene welding			8	10	18
Total					

Form 22.2. Problem Areas Classified Under the Major Phases of Agriculture Mechanics, with Time, Year, and Season Allocation[1]

Phases and Problem Areas	Days[2]	Year of School	Time of Year to Teach
1. Introduction to agriculture mechanics.	2	9th	Fall
2. Developing a home shop.	15	9th and 10th	Fall
a. Organizing.			
b. Selecting a location.			
c. Reconditioning tools.			
d. Selecting tools.			
3. Welding.	10	10th and 11th	Any time
4. Metal projects.	15	10th and 11th	Any time
a. Planning.			
b. Constructing.			
c. Repairing.			
5. Sheet metal projects.	5	9th	Spring
a. Planning.			
b. Constructing.			
c. Repairing.			
6. Farm power.	15	12th	Winter
a. Planning.			
b. Operating and adjusting.			
c. Maintaining.			
d. Making minor repairs.			
e. Selecting.			
7. Farm machinery.	60		
a. Planning.	(6)		
b. Operating, maintaining, and repairing.			
(1) Tillage equipment.	(18)	9th, 10th, 11th	Late winter
(2) Seeding equipment.	(18)	9th, 10th, 11th	Late winter
(3) Harvesting equipment.	(18)	9th, 10th, 11th	Early fall to winter
8. Farm carpentry projects.	40	9th and 10th	Fall and spring
a. Planning.			
b. Constructing.			
c. Painting.			
9. Farm buildings.	15	12th	Fall or spring
a. Planning.			
b. Repairing.			
c. Remodeling.			
10. Farm conveniences.	15	11th and 12th	Any time
a. Planning.			
b. Repairing.			
c. Remodeling.			
d. Installing.			

(Continued)

Form 22.2 (Continued)

Phases and Problem Areas	Days[2]	Year of School	Time of Year to Teach
11. Fencing. a. Planning. b. Building. c. Repairing.	3	11th	Fall or spring
12. Electricity. a. Planning electrical installations. b. Planning electrical installations needed on home farms. c. Wiring these installations or models of these installations.	15	10th and 11th	Any season
13. Soil and water management. a. Providing drainage. b. Preventing soil erosion by mechanical devices. c. Establishing ponds.	20	12th	Early spring

[1]The problem areas are the agriculture mechanics problem areas anticipated in a four-year agricultural education program for a certain school.

[2]Estimated number of days of instruction.

Form 22.3. An Example of the Allocation of Time by Years for the Major Phases of Agriculture Mechanics

Basic Agriculture Course

	Days
Introduction to agriculture mechanics	2
Developing a home shop	10
Sheet metal projects	5
Farm carpentry projects	20
	37

Agricultural Business Course

	Days
Developing a home shop	5
Welding	5
Metal projects	5
Farm machinery	20
Farm conveniences	5
Fencing	3
Electricity	15
Soil and water management	10
	68

Agriculture Science Course

	Days
Welding	5
Metal projects	5
Farm machinery	20
Farm carpentry projects	20
	50

Agriculture Industry Course

	Days
Metal projects	5
Farm power	15
Farm machinery	20
Farm buildings	15
Farm conveniences	10
Soil and water management	10
	75

mechanics needs to be integrated into all courses. However, with the broadening of the concept of vocational education in agriculture, certain schools are also offering courses in agriculture mechanics in addition to the integrating of agriculture mechanics as part of all courses. These courses in agriculture mechanics are needed and can be justified in certain programs. When they are offered, teachers need to develop and plan for the use of shop facilities to avoid excessive use of these facilities at certain time periods.

Form 22.4. Plans for Group Activities and Demonstrations for the Farm Carpentry Phase of Agriculture Mechanics

Problem Areas—

1. Planning.
2. Constructing projects.

	In School	*On Farm*	*In Agribusiness*
a. Possible projects.			
(1) Bull pen.		X	
(2) Trailer box.	X	X	
(3) Tool shed.		X	
(4) Hog houses.	X	X	
(5) Tool box.			X

b. Group activities.
- (1) Selecting lumber.
- (2) Storing and grading lumber.
- (3) Mixing paint.
- (4)
- (5)

c. Demonstrations.
- (1) Using glue to strengthen buildings.
- (2) Using power saws.
- (3) Painting.
- (4)
- (5)

The primary value of developing anticipated course materials in agriculture mechanics, such as those indicated in Forms 22.1 to 22.4, is that it crystallizes thinking and the development of goals regarding the amount of time to be spent and the year in which the development of various abilities will be undertaken. Actually, it is impossible to develop a course outline for agriculture mechanics that can be rigidly followed. To develop an adequate course outline for agriculture mechanics would necessitate a separate course plan for each student, and even this could not be followed rigidly because the time required for the development of various abilities depends to a great extent upon the type of project which the student undertakes in the school's agriculture shop. Therefore, course outlines in agriculture mechanics serve only as rough guides to action. Course plans need to be revised constantly as the instruction and program develop and progress.

ANTICIPATING COURSE CONTENT FOR YOUNG FARMERS

Agriculture mechanics instruction should be an integral part of a three- or four-year program of young farmer education. It should not, however, be the total educational program for young farmers. They have many educational problems that do not involve agriculture mechanics.

Young farmers do have a need of some agriculture mechanics instruction to extend the training they received in high school classes, to meet the needs of their expanding farming programs, to provide advanced training in some agriculture mechanics abilities, and to keep them up-to-date regarding mechanical developments. To meet these needs, they may profit by 20 to 40 hours of agriculture mechanics instruction a year for the duration of their young farmer program.

Considerable teacher-student planning should be involved in the agriculture mechanics activities of young farmers. The steps in anticipating the curriculum for young farmers, however, are nearly identical to the steps outlined for anticipating course content for high school students.

Following is one example of the agriculture mechanics activities outlined for a four-year young farmer program. In this program, the agriculture mechanics activities will require approximately one-fourth of the total hours of instruction for young farmers each year.

First Year:
1. Maintenance, repair, and adjustment of farm machinery.
2. Painting.

Second Year:
1. Welding.
2. Home-farm shop.

Third Year:
1. Tractor maintenance and adjustment.

Fourth Year:
1. Farm electricity.

ANTICIPATING COURSE CONTENT FOR ADULTS

An agriculture mechanics course for adult farmers or for workers in jobs requiring knowledge and skills in agriculture mechanics is usually designed to develop some specific mechanical ability. Courses such as welding, ignition and carburetion of tractors, electrical wiring, repair and adjustment of plows, repair and adjustment of mowers, construction of small wooden structures, rafter cutting, sharpening of tools, and maintenance and adjustment of combines have proven popular with adults.

When adults have a need for a specific mechanical ability, they are not usually interested at that time in developing other mechanical abilities. From the standpoint of teaching, it is nearly impossible to organize and teach effectively several mechanical abilities at one time. If several mechanical abilities are taught consecutively, a course may become too long.

Teachers of agriculture should study the mechanical abilities in agriculture needed and desired by farmers and off-farm agricultural workers in their communities. The general advisory council for agriculture should be of considerable help in determining these needs and desires. Agriculture mechanics courses for adults are often planned for a four- or five-year sequence. Most pressing mechanical needs are met first. Following is a school's program of agriculture mechanics courses for adults covering a four-year period.

First Year:

1. Basic welding.
2. Maintenance and adjustment of tractors.
3. Construction of small wooden structures.

Second Year:

1. Advanced welding.
2. Ignition and carburetion of tractors.
3. Rafter cutting.

Third Year:

1. Electric wiring.
2. Concrete work.
3. Repair and adjustment of plows.

Fourth Year:

1. Repair and adjustment of mowers.
2. Installation of farm conveniences.
3. Construction of labor-saving equipment.

This series of courses, with revisions as needed, would be repeated every four years. If a schedule of courses is publicized in a community, farmers and other adults may plan ahead for the courses in which they will enroll. Yearly evaluations should be made of each course so that the course offerings may be kept in line with the needs and desires of the farmers and other adult agricultural workers in the community.

ANTICIPATING COURSE CONTENT FOR WORKERS IN AGRICULTURALLY ORIENTED BUSINESSES AND SERVICES

The basic mechanical abilities to be taught at the high school level would be similar for both prospective farmers and prospective off-farm workers who need knowledge and skills in agriculture mechanics. Therefore, the content would not need to differ to any great extent. Some adjustments may need to be made in the type of individual projects selected by the students, however. The "slant" given the instruction would also differ.

The depth of the instruction provided may be considerably different. For example, a high school student, a post-secondary student, or an adult working as an agricultural mechanic in an agricultural equipment business or preparing to work in such a business would need more specific and specialized instruction than would a typical production agriculture–oriented student.

CHAPTER

23

How to Conduct an Agriculture Mechanics Program

AGRICULTURE SHOP PROCEDURES

Shop Dress—Effective work in a shop is impossible when students are worrying about protecting their clothes from paint, grease, and dirt. Adult students may be encouraged to wear work clothes to their classes. Coveralls may be worn by high school students as a means of protecting their school clothes. The appearance of high school agriculture mechanics classes is improved if all students are dressed alike. Some schools encourage all class members to provide themselves with coveralls of a uniform type. Many persons prefer blue denim coveralls, but such material has a tendency to fade on white clothing when a worker perspires. White coveralls show dirt very readily. Khaki or striped coveralls seem to be the most desirable type.

Class members should place their names in small letters on their coveralls to prevent mixups and losses. A good place for their names is under the collar. Class members should be provided lockers or hooks for storing or hanging their coveralls. In warm climates, shop aprons or overalls may be more satisfactory than coveralls.

A lightweight shop or laboratory coat about 50″ in length is very satisfactory for a teacher to wear. Such coats protect the clothing, are convenient, and are reasonable in price.

All class members should be encouraged to wear caps as a safety measure. Shop caps are very inexpensive and provide protection while working. Black or striped caps are often preferred since they do not show soil as readily as caps of a lighter color.

Organizing Shop Work—At the beginning of shop classes, many teachers assemble the class members for a short period in a corner of the shop or in the classroom if it is near the agriculture shop. This period may be used to discover problems of class members and to ascertain if everyone has a job of educational value to perform. This procedure motivates class members to anticipate and prevent many problems. It allows a teacher and class members to plan their activities so that everyone is engaged in a worthwhile, educational task, and it also motivates class members to begin their shop activities promptly.

Some shop projects may be sufficiently large or difficult to necessitate two or more class members working together. If a project requires more than one class member, each person should have definite responsibilities for the success of the project. Instructors must make certain that all class members have opportunities to develop the skills and abilities they need. Some class members hesitate to take the lead in a project on which they are working with others. The result is that they do not develop necessary skills and abilities in agriculture mechanics. There is no definite answer to the question regarding the number of persons who can profitably work on a project. It depends on the size and type of project and the personalities of the persons working together. It is usually better, however, to have too few working on a project than to have too many. Two is the maximum number of persons who should work together on the vast majority of projects.

Securing Tools—Checking out tools to class members has many disadvantages. It is usually better to permit the students to help themselves to the tools they need. Some of the advantages of this procedure are as follows:

1. It saves time since checking is eliminated.
2. There is less confusion because students do not have to stand in line and wait to check out tools.
3. It places the class members on their honor.
4. It permits the sharing of tools. (When tools are checked out to students, they do not care to trust others to use them until they have checked them in.)
5. Discipline problems involving the students and the person who is checking tools are prevented.
6. Shop space is saved. If a check-out system is used, a tool room is necessary, which uses considerable floor space. When students are allowed to help themselves to the tools they need, wall cabinets and tool dollies may be used. The value of tool dollies is that they may be rolled close to the projects in process.

The argument for checking out tools to class members is that it prevents the loss of tools from a shop. If a class member is assigned to see that all tools are in their proper locations at the end of a class session, if all tools are marked, and if the instructor also checks to determine if all tools have been replaced before a class leaves, very few shop tools will be lost.

Tools from a shop may be lost in a number of ways. The shop may be burglarized or vandalized. Some shops cannot be made burglar- and vandal-proof, but certain precautions may be taken. The teacher should have the local sheriff's department or the local police department check the shop facilities and suggest ways of providing increased protection to the contents of the shop. The shop should be kept locked and others should not be permitted to have keys. Persons should not be allowed to work in the shop unless a teacher of agriculture is present.

Most tools are lost by being carried away in the pockets of the students. All tools should be silhouetted and stored where they are visible and can be checked with a glance. Students should check at the beginning of each class for missing silhouetted tools and they should repeat this check at the end of each shop period. If a tool is removed from the shop, the teacher should put a tag on the silhouetted spot where it belongs.

Shop Supplies—Students in a class should be requested to have their materials at the agriculture shop before class time. High school students should not expect to use class time to buy supplies at a store. Allowing students to go to a store to purchase supplies during class reduces materially the instructional time available for agriculture mechanics. Often the people in a community or the administrators of the school do not approve of students leaving the campus without an instructor.

A few of the more common pieces of lumber and a few of the more common kinds of nails, bolts, hinges, screws, and paints may be kept on hand in a shop so that if anyone runs out of material, the instructor can furnish it, thus preventing delays in the projects in process and preventing requests to go to a hardware store or lumberyard for extra supplies during the shop periods.

A school may provide a revolving fund to pay for these supplies. As the instructor sells the supplies to the students, the money is collected and deposited at the school's office where it is credited to the revolving fund. When more supplies are purchased, these are charged to the same fund. Sometimes supplies are sold with a 10 per cent markup to allow for waste. When it is a general policy for a school to pay similar charges for other departments in the school, a markup is not used. A form may be developed for keeping a record of any materials purchased from a school by a class member.

Some supplies, such as welding rods and electrodes, are usually furnished by schools. With adult students the costs of such supplies are usually paid by the students through a fee for consumable supplies.

Using a Shop Whistle—In agriculture mechanics instruction there is often so much noise that instructors find it rather difficult to obtain the attention of everyone when they wish the students to stop work. An ordinary whistle of the type used by athletic directors is very effective for this purpose. Using a whistle is much easier for an instructor than shouting at a class.

Cleaning a Shop—Good housekeeping is an important part of the training in agriculture mechanics. About 10 minutes before the close of a shop period, a whistle may be blown signaling that all tools and materials are to be put away and that the shop is to be cleaned. Students should clean around the projects on which they have worked and put away any tools they have used. A rotational system may be developed so that all class members serve as sweepers over an equal period of time for the duration of a course. Two students may be assigned as sweepers for a week or so at a time. The shop should be well cleaned, all lumber and projects neatly arranged, and all tools returned to their proper places before a class is dismissed.

Maintaining Equipment—Good equipment helps to make students better workers, but equipment cannot stay in good condition unless it is given proper care. In order to insure long life, economical use, and satisfactory service from equipment, it is imperative that it be properly maintained. Students need instruction in how to keep equipment properly lubricated and adjusted and free from rust, dirt, and grime. They should recondition or replace worn parts as soon as needed. The proper maintenance of tools and equipment in a shop is an important part of the students' training. The students should take pride in keeping the tools and equipment in good condition. They will obtain much satisfaction from using such equipment, and its use will contribute to good work quality.

Shop Safety—Many accidents have occurred because of the improper use of equipment. A sufficient number of fire extinguishers should be kept in a shop at all times, since many fires have been started in shops through the improper use of equipment. *All possible precautions should be taken to make a shop a safe place in which to work. Accidents are caused; they do not just happen.* The recommendations of the manufacturer should be followed in the safe use of shop equipment.

Safety talks, posters, and regulations help in preventing accidents in a shop, but they are not adequate. Students need to understand safety precautions. The teacher may develop this understanding at least partially by allowing the students to develop their own safety regulations for the shop. These

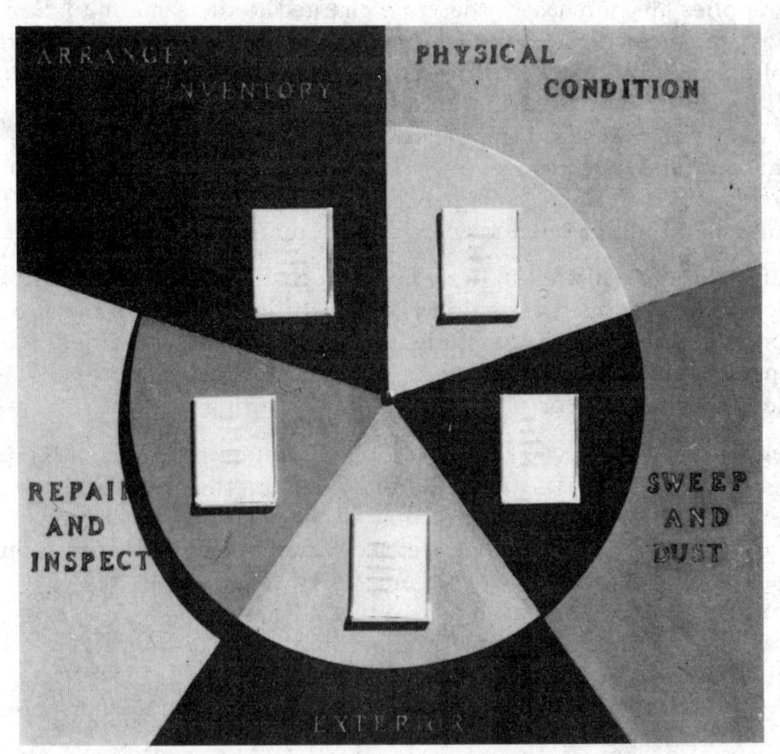

(Photo from New Mexico State University)

Fig. 23.1. A work organizer. The work organizer may be used to keep a record of the work responsibilities of students. It may also be used to rotate responsibilities.

safety regulations would develop from discussions and thinking concerning necessary precautions. If students participate in developing regulations, they will probably more completely understand them and be more willing to observe them. Following are a few examples of safety regulations which might originate from the students:

1. Treat injuries immediately.
2. Keep the shop clean and in order.
3. Remove all nails projecting from boards.
4. Wear goggles when using a grinder.
5. Wear a hood while arc welding.
6. Never use any power equipment unless safety guards are in place.
7. Always stop equipment before making adjustments.

These safety precautions are general. Specific safety precautions may also be developed for each piece of equipment and each operation in a shop. The safety precautions or regulations may also contain statements of the reason for the regulations.

Each class needs to develop its own safety regulations if the members of the class are to understand and respect them. Materials which may be used by students as references during the time they are developing their safety regulations may be obtained from many sources. The National Safety Council in Chicago has numerous publications on safety. The instructional manuals for the different types of shop equipment contain many suggestions.

Student Behavior—With adults and post–high school youth, the only behavior problem that usually concerns a teacher is the observance of safety precautions. Observance of safety precautions requires constant vigilance on the part of a teacher because even young and older adults are sometimes forgetful regarding safety.

Usually there are no behavior problems with high school students working in a shop because they are interested in their work. If behavior problems do develop, the principles of handling and preventing them presented in Chapter 7, "How to Teach Effectively," are applicable. A shop class cannot be as quiet as other classes; in fact, it should not be. If two students are working together on the same job, some conversation pertaining to the job is necessary. Loud talking, whistling, singing, or other unnecessary disturbances, however, should be discouraged.

References—Reference materials are often needed in a shop. A library shelf for such materials may be maintained in a protected spot in a shop. For a discussion of reference materials for agriculture mechanics, see Part X, "Providing and Using Facilities, Equipment, Supplies, and Teaching Aids."

Tools, Equipment, and Facilities—For a discussion of the tools, equipment, and facilities needed for conducting an effective agriculture mechanics program, see Part X.

TEACHING PROCEDURES

The general principles of teaching presented in Chapter 4, "What Is Good Teaching?" and Chapter 5, "How to Plan for Effective Instruction," are applicable in teaching agriculture mechanics. In agriculture mechanics, teachers spend most of their time providing individual instruction, presenting demonstrations, and developing the skills of class members. Discussion procedures are not used as extensively in teaching agriculture mechanics as they are in teaching managerial problems; however, discussion periods and study periods are often needed.

Problem-solving—Problem-solving abilities may be developed in agriculture mechanics. Farmers and many off-farm agricultural workers have problems in agriculture mechanics each year. If agriculture mechanics is effectively taught, attention will be given to the solution of these problems, and the students will receive instruction and develop skill in solving these problems. Skill in problem-solving which is developed in agriculture mechanics should be useful in solving other problems which the students encounter.

Some of the common types of problems which a student may meet are as follows:

1. How do I time a tractor?
2. How do I adjust the cutter-bar on a combine?
3. How shall I cut rafters?
4. What tools and equipment shall I need for my home shop?
5. What job simplification practices should I use?

These are only a few of the many problems which are encountered in agriculture mechanics.

The instructor may help a student in solving problems in agriculture mechanics by:

1. Having the student state the problem in the form of a question and in a clear and concise manner. (The problem should grow out of the occupational experiences of the student, be of interest to the student, and call for superior thinking.)
2. Developing with the student, or students in the case of class instruction, a number of questions or factors which will need to be considered in reaching a satisfactory solution to the problem.
3. Assisting the student in selecting suitable references or other teaching aids.
4. Conducting a supervised study period in which the student reviews and evaluates information. Problem-solving under this method becomes a procedure of seeking the best answers to the questions and factors pertaining to the problem, weighing the information, drawing inferences, and making decisions needed in the solution of the problem.

Some of the activities in which a student may wish to engage in prior to working on a particular job in the shop are:

1. Anticipating budget costs and probable use of equipment to be constructed.
2. Making trips to implement dealers, lumberyards, and nearby farms to observe equipment or materials involved in the solution of the student's problems.
3. Holding individual conferences with the teacher or with other persons who have had similar problems.
4. Inviting the teacher to the home farm or place of employment to discuss the best possible solutions to the student's problems.
5. Evaluating the experiences of others.
6. Testing certain practices.

7. Reading references in search of suitable information pertaining to the student's problems.

If a student engages in these activities prior to doing a job in the shop, there will be a better understanding of what is being done and why. All agriculture mechanics activities should involve thinking and problem-solving. Mere busywork is inexcusable. For a more complete discussion of problem-solving, see the section on that topic in Chapter 4, "What Is Good Teaching?"

Teaching Fundamentals—Students need many fundamental shop abilities if they are to work effectively in a shop. The choice of times to teach these fundamentals, such as how to use a saw or an arc welder, is often a problem. If the instruction precedes the work on actual projects in the shop, the students are often poorly motivated for the instruction because they have no immediate use for the ability. Learning the kinds of lumber and the sizes and kinds of nails, screws, bolts, and hinges before a project has created a need for this knowledge is a monotonous, uninteresting task. If students need this knowledge to carry out effectively agriculture mechanics projects in the shop, they are highly motivated. Learning is efficient. On the other hand, a teacher cannot allow students to go ahead too far on projects without fundamental information and skill. A skillful teacher allows students to proceed in the planning and execution of their projects until they need fundamental information and skills. The teacher then calls individuals, groups, or an entire class together and teaches the fundamentals needed at that time. This spreads the teaching of fundamentals over an entire course. When this procedure is used, the students are highly motivated.

Individual and Group Instruction—Both individual and group instruction are important and must be used for successful results. Often class members need individual help. At other times, a problem may be so general that everyone can benefit from the help of the instructor. Instruction in sharpening a plane or filing a saw may be given to a class. Later, if someone has difficulty with one of these jobs, individual help should be given. The two types of instruction are hard to separate—hardly a shop day will pass without both types of instruction being used.

When to Give a Demonstration—In general, a demonstration should be given by an instructor whenever the opportune time occurs. An instructor should always endeavor to give a demonstration of any new skill immediately prior to the time the skill is needed. The main purpose of demonstrations is to create interest and to aid the students in knowing *what to do* and *how to do it*. A demonstration to an individual may be given whenever it is observed that a student is doing something wrong. For instance, if a student is making a mistake in cutting rafters or in striking an arc, a demonstration should be given. Often an entire class may be halted and the demonstration given to all. Consequently, on some days an instructor may give several demonstrations which were not planned for that day. After a demonstration is given, the teacher should check to see that the students are doing the job properly.

Shop Project Plans—Simple drawings should be made of a construction project (unless other suitable plans are available) before work begins on the project. A teacher may stimulate the development of these plans by inquiring regarding the dimensions, the kinds of materials that will be used, and the approximate cost. A discussion may also be conducted regarding the desirability of various dimensions and materials. Usually a student should also be motivated to compare the cost of construction with the cost of the project if it were purchased.

Quality of Work—Good quality of work in agriculture mechanics is essential if a student is to develop the needed mechanical abilities. If the quality of work in a shop is inferior, the parents and other adults will refuse to allow agriculture mechanics classes to work on their machinery and equipment. The teacher can encourage quality work by discussing its value with classes or with individuals. Discussions may also be conducted to create understanding of the standards for good work. If students share in developing standards for quality work, they accept these standards and attempt to follow them. A class discussion of quality work standards may produce standards such as the following partial list:

1. Square a board by marking before sawing.
2. Use only materials of proper kinds and dimensions.
3. Use bolts when necessary.
4. Prevent bad hammer marks, bent-over nails, and nails clinched on an outer surface.
5. Use the correct number of nails of the proper size.
6. Stress durability at all times.
7. Complete all jobs which are started.
8. Finish all projects before they leave the shop.

Pride in quality of work needs to be emphasized, and a teacher's actions and attitudes should set an example for the students.

Jobs Away from a Shop—Often agriculture mechanics instruction may be broadened in scope and made more realistic and practical by the taking of classes to farms or other work locations for performing certain mechanical jobs. This is a good procedure if:

1. Too much time is not lost in going to and from a farm or another work location.
2. All class members can be taken and given definite jobs which have been planned in advance.
3. Suitable education is provided.
4. The class members go and return in a group with the instructor.
5. Order prevails.
6. The class period is sufficiently long to justify taking a class away from the shop.

When agriculture mechanics instruction is provided, for example, on a farm or at an agricultural business, time is lost going to and from the farm or business. Consequently, insofar as possible, the students should be encouraged to bring their machinery and their construction jobs to the school's agriculture shop. Shops with adequate space and sufficiently large doorways permit a large percentage of the agriculture mechanics jobs involving construction or repairing to be done in the shops.

TEACHING PLANS

The general principles regarding teaching plans presented in Part II are applicable in agriculture mechanics. These discussions may be consulted for a more thorough presentation of the development of teaching plans.

Careful planning is especially important in teaching agriculture mechanics because a number of projects are usually in progress in a shop.

Short-Time Teaching Plans—A teaching plan for a discussion of a problem developing from an agriculture mechanics project may be of the same kind as those plans used for other types of agricultural problems. For examples of teaching plans, see Chapter 5, "How to Plan for Effective Instruction."

Skill Breakdown—An instructional device known as a "skill breakdown" may be used in teaching a skill in agriculture mechanics. It involves dividing a skill into the basic *steps* necessary to perform it and listing the *key points* which will describe *how to do it* to avoid injury, to make the job easier, and to make the skill readily understood. "Skill breakdowns" should be very helpful to a teacher in presenting demonstrations.

Form 23.1 is an example of a breakdown of a manipulative skill.

Form 23.1. Adjusting Tractor Cultivator (Soil Engaging Mechanism)

Important Steps (What you do)	*Key Points* (How you do it)
A. Prepare for job.	1. Draw parallel lines on level floor or ground space to simulate rows to be cultivated. 2. Draw lines to represent centers of rows. 3. Draw lines to make boxes from the parallel lines.
B. Set tractor.	1. Place wheel tread of tractor so that wheel centers are twice the distance between rows.
C. Attach cultivator.	1. See operator's manual.
D. Place cultivator.	1. Place tractor on diagram and center gangs with rows.
E. Prepare to adjust cultivator.	1. Block tractor wheels at desired cultivating depth and lower gangs.
F. Adjust shovels or sweeps.	1. Set inside shovels or sweeps at desired distance from row. See operator's manual. 2. Set other shovels or sweeps to work remaining space. 3. Set angles of shovels or sweeps. See operator's manual.

Supervising Practice in Agriculture Mechanics—The supervision of activities in agriculture mechanics is as much a part of good teaching as the supervision of practice in any other agricultural activities. Supervision of activities in an agriculture shop is generally accepted as essential. On-farm or on-job supervision of a student's agriculture mechanics activities is also essential. Follow-up of instruction of the students is often necessary to obtain successful use of skills and abilities learned in classes in agriculture mechanics. It is also a means of correcting mistakes before they become habits and of solving individual difficulties.

Supervising activities in agriculture mechanics during home or job visits is a good way of locating problems which may be considered in a shop class. It is also a good way for instructors to develop their own skill and understanding of mechanical problems. Teachers who concern themselves with the mechanical problems of farmers and other agricultural workers during visits will learn many mechanical skills. They will also encounter mechanical problems new to them which they will have to think through or receive help in solving. This is one way of keeping informed concerning new developments in agricultural machinery.

THE HOME SHOP

A home shop promotes the use of the abilities developed in agriculture mechanics. It makes the follow-up of activities in agriculture mechanics easier and more effective. Since an average agricultural worker engages in a large number of mechanical activities and since tools and equipment are necessary to do these jobs, a home shop is very important. It is becoming of more importance because of the increasing use of agricultural machinery. A good home shop affords a farmer or other agricultural worker an opportunity to do many repair and construction jobs during winter months. It saves time, money, and inconvenience. One of the important aims of the instruction in agriculture mechanics is the encouragement of students to provide and maintain shops at home.

Equipping Home Shops—Students should be encouraged to first renovate shop tools and equipment already available. These tools may then be supplemented by other tools and equipment of standard sizes and brands. Often instructors can render a very fine educational service by accompanying class members to a hardware store and helping them select their equipment and tools.

PART

Conducting a Guidance Program

CHAPTER

24

What Are the Guidance Responsibilities of Teachers of Agriculture?

INTRODUCTION

What Is Guidance?—Guidance may be defined as the process of assisting individuals to make wise choices and adjustments. Individuals have vocational problems, educational problems, health problems, financial problems, personal and social problems, ethical and moral problems, recreational and leisure-time problems, and problems of civic responsibility which require choices and decisions.

Guidance is an essential part of education. Vocational guidance, an important aspect of vocational education in agriculture, is the process of assisting an individual to choose an occupation, prepare for it, adjust to it, and progress in it.

Need for Guidance—It is only necessary to talk to high school youth, young farmers, adult farmers, and other workers requiring knowledge and skills in agriculture to realize their need for guidance regarding decisions of choice and adjustment. Age or status does not determine the number of problems calling for guidance which confront individuals. Adults, as well as high school youth, have problems. The difference is in the type of problems.

Guidance is the joint responsibility of the *home*, the *school*, and the *community*. The increased prosperity of fortunetellers, palmists, and graphologists is an indication that efforts to assist individuals with their problems of choice and adjustment cannot be relaxed.

The number of problems is always greater during periods of change or stress. The present unsettled times will increase the need for guidance in schools.

The Responsibility of a School—The home, the church, and the community recognize their responsibilities for guidance, but their efforts are inadequate. One of the reasons for this inadequacy is lack of information. They lack information particularly in the area of occupations.

Most schools have accepted responsibility for assisting the individuals they are serving in making choices and adjustments. Many schools have established guidance organizations with directors of guidance and staffs to help teachers provide guidance services to individuals. In such schools, teachers may also use the guidance department as a referral agency. In some of the schools in which teachers of agriculture work, funds are not available for the employment of adequate personnel for guidance services.

Responsibilities of Agriculture Teachers—For a guidance program to be satisfactory, every teacher must cooperate. Because of their training in technical agriculture, their knowledge of agricultural occupations, and their individual contacts with high school, young adult, and older adult students, teachers of agriculture may be the key individuals in a school's guidance program for the people of the community in agricultural occupations and for those with agricultural interests. Teachers of agriculture have many opportunities for guidance, because they receive many requests for help from individuals in their communities. Because they visit the homes of students and because they work with their students intensively, they also frequently have opportunities to contribute information valuable to other persons in the school who are providing guidance services.

Some students have problems in the area of guidance that are too specialized or difficult for an average teacher of agriculture to handle. Teachers should not attempt to guide students in areas in which they are not qualified. One characteristic of effective and successful guidance personnel is that they take advantage of referral opportunities. Teachers of agriculture may improve their guidance activities by taking full advantage of the specialized abilities of the counseling personnel in their schools and communities. Teachers of agriculture will probably also find that others in guidance work will take advantage of their special abilities by referring individuals to them for counseling.

Phases of Guidance—The phases of a good guidance program are as follows:

1. Helping individuals to understand themselves.
2. Providing career and occupational information.
3. Counseling.
4. Providing for exploration of educational opportunities.
5. Providing a placement service.
6. Evaluating guidance activities.

The part teachers of agriculture play in developing and providing these services are presented in this chapter.

GUIDANCE PROBLEMS OF SECONDARY AND POST-SECONDARY AGRICULTURE STUDENTS

Secondary and post-secondary students encounter many problems of adjustment and choice. These problems are often all-important to an individual and must be met satisfactorily before the individual is emotionally ready to benefit from the course work. Teachers of agriculture have a moral responsibility to work with the rest of the teachers in the school, the specialized guidance personnel in the school, and others in assisting students in resolving their problems intelligently and effectively. Some of these problems may not be very closely related to agriculture, but often they must be resolved before students are in a position to study agricultural problems. Teachers need to become sensitized to problems in the area of guidance so that students may be helped to resolve their difficulties even though the students and their parents are unable to verbalize their concerns.

Orientation to High School—Starting high school is a period of adjustment both for parents and for young people. A teacher of agriculture can help in dealing with many of the concerns it produces. Sensitivity to them will be greatly appreciated by the students and their parents and will assist in developing the rapport necessary for future education in agriculture.

A partial list of problems of choice and adjustment in orientation to high school which commonly worry a student (as well as his/her parents) follows:

1. Should I go to high school?
2. What courses should I take in high school?
3. How, when, and where do I register for high school?
4. What should I wear?
5. Should I enroll in agriculture?
6. Should I become a member of the FFA?

School, Personal, and Social Problems—Going to school and growing up produce many stresses and strains. Following is a partial list of the more common personal and social problems which develop:

1. Should I attempt to make the school's athletic teams, or should I devote this time to my supervised occupational experience program?
2. Should I attempt to achieve the advanced FFA degrees?
3. How should I use the money I earn from my supervised occupational experience program?
4. How can I earn better grades in school?
5. How can I study more effectively?
6. How should I act at social affairs?
7. How should I meet and associate with other young people?
8. How can I work with others more effectively?
9. How can I develop confidence in my ability?
10. How can I make friends more easily?
11. How should I act so that I can get along with my family?

Teachers of agriculture do not have the time or the qualifications to deal adequately with some of these concerns. They need to be sensitive to their existence, however, so that individuals may be referred to guidance personnel who have the time and qualifications necessary for providing assistance. It is necessary to remember that students cannot effectively develop supervised occupational experience programs while they have other concerns that are *all-important*.

Vocational and Supervised Occupational Experience Problems—The qualifications of teachers of agriculture make them the school's key figures in assisting students with problems of vocational choice related to agriculture. Some of the more frequent problems of this type follow:

1. Should I farm? Should I prepare for an off-farm job requiring knowledge and skills in agriculture?
2. For what type of farming or off-farm agricultural occupation should I prepare myself?
3. What should be the major and minor activities in my supervised occupational experience program?
4. Should I go into debt for my supervised occupational experience program?
5. How much should I expand my supervised occupational experience program?
6. Should I go into partnership with my parents?
7. Should I reinvest my profits in my supervised occupational experience program?
8. What agricultural abilities should I try to develop?

Orientation to the Next Step—The national and world situation produces many complications in planning for the next steps after graduation from high school. Any change produces stresses and strains. The problems are likely to be more severe in the years ahead because of increasing uncertainty as to what the future holds. Schools and teachers of agriculture cannot overlook their responsibility for helping students adjust to these next steps. Following are a few of the more common problems related to next steps after leaving school:

1. Should I go to college?

(Photo from Robert W. Walker, Pennsylvania)

Fig. 24.1. Possible careers in agriculture provide many opportunities for effective guidance and counsel. In public schools, teachers of agriculture are the best qualified persons available for providing guidance and counsel regarding agricultural career opportunities. Shown are two agriculture students considering the possibilities of careers in dairying or in occupations closely related to dairying.

2. In what college or university should I enroll?
3. How do I enroll in college?
4. How may I further my education after I leave school?
5. What part should I take in the affairs of the community?

GUIDANCE PROBLEMS OF YOUNG ADULTS

Vocational agriculture recognizes the importance of providing young, out-of-school adults with continuing educational opportunities in agriculture. A successful teacher of young adults realizes that an important part of the program for young adults is assisting them to plan, to make choices, and to adjust to agricultural occupations. Many of the problems of choice and adjustment encountered in high school will continue into, or reappear in, the program for young adults. Following is a partial list of continued or new problems in the area of guidance which a teacher must help a young, out-of-school adult resolve:

1. Should I try to become established in an agricultural occupation?
2. How can I become established in an agricultural occupation?
3. Should I go into debt to become established in an agricultural occupation?
4. How far into debt can I safely go?
5. When should I get married?
6. How may I further my education?
7. What immediate steps should I take in becoming established in an agricultural occupation?
8. What part should I take in community affairs?
9. How much and what kind of insurance should I have?

GUIDANCE PROBLEMS OF ADULTS

Adults have problems of choice and adjustment. Medical doctors, religious leaders, bankers, teachers, and other leaders receive many requests for help from adults on problems related to planning, choice, and adjustment. Much of the casual conversation of adults reflects their concern about these problems.

Teachers of agriculture who work effectively with adults cannot avoid receiving requests from adults for help regarding plans, choices, and other adjustments. Teachers, therefore, need to prepare themselves for helping farmers and other adults in agriculturally oriented occupations with these problems. One way teachers may prepare for the guidance of adults is to become acquainted with other persons and agencies in the community that may assist in helping individuals with problems in areas in which they are not qualified.

Some of the problems of an adult farmer in the areas of planning, choosing, and adjusting that are commonly referred to a teacher of agriculture are as follows:

1. Should I continue farming?
2. Should I expand my farming operations?
3. How can I help my children grow into farming or another agricultural occupation?
4. How can I help my children become established in farming or another agricultural occupation?
5. Should I change occupations?

6. Should I engage in another type of agricultural occupation?
7. Should I send my children to college?
8. How should I plan for retirement?
9. Should I retire on the farm?
10. What type of partnership agreements should I develop with my children?
11. What part should I take in community affairs both before and after retirement?
12. How can I make provisions in my will for the continued welfare of my family and farm?
13. How much and what kind of insurance should I have?

Some of the problems of an off-farm agricultural worker in the areas of planning, choosing, and adjusting that are commonly referred to a teacher of agriculture are as follows:

1. Should I continue in my present job?
2. What are the job opportunities in off-farm occupations requiring knowledge and skills in agriculture?
3. What additional agricultural knowledge and skills do I need to advance?
4. Should I engage in part-time farming?
5. Should I go into an agriculturally oriented business for myself?
6. Should I send my children to an agricultural college?
7. Should my children be enrolled in agriculture in high school?

Adults in off-farm agricultural occupations also have guidance problems similar to the problems of adult farmers in the areas of family living, insurance, community affairs, and so forth.

CHAPTER

25

How to Assist in Making Plans, Choices, and Adjustments

KNOWING THE INDIVIDUAL

Before teachers are in a position to assist students with their problems in making plans, choices, and adjustments, they need to know as much as possible about each individual. This background information makes it possible for teachers or guidance specialists to counsel and guide individuals intelligently, effectively, and efficiently.

Collecting Information—Teachers of agriculture may help in collecting information about individual students. However, before teachers begin to gather background information systematically, they should find out the type and amount of data collected through the guidance program of the school. The facts they gather should supplement, and not duplicate, this information. Many schools collect information which indicates the following characteristics of individuals:

1. Goals, plans, and stability of purposes.
2. Aptitudes and abilities.
3. Physical and health condition.
4. Educational achievement and experiences.
5. Work experience.
6. Personal and social adjustment.
7. Home and community situation.
8. Interests.
9. Financial situation.

The background information for use with students of all ages which is of the most value to teachers of agriculture for the type of guidance service they are most frequently asked to render is presented in Form 25.1.

Form 25.1. Background Information Regarding Individual Students

Personal Information

Name ______________________ When born ______________

Where born ______________________________

Location of home ______________________________

Telephone number ______________

Living with ______________________________
(parents, father, mother, brother, sister, husband, wife, stepfather, stepmother, etc.)

Parents

Name of father (if living) ______________ Date born ______________

Highest level of education ______________________________
(elementary school, high school, college)

Health—good ______________ fair ______________ poor ______________

Language (other than English) spoken or written ______________

Occupation ______________________________

Special interests ______________________________

Name of mother (if living) ______________ Date born ______________

Highest level of education ______________________________

Health—good ______________ fair ______________ poor ______________

Language (other than English) spoken or written ______________

Occupation ______________________________

Special interests ______________________________

Brothers and Sisters

Number of brothers __________ Number older __________ Number younger __________

Number of older brothers at home __________

Number of sisters __________ Number older __________ Number younger __________

Number of older sisters at home __________

Number of brothers and sisters graduating from high school __________

Number of brothers and sisters who attended college __________

Education

Amount of formal education ______________________________

Scholastic standing ______________________________

Subjects liked most ______________________________

Subjects liked least ______________________________

Reading ability—good ______________ fair ______________ poor ______________

Interests, Attitudes, and Traits

Hobbies ______________________________

Membership in organizations ______________________________
(list)

Degree of participation in organizations and clubs ______________
(much, some, little, none)

(Continued)

Form 25.1 (Continued)

Offices held ____________________

Work experience ____________________
(kind and amount)

Special abilities ____________________
(music, art, etc.)

Interest in sports or games ____________________
(much, some, little, none)

Favorite type of recreation ____________________

Interest in agricultural work ____________________
(much, some, little, none)

Interest in machinery ____________________
(much, some, little, none)

Source of spending money ____________________

Attitude toward school ____________________

Attitude toward family ____________________

Health

General health condition—good __________ fair __________ poor __________

Vision—good __________ fair __________ poor __________

Hearing—good __________ fair __________ poor __________

Physical defects ____________________
(list)

Absenteeism due to illness ____________________
(much, some, little, none)

Overweight __________ Underweight __________

Adequate rest obtained ____________________
(yes, no)

Future Plans

Finish high school ____________________

Go to college ____________________

Farm ____________________

Work on farm at home ____________________

Work on farm at home for wages ____________________

Work on farm away from home ____________________

Farm in partnership with a relative ____________________

Rent land for farming ____________________

Buy a farm ____________________

Obtain off-farm agricultural work __________ Kind __________

Obtain non-agricultural work ____________________

Type of off-farm agricultural occupation planned ____________________

Source of guidance regarding future plans ____________________

Interest in guidance regarding future plans ____________________
(much, some, little, none)

Teachers of agriculture have many unusual opportunities to obtain the information called for in Form 25.1 plus other background information about individuals. They visit the homes and jobs of students; interview students and their families; have supervised occupational experience program plans, autobiographies, and diaries of students available; and know the activity schedule of their students. In addition to these sources of information, teachers should use the data collected through the school's guidance program. Some teachers waste considerable time gathering information about individuals through formal questionnaires when this information has already been collected or is available as an outcome of the normal activities of teachers. Formal questionnaires should be used by agriculture teachers to obtain only the background information not presently available or not easily obtained through the use of other procedures.

If a school's guidance program has as one of its services the collection of background information about individuals, teachers of agriculture should not only use this service but also aid in collecting such data. Teachers of agriculture need certain types of information not ordinarily collected through a school's guidance program. They may obtain this information through home or job visits, interviews, and questionnaires and make it available to the school's staff to be placed in the cumulative folders for individuals which are maintained by the school. Some of the information needed by teachers of agriculture and not ordinarily collected through a school's guidance program is that pertaining directly to agricultural occupations, for example, the information pertaining to agricultural occupations in Form 25.2. Teachers of agriculture also need specific information regarding the opportunities high school students or young adults have for developing supervised occupational experience programs and for becoming established in occupations requiring knowledge and skills in agriculture. Form 25.2 calls for this type of information. The data for completing Form 25.2 may be obtained from supervised occupational experience program plans, from home and job visits, and from interviews. A few of the items of information may be obtained most efficiently through the use of a questionnaire.

Tests—Standardized tests of various types are available. Several thousand tests are on the market. These tests may provide information of value to teachers of agriculture in counseling their students. Published tests may be classified as follows:

1. General intelligence tests.
2. Intelligence or aptitude tests yielding multiple scores.
3. Reading tests.
4. Achievement tests.
5. Interest and aptitude inventories.
6. Personal adjustment inventories.
7. Predictive tests in certain school subjects.

Administration and interpretation of tests are usually a part of a school's guidance program. Teachers are expected to cooperate with the school's testing program, but they usually have no great amount of responsibility for it other than the intelligent use of results. If teachers have greater respon-

Form 25.2. Information Related to Possibilities for a Supervised Occupational Experience Program and Establishment in an Agricultural Occupation

---

Name ______________________________

Home Farm

1. Size ______________
2. Kinds of livestock raised
   a. ______________ Amount ______________
   b. ______________ Amount ______________
   c. ______________ Amount ______________
   d. ______________ Amount ______________
   e. ______________ Amount ______________
3. Principal crops grown
   a. ______________ Amount ______________
   b. ______________ Amount ______________
   c. ______________ Amount ______________
   d. ______________ Amount ______________
   e. ______________ Amount ______________
4. Number of acres of pasture ______________
5. Acres owned ______________
6. Acres rented ______________
   Name of owner ______________ Address ______________
7. Size of family obtaining a living from the farm ______________

Family Plans

1. Mother's plans for son or daughter ______________
2. Father's plans for son or daughter ______________

Opportunities for Establishment in Farming

1. Opportunity for partnership in present farming operation ______________
2. Opportunity for renting another farm ______________
3. Opportunity for expanding (vertically) the present farming operation ______________
4. Opportunity and possibility of buying a farm ______________
5. Possibility of inheriting a farm ______________
6. Possible sources of credit for becoming established ______________
7. Other potential opportunities for establishment ______________

Opportunities for Establishment in an Off-Farm Occupation Requiring Knowledge and Skills in Agriculture

1. Opportunity for a job in an off-farm agriculturally oriented business ______________
2. Opportunity for a partnership in an off-farm agriculturally oriented business ______________
3. Opportunity for starting an off-farm agriculturally oriented business ______________
4. Opportunity for a job in an off-farm agriculturally oriented service (local, state, or federal job involving agriculture) ______________

---

sibilities than this, they may properly prepare themselves by studying carefully the manuals on giving and interpreting the tests, by studying books on testing, and by taking courses in guidance and testing.

Interpreting Information—Hasty conclusions based on partial information should not be made. Isolated test scores and other bits of information cannot be used as the only bases for conclusions. Background information is useful to teachers in helping them assist students in thinking through their problems in adjustment and choice. Test data and other background information will not give the answers. The accumulation of these data is not an end in itself, but background information may help teachers to view the problems of students objectively instead of emotionally. In the interpretation and use of background information, the pattern of development of an individual is of considerable importance.

Background information should be used to help individuals help themselves. It must be held in strict confidence. The betrayal of personal confidences may not only be damaging to individuals, but it may also create situations in which individuals will not give teachers needed background information about themselves.

GROUP TECHNIQUES

Some problems of choice and adjustment may be profitably handled in groups rather than through individual counseling. For some problems, group techniques are even superior to individual counseling. Group techniques may save the time of an instructor. They may help students to recognize, define, and verbalize their problems. In some instances individuals are more willing to discuss and think through problems of choice and adjustment with their peers than with a teacher or counselor. The following sections present some of the group techniques used by teachers of agriculture.

Elementary School Visits—Some teachers assist in orienting students to high school by visiting elementary schools and discussing with the eighth grade students (1) their entrance into high school, (2) course offerings, (3) school activities, and (4) activities in agriculture. The visits should be for the purpose of helping the students to make intelligent choices and happy adjustments. Some high school agriculture departments allow advanced high school students to visit elementary schools to help eighth graders prepare for the transition from elementary school to high school.

Visiting Days—Many high schools have visiting days for prospective students. If this is not a practice of a school, the department of agriculture can usually obtain permission to sponsor a visiting day for prospective students from the elementary or junior high schools.

FFA Activities—Many FFA chapters invite prospective students to visit certain FFA meetings and events. Some chapters sponsor educational and social meetings during the summer to assist prospective students of agriculture in making adjustments. A chapter may also provide a program for the local 4-H clubs as a means of helping the younger members of these clubs to learn more about agricultural education and the high school.

Orientation Units—Most teachers provide time in their course outlines for orientation units dealing with the school, the agriculture department, the FFA, and the concept of supervised occupational experience. Following is a problem area breakdown for these units:

1. *School and Agricultural Education.*
   a. Finding one's way around the school.
   b. Understanding school regulations.
   c. Obtaining supplies and equipment.
   d. Studying in high school.
   e. Learning in agriculture courses.
   f. Understanding objectives of agricultural education.
   g. Developing individual objectives in agricultural education.
2. *FFA.*
   a. Understanding aims and purposes.
   b. Determining the meaning of the creed and the emblem.
   c. Understanding degrees and qualifications.
   d. Discovering nature and scope.
   e. Planning activities and a program of work.
3. *Supervised Occupational Experience Program.*
   a. Defining occupational experience.
   b. Determining objectives.
   c. Determining possibilities for supervised occupational experiences.
   d. Selecting exploratory experiences.
   e. Selecting production projects.
   f. Selecting improvement projects.
   g. Selecting supplementary practices.
   h. Securing placement for occupational experiences.

Farming and Off-Farm Agricultural Occupations—Some group instruction is needed by students who are deciding whether to enter farming or an off-farm agricultural occupation. This instruction is usually offered in beginning courses in agriculture and in courses for young, out-of-school adults. Some of the problem areas in this unit are as follows:

1. Determining types of farming.
2. Determining occupations requiring education in agriculture.
3. Understanding major qualifications for entering farming and various off-farm agricultural occupations.
4. Determining opportunities for becoming established in various types of farming.
5. Determining opportunities for becoming engaged in off-farm occupations requiring knowledge and skills in agriculture.
6. Evaluating tentative choices.
   a. Personal qualifications.
   b. Value of the occupation to society.
   c. Earnings (immediate and long-time).
   d. Security provided.
   e. Steps in becoming established.
   f. Education required, and cost.
   g. Experience required.
   h. Skills and abilities required.
   i. Safety of the occupation.
   j. Effect on health.
   k. Opportunities for recreation.
   l. Opportunities for family life.

m. Working conditions.
n. Retirement opportunities.
o. Living conditions.
p. Opportunities for becoming established.
q. Capital required for becoming established.

Evaluating tentative choices of occupations is of considerable importance. Young people need to think seriously and to consider many factors before choosing their occupations.

Agricultural Occupations Courses—Some schools offer one-semester courses in agricultural occupations as a means of providing group guidance regarding farming and off-farm agricultural occupations. Such courses may also provide students an opportunity to develop an understanding of agricultural problems.

Guidance in Young Adult Classes—A year-round program for young adults, continuing for four or more years, should contain many units of value in guidance. Most young adult groups are interested in considering more thoroughly the procedures in getting established in farming or in off-farm agricultural occupations, forming partnerships, obtaining capital, and obtaining and using credit.

New problems or more meaningful problems will develop regarding obtaining further education, participating in community affairs, and establishing a home. One of the most severe criticisms of most young adult programs is that no attention or inadequate attention is given to units of instruction which are of value in guidance. If more units related to choices and adjustments in becoming established in a career and in establishing a home were included in young adult programs, interest would probably increase materially.

Group Guidance Opportunities with Adults—Adult courses in agriculture may be taught so that they will have guidance value. The problem area on developing partnership agreements may be a part of an agriculture management course for adults. A discussion of wills may be a part of an adult course on agricultural law. Whole courses may be taught on topics such as expanding operations and planning programs so that the productive capacity of farms or agribusiness firms will be maintained for the children and the grandchildren of the operators.

Many of the problems of a parent, such as (1) how I can help my son or daughter grow into farming, (2) how I can help my son or daughter become established in an agricultural occupation, and (3) whether I should send my son or daughter to college, are discussed in meetings with parents of students enrolled in agriculture courses. For a more complete discussion of meetings for parents and how to organize them, see the section on meetings for parents in Chapter 15, "How to Develop Supervised Occupational Experience Programs in Agriculture."

COUNSELING

Definition—Counseling is a person-to-person, face-to-face relationship in which a counselor, a qualified or professionally trained person, helps individuals to make plans, to arrive at intelligent choices, and to adjust to situations by helping them learn about themselves and about the situation in which they find themselves. The interview is the basic technique of counseling. Counseling is one method of providing a guidance service for individuals.

Importance—The importance of counseling is indicated by the number of agencies and institutions that exist for providing all types of counseling services. We have in the schools and outside the schools vocational counselors, educational counselors, psychiatrists, business counselors, religious counselors, social workers, and visiting teachers. The fact that these counselors keep busy, often on a fee basis, indicates the importance of, and the need for, counseling services. Much of the work of a teacher involves counseling. Good teachers have always been considered counselors by their students. Some teachers do their most effective teaching on a person-to-person basis.

Some guidance problems may be recognized or even resolved through group guidance techniques. In many instances, however, individual counseling is required for resolving a situation satisfactorily. Counseling may also be necessary because of the nature or the individual character of a situation.

Agriculture Teachers' Responsibility—The vocational education in agriculture program has always recognized the importance and necessity of counseling by teachers. This is one of the reasons why teachers of agriculture are expected to visit homes and jobs, provide for supervised study in the classroom, and confer with individuals at school. Time is allotted for supervised study and in-school conferences, and mileage is usually paid for home and job visits. Supervised study, in-school conferences, home visits, and job visits provide opportunities for individual instruction and counseling. Problems involving plans, choices, and adjustments must be resolved before an individual is emotionally ready for instruction. Teachers of agriculture are also consulted by other teachers and agencies as a referral resource for vocational counseling regarding farming and off-farm occupations requiring knowledge and skills in agriculture.

Purpose of Counseling—Counseling is the person-to-person, formal consultation aspect of a guidance program. Its general objectives are the same as the objectives of the total guidance program of a school and the objectives of a school's department of agricultural education. Counselors are to assist individuals during private consultations to plan, make choices, and adjust to situations. Through counseling, it is possible for counselors to help individuals to learn about themselves, understand themselves, evaluate their personal objectives, and in other ways release tension. Counselors assist individuals in becoming intelligently self-directive.

Abilities Required—Teachers of agriculture, when performing the duties of counselors, need to have the ability to listen intently. Allowing counselees to talk about problem situations releases tensions and puts counselees into the correct mood for attacking their problems intelligently. Counselors must have the ability to view the problems of counselees objectively and not as judges. If counselees feel that counselors are blaming or criticizing, or will blame or criticize, they will be unwilling to work with the counselors in trying to solve their problems. Teachers acting as counselors must be able to guide conversations without appearing to be cross-examining the counselees or dictating the direction of the conversation.

Counselors need the ability to understand background information about counselees and to use this information unobtrusively in helping the counselees to understand themselves.

Some of the other abilities needed are:

1. The ability to start a conversation.
2. The ability to direct a conversation toward the guidance problems of counselees.
3. The ability to encourage constructive planning during interviews.

Knowledge Required—Teachers of agriculture need to know, understand, and be able to use effectively the principles and techniques of guidance and counseling. They need also to have some kinds of specialized knowledge which other teachers or counselors are not expected to have. They need information regarding the opportunities in farming and off-farm agricultural occupations in the community. They need to know the number of farms in the area, the average age of farmers, the farmers who intend to retire or leave farming in the next few years, the farmers who are looking for someone to take over their farming operations, the farmers who have no one to take over their farms when they quit farming, and the farmers who need hired help. They need similar information regarding all the other jobs in the area which require knowledge and skills in agriculture.

Teachers of agriculture need information regarding agricultural schools and colleges, forestry schools, and veterinary colleges. They need to use the referral agencies that counsel youth and adults regarding government regulations affecting agricultural workers. Referral of students to others who counsel regarding the rulings of governmental agencies relieves teachers of the responsibility of keeping informed regarding changes in regulations and of the responsibility of interpreting these changes to students.

Characteristics of Good Counselors—If teachers of agriculture expect to be successful as counselors, they must be approachable. One way of developing an approachable manner is by being consistently friendly. Teacher-counselors must be able to secure the confidence and respect of others. Emotional maturity is essential. Problems must be treated objectively but sympathetically. Teachers cannot allow themselves to become involved emotionally in the solution of problems.

Teacher-counselors must be interested in the welfare of the counselees and respect their point of view. One evidence of this respect and interest is a willingness to listen. Consistency of attitude and action is of considerable importance. Pleasing personal appearance is desirable. One of the most important characteristics needed for developing confidence and respect is the willingness to work unselfishly to assist others.

Techniques—Counselors cannot make plans, choices, and adjustments for counselees. Only the individuals can satisfactorily make them. If counselors attempt to dictate, the counselees will become resentful, and one more emotional block will be erected between the counselors and the counselees. Counselors instead assist individuals by (1) helping them to understand emotional blocks, (2) helping them to locate and define their problems, (3) encouraging them to define and analyze their goals, (4) encouraging them to form hypotheses and to think through their consequences, (5) supplying additional information, (6) arranging for tryouts of tentative choices whenever possible, and (7) encouraging them to plan their next steps carefully. Following is one example of a teacher of agriculture who did not follow these techniques:

> The teacher advised a state farmer to start farming immediately instead of going to college first. The student accepted the advice but later resented it and was dissatisfied with the decision. The student was told instead of being helped to think through the decision.

Successful counselors attempt to concentrate conversations on one problem at a time. They select and use words which counselees understand. They listen intently and are interested in the problems and in the comments of the counselees. They never lecture or talk down to counselees. When it is necessary for them to add information, they present only essential ideas and facts. They understand that no one can absorb or comprehend more than a few new ideas at one time. They try to understand the attitudes and feelings of counselees. They indicate by a simple comment that they understand these attitudes and feelings, but they refrain from passing judgment on their worth or correctness. Counselees are guided toward the realization that they are responsible for making final plans, choices, and adjustments. They are guided toward the realization that the counselors will assist them but that there is a limit to what they know or what they can do for them. Successful counselors conduct their conferences with individuals in private. These conferences are unhurried, but they do not drag on indefinitely.

In conducting conferences with individuals, teachers frequently encounter the following problems:

1. *Opening a discussion.*

   Teachers of agriculture must remember that adult or high school students may be ill at ease at the beginning of conferences. Courtesy and good manners will help "break the ice." The location and purpose of conferences will determine the approach. If conferences are initiated by counselees, a simple question such as, "What can I do for you today?" or, "What do you have on your mind?" will usually suffice. If conferences are on farms or jobs and are initiated by teachers, the conferences may be started with a question such as, "How has your work been going recently?" Teachers may then lead into the problem area by asking a question such as, "Have you done any thinking or planning about ____________ recently?" Such questions will usually relate the conversation to the problem to be discussed.

2. *Wandering off the subject.*

   It is occasionally necessary to lead counselees back to the subject if the conversation wanders. This can usually be accomplished by a statement such as, "Your previous statement was ____________," or by a question such as, "What was the last question we were discussing?" Counselors do not usually need to conceal the fact that attempts are being made to keep the conversation on the subject. Usually a conversation is unintentionally sidetracked.

3. *Obtaining background information.*

   Teachers of agriculture often need additional background information in counseling. In obtaining this information, they must exercise care that counselees do not get the impression that they are being cross-examined. It is usually not essential to obtain all needed information at once. If questions for additional information are spaced throughout a conference or over several conferences, resentment will be avoided.

4. *Wording questions.*

   Some teachers have difficulty wording their questions in counseling so that a conversation is generated or continued. Answers tend to stop a conversation. Questions may be worded so that a "yes" or "no" answer is impossible. For example, "What do you plan to do next regarding ____________________?"

5. *Putting words into counselees' mouths.*

   Often individuals have difficulty stating their problems, attitudes, and feelings. Counselors are often tempted to help them state their difficulties or make their comments. This is usually a mistake. Sympathetic statements of encouragement such as, "I see," or "I understand," while counselees are trying to express themselves, usually produce better results than attempts to state the difficulty or position for counselees.

6. *Promoting counselees' confidence.*

   The confidence of counselees has to be bolstered. A friendly, objective, sympathetic attitude will usually raise the confidence of counselees. An unhurried attitude is usually helpful. Sometimes one or two conferences devoted to "visiting" are necessary to develop the confidence of counselees in counselors. Teachers of agriculture seldom have this difficulty with their advanced students. It may occur, however, when teachers are working with referral cases and with new students.

7. *Allowing for silences.*

   Teachers often worry about periods of silence when counseling. Silence is often necessary for thinking. Counselors do not need to worry about periods of silence because a silence can always be broken with a question.

8. *Breaking bad news.*

   Sometimes teachers have to feed into a conference information which is bad news to the counselee, such as the difficulty of obtaining placement on a farm or in a certain occupation requiring knowledge and skills in agriculture. If a conference is to be of value and if the counselee is to make sound plans, choices, and adjustments, all the facts must be honestly considered. There is no place for wishful thinking in a counseling conference.

9. *Dealing with lack of information.*

   Teacher-counselors are not expected to have all the necessary information for helping individuals resolve all types of problems. Counselors should not bluff. The teacher-counselors and the counselees may work together to find the information required, or the individuals may be referred to other counselors or agencies that have the information required.

10. *Promoting thinking.*

    Counseling involves the supplying of information, but primarily it promotes thinking. When persons are emotionally upset, it is sometimes difficult for them to think. Counselors need to help individuals analyze and evaluate their feelings, attitudes, and problems. Sometimes counselors may promote a sounder evaluation of them by reflecting attitudes or feelings back to the persons. If students indicate by their comments that they believe with reservations that they should enroll in college, the teacher may comment, "You feel then that you should go to college, but you are not sure because ____________________." Then the students are able to see the reflection of their attitudes and can often begin to think objectively about their problems.

Thinking may be promoted by the asking of questions so that counselees will locate and define their problems; develop goals; formulate, try out, and revise hypotheses; and plan next steps.

11. *Initiating action.*

Planning the next steps is often neglected in counseling. For example, it is not enough to decide to obtain certain experiences in animal nutrition in a supervised occupational experience program. Plans must also be made for these occupational experiences.

12. *Summarizing counseling conferences.*

For best results, conferences should be summarized at their conclusion. It is usually best for the counselees to summarize conferences. Counselors may promote these summaries by asking, "What have we accomplished in our discussion today?" or, "What have we decided today?"

13. *Ending conferences with individuals.*

The summaries of conferences are usually sufficient to indicate to counselees that the conferences have been completed. Counselors must be careful not to proceed with summaries before the counselees have reached some decisions, but counselors must be careful to protect their time by preventing conferences from "dragging on" just because counselees want to talk. Conferences on farms or jobs may be ended easily because the teachers, rather than the counselees, are the ones to leave.

Ethics for Counselors—Counselors become acquainted with the personal attitudes, feelings, and business problems of their counselees. Most of these matters are presented to teachers of agriculture in confidence. Counselees in giving this information are confident that the teacher-counselors will not reveal, or allow anyone else to have, this information. Teachers may be tempted to tell about counseling experiences at home, at social gatherings, or in class meetings. This is a betrayal of confidence. Shop talk about counseling experiences with others is dangerous and unethical. The best rule is not to talk about counseling experiences at all and to safeguard records carefully.

Records of Counseling Interviews—The counseling activities of teachers of agriculture usually involve many conferences with counselees over a period of years. Memory is not infallible from conference to conference. Some record keeping system is essential. Teachers should develop a system. Some counselors keep notes of the following items for each conference:

1. Problems recognized by the counselee.
2. Basic feelings and attitudes discovered.
3. Changes in plans, attitudes, and feelings since the last conference.
4. Problems discovered during the conference.
5. Plans developed during the conference.
6. Objectives of the counselor.

Follow-up—Changes in people involving attitudes and feelings are slow. Since many of the problems considered in counseling involve adjustments in attitudes and feelings, it is usually impossible to resolve these problems in one conference. If one conference is worthwhile, it is also worthwhile to follow up the conference to check progress. Follow-up may be continued in a number of ways. It may be done through another conference during the school day, during a supervised study period, or during a home or job visit. It may be possible to discover results of a conference during class instruction. Written work and behavior are also often good indications of the results of conferences. Supervision of occupational experience programs provides many opportunities for follow-up. Young farmer instruction provides many opportunities for follow-up of counseling done during the period the young farmer was in high school.

Improving Counseling Skills—Most teachers of agriculture receive little or no training in counseling. Skill in counseling must be learned on the job. Developing any skill involves practice, correction of mistakes, and more practice. Evaluation is necessary for teachers to discover mistakes. Evaluation of counseling techniques is difficult but not impossible. Independent study of the literature relating to counseling is a form of evaluation. It is a source of ideas which may be checked against present practices. Experimentation with techniques involves evaluation and is one way of improving skills in counseling.

Some counselors analyze each conference in writing. This is usually an effective self-evaluation device.

PLACEMENT

Vocational education in agriculture has always recognized establishment in farming or an off-farm occupation requiring knowledge and skills in agriculture as a primary objective. Placement is a part of establishment, and placing students is a guidance service. Opportunities for placement are few in many communities, and often these few opportunities in a community are not known to the teachers of agriculture. If a vocational education in agriculture program is to be effective in assisting its students in establishment in gainful employment, steps must be taken to find out about the opportunities in agriculture in the community. A teacher of agriculture needs to know how a renter is selected when a farm in the community becomes available to rent. The teacher needs to know who owns the land for rent, who is planning to quit farming, who needs hired help, who has land for sale, who does custom work, and who has custom work to be done. If farm managers operate in a community, the teacher needs to be personally acquainted with them. If the teachers in a department have this type of information, farm managers, landowners, and persons trying to become established will seek their advice.

A teacher of agriculture also needs to have information regarding the placement opportunities in off-farm agriculturally oriented businesses and services. All teachers should become personally acquainted with the managers and personnel directors of the off-farm agriculturally oriented businesses in the community.

Studying a Community—Studying a community to discover opportunities for placement should be continuous; however, it may be systematized so that it is not burdensome. Periodically a survey may be made of the agricultural opportunities in a community. This survey will provide information about the placement situation in a community and also inform the public of the department's interest in placement. Young farmers and high school youth may conduct surveys of this type. Since they are interested in establishment, helping with the survey is of considerable educational value to them. For information on how to conduct surveys, see Chapter 39. The following forms are designed to obtain information regarding agricultural opportunities, both on and off the farm. Form 25.3 is designed to obtain the farming intentions of present farmers. This information is useful in predicting the farms that will become available in a community.

Form 25.3. Farming Intentions

Age ________ Years a farm operator ________ Acres ________

Owner ________ Tenant ________ Part owner ________

Do you plan to continue farming for more than five more years? Yes ______ No ______ Undecided ______

If the answer is no, when do you plan to quit? One year ______ Two years ______ Three years ______ Four years ______ Five years ______

If you intend to continue farming, do you intend to farm the same acreage ________, an increased acreage ________, a decreased acreage ________?

Do you intend to increase your livestock production ________, decrease your livestock production ________?

Owners only

When you retire do you expect to continue ownership of your farm? Yes ______ No ______

Do you have a relative in mind to take over when you retire? Yes ______ No ______

Do you have anyone else definitely in mind to take over the farm? Yes ______ No ______

Form 25.4 is designed to obtain from farm managers and landlords information regarding the probable number of farms they will have for rent during the next five-year period and the qualifications required of the renters of these farms.

The use of Form 25.5 will provide information regarding farm labor needs and the supply of farm labor, in addition to information concerning the probable future supply of farms. Information regarding labor needs is of value in helping students to obtain work as hired laborers. It also has guidance value in developing students' supervised occupational experience programs.

Form 25.6 is designed to obtain an indication of the opportunities in a community for placement in off-farm occupations requiring knowledge and skills in agriculture. This type of information is of special value in communities with a surplus of young people who cannot be absorbed in farming.

Form 25.7 is also designed to obtain an indication of the opportunities in a community for placement in off-farm occupations requiring knowledge and skills in agriculture. It is for use with persons in agricultural industries, businesses, and professions.

Form 25.4. Data Sheet for Farm Managers and Landlords

How many farms do you own or manage? ________

Approximately how many farms do you have to rent in a five-year period? ________

Approximately how many farms do you estimate you will have to rent in the next five years? ________

Do you give preference, all other things being equal, to tenants who have received agricultural education in school? ________

What are the requirements for becoming a tenant on one of your farms?

1. ________
2. ________
3. ________
4. ________

Form 25.5. Labor Needs and Supply

Age ________ Years a farm operator ________ Acres ________

Owner ________ Tenant ________ Part owner ________

Present Labor Situation and Needs

Time Period Involved	Months of Labor	
	All Family	Hired
Last year (actual)		
Last year (needed)		
Needs in five years		

Future Supply of Labor

During the next five years, how many children will you have that will become old enough to do farm work? ________

How many will likely remain on the farm? ________

How many of your children now doing farm work will likely be leaving the farm in the next five years? ________

How many children do you have in the armed forces? ________

How many of these will return to farming? ________

How many children do you have working off the farm one-half time or more? ________

How many of these will return to the farm full-time? ________

How many of these children growing into farming, working on the farm at present, and returning to the farm will need some special education or training? ________

What special kinds of education or training should they have? ________

Form 25.6. Opportunities in Off-Farm Agricultural Occupations[1]

Data Sheet for Farmers

Age ________ Years a farm operator ________ Acres ________

Owner ________ Tenant ________ Part owner ________ Farm worker ________

Farm Services

Please indicate the number of additional persons who might be used in the community in supplying services to farm persons. Include the number needed for replacement, for expansion, and for starting new services. Define "community" carefully as to area and number of farm families to be served.

Services	No. of Persons	Check[2]
Storage locker service		
Canning and dehydrating service		
Veterinary service		
Farm record and income tax service		
Landscaping service		
Cow testing and dairy herd improvement service		
Sow testing service		
Soil testing service		
Hatchery service		
Grinding and feed mixing service		
Seed cleaning service (treating)		
Sheep shearing service		
Custom fruit spraying, pruning, etc., service		
Soil conservation and erosion control service		
Farm machinery repair service		
Auto, truck, and tractor mechanics service		
Rural electrician service		
Farm building service		
Carpentry service		
Masonry and cement work service		
Plumbing service		
Livestock trucking service		
Limestone trucking service		
General trucking service		
Custom machine operation service		
Oil and gas service		
Delivery service		
Sawmill worker service		
Grain elevator worker service		
Cream, poultry, and egg dealer service		
Cooperative service (list types)		
Artificial insemination service		
Dead animal disposal service		
Implement dealer and employee service		
Lumber dealer and employee service		
Seed, feed, and fertilizer dealer and employee service		
Hardware store and employee service		

(Continued)

Form 25.6 (Continued)

Modernizing[3]			*Remodeling and Repairing*[4]		
Type or Kind	Amount or Size	Percentage of the Labor to Be Supplied from the Farm	Type or Kind	Amount or Size	Percentage of the Labor to Be Supplied from the Farm

New Buildings			*Land Improvement*[5]		
Type or Kind	Amount or Size	Percentage of the Labor to Be Supplied from the Farm	Type or Kind	Amount or Size	Percentage of the Labor to Be Supplied from the Farm

[1]Data sheet for determining need for labor on farms in the next few years for constructing new buildings; repairing, remodeling, and modernizing existing buildings; improving the land; and so forth.

[2]Check the services you would like to see established in the community.

[3]Examples of modernizing: installation of furnace, running water, sewage system, wiring, toilet and bath, stanchions in cow barn, etc.

[4]Examples of remodeling and repairing: installing new roofs, painting, etc.

[5]Examples of land improvement: fencing; fertilization; application of lime; construction of grass waterways, dams, and terraces; ditching; etc.

Form 25.7. Opportunities for Persons with Agricultural Education in Agricultural Industries, Businesses, and Professions

Type of business ____________________

How many persons do you employ? ____________

How many persons do you need? ____________

How many persons do you estimate you will need in five years' time if we experience neither depression nor inflation? ____________

How many of your employees have had experience in farming? ____________

How many of your employees have had some special education or training? ____________

What kinds of education or training should they have? ____________

____

Do you have any employees that should have additional education in agriculture?

Yes ________ No ________ How many? ____________

Information may also be obtained regarding farming and other agricultural business opportunities in a community from census and other available data. From data on hand, it should be possible to calculate for a community:

1. Average age of farmers and other agricultural workers.
2. Average size of farms and other agricultural businesses.
3. Number of farms and number of agricultural businesses.

The advisory council for an agriculture department may be used to collect and study data about the agricultural opportunities in a community. It also may help in interpreting the data collected in surveys and the data secured from other sources.

Classroom Instruction—Much of the assistance related to placement problems may be given adult farmers, young farmers, workers in off-farm agricultural occupations, and high school students through classroom instruction. Much of the class instruction in a program for young adults may properly be related to the problems of placement. Young adults enjoy and appreciate an opportunity to discuss the following problem areas related to placement:

1. Becoming acquainted with placement opportunities.
2. Understanding methods of becoming established in farming and off-farm agricultural occupations.
3. Developing partnership agreements.
4. Developing desirable leases.
5. Making applications to landlords or farm managers for farms which are available for renting; applying for jobs.
6. Understanding opportunities for vertical and horizontal expansion on home farms.
7. Protecting against risks.
8. Obtaining capital.
9. Accumulating equipment.
10. Obtaining and using credit.
11. Participating in the social and organizational life of a community.
12. Expanding farming programs.

Many opportunities develop through the supervised occupational experience programs of high school students for classroom instruction related to the problems of placement. Some of the problem areas related to placement which are commonly discussed in high school classes are as follows:

1. Choosing an occupation.
2. Growing into farming or another occupation requiring knowledge and skills in agriculture through a supervised occupational experience program.
3. Developing agreements in a supervised occupational experience program.
4. Becoming acquainted with placement opportunities.
5. Understanding how previous agriculture students became established in an agricultural occupation.
6. Obtaining and using credit.
7. Developing a favorable reputation in a community.

Placement for Farm Experience—Since students in agricultural education are often engaged in farming activities, the problem of placement for farm experience is not great. However, students living on small farms or in urban areas may need to be placed on farms for tryout experiences or for more extended experiences. Often students living on farms desire to engage in specialized types of farming. Many times the best guidance service for these individuals is to help them obtain part-time jobs on specialized farms for tryout experiences. For more details on placement for farm experience, see the sections on this topic in Chapter 14, "What Are Supervised Occupational Experience Programs in Agriculture?" and Chapter 40, "How to Evaluate and Test in a High School Program."

Counseling About Placement—If teachers of agriculture study the placement problems in their communities and take an interest in helping their students, they will be called upon often for help. Young adults and high school students will routinely seek their advice. If they try to help them become established, it will not be long until landowners and managers of off-farm agricultural businesses will be seeking their advice regarding prospective renters and employees.

In counseling persons who are seeking assistance in obtaining farms or jobs, teachers must be careful that they remain counselors and do not become givers of advice. They will be asked by landlords and farm managers about persons who wish to rent farms. They must give them honest help. One way of giving information about prospective farmers to landlords and farm managers is to describe how the individuals under consideration have reacted under various situations and to let the landlords or farm managers form their own conclusions. This procedure is usually superior to offering personal opinions of the qualifications of various individuals. In counseling prospective farmers regarding landlords or farm managers, teachers may use the same procedure. Teachers, in counseling regarding placement, cannot afford to have favorites, either employers or employees. The objective of counseling about placement should be successful placement and not just placement.

Clearinghouse on Placement—A department of agriculture may serve as a clearinghouse for those with opportunities to offer in agricultural occupations and for those looking for opportunities in agricultural occupations. A department may arrange for the two groups to get together.

To start such a clearinghouse, a department needs to let its community know that it has students who are trying to become established in agricultural occupations. Gradually those persons in a community who have opportunities to offer will learn that the department can serve as a clearinghouse. This process develops more rapidly when the teacher or teachers of agriculture in a department contact landlords, farm managers, prospective landlords, and agricultural businesses and inform them about students who are looking for opportunities in agricultural occupations.

A department of vocational education in agriculture should serve as a placement clearinghouse both for off-farm agriculturally oriented occupations and for farming.

EVALUATING A GUIDANCE PROGRAM

The principles of evaluation found in Chapter 39, "How to Evaluate a Program of Education in Agriculture," Chapter 40, "How to Evaluate and Test in a High School Program," and Chapter 41, "How to Evaluate Programs for

Form 25.8. Occupational Record of Vocational Student After Leaving School

Name ______________________________ Address ______________________________
(Last) (First) (Middle)

Change of address and dates ______________________, ______________, ______________

Year	At Home with Definite or Indefinite Allowance	Farm Laborer with Specific Wages		At Home with Income from One or More Enterprises	Partner in a Farm Business		Renter and Operator of a Farm	Owner and Operator of a Farm	Manager of the Farm of Another Party	Other Status	Type of Farm	Size (Acres)	Other Occupation Requiring Knowledge and Skills in Agriculture (Give Job)	Continuation of Education					Non-agriculture Occupation (Give Job)
		At Home	Away from Home		At Home	Away from Home								Preparatory	Supplemental	Agricultural College	Other College	Other	
1	2	3	4	5	6	7	8	9	10	11	12	13	14	15	16	17	18	19	20
19—																			

Young and Older Adults," apply in the evaluation of a guidance program. These chapters indicate the methods of evaluating individual growth which will not, therefore, be described again.

Some special system or program is necessary for following up individuals to obtain a long-time view of the guidance activities of a department. If a school has designated guidance personnel, they may adequately handle this follow-up program. Some teachers of agriculture, however, are employed in schools with few special guidance personnel. Interviews or mailed questionnaires are often used to find out how former students and graduates are carrying out their choices, plans, and adjustments. The purposes of this type of follow-up by a department are (1) to ascertain the need for further assistance to former students, (2) to obtain information that will be useful in improving the instructional and guidance program of the department, and (3) to obtain value opinions from the former students regarding the guidance program of the department.

PART

Conducting Post-secondary and Adult Education in Agriculture

CHAPTER

26

How to Conduct Technical Education Programs in Community Colleges and Technical Institutes

---

NEED

Most occupations are becoming more complex and technical. To be successful in them often requires considerable technical knowledge, skill, and understanding. The occupations in production agriculture, agribusiness, and renewable natural resources are not exceptions. These occupations each year are requiring personnel with increasing technical knowledge and skill in agriculture. A large percentage of the jobs in the off-farm sector require education in agriculture beyond the secondary school level. Most production agriculture, or farm and ranch work, involving large-scale operations requires workers with education in agriculture beyond the secondary school level.

Fortunately, both employers and prospective employees for agribusiness and renewable natural resources recognize the need for relevant education in agriculture beyond the secondary school level. As relevant, practical, and realistic technical education in agriculture programs are established at the post-secondary level, employers in agribusiness and renewable natural resources are depending on the graduates of these programs for their new and replacement employees.

Persons interested in employment in production agriculture, agribusiness, and renewable natural resources are also recognizing, in increasing numbers, the need for post-secondary technical education in agriculture and are seeking opportunities to enroll in relevant and practical technical education in agriculture.

ESSENTIAL CHARACTERISTICS OF A PROGRAM

An essential characteristic of technical education in agriculture at the post-secondary level is that it prepares students for immediate entry into certain jobs or clusters of jobs in production agriculture, agribusiness, and renewable natural resources. A program or course of study for a certain job or cluster of jobs must realistically prepare workers for the job or job cluster. This necessitates a clear understanding by program planners of the knowledge and skills required. Since most post-secondary institutions offer several programs or curriculums in agriculture for different jobs or job clusters, it is often impossible for the program or curriculum planners to have sufficient firsthand and up-to-date knowledge of the requirements of the jobs or job clusters. Advisory committees of employees and employers in the jobs or job clusters need to be used so that relevant and realistic programs or curriculums are established and kept up-to-date.

In post-secondary education in agriculture, it must be assumed that the students will enter the world of work immediately upon completing the program and will not need further experience or class work. In secondary education in agriculture, this is not the situation. At the secondary level, it must be assumed that a large percentage of the students will need and seek further specialized or technical education in agriculture and root disciplines before employment.

All programs or curriculums at the post-secondary technical education level need to provide supervised occupational experience on the job. This means that each student will have a placement experience on a job where he/she works under the close supervision of an experienced worker and with overall supervision of an instructor from the post-secondary institution. The placement experience needs to be planned so that it will provide a training program for the student. It needs to be designed to provide firsthand, actual work experience with all or most of the tasks involved in the job. It must be designed so that it is not repetitive. If it is repetitive, the student will not receive the breadth of experiences necessary to learn to handle the various tasks involved in a job. Often one-third to one-half of the time in a curriculum is needed for placement experience.

At the post-secondary level, a student is often placed on a job as a learner in an agribusiness or a natural resource firm on a full-time basis for a quarter or semester at a time. Part-time placement in a job, permitting a student to enroll in courses that meet regularly on campus, is not often permitted.

In post-secondary technical education in agribusiness and natural resources, the courses provided must emphasize the knowledge and understandings needed without slighting the teaching of the skills needed for a job or cluster of jobs. A post-secondary curriculum should produce students who have the knowledge and skills necessary for effective performance of a job, plus the theory necessary to explain the knowledge and skills.

Information supplied at the post-secondary level should be given in a way that it can be generalized to other situations. The best way to teach for generalization is to base instruction on real problems related to the job.

TYPES OF PROGRAMS

As indicated in the section on essential characteristics of technical education at the post-secondary level for production agriculture, agribusiness, and renewable natural resources, it is not sufficient or adequate to offer a general curriculum in agriculture. This is not what is needed. Specialized programs are needed for specific job clusters in agriculture. The types of programs needed depend to a considerable extent on the types of agricultural jobs available in a 50- to 100-mile radius of the post-secondary institution. However, for certain essential and critical jobs requiring technical education but offering limited employment opportunities, one institution may offer the program for a whole state or for several states.

Programs should be of varying lengths, from a few weeks to 24 months. The length of a program for preparing persons for a certain cluster of jobs should be dependent on the requirements of the occupation. A program should not be any longer than necessary to prepare technically a worker with the knowledge, skills, and theory necessary for successful work performance.

Curriculums for many occupations might be geared to the eight broad agriculture areas with spinoff options in the later part of the educational period for more narrow job preparation. These eight curriculums are:

1. Agricultural Supply.
2. Agricultural Marketing.
3. Agriculture Mechanics.
4. Agricultural Processing.
5. Ornamental Horticulture.
6. Agricultural Production Management.
7. Forestry.
8. Natural Resource Management.

In some post-secondary institutions, it might also be desirable to have certain specialized curriculums that are spinoff options of the preceding eight broad curriculums. An example of such a curriculum is horse science. As one example, this curriculum might prepare persons for horseshoeing. Another example, which would be appropriate in some areas, is wood technology. Other examples are animal laboratory technology and meat cutting.

Following are some of the curriculums or types of programs found in post-secondary institutions, such as technical colleges, community colleges, and junior colleges. These curriculums may be separate programs or spinoff options of broader based curriculums.

1. Agricultural Equipment Technology.
2. Agricultural Business Management (off-farm).
3. Turf Management Technology.
4. Crop Genetics Technology.
5. Animal Laboratory Technology.
6. Floriculture Technology.
7. Landscaping Technology.
8. Greenhouse Technology.
9. Fertilizer Production Technology.
10. Fertilizer Sales and Application Technology.
11. Agricultural Construction and Maintenance Technology.
12. Food Processing Technology.

13. Nursery Operation and Management Technology.
14. Arboriculture Technology.
15. Non-food Agriculture Processing Technology.
16. Agricultural Automation Technology.
17. Production Agriculture Technology.
18. Feed Processing Technology.
19. Soil Conservation Technology.
20. Horse Science Technology.
21. Agricultural Chemicals Technology.
22. Environmental Quality Technology.
23. Wildlife Technology.
24. Forestry Technology.
25. Forest Protection Technology.
26. Water Management Technology.
27. Wood Utilization Technology.
28. Range Management Technology.
29. Fish and Fishing Technology.
30. Natural Resource Recreational Technology.
31. Agriculture Related Tourism Technology.

CHARACTERISTICS OF STUDENTS

Post-secondary students in technical institutes, community colleges, and junior colleges are usually persons who have decided on the occupational technology area in which they want to work. They may select another occupational area later, but for the present they are committed. They are going to school for a purpose. Their educational program has meaning for them, and they insist on relevant, realistic courses and experiences. Because of their commitment to preparation for employment in a certain occupational area, they want to learn; they are willing to put forth much effort and will not tolerate poor teaching for very long. They insist that their teachers know the content area they teach and the ways to teach efficiently and effectively. They are often more dedicated, serious, and mature than persons of an equivalent age who have not made an occupational choice.

Teachers teaching such students must continuously help them to relate what they are learning to the occupations for which they are preparing. When this is done adequately, they are a joy to teach.

ORGANIZING PROGRAMS

In organizing programs, individuals must first determine the need for each program. Is there a demand at present for well prepared persons in the occupation? If the demand is not present, will it develop if well qualified persons are prepared? In other words, is the lack of demand due to the fact that in the past there has been no supply? Will the demand continue? Will the demand increase? These last two questions relate to the continuation and development of the type of agribusiness the curriculum or program is designed to serve.

A survey is often used to determine answers relating to the need for a program or a curriculum. A survey is usually needed, but it is not sufficient to determine need. An advisory committee of employers in the program area being considered is needed. Such a committee can be used to help design the survey questions and obtain acceptance for the conduct of the survey. Most important, it can be used to interpret the results from the survey.

The committee can also be used to answer questions regarding demand or need for a curriculum, which are very difficult to include in a survey instrument. If a committee is representative of all employers, it is especially helpful in answering questions such as (1) "Will demand for well qualified workers increase if they are prepared?" and (2) "Is the demand for such workers increasing or decreasing?"

If a need for a program is established, the second task is to design a curriculum. This requires the establishment of measurable behavioral objectives. Again a representative advisory committee is essential. This advisory committee should be composed of both employers and employees. It should advise regarding the knowledge and skills prospective workers must acquire if they are to be successful performers on the job.

The final task is to obtain facilities, organize courses, provide placement experiences, obtain teachers, and enroll students. These are relatively mechanical steps. The first two tasks are the crucial ones.

ON-THE-JOB TRAINING

In technical education in agriculture, an essential ingredient of the program is on-the-job placement for training. It is difficult to imagine a successful program to prepare persons for successful entry into a specialized job that does not utilize on-the-job placement for training. And this on-the-job placement for training should be of a relatively long duration.

(Photo from Jasper Lee, Mississippi)

Fig. 26.1. Students inspecting turf at a retail garden center.

A partial list of the objectives of this portion of the technical education in agriculture program follows:

1. To provide students with practical and realistic experiences related to the theoretical content of the program.
2. To help students develop the abilities, attitudes, and knowledge for successful adjustment when they cease being students and become workers.
3. To help students become aware of the mobility of labor, the societal pressures in the world of work, and the continuing need to upgrade abilities and skills.
4. To assist students in the process of refining their career goals.
5. To help students develop work habits necessary for success in the world of work.
6. To teach students those details relating to knowledge and skills which are almost impossible to teach except on a job.

Organization—It is an institution's responsibility to organize and supervise the on-the-job placement for training. It is an integral part of the total educational program. This task is usually assigned to one or more teachers in a program. The responsibility consists of the following tasks:

1. Developing instructional content to inform students of the importance of the on-job training experiences and the procedures to be followed in implementing this phase of their educational program.
2. Informing agribusiness firms regarding the program, its purpose and importance, and the procedures related to its operation.
3. Selecting cooperating firms and obtaining their cooperation.
4. Developing a written memorandum of agreement with the firms that will be involved in the program. This memorandum of agreement should relate to the objectives of the program, the type of training to be provided, supervision to be provided, pay of the student, records to be kept, and so forth.

Agribusiness firms are often not accustomed to working with schools in educational endeavors. Therefore, considerable instruction needs to be provided in group meetings and individually prior to and during an on-the-job training period.

Advisory Committees—Each technical education program in agriculture should utilize an advisory committee of employers and employees. If unions and trade associations are involved, they should be represented on the advisory committee. A very important task of this committee is to advise regarding the organization and conduct of the on-job training program. It should be asked to advise regarding:

1. Publicity in relation to the program.
2. Recruitment of firms to provide occupational experiences for students.
3. Selection of firms in which students will be placed.
4. Contents of the memorandum of understanding between the institution and the firm.
5. Contents of the training plan agreement to be developed by the student, firm, and school.
6. Observation, supervision, and evaluation of the student.

Training Agreement—Each student placed for on-the-job training should have a training agreement developed cooperatively by the student, the firm where the work is to be done, and the institution. This agreement should indicate in some detail what the student agrees to do, what the firm agrees to do, and what the institution agrees to do. The agreement should indicate pay and hours of work involved. It should indicate the progression of work experiences to be provided so that the student will obtain the breadth of experience needed. Busywork and excessive repetitive activities need to be avoided to the extent possible. The training plan should indicate the records to be kept, the supervision to be provided by both the firm and the institution, and the federal, state, and local laws and regulations to be observed.

Teacher Responsibility—The teacher who is responsible for organizing, conducting, and supervising the on-the-job phase of the total technical education program needs allocated time to do the job. It is an essential and critical job for the success of any technical education in agriculture program. Arrangements need to be made for applications by students for on-the-job training. Although on-the-job training should not be an optional part of a curriculum, applications are needed to provide background information regarding each student. This background information should be provided to the employer. An application is needed to determine interests and desires of the student so that a good job can be done in placing the student in an appropriate firm and with an appropriate employer.

A teacher-coordinator also needs to keep the school, the students, and the cooperating firms informed regarding federal, state, and local laws and regulations relating to employment of students. These should also include the regulations of local unions and trade associations.

For additional information regarding supervised occupational experience programs see Chapter 14, "What Are Supervised Occupational Experience Programs in Agriculture?"; Chapter 15, "How to Develop Supervised Occupational Experience Programs in Agriculture"; and Chapter 16, "How to Conduct Off-Farm Supervised Occupational Experience Programs."

Courses and Competencies—A technical education curriculum for a certain cluster of jobs in agriculture needs to contain the courses that will develop the competencies necessary for successful performance in these jobs. Most institutions provide course credit for the on-the-job training portion of the curriculum. Careful attention needs to be given to the total spectrum of competencies needed. It is not enough to consider only the agricultural knowledge and skills needed. The competencies related to utilizing the knowledge and skills on a job also need to be developed. In agricultural supply businesses, many employees need specialized communication abilities related to the agricultural products they are handling or distributing. Special sales abilities, for example, may be needed.

Following is a list of competencies found to be desirable, and which should be taught at the post-secondary level, adapted from a research study by David Williams. These competencies relate to employees in agricultural supply firms. These are in addition to the basic agricultural knowledge usually identified:[1]

1. Understanding how human relations factors influence the way an employee works with present and potential customers of an agricultural supply firm.

---

[1]Williams, David L., *A Competency Pattern Approach to Curriculum Development in Agribusiness*, Interim Report No. 1, Project No. PDC-A1-043, Agricultural Education Division, Department of Vocational and Technical Education, University of Illinois, Urbana–Champaign, 50 pp.

2. Ability to build sound working relationships in "forced" associations.
3. Understanding the function of reports.
4. Ability to make out and file written reports.
5. Ability to help customers fill out credit application forms.
6. Ability to plan and conduct an educational meeting for an agricultural forum.
7. Ability to determine which type of meeting is most effective for a given product or group of products.
8. Ability to interpret merchandise guarantees and directions to customers.
9. Ability to interpret and explain time payment principles that apply to various credit arrangements.
10. Ability to study specific information in ads and use advertised facts effectively in selling.
11. Understanding the credit policies, terms, and credit plans of the firm.
12. Ability to use the terminology and develop a vocabulary descriptive of the product or service being sold.
13. Understanding why customers have different needs.
14. Understanding that brand or trade names are an advertising device used to encourage customer retention.
15. Ability to anticipate the needs of present and potential customers.
16. Understanding the methods of financing sales.
17. Ability to translate technical words concerning an item of merchandise into customer's language.
18. Understanding that the effects of underselling are often as harmful as the effects of overselling.
19. Understanding how to employ season or storewide themes in department displays.
20. Ability to select merchandise for advertising that is seasonal and timely.
21. Understanding that one must read newspaper advertising in order to keep informed of the advertising done by one's own store and its competitors.
22. Understanding that the available quantities of advertised merchandise should be checked before an ad runs.
23. Understanding that advertising helps stabilize volume by maintaining customer interest during a slow selling period.
24. Understanding the ways in which past advertisements can be helpful in planning future ads.
25. Ability to develop effective advertising, demonstrating, and other promotional procedures.
26. Understanding the values of advertising information to the salesperson.
27. Understanding how to obtain maximum customer exposure to merchandise by arranging temporary displays in other than normal department locations.
28. Ability to use known media effectively in advertising.
29. Understanding that special customer services and accommodations build customer good will and help increase sales.
30. Understanding that when purchasing display supplies or fixtures, one must consider the store's image.
31. Ability to take advantage of promotion and advertising offered by the supplier.
32. Understanding that adequate merchandise information will build customer confidence in the merchandise as well as in the store.
33. Ability to use periodicals, direct media, sign media, and radio and television broadcasting in promotional advertising.
34. Ability to select advertising media best suited to the product, merchandise, or service being advertised.
35. Understanding the methods used to determine needs of customers.
36. Understanding the meaning of the purchasing function and its objectives related to a firm.
37. Ability to use standards and specifications in buying.
38. Understanding that the purchasing function includes more than buying.
39. Understanding how the retailing aids offered by the supplier affect the choice of a vendor.
40. Ability to find information needed to compare related suppliers.

41. Understanding the importance of affiliation in selecting a supplier.
42. Ability to determine stock quantities necessary for seasonal or year-round selling.
43. Understanding the role of insurance in an agricultural firm.
44. Ability to determine the proper time for purchasing additional products for the firm.
45. Understanding how purchasing functions may vary among different types of firms.
46. Ability to keep records of merchandise sold by classification—use of ticket stubs or special forms.
47. Understanding the advantages of consolidating purchasing in a firm.
48. Ability to determine the price of merchandise being purchased in a lesser quantity than originally multiple-priced.
49. Ability to compute accurately employee discounts, delivery charges, etc., when computing sales.
50. Understanding livestock and crop prices and price trends.
51. Understanding the intrafirm competition between products.
52. Understanding that merchandise guarantees and sanctions protect both the customer and the store, and help increase sales.
53. Understanding the use of purchase orders, shipping statements, and invoices used to process the products coming into the firm.
54. Ability to record the transfer of merchandise or stock to branch stores to prevent inventory shortages.
55. Understanding that unit inventory control systems must be kept up-to-date if they are to be useful in planning and making purchases.
56. Understanding the uses of the information available from unit inventory control systems.
57. Understanding the nature of standards and specifications and the reasons for their use.
58. Ability to recognize that different organizational patterns exist.
59. Understanding the ways to handle special orders of merchandise for customers.
60. Ability to analyze customer demand.
61. Understanding the store's procedures for recording markups and markdowns.
62. Understanding the various pricing techniques and policies used in the firm.
63. Understanding the laws affecting the sale and distribution of agricultural products.
64. Understanding how various activities within the firm are related to the purchasing function.
65. Ability to determine in various situations the most efficient way to get the job accomplished.
66. Understanding federal wage and hour laws.
67. Understanding that although management plans expense control budgets, the actual control must be carried out by the cooperative effort of all employees.
68. Understanding the major techniques used in determining advancement and promotions.
69. Ability to evaluate the compensation, incentives, and benefits offered by one employer and to compare them to those of another.
70. Ability to handle slow payers or noncollectable credit accounts tactfully.
71. Understanding the role of labor unions.
72. Understanding how labor laws and labor unions affect agricultural firms.
73. Understanding what is involved in the pricing of individual items.
74. Understanding the different methods of bill collection used by agricultural firms.
75. Ability to differentiate between the primary and secondary products and services of the firm.
76. Ability to follow procedures for reporting and handling damaged merchandise.
77. Understanding the marketing trends of farm products.
78. Ability to fill out credit instruments properly.
79. Ability to determine the proper quantity of a product to purchase.

80. Understanding state and federal regulations related to the product.
81. Understanding of governmental agricultural programs and their effect on sales and collections.
82. Understanding that standardization provides a base upon which grading can be determined and helps customers by providing guaranteed services to fit their needs.
83. Understanding current merchandise, trends, and product innovations.
84. Ability to explore the community for new or additional service.
85. Ability to determine the market area situation of the firm.
86. Understanding that labels taking the form of tags, stamps, wrappers, etc., identify products as to their contents.
87. Ability to determine prices for the products and services of the firm.
88. Understanding the value and limitations of using computers in a firm.
89. Understanding that manufacturer representatives are a source of market, merchandise, and product information and consumer information.
90. Ability to keep informed of competitive conditions in the market area served by the firm.
91. Ability to keep up-to-date on trends through trade journals and central buying office aids.
92. Ability to make effective use of current trends in sales, customer buying habits, and styles.
93. Understanding the significant segments of the purchasing function.
94. Ability to determine the demand of products based upon seasonality.
95. Ability to participate effectively in devising a coordinated plan of action for selling.
96. Ability to evaluate suppliers on the basis of the business services they offer.
97. Understanding the policies of suppliers relative to the return of slow-moving merchandise.
98. Ability to recognize possibilities for improving the existing delivery system within a firm.
99. Understanding the importance of transporting products when making buying agreements.
100. Ability to select the proper transportation method for a given product.
101. Ability to recognize how product characteristics affect their handling methods, and to choose the best of those methods available.
102. Ability to operate the product handling, storage, and processing equipment in a manner consistent with acceptable safety practices.
103. Understanding the delivery area served by the store, delivery schedules, and delivery charges.

In addition to these competencies to be taught at the post-secondary level for prospective employees in agricultural supply firms, Dr. Williams identified 241 competencies in these areas that should be taught at the secondary level.

Competencies needed should be identified for each curriculum to be offered. The competencies for agricultural equipment technology, for example, would be somewhat different from the preceding competencies identified for agricultural supply technology.

After competencies are identified, they need to be organized into courses, and the courses need to be developed into a curriculum.

Curriculum—Following is an example of the curriculum for an Agricultural Equipment Technology program at Lake Land Community College, Mattoon, Illinois:

1. Introduction to Agricultural Occupations.
2. Agricultural Technician Problems and Computations.
3. Agricultural Mechanical Skills.
4. Communication Skills in Agriculture I and II.

5. Introduction to Gas Engines.
6. Acetylene and Arc Welding.
7. Ignition and Electrical Systems.
8. Tractor Tune-up and Repair.
9. Hydraulics.
10. Assembling, Handling, and Adjusting New Equipment.
11. Diesel Engines.
12. Human Relations.
13. Business Relations.
14. Transmissions.
15. Painting Farm Equipment.
16. Advanced Tractor Overhaul.
17. Machinery and Parts Supply.
18. Shop Supervision.
19. Supervised Occupational Experience I, II, and III.
20. Agricultural Equipment Technology Seminar I, II, and III.

Student Organizations—If organizations for students in agriculture are important at the secondary level and at the four-year university level, they are important at the technical education level. The type and form of the organizations are dependent on local situations. However, student organizations are needed to "round out" the curriculum. They provide opportunities to develop many abilities that are difficult to develop in other ways. They provide opportunities to develop leadership abilities, speaking abilities, parliamentary procedure abilities, citizenship abilities, and agricultural abilities. Students in technical post-secondary programs will be expected to be members of various organizations related to their jobs after they finish their present educational programs. They need opportunities to develop the abilities in student organizations that they will be expected to possess later.

Teaching Procedures—Approved teaching procedures for problem-solving and skill development are vital to the success of technical education in agriculture at the post-secondary level. Teachers often assume that because of the career-directed motivation of the students, they do not need to give much attention to their teaching procedures. The result is that they gradually develop some unproductive teaching habits. They begin to tell or lecture instead of teach. They begin to imitate the worst feature of four-year university professors—presenting lectures.

When junior college, community college, and other post-secondary teachers who are telling and lecturing, instead of teaching, are asked why they are using this procedure, they often reply that problem-solving teaching is not appropriate in post-secondary technical education in agriculture.

This is a false assumption. Teacher evaluation studies show that problem-solving teaching is the most effective teaching procedure. It is the most effective teaching procedure from kindergarten through university levels and in adult continuing education. The reason why many professors in four-year universities resort to telling and lecturing instead of using more appropriate teaching procedures is that most of them have had no preparation for teaching. If they do use good procedures, they have developed their techniques through trial and error. Since trial and error does not often produce good teachers, junior college and community college teachers should not use four-year university teachers as their models.

Technical education teachers of agriculture who are interested in improving their abilities as teachers should review the following chapters in this book:

Chapter 4, "What Is Good Teaching?"
Chapter 5, "How to Plan for Effective Instruction."
Chapter 7, "How to Teach Effectively."
Chapter 8, "How to Teach Young and Older Adults."
Chapter 9, "How to Teach Persons with Special Needs."

It is important for teachers at the technical education level to use effective teaching procedures, because their instruction is very closely related to the success of the students in their various future careers in agriculture.

CHAPTER 27

What Is Agricultural Education for Young and Older Adults?

TYPES PROVIDED

Agricultural education for young and older adults may be of many types. A partial list follows:

1. Vocational.
   a. Courses for young farmers becoming established in farming.
   b. Courses for young adults preparing for off-farm occupations requiring knowledge and skills in agriculture.
   c. Courses for young persons living on farms who do not have crystallized agricultural objectives.
   d. Courses for older adult farmers.
   e. Courses for adults employed in off-farm occupations requiring knowledge and skills in agriculture.
   f. Courses for older adults preparing for off-farm occupations requiring knowledge and skills in agriculture.
2. Non-vocational.
   a. Avocational courses in agriculture.
   b. Practical arts courses in agriculture.
   c. Citizenship and consumer education courses in agriculture.

Ball and Cushman[1] have classified adult education courses in agriculture into three models. The models are:

1. The business management model.
2. The employee training model.
3. The self-fulfillment model.

---

[1]Ball, J. P., and H. R. Cushman, *Teaching Adult Education Courses: The Business Management Model, the Employee Training Model, the Self-fulfillment Model*, New York State College of Agriculture and Life Sciences, Cornell University, Ithaca, New York.

The purpose of the courses following the business management model would be to assist owner-operators or managers of agricultural businesses or farmers in becoming established successfully or in improving their operations. The purpose of the courses following the employee training model would be to teach present and prospective employees to perform the operations their present or prospective jobs require. The purpose of the courses following the self-fulfillment model would be to assist the enrollees in pursuing the interests in agriculture which they believe will add meaning to their lives. These interests may help the learners to advance culturally, occupationally, physically, politically, and/or spiritually.

In several states, the farm business management type course has been very successful. Some schools have employed teachers full-time to teach farm business management courses. These courses enroll all persons involved in the operation of farms. This includes husbands, wives, and farm partners. Group and individual instruction is provided throughout the year. The first stage of the instruction is the keeping of farm records and accounts. The second stage is the analysis of farm goals and family goals. The third stage is the analysis and interpretation of the farm business records and accounts. The fourth stage is the planning, replanning, and reorganizing of the farm business, using the analysis of the farm business records and accounts. Support services for summarizing the farm business records and accounts are important in making this type of course successful.

Courses for young and older adults may be provided for persons who wish to go to school full-time or part-time. These may be short courses, or they may be a semester or a year long. They may be provided by high school agriculture departments, community colleges, or area vocational and technical schools. The content of the courses may involve any phase of agriculture.

HISTORY AND DEVELOPMENT

History—Adult education in agriculture did not result from the Smith-Hughes and Smith-Lever acts. In this country, it has had a long historical development.

In 1785, the Philadelphia Society for Promoting Agriculture was organized to encourage "a greater increase of the products of land within the American States, and for this purpose the society would print memoirs, offer prizes for experiments, improvements, and agricultural essays, and encourage the establishment of other societies through the country."[2] By 1860, there were 941 active agricultural societies in the United States. Fairs for the sale of agricultural products have been held since colonial times as one educational procedure.[3]

In 1826, the lyceum movement was originated by Josiah Holbrook. A lyceum was an organization of adults which sponsored meetings, instituted

---

[2]True, Alfred Charles, *A History of Agricultural Education in the United States, 1785–1925*, U.S. Government Printing Office, Washington, D.C., 1929, p. 7.

[3]*Ibid.*, p. 31.

regular courses, procured books and apparatus, and established institutions for applying the sciences to agriculture.[4] By 1831, about 900 towns had lyceums.[5]

Farmer institutes were begun about 1870 and developed into a regular system of meetings under public control. In 1874, the chautauqua movement started. It provided lectures and entertainments. In 1894, extension work was begun in New York State. True points out that by 1902, there were 29,792 persons enrolled in the farmers' reading course and 9,500 in the farmers' wives' reading course in New York State.[6]

The Agricultural High School of Baltimore County at Sparks Station, Maryland, was opened in 1909 and was among the first public high schools to introduce instruction in agriculture. This school provided for the adult farmers a 10-meeting course, with an average attendance of 125 men and women. Monthly meetings were held on Saturday afternoons for the farmers' wives, with an average attendance of 85 women. They studied home economics, carpentry, home crafts, or modern literature.[7]

Vocational education in agriculture for adults provided by the public schools and stimulated by the Smith-Hughes Act was a natural development in the long process of adult education in agriculture.

Present Status and Trend—Interest in general adult education and in adult education in agriculture is expanding rapidly. An increasing number of states provides state aid for general adult education. Adult education is becoming more widely known and discussed than at any time in history. This is also true regarding adult education in agriculture.

The 26th Yearbook of the American Association of School Administrators states:

> "The next half century will emphasize adult education. The Nation's educational development prior to 1900 was characterized largely by the growth and expansion of elementary education. In the first half of this century the outstanding development has been in secondary education. It may well be that the last half of the twentieth century will witness a major expansion in post-secondary education."[8]

The adult program in agriculture has reached a high level of development. The trend is toward increasing attention to this phase of the program of agricultural education.

WHY PROVIDE AGRICULTURAL EDUCATION FOR YOUNG AND OLDER ADULTS

Need—Our present national and world culture with its complexities de-

---

[4]*Ibid.*

[5]*Ibid.*, p. 32.

[6]*Ibid.*, p. 277.

[7]*Ibid.*, p. 353.

[8]*The Expanding Role of Education*, 26th Yearbook, American Association of School Administrators, Washington, D.C., p. 79.

mands adult education. We cannot wait to educate another generation. Even if we could, it is impossible to prepare for the future when changes are so rapid.

Most of the problems in America are the problems of the world or are related to worldwide problems. If we are to survive, our citizens must learn about and understand these problems. Adults can no longer depend upon the random experiences of daily life as their chief sources of learning. Modern society is too complex and is changing too rapidly for this to suffice. Also, we cannot depend on elementary and secondary education because new knowledge, skills, and understandings are developing so rapidly that the abilities of youth are often outdated soon after they graduate from school.

Technological changes in agriculture make it necessary for adults to learn, and they do learn. Adults need opportunities to study ideas if they are to become capable of evaluating subversive ideas promulgated by rumors, whispering campaigns, and outright propaganda. Adult education is needed and provides opportunities for citizens to go on learning despite their schooling or educational backgrounds.

The same political and economic needs which justify public schools for children can be used to justify adult education. Adults are never too old to learn, and they are never too old to need to learn.

The further need for adult education is indicated by the present educational level of adults. In most states only a small percentage of the present adult workers in agriculture have had formal agricultural training while in high school.

Many of our most intelligent agricultural workers who may profit materially from adult education did not go to college. In many communities, for every high school graduate who ranks in the upper 10 per cent of the class and enters college, another graduate who also ranks in the upper 10 per cent of the class does not enter college. Among the graduates in such communities who rank in the upper 30 per cent of their classes, often only one-third attend college.

Even though we have several agencies involved in educating adults for agricultural occupations and all are doing a good job, many adults are not being reached. In Illinois, it is estimated that the Extension Service reaches systematically about one-third of the rural population over 21 years of age. There is plenty of room for expansion of adult educational opportunities.

Economic conditions do not alter the need for agricultural education for young and older adults. Adults need education during periods of adversity, and they also need education during periods of prosperity. Problems do not decrease during prosperity—they are just different.

Demand—The demand for adult education and for adult education in agriculture is increasing because the span of life is lengthening and the leisure time of adults is increasing. The demand for adult education for agricultural occupations will continue to be strong because it is characteristic of the American agriculturalist to try to get ahead. Since the times are becoming increasingly complex, the desire for security will increase this demand.

Adults employed in agricultural occupations, according to surveys, attend adult courses because they (1) receive mental stimulation from the courses, (2) want to earn more money, (3) believe more education is needed to ensure success, (4) desire more security, or (5) want to improve their personalities and to understand other persons. If teachers of agriculture properly organize and conduct systematic instruction for adults, the departments of agriculture will be swamped with adult enrollees.

One of the conclusions regarding adult education in the armed forces was that the more education persons have, the more they demand. If this is true, we are due for a drastic upsurge in the demand for adult education. Our general level of years of education completed is increasing. More and more persons are experiencing education as adults.

Value—Education for adults puts zest into life, for the best way to relieve the monotony in a job is to study ways of improving it. Adult education in agriculture can increase the efficiency of agricultural workers, who may need to increase their efficiency in the near future to maintain their present standard of living.

Much information regarding improved methods of production agriculture and agribusiness is present in the minds of the adults of a community. Systematic instruction in agriculture brings these minds together and gives them a chance to react to one another. If an instructor were merely to stimulate this reaction, a course for adults would be worthwhile. When the ideas of a teacher are added to those of the class members, the results may be startling. A backward agricultural community may be changed to a progressive community. A community may be produced with agricultural workers who are almost equally progressive, instead of a community with only a few outstanding agricultural workers. The leadership ability of the individual farmers and other adults in agriculture may be greatly developed through vocational education in agriculture classes.

Adult education in agriculture has many guidance values. Farmers and other adults in agriculturally oriented jobs will seek guidance regarding their personal and agricultural problems if given an opportunity. Adult education has a special guidance and educational function in helping aging farmers and other workers in agriculture to live out their lives in a useful capacity. In many areas, the trend is for farmers to retire gradually on their farms. This is creating many guidance and educational problems that must be solved if farmers are to maintain a healthy mental outlook while gradually turning their farming responsibilities over to others.

Advantages over a High School Program—Agricultural education for youth is essential. However, agricultural education for young and older adults has many advantages. Thorndike listed the following:

> "1. A better selection of persons to be taught can be made.
> "2. A better selection of the content of instruction can be made.
> "3. A better sequence of learning can be provided.
> "4. A loss of abilities by forgetting or of time of relearning can be prevented.
> "5. The lag of schooling behind science and technology can be lessened.
> "6. Learning satisfies some real need, benefits some cherished purpose, and is made use of at once."[9]

---

[9]Thorndike, Edward L., and others, *Adult Learning,* New York: Macmillan, 1928, Chap. XIII. By permission of Elizabeth M. Thorndike.

Farmers and other workers in agriculture are often in a position to adopt approved practices immediately. High school students may have to wait 10 or 15 years before they are in a position to practice some of the things they have heard about in classes in agriculture. At least this is often true regarding the adoption of approved practices on a practical scale. Another reason that a teacher's efforts are more effective and rewarding with adults is that there are no discipline problems.

Advantages to a Teacher—Teaching adults makes better teachers. It keeps them practical. They become acquainted with real agricultural problems. A teacher of adults does not have to resort to textbook teaching in high school classes. The teacher learns a lot of agriculture from the adults enrolled. Effective teachers of adults soon gain the respect and confidence of the people in their communities. Respect and confidence make all teaching easier, including high school teaching. The result is often higher pay and longer tenure in a community.

The really good jobs in agriculture frequently go to teachers who have been effective teachers of adults, because good administrators want teachers who can work with adults. These administrators realize that a teacher of agriculture is a school's primary contact with the farmers and other agricultural workers in a community.

Advantages to a School—If the teaching of adults improves the teacher, the school is thereby benefited. An adult education program sponsored by a public school system will not only improve the teaching in the school system, but will also make the school the educational center of the community. If a school is the educational center of a community, it will probably be more adequately supported financially. People will support their schools if they understand what they are doing, if they receive some personal educational benefits from them, and if they become interested in their activities.

A PHILOSOPHY OF AGRICULTURAL EDUCATION FOR YOUNG AND OLDER ADULTS

Teachers of agriculture need to understand, and help their communities and school administrators understand, the following characteristics and philosophy of agricultural education for young and older adults:

1. Farmers and other adults in agricultural occupations will welcome adult educational opportunities and enroll in large numbers.
2. It is the public school's responsibility to provide adult education in the nonprofessional occupations the same as it is the public's responsibility to provide education for the professions.
3. Adult education, when compared with other types of education, is relatively inexpensive.
4. Adult education can be made interesting.
5. The school is the institution for educational affairs and therefore should provide adult education.
6. The school has persons who are specially trained as teachers and who are, therefore, the logical ones to teach adults.
7. The school is discriminating against a large part of its community if it does not provide for adult education.

8. The school should provide adult education. It has nothing to sell but the truth.
9. The school belongs to all the people, who have a right to participate in its activities.
10. Adult education in agriculture is going to be provided. The school can do it with less money because of its investment in buildings, facilities, and professionally trained personnel.
11. Education is an important function of a community, a state, and a nation. Society cannot afford to allow an important area of education, such as adult education, to become the sole concern of persons and groups other than the whole public. Since public schools represent the interests of the public, adult education opportunities should be provided by schools.

Objectives—The objectives of adult education in agriculture are as broad as the objectives for education. Many people assume that adult courses in agriculture have as their only objective the increasing of production. This is untrue. It is true that one of the principal objectives of vocationally oriented courses in agriculture is to make farmers and other agricultural workers more economically efficient and secure by increasing their knowledge, understandings, and skills. This objective may result in more efficient production. In war times, increasing production may be of primary importance, but in peace times other objectives become more important.

Following is a summary of the objectives of adult education in agriculture:

1. Development of the ability to be economically efficient.
2. Development of the consciousness of adults regarding their civic responsibility in their local community, the state, the nation, and the world, and the ability to participate effectively in discharging this responsibility.
3. Development of consciousness of the values of democracy.
4. Development of the ability to live happily.
5. Increase of interest, knowledge, and understanding regarding safety, health, and physical fitness.
6. Increase of ability in the use of the fundamental educational tools and an increased knowledge of other agricultural education agencies available.
7. Increase of interest in, and appreciation of, agriculture.
8. Increase of interests other than vocational interests.

The objectives of an agriculture course for adults should depend on the agricultural and personal needs of those enrolled. It is conceivable that farmers and other workers in agriculture may need and request courses in the following areas of learning:

1. Agricultural subjects.
2. Citizenship responsibilities.
3. Community affairs.
4. General education.
5. Home and family life.
6. Leadership.
7. Music, drama, and fine arts.
8. Crafts and avocations.
9. Recreational and leisure-time activities.

Teachers of agriculture may contribute to several of these areas of learning in their courses for adults, but they are primarily concerned with the area of agriculture. They should, however, help and encourage the school in which they teach to meet the needs and requests in the other areas of learning.

The adult education in agriculture provided by programs of vocational education in agriculture over the years has developed confidence among farmers and others in agricultural occupations in the effectiveness of agricultural education for adults. Schools having programs of agriculture should provide:

1. Adult courses developed on a long-time basis and conducted every year.
2. Courses when and where class members desire them.
3. Qualified special instructors to assist the regular teacher.
4. "Action" or "doing" rather than "talking" or "lecturing" courses.
5. Courses based on the individual interests, needs, and capabilities of those enrolled.
6. Courses held throughout the year.

Systematic instruction in agriculture may profitably be offered throughout a year and over a period of years for the same group of adults.

Local school administrators should encourage adult courses by allowing teachers of agriculture time to conduct and supervise such courses. It is the responsibility of schools with agriculture departments to promote adult courses, and these courses should be considered as an integral part of the program of agricultural education. It is the function of schools to provide for and fulfill the educational needs of communities. One of the best ways to accomplish this is through adult education. Local administrators should visit the adult courses occasionally to become acquainted with the program and to help promote interest in these courses. All teachers of agriculture should teach adults.

POTENTIALITIES AND DEVELOPMENTS

If all the agricultural education needs of communities were met adequately, we would need several additional teachers of agriculture in many schools. A full-time teacher can probably teach only 50 to 100 adults in year-round courses if optimum individual instruction is provided. Fifty young farmers could provide a teacher with full-time employment. One hundred adult farmers or other adults interested in agricultural education could also provide a full-time job for one teacher. The following groups of adults need agricultural education:

1. Older adult farmers.
2. Young farmers.
3. Small-scale farmers (part-time farmers).
4. Farmers' wives.
5. Retired landowners living in towns.
6. Businessperson-farmers.
7. Women landowners.
8. Specialized farmers, such as gardeners and poultry producers.
9. Adults who do not farm but who have financial interests in farming.
10. Workers in off-farm occupations requiring knowledge and skills in agriculture.
11. Adults with avocational interests in agriculture.
12. Adults with civic or cultural interests in agriculture.
13. Adults with nonfarm financial interests in agriculture.

When we add all these groups together, we have several hundred adults to serve in each community. Assuming that we have a community with 600 persons in these groups and assuming that a department of agriculture could reach one-third of these adults each year if adequate courses were offered, two to four full-time teachers of adults would be required. Some agriculture departments are reaching many more than one-third of the adults in their communities. In some communities the number of adults engaged in occupations requiring knowledge and skills in agriculture is several times 600. The opportunities for expanding agriculture by meeting the needs of adults are almost unlimited.

Some of the developments in agriculture for adults which are designed to improve the program and meet the needs of all adults in agriculture are as follows:

1. Courses organized for a period longer than one year.
2. Year-round courses.
3. Courses meeting 30 to 40 times a year.
4. Courses meeting several hours per day and being completed in about two weeks.
5. Courses on one subject instead of courses covering several subjects or topics.
6. Forums to supplement unit courses and to meet the demand for complete coverage of the new developments in the various fields of agriculture.
7. Programs providing for a sequence of courses over a period of years.
8. Courses to provide education supplementary to the programs of agricultural organizations (for example, a swine production course for the members of a swine improvement association).
9. Courses for specific groups, such as couples, women landowners, agricultural leaders, employers in agribusiness, employees in agribusiness, and persons with avocational, civic, political, or financial interests in agriculture.

VOCATIONAL AGRICULTURE FOR YOUNG AND ADULT FARMERS

Instruction for out-of-school young persons who are becoming established in farming and for older adult farmers is one of the most important phases of vocational education in agriculture. If done adequately, the teaching of young farmers and adult farmers requires more time than any other job a teacher of agriculture performs. Young and adult farmers need, want, and are in a position to use, agricultural instruction.

Definition—Vocational education in agriculture for adult farmers and young farmers is not an afterthought. The sponsors of the Smith-Hughes Act probably considered first the need of farmers for vocational education as indicated in the act. The act states that *"such education shall be of less than college grade and be designed to meet the needs of persons who have entered upon or who are preparing to enter upon the work of the farm."* The reason that the high school phase of vocational education in agriculture developed more rapidly in many states than the young and adult farmer phase is that it was easier to organize.

Vocational education in agriculture for adult farmers is not in conflict with, or a repetition of, any adult farmer education activities made possible by federal acts that preceded or followed the Smith-Hughes Act. The Smith-Hughes Act and the subsequent vocational education acts provide for a definite educational need for which other agencies are not designed to provide. Vocational education in agriculture for adults is designed to provide systematic instruction carried on in schools or classes. Part of this systematic instruction must be the supervision of practice in the farming activities for which instruction is being offered in a school or class. Agriculture teachers may receive occasional calls for individual help from farmers in their patronage areas who are not enrolled in courses, but this type of activity is not systematic instruction and, therefore, should not be considered a part of the agricultural education program. Systematic instruction, as defined, requires courses of at least two weeks' duration with related supervision of practice. General farmers' meetings and farmers' institutes are not considered systematic instruction. The instruction is systematic when a series of meetings or classes is provided on related topics; when the content dealt with in the different meetings is unified, interacting, and interdependent; when the various meetings are designed to contribute to the same predetermined objectives; and when understanding of the instruction provided at a meeting is based to a great extent on the instruction provided at previous meetings.

The Smith-Lever Act, providing for an educational program for farmers under the Agricultural Extension Service, was passed prior to the Smith-Hughes Act. The Smith-Lever program is not in conflict with the vocational education in agriculture program because it serves a different purpose and uses different procedures.

The purpose of the Extension Service as stated in the Smith-Lever Act is "to aid in diffusing among the people of the United States useful and practical information on subjects relating to agriculture and home economics, and to encourage the application of the same." Extension work does not usually involve systematic courses of instruction. It deals with the special problems of a farm or a rural community rather than with systematic instruction, which includes the application and follow-up of the details of practice. The program of the Extension Service is designed to provide individual help and general farmers' meetings. The Extension Service disseminates new information and information about special problems. It ignites or fans the spark of interest for better farm practices and rural life. The program of vocational education in agriculture for young and adult farmers is designed to nurture this spark of interest through systematic instruction in the classroom and through supervision of practice on the farm. Both are effective agencies of adult farmer education, but they provide different types of educational service. The Extension Service is ideally organized to disseminate new information and assist with special problems which confront many individuals at the same time. Teachers of agriculture are in an ideal position to provide systematic instruction and supervision of practice. They live in the community where they teach. Their community is often relatively small compared with the area served by a county agent, and they can become well acquainted with their area and the people they teach. Teachers of agriculture should confine their activities with adult farmers to systematic instruction. Both agriculture teachers and extension agents should try to provide the type of educational service for which their respective programs are ideally suited. If this is done, there will be no duplication of educational services to farmers.

This interpretation of the division of responsibility between the extension program and the vocational education in agriculture program was issued as early as 1921. At that time, a committee representing the agricultural section of the National Society for Vocational Education, the Department of Rural Education of the National Education Association, and the Association for the Advancement of Agricultural Teaching made the following statement:

> "Where the school provides a comprehensive program of agricultural and home economics education which meets the needs of children and adults, through systematic instruction and supervised practice, the extension forces of the land-grant colleges shall not be duplicating such work of the schools but shall rather cooperate with the schools by providing, on request, subject matter, special lectures, conferences, and other similar services. This shall not be interpreted to limit the freedom of the extension forces to prosecute their extension work through local organizations of farmers."[10]

Vocational education in agriculture for adult farmers is not a new idea, a new frill, or an addition to the program of vocational education in agriculture. As indicated earlier, adult farmer education was one of the principal objectives, if not *the* principal objective, of the Smith-Hughes Act. Adult and young farmer courses were organized soon after the Smith-Hughes Act was passed, and there has been a steady growth in courses and enrollment.

VOCATIONAL AGRICULTURE FOR OFF-FARM ADULTS

Adults in many occupations require knowledge and skills in agriculture to perform their work. Courses for these adults should be provided. When provided they are welcomed by the owners and operators of agriculturally oriented businesses.

Courses of the following types may be offered:

1. Plant nutrition for fertilizer salespersons, garden center workers, ornamental horticulture workers, and others.
2. Animal sanitation for farm supply workers, pet shop workers, riding academy employees, animal laboratory technicians, veterinary assistants, and others.
3. Agriculture mechanics for farm equipment employees, garden center employees, agricultural construction employees, and others.
4. Agricultural distribution for grain elevator employees, stockyard and auction barn employees, farm supply employees, and others.

Many other courses in vocational agriculture of a specific nature may be designed to meet the unique agricultural education needs of off-farm workers who require knowledge and skills in agriculture.

---

[10]True, *History of Agricultural Education*, p. 376.

CHAPTER

28

How to Design a Comprehensive Program

DEFINITION AND DESIGN

Definition of a Comprehensive Program—A comprehensive program of adult education in agriculture is one that provides for all agricultural workers and others in a community who wish to enroll in agriculture courses and who can profit sufficiently from the instruction to justify the public's further investment in their education. Staffs in departments of agriculture are small. An adult education program, to be effective, must provide intensive instruction to any person enrolled in the program. It is, therefore, impossible at present to provide instruction in agriculture to everyone who may want instruction. The personnel of a school will have to determine, with advice from others, the most pressing needs in their community and the nation. Standards should then be established regarding who can profit sufficiently from the instruction planned to qualify for enrollment. Standards will also have to be established for progress necessary for staying in a program. With increasing demand for education in agriculture, we cannot continue to provide adult education cafeteria style. We can probably most adequately meet the demand by providing intensive training for a certain age group with limited training after that. We will have to help adults to develop the ability to educate themselves so that they will be less and less dependent on formal education programs.

A comprehensive program might provide courses as needed for the following groups:

- I. Agricultural groups.
  - A. Adult farmers.
    - 1. Tenants.
    - 2. Owner-operators.

3. Employees.
4. Small acreage or part-time farmers.

B. Young farmers.
1. 14–18 age group not in school.
2. 18–28 age group who want to start farming.
3. 18–28 age group who are just getting started in farming.

C. Farm managers who are not farming.
1. Retired farmers.
2. Businesspersons.
3. Women.
4. Others.

D. Off-farm agricultural workers.
1. Employed.
2. Self-employed.

II. Businesspersons and others who are not farming or managing farms but who are interested in the welfare of agriculture.

III. Adults with avocational, recreational, and practical arts interests in agriculture.

IV. Adults with consumer interests in agriculture.

Approval—Approval for an agricultural education program for young and older adults should be obtained by a teacher from the school administrators and the school board before the details of a program are planned.

Asking a board in a school that has sponsored little or no adult education for approval to conduct an adult program in agriculture involves the board in a question of major policy. Approval places the board on record in favor of school-sponsored adult education although only the agricultural adult program may be attempted at present. A board should understand that approval of an adult program in agriculture may establish a precedent for adult education in other areas in the school. A board, therefore, should consider carefully its statement regarding overall policy for adult education sponsored by the school.

After approval is received, the administrators should be kept informed regarding the details of the adult program in agriculture as they develop. Administrators and teachers should understand that the administrative officials of a school have the prerogative of vetoing or advising changes in these details.

Advisory Council and Committees—An advisory council for a local agricultural education department is frequently used in designing the overall agricultural education program for young and older adults. Its first job would be to determine, with the aid of the community, the needs for education in agriculture. The council then should decide, with the help of others, what are the most pressing needs. An advisory committee for each of the more pressing needs may then be established. Membership in an advisory committee for an adult education course may be composed of three or four of the members of the general council, or it may be composed of a chairperson from the council and three or four other persons not in the council. Advisory committee members are selected for a committee because of their interest in a particular educational need. For example, if a need is the improvement of ability in swine production, the committee members should feel a personal need for an educational program to help in meeting this need.

The use of a special advisory committee to organize a course in an instructional area helps to assure that the course will be designed on a sound educational basis. If the overall advisory council for agricultural education is used to organize courses, it is difficult, because of the diversified interests of the members, to prevent the establishment of topic or "shotgun" courses—courses in which a different topic is considered each meeting. For example, swine are discussed at one meeting, dairying is discussed at the next, soil is the topic of the following meeting, and so forth throughout a course. This type of course is not educationally sound, and it does not make possible systematic instruction. It approaches very closely the adult education provided by the Extension Service. If we provide this type of educational service, we are duplicating the work of the Extension Service. When courses are held in a neighborhood meeting place, such as a grange hall, a country church, a home, an agribusiness firm, or a local school, a neighborhood committee of three to five adults may compose the advisory committee. Some of the functions of an advisory committee are as follows:

1. Assisting in securing qualified instructors.
2. Suggesting a suitable meeting place.
3. Assisting in recruiting enrollment.
4. Assisting in providing adequate facilities.
5. Suggesting the time of year to conduct courses and the frequency of meetings.
6. Participating in the discussions as resource persons and helping keep the discussions on the subject.
7. Finding out the needs for adjustments in a course and relaying this information to the teacher of agriculture.

When a teacher has an experienced council that understands the agricultural education program for adults or when a teacher has board policies that establish the type of agriculture courses the council is to plan, it is often desirable to have the general advisory council for agriculture plan a three- or four-year program of adult education courses in agriculture. This program would be reviewed each year.

The general advisory council for agriculture in a school should assist in determining the objectives and evaluating the outcomes of the total adult agricultural education program. The advisory committees used to organize and develop specific courses may do likewise for their particular courses. All general policies, within the framework of a board's policy for adult education, regarding the operation of a total adult program in agriculture should originate with the general advisory council or be referred to the council for its advice. The decisions of a council are subject to the approval of the administrators of a school. Policies recommended by a council which are outside the framework of the board's policy should be given to the board for its action before they are put into use. Questions regarding the use of special teachers, the division of responsibility in multiple-teacher departments, the use of specialists, and the number of courses to offer are examples of questions of policy usually considered by advisory councils.

Multiple-Teacher Departments—Most departments of agriculture are not sufficiently staffed to meet all the needs for adult education in agriculture. One of the best ways of providing an adequate staff for adult courses is to hire additional full-time teachers of agriculture. It is probably unwise, however, to have one or more teachers work full-time with agriculture courses for adults. All teachers in a department need experience with adults if they are to do their best with high school students. A variety of teaching responsibilities will also relieve any monotony in teaching.

Special Instructors—Often a large agriculture program for young and older adults has to be developed before a community can be convinced that it needs additional full-time qualified teachers of agriculture. Some departments have been able to develop their adult programs by using part-time instructors for teaching one or more courses.

Farm machinery and tractor mechanics have been used as special instructors of farm machinery courses. Frequently housewives who have had considerable experience in food preservation have been used to teach food processing courses. Successful farmers have frequently taught enterprise courses, such as swine production, beef production, and corn production.

Many special instructors have not received professional or formal technical training; consequently, they need considerable help with activities such as the preparation of teaching materials, the effective use of teaching aids and devices, and the organization and conduct of classes. It is the job of the teachers of agriculture, as the local supervisors, to provide this assistance.

Should Special Instructors Be Secured?—Whether special instructors should be secured will depend upon the needs of the community, the number of teachers of agriculture in the department, and the time for adult education available to these teachers. In deciding whether to secure special instructors, a department of agriculture should also consider whether money is available for payment of salaries, whether sufficient equipment and housing facilities are available, and whether qualified special instructors can be secured.

If a community study indicates a need for an extensive program of adult courses in agriculture, every effort should be made to meet this need. A much more extensive program of adult education in agriculture is possible when special instructors are used. The use of special instructors makes it possible for teachers of agriculture to supervise a large number of courses and meet more fully the agricultural education needs of the community.

Persons used as special instructors should have (1) successful occupational experience in the area to be taught, (2) community respect, (3) ability to get along well with people, (4) ability and willingness to learn from others, (5) available time for teaching, and (6) appreciation of the importance of adult education in agriculture.

Professional training and teaching experience, in addition to these qualities, are especially desirable. Qualified persons living in a community should be employed if possible because they are then available for providing related individual instruction.

Upgrading Special Instructors—Even though all the criteria for selecting special instructors are observed, a thorough plan of in-service education and supervision of these instructors is necessary. The following methods of upgrading special instructors in a department are suggested:

1. Enrollment of special instructors in short intensive courses offered by the state teacher education institution.
2. Enrollment of local supervisors and special instructors in workshops offered by teacher educators or supervisors.
3. Enrollment of the special instructors in courses taught for their benefit by teachers of agriculture.
4. Attendance of special instructors and local supervisors at meetings conducted by teacher educators or supervisors.
5. Group and individual conferences for the special instructors sponsored by the teachers of agriculture.
6. Visits to the classes of the special instructors by the teachers of agriculture.
7. Outlines developed cooperatively by the special instructors and their local supervisors, the teachers of agriculture.
8. Source units on the units being taught made available to the special instructors.
9. Encouragement of special instructors to observe one another's teaching and that of the teachers of agriculture.

Responsibilities of Special Instructors—The following is a suggested list of the responsibilities of the special instructors in a department:

1. Assisting in organizing the courses.
2. Assisting in recruiting enrollees.
3. Asking the teachers of agriculture for assistance in planning course materials and in making teaching plans.
4. Reporting at once all equipment maintenance needs to the agriculture teachers.
5. Seeing that needed instructional supplies are on hand.
6. Seeing that sufficient appropriate projects, jobs, and problems are on hand for effective instruction.
7. Always meeting the groups when and where scheduled; *being on time.*
8. Keeping equipment in good working condition.
9. Becoming acquainted with enrollees and their problems.
10. Preparing and using instructional aids, such as charts, 2" x 2" slides, exhibits, and posters.
11. Keeping necessary records.
12. Formulating and enforcing safety rules.
13. Organizing groups so that maximum training can be provided with the equipment and the facilities available.
14. Doing an effective job of teaching, including *a good job of housekeeping.*
15. Providing individual instruction.

The state plans in some states do not provide for the use of special instructors.

Local Supervision—A teacher of agriculture should be the local supervisor of the special instructors. A local supervisor should:

1. Survey the community and determine with the help of the local advisory council the courses needed.
2. Arrange for proper facilities.
3. Locate special instructors.
4. Assist in planning the content of the courses.
5. Provide adequate teaching materials, aids, and devices.
6. *Meet with the special instructors frequently and discuss teaching methods, class organization, course content, safety precautions, sanitary measures, and standards of work quality.*
7. Visit the first meeting of each class and introduce the instructor; explain the purposes of the course, the goals to be attained, and the general plans for conducting the meetings.
8. Visit classes as frequently as possible in order to give the special instructors any help needed.

9. See that complete and accurate records are kept, including attendance records and records of accomplishments.
10. Visit the last meeting of each class and see that the course is properly closed. Make sure all equipment is checked, reconditioned, and properly safeguarded.
11. Make all necessary reports to the state office accurately and promptly.
12. Assist the special instructors in developing a publicity program.

Use of Specialists—In systematic courses in agriculture, specialists should be used sparingly. There may be certain occasions when it is desirable to invite a specialist in a particular field, such as dairying, to participate in a class discussion of special problems. Experience indicates, however, that when specialists participate in a course, the results are often not encouraging because (1) the specialists stand before the group and lecture—*a telling process,* (2) the specialists deal with generalities which are not applicable to the enrollees' situations, and (3) the enrollees do not get a chance to ask questions or to enter into the discussion. *If a specialist is used in a course, he/she should be asked to sit with the group as a resource person and to participate in the discussion led by the instructor.*

Having specialists sit with a group and act as resource persons is usually better than having them give a formal lecture, and this procedure is normally preferred by the adult enrollees and the specialists. Often it is easier to obtain a specialist to act as a resource person than it is to obtain a specialist to give a speech.

Adults, especially adult farmers, often do not discuss their problems freely when a specialist is present. It is usually more desirable for a teacher of agriculture to obtain needed information from specialists and relay this information to the class than it is to use a number of specialists in a course.

Number of Courses to Conduct—Systematic instruction in agriculture should be provided for all the adults in a school area who desire it and who can profit from it. The number of courses to conduct in a community will depend on:

1. The needs of the community.
2. The facilities and finances available.
3. The interest in courses.
4. The available time of the teacher or teachers of agriculture.
5. The special instructors available for employment.

The farmers in most rural communities will enroll in sufficient numbers to support each year at least one to five courses related to farm enterprises, one to three courses in farm mechanics, and one young farmer course. Most communities will also have a need for at least one or two courses in agriculture for non-farmers and off-farm agricultural workers.

Time for organizing and teaching courses is often the limiting factor in a program of agricultural education for adults. Several techniques have been developed to alleviate this lack of time. The use of special instructors is one of these techniques.

When teachers of agriculture devote a part of their available time to the local supervision of special instructors of adult courses in agriculture, it is possible to sponsor a large number of courses and in this way more nearly meet the agricultural education needs of a community. Some instructors are employed to teach only two high school classes and to spend the remainder of their time teaching young and older adults. Instructors employed on this basis have time to teach many more courses for adults than those who have teaching duties with high school groups during the entire day.

Offering a sequence of adult courses in agriculture over a period of years and alternating the location of these courses over a community constitute an effective procedure for spreading the work in adult education so that the teacher personnel for a quality program can be provided.

Length of Courses—The length of a course must be based on the needs and desires of the group of persons enrolled. The time required to cover adequately the contents of a course should also affect the length of a course. Some adult courses in agriculture have been continued over a number of years for the same group of enrollees. Generally, however, an adult course in agriculture covers a one-year period. Experience has shown that a group of adults enrolled in a year-round course will usually attend willingly from 20 to 25 class sessions during a year.

Frequency of Meetings—The frequency of class sessions in adult courses varies from course to course and from community to community. Courses have been conducted that have met daily over a period of time. Many successful adult courses have been conducted with class sessions once every two weeks. An increasing number of courses are being organized to meet once a month throughout the year.

For most courses, weekly class sessions during the period or periods of the year when work and other activities are least pressing have been found most desirable. These weekly sessions may then be followed with monthly meetings during the remainder of the year to observe, evaluate, and discuss results obtained from approved practices adopted because of the instruction received in the weekly meetings and through individual instruction.

In agriculture mechanics courses, many adults prefer to meet twice a week. There are even some communities where the adults enrolled in agriculture mechanics courses prefer to meet every day for a period of two or three weeks.

A somewhat different situation exists in food processing courses, since the food has to be processed at the time it is ready. Consequently, there may be certain times when it is necessary to permit the enrollees to meet three or four times a week. In most instances, however, twice a week should meet the needs of most enrollees.

Length of Sessions—The length of the sessions in adult courses in agriculture should vary with the type of education offered. Class periods of the following lengths are usually satisfactory:

1. Enterprise courses—1½ to 2 hours.
2. Agriculture mechanics courses—3 to 5 hours.
3. Food processing courses—3 to 4 hours, except for courses in meats, which require a longer period.
4. Skill courses, such as sheep shearing—3 to 5 hours.

Time of Day to Hold Meetings—Courses may be held at any time of the day enrollees will attend and instructors are available. Most courses in agriculture have been held in the evening, because regular teachers of agriculture are occupied with high school students during the day and because adults prefer evening meetings in order that they may work during the day. Special instructors often teach their courses in the daytime, however. Daytime classes are especially desirable for courses in food processing and agriculture mechanics.

Instructors of agriculture who are not occupied teaching high school classes during the entire day often teach young farmer classes, food processing classes, or agriculture mechanics classes during the day. During seasons when farm work is not pressing, farmers may even prefer daytime classes. Daytime adult courses are desirable from the standpoint of many teachers because their evenings remain free for other activities. Employers in agribusinesses often are willing to send their employees to classes meeting during the day.

Location of Meetings—Adult courses should meet at places convenient for the enrollees where adequate facilities can be made available. Adults generally prefer to meet in their home neighborhoods rather than at the school, when suitable facilities are available in their neighborhoods. Older adults will not travel many miles at night to attend a class.

Courses are frequently held in local elementary schools, grange halls, country churches, and homes. Adults often feel free to attend meetings in these centers without "dressing up" for them. If a school district is large, it is often desirable to locate courses in a number of centers in the area surrounding the school and served by it. When but one course is held in a community, it is usually best for the meetings to be held at the school.

Any location used for adult courses, such as local elementary schools, grange halls, churches, and homes, should have tables and chairs of adult size, be heated comfortably, and have electricity so that adequate lighting may be provided and films and slides may be shown. A place for displaying references, bulletins, and other teaching materials may usually be provided. A chalkboard should be available. If a meeting room does not have a permanent chalkboard, a portable board may be moved into the room.

Agriculture mechanics courses have to be held where facilities are available. Departments of agriculture should have agriculture mechanics shops of sufficient size to accommodate high school and adult classes. If a high school does not have the facilities for agriculture mechanics courses, it may be possible to rent a separate building for the courses, such as a vacant building in town, a local garage, or a repair shop. Any equipment placed in rented shops, as well as in school shops, should be carefully stored and kept under lock and key when classes are not in session.

Sizes of Classes—When the enrollment in a course is very large, it is impossible for all class members to enter the class discussions. Most instructors obtain more discussion in their courses when they keep the enrollments below 25. Special instructors, because of their lack of experience, are especially handicapped in leading discussions when the enrollments in their courses are large.

About 12 to 18 enrollees are all that can be effectively taught in a course in agriculture mechanics. It is preferable from the standpoint of economic efficiency to maintain an enrollment of at least 10 in all courses.

Financing Adult Courses—Many school administrators recognize that courses for adults are an integral part of the program of agricultural education and that the public schools are responsible for adult education. These administrators do not hesitate to finance adult education programs in their schools from general school funds if state laws permit. Nearly all schools supply classrooms, heat, light, janitor services, and teaching supplies for adult courses. Paying the salaries of instructors is more of a problem, however. Most state agencies for vocational education reimburse the schools liberally from state and federal monies for the salaries of instructors teaching vocational agriculture courses for adults. The portion of a teacher's salary for an adult course which is not reimbursed is obtained by a school from its regular school funds or from tuition fees charged the adults enrolled in the courses offered. It is usually considered undesirable to charge a tuition fee to pay the nonreimbursable costs of an adult course. It may put a teacher on the spot. It increases the difficulty of obtaining enrollment, and the adults may resent a tuition fee. As taxpayers, they may feel that their school owes them some educational service.

Adult education in agriculture is relatively inexpensive compared with other types of education. Teachers should remember that it is possible, even though undesirable, to finance an adult program with tuition fees if no other sources of money are available. Some teachers believe a small fee to cover expenses such as postage and refreshments is desirable.

The method of paying a regular agriculture teacher's salary for instruction of young and older adults is a problem to teachers, local school administrators, and state boards of education. An increasing number of teachers, school administrators, and state agencies for vocational education are realizing that adult education in agriculture is a part of every teacher's job. Therefore, teachers of agriculture should be given time to provide adult education, and their salaries for this part of their job should be an undesignated part of their total salary. When a teacher receives extra compensation for adult education, this part of the job tends to become an overload. The extra pay most teachers receive for their adult courses is insufficient to pay adequately for the hours of work devoted to this phase of the program in agriculture.

The salary of a special instructor is usually paid by a local school. If federal funds are available, a school may be reimbursed, in most states, for a part of a special instructor's salary. This is an administrative problem to be worked out in each state.

In agriculture mechanics courses, enrollees usually pay for all repair parts, materials, and supplies used. The adults enrolled in such courses should put all tools away and clean the shop properly before leaving. Consequently, a janitor should not be needed.

Awarding Certificates—Some kind of a certificate may be awarded the enrollees who have completed a course of instruction. Certificates may be awarded at the last meeting of a course, but in most instances it is more desirable to withhold certificates until the supervised or directed practice work is completed. Many adults appreciate this recognition very much and prize the certificates very highly.

Form 28.1. Adult Course in Agriculture Certificate

DEPARTMENT OF VOCATIONAL AGRICULTURE

THIS IS TO CERTIFY THAT

____

has been granted this

CERTIFICATE

as evidence of having completed the prescribed work of the

ADULT COURSE IN AGRICULTURE

offered in the ____________________________________ School

____________________ President

____________________ Superintendent-Principal

____________________ Instructor

____________________ Date

Recreation—Some teachers hold a short recreational period with activities such as basketball or volleyball at the close of each meeting; others withhold all recreation until the last meeting. In some communities, recreational activities are sponsored for enrollees at times other than when instruction is provided. This is often the procedure for providing recreational activities in a young farmer program.

Recreational activities are not essential to the success of an adult program in agriculture. Care must be exercised not to have a group attend a course just for the recreational activities. The author is of the opinion that the best procedure is to have recreational activities on nights when instruction is not provided, although limited use of appropriate recreation or entertainment after class meetings may be desirable in some communities.

Refreshments—Refreshments, such as coffee and doughnuts, at adult class meetings are usually considered desirable. Some teachers have coffee and doughnuts or other refreshments served during a class meeting or at a "break period" in a meeting. Others have refreshments served following the instructional meetings. Refreshments during or after meetings may help class members become better acquainted and feel more relaxed. If they do this, better class discussions will result.

School-sponsored Organizations—Occasionally the best method of teaching an ability or skill is to sponsor an organization among the adults enrolled in a course. Some examples of school-sponsored organizations that have been created to facilitate instruction in courses are swine herd improvement associations, cow testing associations, boar and bull rings, cooperative purchasing associations, and cooperative marketing associations.

School-sponsored organizations are often advisable, but definite precautions should be observed in promoting and operating these organizations. Any organization developed should grow out of an adult course and should be for the purpose of facilitating the instructional program in the course. The only purpose of a school is education. A public school is not established to sponsor organizations unless these organizations are essential to the successful conduct of the educational program. If this principle is followed, then all school-sponsored organizations should be discontinued at the time the educational programs from which they developed are discontinued. If a school-sponsored organization is operated to facilitate the education of the adults in a course, then membership in the organization should be limited to the members of the course. A school-sponsored organization should cooperate, and not compete, with existing community organizations. If a school-sponsored organization competes with an existing organization, the need for the school organization is doubtful. The membership of a school-sponsored organization in a state, regional, or national organization is of doubtful value. An organization sponsored by a school should engage only in those activities for which it is created, and these activities should be closely related to the educational objectives of the school. Such organizations should not be involved in political activities or large business ventures.

SUMMER PROGRAM

During the summer teachers of agriculture may increase the amount of time devoted to adult education in agriculture because high school classes do not meet. This does not mean that during the summer teachers should neglect the supervision of the occupational experience programs of high school students. This responsibility is present even though classes are not in session.

A large number of class meetings for adults may be held during the summer months. This period of the year is especially suited for adult class meetings because of the following situations:

1. The time schedules of teachers are not so rigid.
2. The weather is generally favorable.
3. The roads are usually good.
4. The evenings are long, and outdoor meetings are possible.
5. Crops and pastures are growing and provide many opportunities for field trips.
6. Modern mechanical procedures produce some slack work periods during the summer.

Young farmer courses often meet regularly on a monthly or biweekly basis during the summer months. Many teachers also hold monthly adult classes in agriculture during the summer months. Tours and field trips for adults are usually held during the summer. The summer months provide many opportunities for holding meetings on farms and in agribusinesses to observe and evaluate practices. Plans may be made during winter meetings for holding summer class meetings on the farms or in the businesses of class members to observe approved practices developed as a result of the instruction. If every opportunity is utilized during the winter series of meetings to schedule summer follow-up meetings, at least monthly meetings in addition to tours and trips will be possible.

Individual instruction for both high school students and adults may be increased during the summer months. The summer is an ideal time for individual adult instruction because it is during this period that adults are attempting to use many of the practices discussed in their class meetings.

Unfortunately, most teachers of non-vocational agriculture are not employed during the summer. If teacher time were available, much adult education in agriculture of a non-vocational nature could also be provided in the summer.

ADMINISTRATION

The administrator of a school is the administrator of a local adult program in agriculture. Most administrators delegate some of this responsibility to their teachers of agriculture. If responsibilities are delegated to a teacher, adequate records must be kept by the teacher.

Following are some of the types of records teachers usually keep on their adult agriculture courses:

1. Number and names of courses.
2. Number and length of meetings in each course.
3. Number of adults enrolled in each course.
4. Attendance.
5. Location of courses.
6. Location of adults enrolled in each course.
7. Age of those enrolled.
8. Outlines of courses.
9. Visits for individual instruction.
10. Miles traveled by teachers in providing individual instruction.
11. Approved practices adopted.
12. Outside specialists used.
13. Problems presented by enrollees.
14. Time requirements of teacher or teachers.
15. Budget.

Developments in an adult program in agriculture should be reported to the school administrator, and the annual written report to the administrator concerning the agriculture department should contain a section on the adult program.

WHO SHOULD SPONSOR ADULT PROGRAMS

In many areas both secondary and post-secondary public schools sponsor adult courses in agriculture. This is desirable. There are functions that both need to perform. The post-secondary schools need to offer courses that are more specialized and more technical in nature. They have the teachers qualified to offer such courses. The secondary schools need to offer courses and programs that are based on the specific problems of the adults in a local community. The courses offered by secondary schools can be made more specific because (1) the teachers often know personally the enrollees and their situations, (2) the classes are often smaller, permitting more effective use of the conference method of teaching, and (3) the enrollees often know each other and are more free to discuss their problems.

Secondary schools are in a position to offer effective levels and types of adult education in agriculture courses which post-secondary schools cannot provide, and vice-versa. Comprehensive adult education in agriculture programs demand the services of both secondary and post-secondary schools.

CHAPTER

29

How to Organize a Program for Young Adults

INTRODUCTION

Among the courses in agriculture for adults, including the courses for the upgrading of adult farmers and the upgrading of workers in the off-farm agricultural occupations, the programs for young adults are given high priority. Teachers enjoy teaching young adults, and the young adults are especially responsive to the instruction provided.

In this chapter two types of programs will be discussed. They are programs for:

1. Young farmers.
2. Young adults who are off-farm oriented.

PROGRAMS FOR YOUNG FARMERS

Definition—*Young farmer courses are established under public supervision and control and are organized for young men and women, regardless of their previous schooling, who are becoming established in farming.* They enroll out-of-school young farmers, usually 16 to 35 years of age, and provide systematic instruction designed to be helpful in becoming established in farming. Persons enrolled in a young farmer course conduct, under the supervision of their teacher of agriculture, farming programs related to their course of instruction.

Instruction for young farmers is the connecting link between the high school and adult farmer courses. Many young farmers are too old to want to go to high school, yet they are not established in farming and are too young and too inexperienced to want to enroll in courses for adult farmers. It is hoped that the time will come when all persons who are interested in becoming established in farming and who can profit sufficiently from the training to justify the expense of the program will have an opportunity to enroll in a three- or four-year young farmer program.

Responsibility of a School—There is present in practically every community where vocational education in agriculture is taught a sufficient number of young people living on farms to justify organizing and conducting a young farmer program. Young farmers who are not in school are just as much a responsibility of the public schools as those who are enrolled in schools. It is the function of a school to meet the educational needs of its community. *The attitude of the young farmers in a community toward the school at present and in the future will largely depend on how well their educational needs are met.*

It is a definite part of the job of teachers of agriculture to provide systematic instruction for young farmers, *regardless of their previous education, attitude toward school, marital status, degree of establishment in farming, or other factors.*

Characteristics of Young Farmers—Young farmers have varying abilities and varying amounts of schooling and farm experience. Some young people on farms are already farming with limited ownership and responsibility, usually on their home farms or as farm workers looking forward to full establishment as independent farm operators. Some of the characteristics of young farmers are as follows:

1. They are out of school.
2. They are interested in becoming established in farming.
3. They live on farms.
4. They are eager to learn.
5. They have acquired some operative skills but lack managerial experiences.
6. They are young enough to form good habits, ideals, and appreciations related to farming.
7. They attend classes for a purpose.
8. Many of them have opportunities to carry out comprehensive farming programs.
9. They do not like too much formality in teaching.
10. They are working on farms in various capacities either at home or away from home.
11. They like to participate in recreational activities involving physical skills.
12. They do not all have equal opportunities at home.
13. They have not all had the same educational opportunities.
14. They need career guidance.

DETERMINING THE NEED FOR A YOUNG FARMER PROGRAM

It too frequently happens that school officials, advisory council members, and teachers feel before studying their communities that there are very few out-of-school youth in their areas who are interested in young farmer courses. Many school districts have sufficient young farmers interested in furthering their education to justify young farmer programs. If not, adjoining districts may develop cooperative arrangements for offering a program for the total geographical area involved. A study of the area served by a school district should be made to find out the following:

1. The number of out-of-school young farmers between 16 and 35 years of age.
2. The age, farming status, and experience of each person.
3. The schooling of each young person.
4. The type of work each young farmer is interested in doing.
5. The possibilities of becoming established in farming.
6. The reasons for being out of school.
7. The needs of the group as a whole as well as of each individual.

Considerable data of this kind may be found for a community in the offices of the county superintendent, the county assessor, the county agent, and the local school. It is important to have data of this kind before starting young farmer courses. After a study of a community is completed, a map of the community showing the location of each young farmer may be made.

A teacher may record information regarding the out-of-school youth living on farms in the community on a form similar to Form 29.1. The information not available from local school data and from other sources for completing Form 29.1 may be obtained through a survey.

Form 29.1. Information on Out-of-School Persons 16 to 35 Years Old Living on Farms[1]

1. Name ______________________________

 Age ______________ Address ______________________________

2. Names of parents or name of guardian ______________________________
3. Highest grade completed in school ______________________________
4. Reasons for leaving school (check one):
 a. Economic reasons .... ( )
 b. Lack of interest in school .... ( )
 c. Graduation .... ( )
 d. Poor health .... ( )
 e. Other: ______________________________ ( )
5. Present farming status:
 a. At home with definite or indefinite allowance .... ( )
 b. Farm laborer away from home .... ( )
 c. Farm laborer at home .... ( )
 d. At home with income from one or more enterprises .... ( )
 e. In partnership away from home .... ( )
 f. In partnership at home .... ( )
 g. Renter and operator .... ( )
 h. Owner and operator .... ( )
 i. Manager of farm of another party .... ( )
 j. Other: ______________________________ ( )
6. Home farm:
 a. Type of farm ______________________________
 b. Size (no. of tillable acres) ________
 c. No. of older brothers or sisters on home farm ________
 d. No. of younger brothers or sisters on home farm ________

(Continued)

Form 29.1 (Continued)

7. Ownership in farming:
   a. Acres of land owned ______ b. Acres of crops being grown this year ______
   c. Kind and number of livestock owned ______________________________

   ____

   d. Equipment owned ______________________________

   ____

8. Names of employers for past three years: Types of work:
   19____, ______________________ ______________
   19____, ______________________ ______________
   19____, ______________________ ______________

9. Education for farming:
   a. Yrs. in 4-H club work ________ Projects ______________________
   b. Yrs. of vocational education in agriculture ________ Projects ____________

   ____

   c. No. of short courses attended ______

10. Are you interested in joining a group of young farmers to study farming problems? Yes ( ) No ( ) Undecided ( )

11. Are you looking forward to becoming established in farming? Yes ( ) No ( ) Undecided ( )

12. In what problems dealing with farm business are you interested? ____________

    ____

13. In what subjects related to agriculture are you interested? ______________

    ____

14. In what occupation other than farming, but related to farming, are you interested? ______

    ____

15. In what recreational or social activities are you interested? ______________

    ____

    ____

16. What time for the meetings would best fit your needs? (Check one):
    a. Morning .... ( )
    b. Afternoon .... ( )
    c. Evening .... ( )

[1]Adapted from a form prepared by a summer school committee for young farmer classes under the supervision of Dr. H. M. Byram, Michigan State University.

DETERMINING THE TYPE OF PROGRAM NEEDED

Occupational Status of Young Farmers—Information regarding the occupational status of young people and the status they aim to reach is essential in planning a program. Following are the kinds of occupational situations in agriculture in which a young farmer may be found:

1. At home with definite or indefinite allowance.
2. Farm laborer, with specific wages, at home.
3. Farm laborer, with specific wages, away from home.
4. At home with income from one or more enterprises.
5. Partner in a farm business at home.
6. Partner in a farm business away from home.
7. Renter and operator of a farm.
8. Owner and operator of a farm.
9. Manager of a farm for another person.
10. Part-time farmer.
11. In an off-farm agricultural occupation.

Opportunities for Placement—The type of instruction offered in a young farmer program should be based not only on the present status of the enrollees but also on the opportunities for placement in a more desirable status. Some attention in a young farmer program must be given to placing young farmer students; otherwise there may be little ultimate gain in offering them training. Young people become established in farming through:

1. Share agreements with farmers who wish to retire.
2. Loans from various sources, such as local banks, the Production Credit Association, and federal land banks.
3. Partnership agreements on their home farms.
4. Help from interested individuals.
5. A series of enterprises carried on at home and expanded into comprehensive farming programs.
6. Special jobs, such as tending a herd.
7. Part-time work off the farm.
8. Family allowance.
9. Working as hired hands.
10. Working at other occupations.

There are many factors which affect the establishment of young people in farming. Some of these are:

1. The amount of available capital.
2. The marital status of the individuals.
3. The ability of the parents to help.
4. The type of farming in the community.
5. The attitudes, aptitudes, and abilities of the individuals.
6. The number of farmers in the community desirous and capable of retiring.
7. The farming possibilities in the community.

DESIGNING A YOUNG FARMER PROGRAM

A young farmer course designed to train young people for establishment will need to continue over a period of three or four years with 20 to 30 class sessions a year. At the end of this period, most of the young farmers should be sufficiently established and old enough to be graduated into an older-adult farmer program. For a discussion on designing courses for adult farmers, see Chapter 31.

Who Should Teach Young Farmer Courses?—The teachers of agriculture in a community should usually teach the courses for young farmers. They are especially trained to teach such courses, and it is their responsibility to see that the instruction is provided. It may be desirable to employ special teachers to teach some phases of a young farmer program. Instruction in managerial jobs, insofar as possible, should be provided by agriculture teachers since they are especially trained in developing problem-solving abilities. It is usually satisfactory to employ a qualified special instructor to teach the agriculture mechanics phase of a course. Special instructors may also be employed to provide other instruction for young farmers when the need justifies it and when qualified instructors can be secured. Other suggestions pertaining to special instructors are given in Chapter 28. Some of the duties of a local supervisor are also discussed in Chapter 28.

Grouping of Young Farmers—The young people on farms in a community may usually be classified into three distinct groups. They are:

1. Persons living on farms who are out of school but who have not yet definitely decided to enter farming.
2. Persons who are living on farms and are out of school. They want to become established in farming but have made few definite steps toward establishment.
3. Persons who are becoming established in farming. They may be beginning farmers or farmers who are in partnership with others. They also may be part-time farmers.

If the number of young people living on farms in a community is large enough, an ideal organization would be to divide them into these three young farmer groups and provide a different program for each group. Often, however, the number of young people in a community is not large enough, or the teacher time available for young farmer instruction is insufficient, to provide three young farmer courses.

Number and Frequency of Meetings—Establishing the number and frequency of class meetings is a problem which must be dealt with locally. Many departments conduct a series of at least 24 to 30 class sessions a year, with meetings at least monthly. During the seasons of the year when farm work is least, the teacher may hold class sessions once a week, twice a week, or even once a day, in addition to, or in lieu of, the monthly meetings. For example, experience indicates that in conducting instruction in agriculture mechanics, a group should meet one to three times a week. During school holidays, young persons will often attend daily meetings for six to eight hours a day for one or two weeks. The recommendations of state agencies for vocational education vary and should be followed in conducting these courses.

Size of Classes—It is better to have 15 students in a course who are really interested in the instruction than to have 25, half of whom are there only to have a good time. A few disinterested students can be a decided detriment to an entire program. A group of 10 to 25 is adequate for a young farmer course.

ORGANIZING A YOUNG FARMER COURSE

Procedures—The first step in organizing a young farmer program is the organization of an advisory committee of young farmers to help study the agricultural education needs of the young farmers in the community. After the major needs of the young farmers have been located, the information collected should be shown to the administrators of the school and their cooperation solicited. The next step is the use of the advisory committee of young farmers to help plan and organize a course. The help of a department's general advisory council is usually solicited in organizing this advisory committee. The chairperson of an advisory committee may be a young farmer member of the department's advisory council. An advisory committee of three to six members is usually considered sufficient. Advisory committee members should be selected on the basis of their interest in furthering their education through a young farmer program. The committee members should also be leaders and should be geographically distributed in a community.

Recruiting Enrollees—A young farmer advisory committee may be of considerable value in enrolling class members. Most advisory committees welcome the opportunity to promote young farmer programs by asking others to enroll. Advisory committee members are in a better psychological position than a teacher to enroll class members. Presumably, they are also enrolling in the course and are asking friends and acquaintances to enroll. Others know that they are sincere because they are receiving nothing for their efforts. Another value of having advisory committee members enroll class members is that several persons are making personal visits regarding a course, and personal visits are essential in obtaining enrollment in young or adult farmer courses. The task of an advisory committee may be decreased if the young farmer program and the manner of securing enrollment are publicized through some of the following:

1. Members of the FFA.
2. Members of adult courses in agriculture.
3. Newspapers.
4. Farmers' organizations.
5. Meetings of parents and teachers.
6. The county agent.
7. Placards in store windows.
8. Agribusiness employers and employees.

After the young farmer advisory committee in a community turns in the names of those it has enrolled, the teacher should personally visit the enrollees to become acquainted and to discover their problems. A reminder letter or card should be sent to each enrollee a few days before the first meeting of the course. For a discussion of the use of news articles and circular letters for publicizing an adult course, see Chapter 31. For a discussion of writing for farmers and other workers in agriculture, see Chapter 11.

Membership cards are often given to enrollees in young farmer and adult courses in agriculture. Possession of a membership card indicates definite enrollment, and it creates a feeling of belonging. Figures 29.1 and 29.2 illustrate a type of membership card often used. Note that the card requires the signatures of the course instructor and of the advisory committee representative who enrolls the young farmer.

Most membership cards are printed and are 2¼" wide by 3½" long.

A form may be printed on the back of a membership card for recording the dates, times, and locations of meetings. If a meeting date, time, or location is changed, the members of a course can then record this change on their membership cards.

Vocational Agriculture Department

______________________________High School

This certifies that______________________________

is enrolled in the Young Farmer Course from July 1, 19______, to June 30, 19______.

____
Instructor

Enrolled by ________________________
Advisory Committee Representative

Fig. 29.1. Membership card.

Before a course is started, the school should apply to the state agency for vocational education for permission to conduct a reimbursable course. A state agency usually desires information on a course regarding the suggested course content, the number of meetings planned, the place, the time, the number enrolled, and the name of the instructor; the agency usually supplies a form for securing this information.

Vocational Agriculture Department
Schedule of Meetings in

____

Date	Time	Location

Fig. 29.2. Information on back of membership card.

When to Enroll Young Farmers—Young farmers should be definitely enrolled in a young farmer course in advance of the first meeting of the course so that the teacher can visit all the enrollees before the course starts. A problem regarding when to enroll new members in a young farmer course develops when the course is continued for three or four years on a year-round basis with 15 to 30 meetings per year. When a course continues for a three- or four-year period, several young persons in the community may become eligible for enrollment in the course before it is completed. A teacher, therefore, is confronted with the problem of deciding whether to enroll new persons during the course or whether to ask them to wait until a new course for young farmers is started. The ideal solution to the problem would be to start another course for young farmers as soon as a group of sufficient size is available for the instruction. In some communities, however, this is not possible.

Most teachers do not enroll new persons in their young farmer courses at any time during the year. Instead they enroll or start new persons once each year. Some teachers start new persons in their young farmer courses once every two years. If new persons are enrolled during a three- or four-year course, it is necessary for the teacher to provide the new enrollees with considerable individual instruction so that they will feel secure in the course and so that they will not hinder the progress of the other persons in the course.

DEVELOPING SUITABLE COURSE CONTENT

Importance of Suitable Course Content—The success of young farmer courses is largely dependent on the following factors:

1. The content of the courses.
2. The effectiveness of the instruction.
3. The facilities, including space and equipment.

The failure to provide adequately any one of these items may be sufficient reason for the failure of a course. Teachers must spend considerable time determining the interests and needs of a group and seeing that effective course content is developed.

Objective of a Young Farmer Course—The primary objective of a course for young farmers is to assist young people in becoming satisfactorily established in farming. This teacher objective implies the development of the ability to:

1. Choose and plan a life career.
2. Choose a farming program composed of activities which will contribute to progressive establishment in farming.
3. Solve the major problems in the development of a farming program.
4. Participate in cooperative activities in agriculture.
5. Work with others engaged in agriculture in the community, including parents.
6. Appreciate the advantages of the occupation of farming.
7. Select, finance, and purchase farming equipment and a farm.
8. Use the services which are provided for farmers by the agricultural agencies.

A young farmer course should contribute not only to the objectives of agricultural education but also to the objectives of general education. A young farmer course may help the young people enrolled develop (1) broadened interests, (2) abilities in the more skillful use of the fundamental tools of learning, (3) ability to think through their problems, (4) abilities in social, recreational, and civic activities, (5) ability to solve successfully the problems involved in marriage and the establishment of a home, (6) ability to live by the principles of democracy, and (7) ability to learn from others.

Developing Course Content—Preliminary planning of course materials by teachers in advance of the time of the instruction is highly essential. Teachers should study the individual needs of the enrollees and develop course materials which will meet these needs. They should then present their findings to the members of the local advisory committees for young farmer education and discuss the proposed courses with them. Following this, the young farmers enrolled in the courses should be given an opportunity to express their desires as to content of the courses.

The following list of areas of instruction for young farmers may be used as a source of problem areas to consider in planning a young farmer course.

• • •

SUGGESTED PROBLEM SOURCES FOR INSTRUCTION IN YOUNG FARMER COURSES[1]

A. *Areas Relating to Occupational Adjustment.*

1. Becoming acquainted with the opportunities in farming and off-farm agricultural occupations.
2. Getting a job to earn money to get started in farming.
3. Deciding whether to enter farming.
4. Deciding whether to enter an occupation related to farming.
5. Increasing one's efficiency as a farm laborer.
6. Discovering opportunities for placement.
7. Determining the possibility of establishing one's self in farming.

B. *Areas Relating to Establishment in Farming.*

1. Working out a partnership agreement in farming.
2. Choosing the type of farming to follow.
3. Finding and selecting a suitable farm to rent or to buy.
4. Deciding how much to invest in a particular farm (real estate).
5. Deciding how much a particular farm is worth.
6. Deciding how much to invest in livestock, machinery, and equipment.
7. Deciding how much operating capital will be needed in a particular farming business.
8. Deciding how to go about purchasing a farm.
9. Using credit facilities in purchasing a farm.
10. Determining the best lease to use for a given renting situation.
11. Using credit facilities in equipping and stocking a farm.
12. Selecting suitable farm equipment and machinery at the lowest possible cost to start in farming.
13. Deciding on the size and scope of farm business to enter.

C. *Areas Relating to Management of a Farm.*

1. Developing a suitable livestock program for the farm.
2. Planning a suitable cropping program for the farm.
3. Planning crop rotations.
4. Planning the farm layout.
5. Keeping farm records.
6. Making and using a farm budget.
7. Analyzing and interpreting farm records.
8. Hiring and managing farm labor.
9. Determining the power requirements of a farm.
10. Preventing farm losses and cutting down wastes.

D. *Areas Relating to Business Management.*

1. Determining the need for production credit.
2. Securing or making use of production credit.

[1]Developed by Dr. H. M. Byram, Michigan State University.

3. Using banking agencies.
4. Dealing with common laws of concern to young farmers.
5. Selecting insurance.
6. Solving mathematical problems encountered in managing the farm business.
7. Writing advertisements for farm products.
8. Building up a tourist business.
9. Displaying and marketing farm products.

E. *Areas Relating to Increasing Efficiency in the Livestock Program.*
1. Selecting livestock for working, feeding, production, and breeding.
2. Improving livestock through breeding and selection.
3. Feeding livestock; balancing rations for livestock.
4. Adjusting livestock production to market demands.
5. Improving marketing efficiency.
6. Improving sanitation and controlling disease.

F. *Areas Relating to Increasing Efficiency in the Cropping Program.*
1. Improving crops through introduction of new varieties and through breeding and seed selection.
2. Finding better ways of using crops.
3. Producing certified seed.
4. Carrying out a soil improvement program.
   a. Building up soil productivity.
   b. Controlling erosion, using cover crops, or strip cropping.
5. Controlling pests and diseases.

G. *Areas Relating to Farm Improvement and to Farm Machinery and Equipment.*
1. Improving the farmstead layout.
2. Beautifying the home grounds.
3. Improving and repairing farm buildings and equipment.
4. Using electricity on the farm.
5. Providing a farm lighting system.
6. Providing a water and sewage disposal system.
7. Heating the farm home.
8. Repairing farm machinery and equipment.
9. Building farm equipment.
10. Establishing a home-farm shop.
11. Operating farm machinery and farm motors.

H. *Areas Relating to Leadership in the Family and Community.*
1. Leading a discussion on farmers' problems.
2. Conducting meetings according to accepted parliamentary procedure.
3. Improving rural-urban relationships.
4. Making the community more interesting and attractive.
5. Organizing young farmers for business, recreational, and service purposes.
6. Understanding government programs relating to agriculture.
7. Understanding the programs of farmers' organizations.
8. Improving schools for rural children.
9. Cooperating in group economic and social undertakings.
10. Developing cordial family relationships.

● ● ●

For a discussion of the principles involved in the development of courses of study, see Chapter 13.

Planning Content with Young Farmers—It is often difficult for young farmers to understand the need for a three- or four-year program. The following procedure may help them understand the importance of a long-time educational program while they are becoming established in farming. The procedure may also help them see the possibility of planning such a program. A teacher should:

1. Ask young farmers individually, probably during farm visits, how far toward establishment in farming they wish to progress during the next three or four years.
2. Ask young farmers to inventory in detail their present status in farming.
3. Ask young farmers to indicate in detail the progress they hope to make each year for the next three or four years. Some of the more important items that should be included in a young farmer's inventory of the present situation and future goals are included in Form 29.3.
4. Summarize the present situation and goals of the enrollees in the program. The summary, when it is presented to the young farmer class, should not identify the present situation and goals of each young farmer.
5. Analyze with the enrollees their common goals.
6. Identify, with the help of the enrollees, the decisions, problems, skills, abilities, and knowledge involved in reaching the common goals of the group.
7. Organize the anticipated problems, knowledge, and skills needed into a logical sequence. The skills and knowledge that are needed first should be identified and supplied near the beginning of the course. The skills and knowledge needed the second year of the program and in the succeeding years should be identified and tentatively located in the course outline.
8. Organize seasonally the content placed in the first year of the program.
9. Revise the tentatively selected content at periodic intervals, and organize it seasonally.

In helping young farmers plan a young farmer program, a teacher must provide them with considerable guidance so that they will not insist on excessive jumping from topic to topic in their course and so that they will avoid the superficial treatment of their problems. If a particular problem area is taught, it should be taught until it is learned. Farmers, especially young farmers, need to have more than a superficial exposure to a problem area or to a new idea.

When young farmers indicate through the process and steps just given the content that they will need each year in a three- or four-year program if they are to receive help in reaching their objectives, it is not usually wise for a teacher to ask them to determine also the arrangement of the content. Teachers of agriculture have had professional training in the arranging of content and in the development of teaching plans and, therefore, should be able to arrange the content of a course so that excessive jumping and superficiality are avoided. Since the young farmers have not had professional training in the organization of content or in the development of teaching plans, it is unfair and unwise to insist that they determine how these things should be done. Periodically, however, a teacher should ask the young farmer enrollees to evaluate the progress of the course as a means of evaluating the way the content is being arranged and the way teaching of the content is being handled. Thus, the young farmer enrollees assist the teacher directly in determining the content of their course but assist only indirectly in determining the organization of the content for teaching and in determining the teaching procedures used.

Form 29.2 is an example of an anticipated outline for a three-year young farmer course. This outline was developed by a process similar to that described in the preceding paragraphs.

Form 29.2. Anticipated Outline for a Three-Year Young Farmer Course

Unit: Getting Started in Farming

PROBLEM AREAS:

First Year

1. Evaluating present farming status (1 or 2 nights).[1]
2. Establishing a home (1 or 2 nights).
3. Selecting suitable land for young farmers (2 nights).
4. Determining whether to buy or rent a farm (1 night).
5. Determining type and scope of farm business (2 nights).
6. Using credit in establishing farming programs (2 nights).
7. Developing leases and partnership agreements (2 nights).
8. Planning livestock programs for the farms of young farmers.
   a. Selection of foundation stock (2 nights).
   b. Sanitation and disease control (2 nights).
   c. Planning of feeding programs (3 nights).
9. Planning the cropping systems for the farms of young farmers.
   a. Crop selection (1 night).
   b. Cultural practices—rate of seeding, tillage, fertilizers (3 nights).
   c. Crop rotations (1 night).
   d. Crop harvesting and storing (2 nights).
10. Keeping, using, and analyzing farm records (3 nights).
11. Selecting and maintaining farm equipment.
   a. Plow adjustment (1 night).
   b. Combine adjustment (½ day, Saturday morning).
   c. Hay-making equipment adjustment (½ day, Saturday morning).
   d. Tractor trouble-shooting (½ day, Saturday morning).

Second Year

1. Determining insurance needs for young farmers.
   a. Life insurance problems (1 night).
   b. Insurance on crops, buildings, etc. (1 night).
2. Planning livestock programs for the farms of young farmers.
   a. Sanitation and disease control (2 nights).
   b. Planning of feeding programs (3 nights).
   c.
3. Planning cropping systems for the farms of young farmers.
   a. Cultural practices—rate of seeding, tillage, fertilizers (3 nights).
   b. Crop rotations (1 night).
   c. Crop harvesting and storing (2 nights).
   d.
4. Keeping, using, and analyzing farm records (2 nights).
5. Selecting and maintaining farm equipment.
   a.
   b.
   c.

(Continued)

Form 29.2 (Continued)

Third Year

1. Determining what farm organizations to join (2 nights).
2. Improving rural-urban relationships (1 night).
3. Developing a recreational program (2 nights).
4. Planning livestock programs for the farms of young farmers.
   a. Feeding program (2 nights).
   b.
   c.
5. Planning cropping systems for the farms of young farmers.
   a. Cultural practices—rate of seeding, tillage, fertilizers (3 nights).
   b.
   c.
6. Keeping, using, and analyzing farm records (2 nights).
7. Selecting and maintaining farm equipment.
   a. Tractor trouble-shooting (½ day, Saturday morning).
   b.
   c.

[1]Suggested number of days or nights to devote to each problem area is given in parentheses.

ORGANIZING SUPERVISED FARMING PROGRAMS

Types of Farming Programs—Young farmers become established under varying conditions. Some of the kinds of farming programs which have been conducted by young farmers are:

1. Farming at home with parents and conducting a number of production projects, such as dairy, swine, beef, sheep, and poultry, in which part or full ownership is involved.
2. Developing improvement projects at home.
3. Farming in partnership or renting additional land.
4. Renting a farm.
5. Purchasing and operating a farm.
6. Working as a hired farm laborer.
7. Working part-time on the farm and part-time in industry or at farm custom work until sufficient capital can be accumulated for use in furthering progress toward establishment.

Instruction on the Farm—Adequate instruction on the farm is essential in achieving desirable outcomes in terms of the objectives outlined for a course. Teachers should organize their on-the-farm instructional programs so that they can do the following:

1. Visit the homes frequently and develop desirable relationships.
2. Visit the young farmers during critical times in the year when the teacher can be of help to them:
   a. In carefully evaluating their programs and in improving and expanding their programs.
   b. In selecting desirable seed and breeding stock.
   c. By counseling each young farmer on any major problems relating to the farming program, such as financing, renting or purchasing land, and securing equipment.
3. Carefully guide the students in developing superior programs in which a large number of approved practices are adopted and put into effect.

Form 29.3. Young Farmer Inventory of Present Situation and Future Goals

Part 1

Item		Status Now	Status Desired 4 Years from Now
1. Home (own home or live with parents, etc.)		______	______
2. Farming status (partner, owner, renter, etc.)		______	______
3. Farm:			
Type		______	______
Size		______	______
Acres of land owned		______	______
4. Crops:			
Corn	acres	______	______
	yield	______	______
Soybeans	acres	______	______
	yield	______	______
Oats	acres	______	______
	yield	______	______
Wheat	acres	______	______
	yield	______	______
Legumes	acres	______	______
	yield	______	______
Permanent pasture	acres	______	______
	yield	______	______
Other	acres	______	______
	yield	______	______
5. Livestock:			
Poultry			
Meat		______	______
Layers		______	______
Swine			
Size		______	______
Type		______	______
Beef			
Size		______	______
Type		______	______
Dairy			
Size		______	______
Type		______	______

(Continued)

Form 29.3 (Continued)

Item	Status Now	Status Desired 4 Years from Now
Sheep		
Size	______	______
Type	______	______
Other	______	______
	______	______
	______	______
6. Buildings and equipment:		
a. Buildings		
(1)	______	______
(2)	______	______
(3)	______	______
(4)	______	______
(5)	______	______
(6)	______	______
b. Equipment		
(1)	______	______
(2)	______	______
(3)	______	______
(4)	______	______
(5)	______	______
c. Machinery		
Tractors		
(1)	______	______
(2)	______	______
(3)	______	______
Combine	______	______
Corn picker	______	______
Baler	______	______
Plow	______	______
Disc	______	______
Harrow	______	______
7. Farm labor:		
Amount used	______	______
8. Miscellaneous:		

(Continued)

Form 29.3 (Continued)

Part 2

Item	O.K.	Needs Improvement (Give examples of improvement desired)	Future Plans	Does Not Apply
1. Farm lease				
2. Partnership agreement				
3. Use of credit				
4. Crop rotation				
5. Farm layout				
6. Farm records				
7. Budget				
8. Insurance coverage				
9. Home grounds				
10. Home improvement				
11. Home-farm shop				
12. Parliamentary procedure				
13. Community improvement				
14. Participation in groups				
15. Participation in, and understanding of, farm organizations				
16. Participation in, and understanding of, schools in the community				
17. Social activities				
18. Recreational activities				
19. Family relationships				
20. Child care				
21. Home life				
22. Orcharding				
23. Gardening				

PROGRAMS FOR OFF-FARM AGRICULTURALLY ORIENTED YOUTH

Young men and women who are interested in establishment in an off-farm agricultural occupation and who are out of school need a "custom-made" program. A teacher of agriculture is often in a position to provide meaningful educational assistance to these young men and women. The type of program often cannot be the same as the type provided for young persons who have entered or are preparing to enter farming.

The techniques of organizing and conducting courses for these young men and women are similar to the techniques of organizing and conducting courses for young farmers. The content and activities of the courses, however, should differ.

Courses for these young men and women should emphasize activities such as the following:

1. Re-exploring the special interests and competencies of the enrollees.
2. Examining the competencies developed in agriculture that would be of value in other occupations.
3. Examining the agricultural competencies needed in different off-farm agricultural occupations.
4. Exploring the opportunities for employment in off-farm agricultural occupations.
5. Determining the non-agricultural competencies needed for off-farm agricultural occupations and for other occupations.
6. Determining the educational opportunities available for preparing for off-farm agricultural occupations and for other occupations.
7. Studying content most useful in becoming established in off-farm agricultural occupations in which employment is desired and most probable, such as:
   a. Principles of agricultural economics as they apply to off-farm agricultural businesses.
   b. Principles of business management in off-farm agricultural businesses.
   c. Operation of agricultural cooperatives.
   d. Principles of animal nutrition. (This knowledge would be of value in feed manufacturing or in farm supply businesses.)
   e. Agricultural chemicals. (This knowledge would be of value in fertilizer and pesticide businesses.)
   f. Agricultural mechanization.
   g. Principles of genetics in animals and crops. (This knowledge would be of value in hybrid seed businesses and in animal breeding businesses.)
8. Studying content useful regardless of type of occupation, such as:
   a. Principles of working with people.
   b. Principles of parliamentary procedure.
   c. Social graces.
   d. Principles of public speaking.
   e. Procedures in applying for a job.
   f. Procedures for managing family income.
   g. Principles of using credit.
   h. Procedures for becoming good citizens at local, state, national, and world levels.
   i. Self-education procedures.

The dropout rate in a program for off-farm agriculturally oriented youth will and should be greater than the dropout rate in a young farmer program. If the instruction is successful, the enrollees will be getting jobs that may take them out of the community. Some will also drop out to enroll in other educational programs specifically designed for the occupations they enter.

CHAPTER

30

What Are Young Farmer Associations and How Are They Organized?

INTRODUCTION

Meaning—In many departments the young people enrolled in a young farmer program have organized themselves into a local young farmer association for the duration of their course. Membership is limited to those members in good standing in the young farmer program.

History—Teachers have recognized for a long time that young people like to belong to worthwhile organizations and feel that they are a part of a group. It has been a common practice to let a young farmer group elect a president to open and close the meetings, introduce speakers, appoint committees, and carry on business. Some teachers have sponsored FFA Alumni Associations.

There have been local clubs, chapters, or associations of young farmers in Ohio since 1927. Also since that time, local young farmer groups have been organized in several states. These groups have often adopted constitutions and bylaws, elected officers, and developed programs of work based on the educational needs of young people on farms who are becoming established in agriculture and in their communities.

Purpose—A local young farmer organization is a method of accomplishing the broader objectives of a young farmer program. It provides a vehicle for developing leadership and intelligent followership. It prepares young people for effective and intelligent participation in adult farmer organizations. Young farmers demonstrate to themselves through an organization the importance of belonging to and participating in adult organizations. Most persons agree that young people need help in developing the desire and ability for participation in adult organizations.

Social and recreational activities are often sponsored by an association, relieving the teacher of the responsibility for this part of a young farmer program. The executive committee of an organization usually acts in an advisory capacity to the teacher regarding the educational aspects of the young farmer program. An organization may also provide support and advice to the FFA. It may sponsor cooperative activities that result from the instructional program. It often provides a vehicle for rendering service in its community. It provides opportunities for the development of attitudes, interests, appreciations, and understandings which are difficult for a teacher to develop through class or individual instruction.

Value to Teachers—Young farmer organizations make the work of teachers with young farmers more effective and relieve the teachers of many responsibilities. Teacher-student relationships are improved. An organization of this type is an effective teaching procedure and not an added responsibility for teachers.

An association will make more work for teachers, but it will also save them work if used properly. The members may save teachers work by organizing and sponsoring demonstrations on their farms or by planning and conducting farm tours and trips. The members also encourage enrollment and attendance at the educational meetings in the young farmer program. This relieves teachers of most of this responsibility. The arguments used to justify a local FFA chapter may also be used to justify a local young farmer association.

ORGANIZATION

How to Organize—A local young farmer association should develop naturally from a young farmer course. Since it is an educational procedure or method of accomplishing the objectives of a young farmer program, an association should grow out of such a program and not precede it. If it precedes the young farmer program, the young farmers may view the association as a pressure or political organization instead of an organization to provide additional educational opportunities. Teachers of agriculture, as employees of the public, cannot sponsor a pressure or political organization as a part of their work.

After a young farmer program is underway, the teacher may discuss the possibilities of a young farmer association with the school administration and the local board of education. When they understand the aspects of a young farmer association, the teacher is justified in discussing with the enrollees in the young farmer course the possibilities of a local association. Some of the following questions might be discussed:

1. What is a local young farmer association?
2. What are the purposes of an association?
3. What could be accomplished through a local young farmer association?
4. Is there a need for an association?
   a. What organizations already exist for young farmers?
   b. What percentage of the class belongs to these organizations?
   c. Are these organizations meeting the needs of the class members?
   d. Would a local association help them become more effective members of these other organizations?

5. What needs of young farmers could an association serve?
   a. Leadership?
   b. Community service?
   c. Recreation?
   d. Social?
   e. Cooperative?

After such a discussion, the members of a young farmer group may wish to visit another local young farmer association or have an association member speak to them. It is usually not wise to rush a group into organizing an association. After a group has had some time to think and talk with others about an association, the question may be put to the group. If the vote is favorable, the group should elect a committee to design the constitution and bylaws. This constitution and these bylaws would be referred back to the group for ratification. The next step would be the election of officers. The officers acting as an executive committee would then select, and the president would appoint, the program of work committees and other standing committees.

Constitution and Bylaws—Following are a suggested local constitution and bylaws. Any constitution and bylaws, before taking effect, should be approved by the administrators of the school.

• • •

SUGGESTED CONSTITUTION AND BYLAWS FOR A LOCAL ASSOCIATION OF YOUNG FARMERS

CONSTITUTION

Article I—Name and Objectives

Section A—Name:

The name of this organization shall be the ____________________ Association of Young Farmers.

The ____________________ Association of Young Farmers is an organization of, by, and for young farmers participating in programs of organized, systematic instruction in vocational education in agriculture under the provisions of the National Vocational Education Acts. It is a nonprofit and nonpolitical organization of voluntary membership.

Section B—Primary Objective:

The primary objective of this association is to develop group and individual responsibilities of out-of-school young farmers in programs of instruction in agriculture designed to meet their needs in becoming established in farming.

Section C—Contributory Objectives:

1. To develop individual and group interests and abilities in financing, planning, operating, and evaluating farming programs of out-of-school young farmers who are members of the organization.
2. To discover and utilize placement opportunities available on a rental, lease, partnership, or purchase basis in helping young people to become established in farming.
3. To develop the leadership abilities needed to participate in activities requiring an understanding of parliamentary procedure, conduct of meetings, public speaking, and other desirable activities for rural young people.
4. To develop an understanding of the ways to secure and utilize the services available to farmers in improving their economic status and their social and family relationships.

5. To develop abilities in producing, marketing, and utilizing farm products; conserving water, soil, and other natural resources; financing and managing farm businesses; maintaining and operating farm machinery and equipment; maintaining and improving the farmsteads; applying farm work simplification practices; and improving farm-family living situations.

Article II—Organization

Section A—The ______________________ Association of Young Farmers is an organization for out-of-school young people who are progressively establishing themselves in farming and who are enrolled for systematic instruction in agriculture in a young farmer class for the duration of the young farmer course.

Section B—The young farmer association shall exist only during the time it is authorized by the school administrators and the board of education.

Section C—The constitution, bylaws, and activities of the ______________________ Association of Young Farmers shall be acceptable to the administration and board of education of the school.

Section D—The ______________________ Association of Young Farmers will automatically be discontinued at the end of the young farmer program.

Section E—The local teacher of agriculture responsible for the local young farmer course shall be the adviser for the local association of young farmers.

Section F—The fiscal year for this association shall be July 1 to June 30.

Article III—Membership

Section A—The membership of this association shall be of two kinds: (1) active and (2) honorary.

Section B—Active membership—Young farmers 16 to 35 years of age inclusive who are out of school, progressively establishing themselves in farming, and members in good standing of a young farmer course are eligible to become active members of the association of young farmers upon receiving a majority vote of the members at a local association meeting.

Section C—An active member will automatically lose membership in the association if the member fails to attend three successive young farmer class sessions or association meetings without presenting a valid excuse for the absences.

Section D—An active member will automatically lose membership in the association if the member fails to attend more than 20 per cent of the young farmer class sessions and association meetings during any fiscal year, unless a valid excuse is presented for the absences.

Section E—An active member will automatically lose membership in the association when dues are in arrears for more than six months.

Section F—Honorary membership—Individuals who have made outstanding contributions to the local association of young farmers and to the general improvement of agricultural conditions may be elected to honorary membership by a majority vote of the members.

Article IV—Officers

Section A—The officers shall be: president, vice-president, secretary, treasurer, reporter, and local adviser. With the exception of the local adviser, officers of this association shall be active members and shall be elected annually by a majority vote of the members.

Section B—Elected officers of the association and the local adviser shall constitute the executive committee.

Article V—Meetings

Section A—Meetings of the association shall be held once a month throughout the year. Special meetings may be called by the executive committee at any time.

Section B—Parliamentary procedure at all meetings of the association will be in accordance with *Robert's Rules of Order*.

Section C—The order of business at regular meetings shall be: call to order, roll call, reading of the minutes, reports of officers and committees, unfinished business, new business, special events, and adjournment.

Article VI—Dues and Funds

Section A—Annual membership dues in the association shall be fixed by the executive committee, subject to approval by a two-thirds majority vote of the members.

Section B—Dues are to be fixed at a minimum rate necessary to cover the cost of consumable supplies and paraphernalia.

Section C—Special assessments are not permissible.

Section D—Funds of the organization shall be handled in the same way as the school handles the funds and accounts of other student organizations.

Article VII—Emblem and Colors

Section A—The emblem of the ________________ Association of Young Farmers shall be ________________ with the following inscription around and near the edge of the emblem: ________________ Young Farmers.

Section B—The colors of the ________________ Association of Young Farmers shall be ____________ and ____________.

Article VIII—Amendments

Section A—A proposed amendment to the constitution or bylaws must be submitted in writing by an active member of the association at least 90 days before action is taken. The amendment or amendments must be read at three regular meetings of the association before being brought to a vote. When this procedure is followed, amendments to the constitution or bylaws may be adopted at any meeting by a two-thirds vote of the active members. Before amendments become effective they must be approved by the administrators of the school.

BYLAWS

Article I—Duties of Officers

Section A—*President.* It shall be the duty of the president to preside at all meetings of the association of young farmers and to serve as chairperson of the executive committee. With the approval of the adviser, the president shall appoint all committees and may serve as an ex officio member of these committees.

Section B—*Vice-President.* It shall be the duty of the vice-president to preside at all meetings of the association in absence of the president and to assist the president at all times in carrying on the work of the association.

Section C—*Secretary.* It shall be the duty of the secretary to keep minutes of the meetings of the association and of the executive committee. The secretary also shall keep a roster of members attending meetings, carry on the correspondence of the association, and fulfill such duties as usually pertain to that office.

Section D—*Treasurer.* It shall be the duty of the treasurer to collect and disburse all funds authorized by the association and to maintain complete and accurate records of all transactions. The treasurer shall present to the association an annual financial statement of the condition of the treasury.

Section E—*Reporter.* It shall be the duty of the reporter to report promptly and correctly to newspapers, other publications, and local radio stations any items of interest relating to the association.

Section F—*Adviser.* The adviser is an ex officio member of all committees. The adviser is an active member of the executive committee of the association of young farmers and assists officers in conducting meetings and other affairs of the association. The adviser reviews actions taken by all committees to determine whether they are in conformity with policies, plans, and regulations pertaining to the program of agricultural education as approved by the state agency for vocational education.

Article II—Committees

Section A—The president of the association shall appoint annually the following standing committees: the nominating committee, the auditing committee, and the program committees. Other special committees may be appointed as needed.

Section B—The nominating committee, after careful consideration of the young farmer association personnel, shall annually place in nomination candidates for the various offices.

Section C—The auditing committee shall examine annually the books of the treasurer and report its findings to the members.

Section D—The program committees shall plan the objectives, activities, and ways and means for the annual program of work. Adoption of the proposed program of work shall be by a majority vote of the members.

Article III—Program

Section A—The primary objective of the program of the association shall be to meet the educational needs of the association's members.

Section B—The association shall not engage in competitive business ventures.

Section C—The association shall not engage in political activities.

Section D—The association shall not engage in competitive sports activities with other organizations.

Section E—The program of the association shall be coordinated with the policies and program of the school and of vocational education in agriculture.

Section F—The program of the association shall be submitted to the officials of the school for their approval.

• • •

Explanation of Constitution and Bylaws—At first, some of the items in the constitution and bylaws may seem trivial and insignificant, but all are there for a purpose and are based on considered judgment. Several are safeguards for the teacher of agriculture, the school, and the young farmer students sponsoring an association.

In Article I of the constitution, the young farmer association is defined as a nonprofit and nonpolitical organization of voluntary membership. This is necessary in a school-sponsored organization because a school is a public institution supported by public funds. A public institution or an organization sponsored by it cannot afford to engage in business or political activities. The purpose of a school and its organizations is educational and must remain that if support of the public is to be maintained.

Extensive business activities involving considerable sums of money should be avoided in young farmer associations. If extensive business activities are sponsored by a young farmer association, it is easy for these activities to encroach on the primary aim of the organization, which is education in agriculture. If there is a need for the young farmers to conduct business activities cooperatively, they should organize, separate and apart from the young farmer association, a cooperative. If this is done, there will be no justification for criticism of the school by businesses operating in the community.

The definition of a young farmer association as a group of young people who are progressively establishing themselves in farming and who are enrolled for systematic instruction protects an association from becoming "watered down" with young people who are not trying to become established in farming. Without this safeguard an association may have a number of members who are there because of social, recreational, and other reasons. The requirement of simultaneous membership in good standing in a young farmer class makes an association a part of the educational program of a school and distinguishes it from other organizations that young people may join. Without this section of the constitution, some young farmers may drift into the habit of attending the association meetings without attending the class meetings. Without the benefits of the class instruction, these young people may have an undesirable effect on the type of program sponsored by an association. The section stating that the association will automatically be discontinued at the end of the young farmer program in a school guarantees that the association will remain a device for broadening the educational opportunities of the young farmer program and not a means of establishing another farm organization.

Article VI of the constitution, regarding dues and funds, prevents dues from becoming prohibitive and safeguards the funds of the association. The provisions for fixing dues at a minimum, for prohibiting special assessments, and for requiring a two-thirds majority to establish the amount of the dues are designed to prevent dues from becoming a financial burden. No young farmers should be denied the opportunities of membership because they cannot afford to belong. A young farmer association should not become an exclusive fraternity or club. It should be available to all the young farmers in a community interested in increasing their education.

The provision prohibiting special assessments assures a prospective member that the association will not become a financial burden at a later date. Organizations have been destroyed because of frequent special assessments for good causes. Some persons will not join an organization that allows special assessments. A young farmer association has little need for funds, so dues should be nominal. Activities of a local young farmer association should usually pay their own way.

The section regarding the necessity of the school's approval of the constitution and program is a further safeguard to prevent the association from engaging in activities that would embarrass the school. It is a safeguard to prevent the neglect of the educational objectives of the association in favor of other objectives.

The section stating that the association shall not engage in competitive sports activities with other organizations is a safeguard for the teacher of agriculture. Teachers are busy, and they are not athletic coaches. Unless the constitution and bylaws prohibit competitive sports, an association may drift until it becomes an athletic association. Young people are interested in sports and may easily point a program of activities in this direction. Since the school is sponsoring the association, the teacher would be obligated to attend these athletic contests. If young farmers wish to engage in competitive sports, they should join or form an organization that is not school-sponsored and has athletics as its function.

Advantages of a Constitution and Bylaws—A constitution and bylaws are means of safeguarding an association. They are also excellent means of educating the young farmers themselves regarding the advantages, limitations, and possibilities of a young farmer association. They are excellent public relations devices regarding a young farmer association and are also means of educating the administration and board of education of a school regarding an association. Preparation of the constitution and bylaws is excellent training for similar activities in other adult organizations.

PROGRAM

Program of Activities—Young farmer association members need to plan their program for a year in advance. The program should be based on the primary and contributory objectives of the association, and it should contribute to the instructional phase of the young farmer program. A balance of activities contributing to the various objectives should be attempted. For example, all the activities of an association should not be social, nor should all be leadership activities.

If the instructional program in a young farmer course is based on establishment in farming, involving problem areas such as financing, renting, partnerships, leases, agreements, and maintaining and adjusting machinery, a program of work for the association might result that would be similar to the following program:

Educational Activities

1. Assist with the instructional program.
   a. Locate materials for study on leases and agreements.
   b. Secure machinery for maintenance, repair, and adjustment.
   c. Secure consultants when needed for discussion meetings.
   d. Provide for on-the-farm meetings related to the course of study.
   e. Provide farm demonstrations related to the course of instruction.
   f. Have members perform class demonstrations related to the course of instruction.
   g. Appoint members to be in charge of movie projection operation.
   h. Sponsor educational field trips related to the course of instruction.
2. Cooperate on matters of education with other agricultural organizations.
   a. Keep other organizations informed of the program and the activities of the young farmers.
   b. Attend educational meetings of other farm organizations.
3. Assist each member in developing a library of new agricultural information.
   a. Discuss at meetings new information in books, bulletins, and articles.
   b. Present sources of new information.

Leadership Activities

1. Present radio and television programs related to the course of instruction.
2. Provide demonstrations and practice in parliamentary procedure.
3. Conduct demonstrations and discussions on how to work with others.
4. Provide a publicity program regarding young farmer activities and accomplishments.
5. Invite FFA members who graduate or drop out of school to become members.
6. Sponsor an FFA officers' training school.
7. Provide speakers for FFA meetings.

Community Service Activities

1. Provide agricultural demonstrations for the community.
2. Conduct a farm safety campaign in the community.
3. Assist with the local agricultural fair.
4. Conduct a fire prevention campaign in the community.

Cooperative Activities

1. Cooperate with adult farmer classes of the vocational agriculture department by having members attend classes and report back to the young farmer association.
2. Cooperate with the Extension Service by attending its meetings.
3. Cooperate with adult farmer organizations by having a young farmer attend their meetings and report back to the young farmer association.
4. Cooperate in purchases of seed and fertilizer.
5. Cooperate in the building of terraces, grass waterways, flumes, and dams.

Meeting Conduct Activities

1. Conduct parliamentary procedure practice sessions.
2. Promote use of good business procedures at all regular meetings.
3. Plan meetings and publish agenda.

Public Relations Activities

1. Submit news articles, following school policy, for releases.
2. Participate in one radio program a year.
3. Hold an annual achievement banquet.
4. Distribute copies of the local program of work.
5. Nominate persons for honorary membership.

Contest and Award Activities

1. Conduct an awards program.
2. Conduct appropriate educational contests.
3. Provide recognition for persons participating in contest and award programs.
4. Develop standards for award programs.

Social and Recreational Activities

1. Conduct one meeting during the year with a neighboring association.
2. Provide refreshments for young farmer class meetings.
3. Sponsor an annual banquet.
4. Sponsor a square dance for members and guests.
5. Sponsor a recreational program following class meetings.

Calendar of Activities—If a calendar of activities for a year were based on the program of activities just suggested and on an instructional program for getting established in farming, for increasing soil fertility, and for maintaining farm machinery, a schedule resembling the following might result:

July

First Wednesday

Planning the program for the year.
Discussion of opportunities for becoming established in farming.
Association business meeting.
Refreshments and recreation.

Third Wednesday
Discussion on obtaining and using credit.
Association business meeting.
Refreshments.

August
First Wednesday
Field trip to observe approved soil practices.
Third Wednesday
Discussion of approved soil practices.
Association business meeting.
Refreshments and recreation.

September
First Wednesday
Discussion of fertilizer practices for wheat.
Association business meeting.
Refreshments.
Second Wednesday
Square dance.
Third Wednesday
Discussion of approved practices for maintaining and increasing organic matter in the soil.
Association business meeting.
Refreshments and recreation.

October
First Wednesday
Discussion of soil conservation practices for the winter.
Association business meeting.
Refreshments.
Third Wednesday
Planning the farm machinery maintenance and repair program.
Association business meeting—organization of a farm safety campaign.
Refreshments and recreation.

November
First Wednesday
Farm machinery maintenance, repair, and adjustment.
Refreshments.
Second Wednesday
Farm machinery maintenance, repair, and adjustment.
Refreshments.
Third Wednesday
Farm machinery maintenance, repair, and adjustment.
Refreshments.
Fourth Wednesday
Farm machinery maintenance, repair, and adjustment.
Association business meeting.
Refreshments.

December
First Wednesday
Farm machinery maintenance, repair, and adjustment.
Refreshments.
Second Wednesday
Farm machinery maintenance, repair, and adjustment.
Refreshments.
Third Wednesday
Christmas party.
Christmas holidays
A welding or farm carpentry short course meeting four hours a day for five days and taught by a special instructor.

January
- First Wednesday
  - Discussion of problems of becoming established in farming.
  - Association business meeting—organization of a fire prevention campaign.
  - Refreshments and recreation.
- Third Wednesday
  - Continued discussion of problems of becoming established in farming.
  - Refreshments.

February
- First Wednesday
  - Continued discussion of problems of becoming established in farming.
  - Association business meeting.
  - Refreshments and recreation.
- Third Wednesday
  - Discussion of approved practices in soil preparation.
  - Refreshments.

March
- First Wednesday
  - Continued discussion of approved practices in soil preparation.
  - Association business meeting.
  - Refreshments and recreation.
- Third Wednesday
  - Discussion of soil fertility.
  - Refreshments.

April
- First Wednesday
  - Discussion of problems of getting established in farming.
  - Association business meeting.
  - Refreshments and recreation.

May
- First Wednesday
  - Continued discussion of problems of getting established in farming.
  - Association business meeting.

June
- First Wednesday
  - Meeting on a farm to observe approved soil and cropping practices.
  - Association business meeting.
  - Refreshments and recreation.
- Third Wednesday
  - Picnic supper.

Developing a Program of Work—Much of a program of work may be developed by committees meeting at times other than at association or class sessions. If this is done, most association meetings may be held after instructional sessions.

To obtain maximum benefits from an association, all members should be delegated some responsibility for the success of the program. This can be accomplished through committee apppointments and individual assignments. Most of these assignments should contribute to personal educational objectives.

State and National Affiliations—Several states have state young farmer associations. Local chapters may affiliate with their state association, usually by paying nominal dues. The purposes of the state associations are to:

1. Coordinate activities of local chapters.
2. Provide educational activities that local chapters have difficulty sponsoring.
3. Provide educational aids.
4. Coordinate statewide functions.
5. Promote exchange of ideas.
6. Increase opportunities for leadership.
7. Promote cooperation with agricultural businesses.
8. Promote participation at the national level.
9. Provide an awards program.
10. Strengthen the public relations program.

At the national level, a National Young Farmer Institute is held each year. Each state chapter may send voting delegates. Local chapter members may attend the National Young Farmer Institute.

SUMMARY

Teacher's Responsibility—The responsibility of a teacher of agriculture to a young farmer association is that of adviser. A teacher of agriculture needs to take the initiative in presenting to a young farmer class the possibilities of a young farmer association. The teacher's advice and help are needed in developing the organization and in developing the constitution and bylaws. Informal officer training is usually necessary.

Other than this, the role of a teacher should be that of an adviser only. Association members are delegated definite responsibilities related to the success of their young farmer program, and the teacher needs to stand aside and let the young farmers learn by performing these duties. A teacher may lessen the work with young farmers by acting as an adviser to them and by refraining from performing the work of the association for them. A young farmer association need not increase the work of a teacher who acts only as an adviser.

A teacher may serve as a catalytic agent for a young farmer association and should provide effective help without the members being unduly aware of it. The teacher should be constantly alert for opportunities to give credit for the success of the association to the young farmer members and should avoid the handling of monies and the negotiating of business transactions for a young farmer association.

Relationships to Other Young Farmer Groups—A young farmer association is not in conflict or competition with other young farmer groups. The objectives of many young farmer groups differ considerably from those of a young farmer association. Young farmer groups subsidiary to farm organizations usually engage in business and political action. Young farmer associations perform neither of these functions.

Even if the objectives are parallel, young farmer education is such a large task and is so important that there is little danger of it becoming overly organized.

CHAPTER

31

How to Organize Adult Courses in Agriculture

Agriculture programs for adults may provide specific courses for the following groups:

1. Adult farmers.
2. Workers in off-farm occupations requiring knowledge and skills in agriculture.
3. Adults with non-vocational interests in agriculture.

This chapter will discuss the procedures for organizing courses for (1) adult farmers and (2) workers in off-farm agricultural occupations.

ADULT FARMER COURSES

Courses in agriculture for older farmers provide systematic instruction concerning practical farm problems and activities. These courses are organized for persons who have entered upon the work of the farm. The enrollees of a course carry on farming activities involving the use of approved practices related to the course of instruction under the supervision of the teacher of the course. *Adult farmer courses are established under public school supervision and control.*

Objectives of Courses for Adult Farmers—The primary objective of courses for adult farmers should be to develop the ability of farmers through systematic instruction to solve their problems intelligently and to perform the manipulative jobs needed on their farms.

Some contributory objectives may be stated as follows:

1. To provide up-to-date information involving approved practices pertaining to farming.
2. To develop abilities of farmers which will enable them to perform their necessary farm mechanics jobs.
3. To develop abilities which will improve the management of their farm businesses.
4. To develop abilities for "farm-family living" programs.
5. To develop abilities in food production and conservation.
6. To develop abilities in cooperative activities which will result in desirable farm practices.
7. To develop abilities which will result in making their farms better places to live.

A teacher's objectives for adult farmer courses may involve the following in addition to those previously listed:

1. To help change or improve certain farm abilities in the community as a whole and to extend the educational services of the school and the program of vocational education in agriculture to a larger percentage of the community.
2. To make new friendships and thus increase the effectiveness of the school's program.
3. To lower the per capita cost for the agricultural instruction.
4. To help create and maintain desirable attitudes between the farmers and the public school.
5. To afford an opportunity for the teacher of agriculture to render educational services in the community.

Types of Courses—*Farm mechanics courses* in the repair, maintenance, adjustment, and construction of machinery and equipment have been very popular among adult farmers. Farmers in this type of course develop the necessary abilities to repair, maintain, and adjust their farm machinery and to construct many labor-saving devices.

In surveys, farmers indicate that they receive the following values from farm mechanics courses:

1. Development of abilities to adjust machinery and make minor repairs.
2. Opportunity to use tools and equipment before purchasing them for their home shops.
3. Development of abilities needed to construct simple farm machines.

Courses in dairying, poultry, swine, field crops, feeds and feeding, soil conservation, and farm management always have been important and will continue to be important. Efficient production will always be essential in successful farming; consequently, farmers will continue to need courses in which they can discuss *approved practices* and efficiency measures of production. In the past, insufficient emphasis has been placed on courses of this type in many communities. A large number of such courses should be promoted in the future if the adult education needs in agriculture are to be met.

Farm-family living and *rural citizenship courses* meet a real need. Adult farmers welcome instruction on the ways to better their farm-family life and on the understanding of local, county, state, and national problems and their relationships to agriculture and to them as farmers.

Food production, conservation, and processing courses for farm families are popular in some communities. The three main advantages often listed for courses in food production and processing are as follows:

1. Training in food preservation is obtained.
2. Equipment for food processing not found at home is available.
3. Time and labor spent in food preservation are reduced.

Farm Business Management Courses—Farm business management courses for farm families have been very successful in several states. These courses are based on the keeping and interpreting of farm records and the reorganization of the farm business, in line with family goals, as a result of the analysis and interpretation of the farm records. This type of course has been most successful where support services are available for summarizing and analyzing the farm account records.

Characteristics of Adult Farmers—Adult farmers may be characterized as follows:

1. They are interested in gaining new knowledge and in developing needed skills. They attend courses for a purpose.
2. They are interested in selecting and adopting approved practices which will work successfully for them.
3. They are interested in relating their experiences if tactfully approached.
4. They want to develop abilities which will assist them in their farming activities. *They desire to learn by doing.*
5. They are capable of thinking through their problems.
6. They desire practical information which they can use.
7. They are interested in cooperating for the good of the community.
8. They have considerable creative ability.
9. They are not interested in fads and frills.
10. They are appreciative of the education provided.
11. They are the persons who have a major part in making an agriculture teacher's job secure.

ORGANIZING AN ADULT FARMER COURSE

Procedures—Before teachers attempt to organize adult farmer programs, they should consult their superintendents, principals, directors of vocational education, and school boards. They should explain to them the aids and values of adult farmer courses, ask for their support, and receive their cooperation before organizing courses. After they have received permission to undertake an adult farmer program, they should meet with an advisory council to determine the needs for instruction. They should then survey facilities and available special instructors.

Teachers over the years have tried all sorts of devices in organizing classes. None has been very successful, with the exception of advisory councils and committees. Following is a summary of recommended successful practices in organizing an adult course:

1. Study community needs with the help of the advisory council.
2. Determine with the help of the council the more pressing agricultural needs of the community.
3. With the help of the council, organize an advisory committee for each of these needs.
4. Use advisory committees in organizing specific adult courses.
5. With the help of each advisory committee, determine the objectives and ways and means of evaluating the adult course it is sponsoring.
6. With the help of the advisory committees, determine the place and time of courses. Locate course centers for the convenience of the enrollees.

7. With the help of the advisory committees, determine the number of farmers to enroll in each course.
8. Ask advisory committee members to enroll class members. Provide enrollment forms. (See Figure 31.1.)
9. Place a preliminary news announcement in the newspapers at the time the advisory committee is enrolling members.
10. Hold another meeting of the advisory committee to check on persons enrolled in the course. Also begin making preliminary plans for the first few meetings of the course.
11. Visit each class member who has been enrolled by an advisory committee member, before the first meeting of a course.
12. Hold an advisory committee meeting to prepare detailed plans for a course.
13. Place articles in the local newspapers, giving time and place of the meetings, a few days before the first meeting of a course.
14. Send out a reminder card announcing the first meeting.
15. Hold advisory committee meetings during a course for the purpose of evaluating the course and making further plans.
16. Place in local newspapers periodic news articles concerning a course.

Several techniques have proved ineffective in recruiting membership for a course. Some teachers hold organizational meetings. These are usually not effective because only a few farmers attend meetings of this type. Cards and letters plus newspaper articles are usually not effective procedures when not used in relation to personal solicitation by advisory committee members.

Vocational Education in Agriculture
____________________ School

This certifies that ____________________
is enrolled in the Adult Farmer Course on ____________________
____
for the school year, 19_____-_____.

____
Instructor

Enrolled by ____________________
Advisory Committee Representative

Fig. 31.1. Adult farmer membership card.

News Items—Occasional news articles are a desirable means of informing farmers of the adult farmer program being conducted by a school. News articles make the work of advisory committee members easier when they are recruiting enrollees for a course. Farmers who have read a news item about a proposed adult course are prepared to discuss their enrollment intelligently when asked to enroll by committee members.

A news article announcing a course also informs prospective class members who are not asked to enroll by a committee member about the course so that they can enroll in the course at the school.

Occasional news articles may also be used during the progress of a course as a means of keeping a community informed.

Circular Letters—A circular letter is sometimes used to announce a course and pave the way for the securing of enrollment by advisory committee members. The following circular letter illustrates one type that may be used.

• • •

____

__________________ 19 _____

As you know, the production of potatoes is the main source of income in this community. We plan to conduct a course at the high school for farmers interested in making greater profits from their potatoes. The first meeting will be held at 7:30 next Tuesday evening, October 14, in the agriculture classroom.

Some problems which have been suggested by potato growers are: When is the best time to harvest potatoes? What methods are most satisfactory in harvesting potatoes? What grading methods are best? What advantages are to be gained by marketing cooperatively? What markets are best for this community? These problems and many others will be discussed by the growers of this community.

I am sure the discussions will be both interesting and profitable. If you desire to enroll in the course, please do so as soon as possible. The enrollment in the course will be limited to 20 farmers. We will be expecting you.

Very truly yours,
R. W. Johnson
Agriculture Instructor

P.S. A potato grading demonstration will be given by two FFA youths Tuesday night.

• • •

For a discussion of the techniques of writing for farmers, see Chapter 11, "How to Develop a Desirable Public Relations Program."

Deciding on Courses to Offer—The courses offered should be based on the interests, needs, and capabilities of the farmers. Courses must be selected for which qualified instructors and adequate facilities can be secured. It is impossible to select courses that are of interest to everyone in a community, as there are many diversified interests in most communities. However, it is important to select courses that are needed and to secure enrollees who are interested in the instruction and who will benefit by it.

Using a general advisory council to study the needs of a community is one of the best procedures for deciding on the courses to offer. After this has been done, an advisory committee for each of these needs may be established to organize adult courses for each need or for those that are most pressing.

DEVELOPING COURSE CONTENT FOR ADULT FARMER COURSES

The general principles of course of study planning are discussed in Chapter 13, "How to Develop Courses of Study." This chapter should be reviewed before a course of study is developed for an adult farmer course.

Proper Content Essential—It is very important in developing the content of a course to make sure that it contains activities which provide for *learning by* *doing*. The success or failure of an adult farmer course is largely dependent on the course content and the teaching procedures used by the instructor. Provision must be made in a course for the development of essential abilities, skills, attitudes, and understandings pertaining to the immediate problems common to the farmers.

Teacher Plans—Planning done prior to the first meeting of a course is of value in getting a course off to a good start. The following procedure is suggested:

1. Review the local situation through surveys, personal interviews, and the like to determine the immediate problems of the enrollees.
2. List the abilities you hope enrollees will develop.
3. Consider the facilities available for developing needed abilities.
4. Decide on the objectives of the course—that is, what you hope to accomplish—and decide on how you propose to achieve the objectives.
5. Consider the qualifications and abilities of the special instructor if one is to be used.
6. List the activities or problems you propose to include in the course.
7. Review these activities with the advisory committee for the course and make any revisions that are necessary.
8. Use the proposed outline as a guide in developing the course content with the enrollees at the first meeting.

Selecting Course Problem Areas—At the first meeting of a course, the instructor should discuss and formulate with the enrollees the objectives of the course. The farmers should then be given an opportunity to suggest the problem areas and activities they think should be included in the course. These activities may be listed on the chalkboard by the instructor.

The instructor and the group should then review this list, keeping the following in mind:

1. The specific needs of the farmers enrolled.
2. The facilities available.
3. The availability of essential experimental data.
4. The activities which will provide for the development of needed abilities.

After these problem areas and activities have been carefully evaluated in terms of need, and after the feasibility of including them in the course has been discussed, selections of problem areas and activities may be made. These may then be listed on the chalkboard by the instructor approximately in the order in which they will be discussed in the course, considering the seasonal sequence of each. Problem areas and activities which are closely related should be taken up consecutively, insofar as possible, in order to bring out interrelated or closely associated information.

PROMOTING SUPERVISED FARMING PROGRAMS OF ADULTS

Every person enrolled in an adult farmer course is expected to conduct a supervised farming program consisting of activities related to the course of instruction. This gives an enrollee an opportunity to apply the knowledge and skills gained through the instruction received in a course.

Kinds of Activities—Activities in the farming program of an adult farmer may be classified as follows:

1. Approved practices which will result in the better conduct of one or more farm enterprises.
2. Approved practices which will result in the improvement of the management of the farm business.
3. Production enterprises not previously conducted on an enrollee's farm, such as growing potatoes or raising swine.
4. Improvement projects, such as growing a green manure crop or building a poultry house.
5. Cooperative activities with other adult farmers which will result in the improvement in the conduct of one or more farm enterprises.

Instruction on the Farm—For a discussion of how to organize on-the-farm instruction, see the section on this topic in Chapter 29, "How to Organize a Program for Young Adults."

OFF-FARM ORIENTED AGRICULTURE COURSES FOR ADULTS

In addition to courses for young and older farmers, most rural and all urban communities need courses of the following types:

1. Retraining vocational courses for adults preparing to enter off-farm occupations requiring knowledge and skills in agriculture.
2. Upgrading vocational courses for adults presently working in off-farm occupations requiring knowledge and skills in agriculture.

The retraining and upgrading courses offered for off-farm agricultural workers would depend on the types of agricultural industries in the community. Some of the courses offered for off-farm agricultural workers are:

1. Servicing farm machinery.
2. Installing farm equipment.
3. Working with farmers.
4. Using agricultural chemicals.
5. Manufacturing fertilizers.
6. Mixing feeds.
7. Planning agricultural credit programs.
8. Serving nonfarm agricultural interests.
9. Diagnosing crop problems.
10. Consulting with farmers.
11. Operating hatcheries.
12. Operating grain elevators.
13. Operating agricultural cooperatives.
14. Processing fruit.
15. Marketing livestock—middleman problems.
16. Handling nursery products.
17. Managing lawns or turfs.
18. Landscaping homes.
19. Growing flowers.
20. Growing perennials.
21. Caring for pets.
22. Gardening.
23. Growing trees.
24. Producing herbs.
25. Preserving food.

26. Investing in agriculture.
27. Controlling pests.
28. Handling and caring for horses.
29. Using and adjusting agricultural and nursery equipment, such as power lawn mowers, sprayers, and weeders.
30. Organizing off-farm agricultural businesses.

The techniques of organizing courses for adults in off-farm agricultural occupations are very similar to those used for organizing adult farmer courses. An advisory council should be used to determine needs, and an advisory committee should be used for each course to obtain enrollment and assist in organizing content. The primary difference is that close working relationships with employers are essential when teachers are organizing and conducting courses for off-farm agricultural workers.

Teachers organizing courses for off-farm workers in jobs requiring knowledge and skills in agriculture should review, because the general principles are the same, the preceding sections of this chapter which are labeled as follows:

1. "Organizing an Adult Farmer Course."
2. "Developing Course Content for Adult Farmer Courses."

PART

Providing and Using Facilities, Equipment, Supplies, and Teaching Aids

CHAPTER

32

How to House Agricultural Education

FACILITIES FOR AGRICULTURAL EDUCATION

New Emphasis in Agricultural Education Demands More Adequate Facilities—The increasing attention to a broadened program of education in agriculture requires more adequate facilities than some schools have provided in the past. In many established departments the facilities will have to be expanded. New facilities should provide space and equipment for comprehensive programs of education in agriculture.

Careful Planning Essential—Many costly errors have been made in constructing buildings. A reliable architect should be employed to draw plans, develop specifications, and supervise the construction of a building.

Architects should be advised by teachers of agriculture, state supervisors, and school administrators regarding the program, the methods used, and the special needs in agricultural education. Many architects do not understand the special requirements of education in agriculture and, therefore, make obvious errors. An architect's plans should be checked carefully before a building is started. Some of the basic requirements of agricultural education buildings or facilities are discussed in the following paragraphs. The essential features of a building must, in addition, meet a state's school building standards.

Location and Architecture—The facilities for agriculture may be a part of the main school building in a community, or they may be located in a separate building. Many communities are providing separate buildings for agriculture which include classrooms, shops, laboratories, and greenhouses. A separate building has a number of advantages, some of which follow:

Fig. 32.1. Agriculture building in Georgia. It includes a classroom, an agriculture mechanics shop, and a school-community cannery.

1. It stimulates the pride of students in their facilities.
2. It eliminates the danger of shop noises interfering with other classes.
3. It concentrates all agricultural activities in one area.
4. It attracts the attention of the community.

If the agricultural facilities are a part of a main school building, a wing location is preferred so that additions may be made as more space is needed. An agriculture mechanics shop is usually built away from the regular classrooms in a school because of the noise from the shop. For best results, no classroom should be placed above a shop. Attaching an agricultural unit to a main building has several advantages:

1. The heat, water, and lighting facilities used in the main building are available.
2. Students do not feel set apart from the rest of the school system as they sometimes do when a separate agriculture building is used.
3. It is easier to maintain desirable behavior in going to and from the agriculture department.

When a separate building is provided for agriculture, it should be located near the main school building. This will save time in passing to and from classes and will lessen the discipline problems at that time. A separate building should fit into the general scheme of the buildings on a school campus. The materials used in its construction and the type of architecture should correspond with the materials and architecture of the other school buildings. However, if too much attention is given to conformity to other buildings in materials and architecture, the lower cost, one of the advantages of a special building, may be lost. Materials such as concrete blocks, cinder blocks, stucco, brick, stone, tile, and wood have been successfully used for constructing facilities for agriculture departments.

Rooms to Include in One Unit—The classrooms, agriculture mechanics shop, office–conference room, storage rooms, washroom, toilets, laboratories, and greenhouses for an agriculture department should be in one unit. The most common type of unit has a washroom, an office–conference room, and a storage room located between the classrooms and the agriculture mechanics shop.

A community may prefer to have an FFA chapter room and rooms for cold storage and processing of agricultural products included in the unit. Some favor having these auxiliary facilities constructed as separate buildings.

Ventilation and Lighting—All buildings should be well ventilated and lighted. A general rule to follow is to have the window area in a room equal to 20 per cent of the floor area. Thirty foot-candles of artificial light should be available for work areas. Exhaust fans for ventilating may be used in rooms which do not have facilities for adequate ventilation. Exhaust fans are usually needed in agriculture mechanics shops.

Heating—An adequate heating system must be provided. Wherever feasible it should be a part of a school's main heating plant. If the central heating plant for a school is used for heating the agriculture building, a cutoff valve may be provided so that the building or unit for agriculture may be heated without heating the main school building. When a separate heating plant for the agricultural facilities is used, it should be of adequate size. It doesn't pay to try to economize on the size of a heating plant. Heating systems requiring blowers are often not satisfactory for classrooms because they make enough noise to disturb class discussions.

For energy efficiency, the facilities should be equipped with thermostats in each area. Storage rooms, agriculture mechanics shops, and classrooms, for example, all require different heating levels.

Size—Adequate space should be provided to meet the needs of a community. The space for agricultural education will depend on a number of factors, such as the following:

1. The number of teachers of agriculture. A one-teacher department will need but one classroom. If there are two or more teachers of agriculture, there is a need for two or more classrooms.
2. The number of students enrolled.
3. The number of young and older adults enrolled.

A community, in deciding on the amount of space for agriculture, should consider the unmet needs for training in agriculture and the probable future demand for space if a program were offered to meet these needs. Many communities have found that their demand for education in agriculture is increased several times after they have provided desirable facilities.

An average community with one teacher of agriculture needs from 5,500 to 8,500 square feet of floor space for classrooms, office–conference rooms, toilets, an agriculture mechanics shop, storage rooms, and a laboratory in order to meet the agricultural education needs of high school students, young farmers, adult farmers, and workers in off-farm agricultural businesses. Additional space is needed if greenhouses are provided.

CLASSROOMS

Classrooms used exclusively for agriculture are desired because they can be organized to meet the needs for education in agriculture. A room can be made

(Photo from U.S. Office of Education)

Fig. 32.2. Agriculture building at Salinas, California.

more attractive and more suitable for effective teaching in agriculture when it is not used for other classes.

When a separate building for agriculture is provided, the agriculture classroom is usually located in this building. If the agriculture classroom in a school is located in the main building, it should be on the ground level. The most desirable location for an agriculture classroom is facing the south on the ground floor, and it is preferable that the room be situated so that people can enter it without going through the rest of the building. When meetings are held in a department, the school does not usually want the people attending to wander all over the school building.

Size and Shape—A classroom 28′ wide by 30′ to 40′ long is adequate for an average community with one teacher of agriculture. Additional classrooms are needed in multiple-teacher departments. A minimum of 45 square feet of floor space is needed for each student in the largest class in a department. Offsets in the walls or L-shaped classrooms are undesirable because they have a bad effect on the acoustics.

Basic Principles of Construction—A classroom should be constructed so that it is possible to have a chalkboard running the full distance of the wall the students will be facing. Adequate provision should be made for running water; duplex convenience outlets; gas; a demonstration table; a laboratory testing area with an acid-resistant table and sink; a bulletin board; and sufficient cabinet space for bulletins, books, notebooks, supervised occupational experience record books, magazines, and supplies. Tables and chairs, rather than fixed seats, are frequently used in agriculture classrooms. They are arranged so that the students do not have to face the light. The windows should be positioned high enough from the floor so that a 32″ cabinet or table may be placed below them.

Ceilings should be treated acoustically and should be approximately 12′ high. The floor in a classroom may be hardwood, tile, or linoleum. A concrete floor is not satisfactory because of noise. An acoustically treated ceiling and a tile or linoleum floor will decrease the noise in a classroom. Noise is an effective deterrent to efficient learning and desirable behavior. A large amount of tack-board space in a classroom will also assist in absorbing noise.

If the agriculture classroom in a department is next to the agriculture mechanics shop, the dividing wall should be soundproof. The placing of a

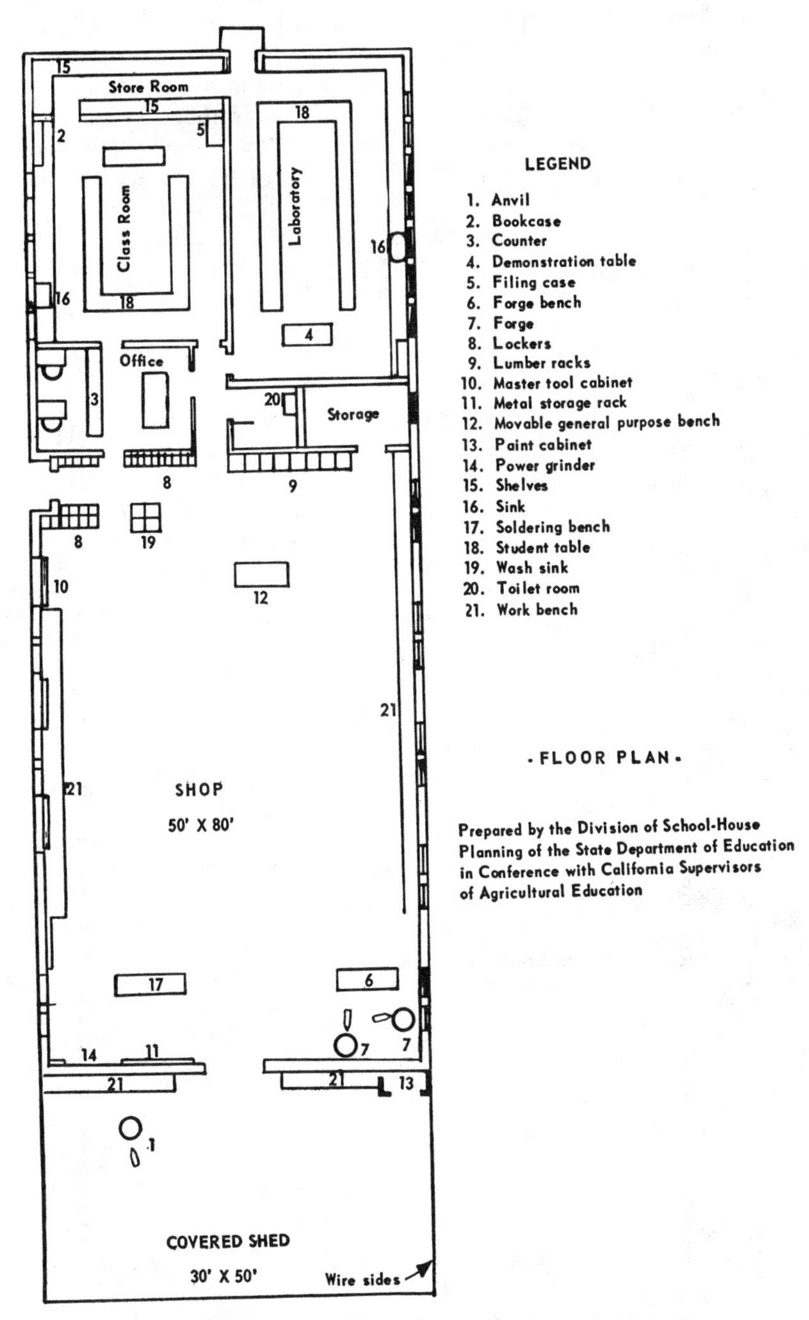

Fig. 32.3. A suggested layout for a two-teacher agricultural unit.

storeroom, an office–conference room, and toilets between an agriculture mechanics shop and a classroom will eliminate most of the shop noises from the classroom. A window between a classroom and an adjoining agriculture mechanics shop is of value so that a teacher may observe shop activities from the classroom and vice-versa. An office–conference room between a shop and a classroom is usually provided with windows so that a teacher can see into the shop or the classroom. If this is done, a clear view of the classroom, the office–conference room, and the shop may be had from any of them.

The *storage room* for a classroom should provide sufficient space for essential equipment, supplies, and teaching aids used in connection with classroom activities. Many of the newer buildings for agriculture have storage rooms for the classrooms having as much as 350 square feet of floor space.

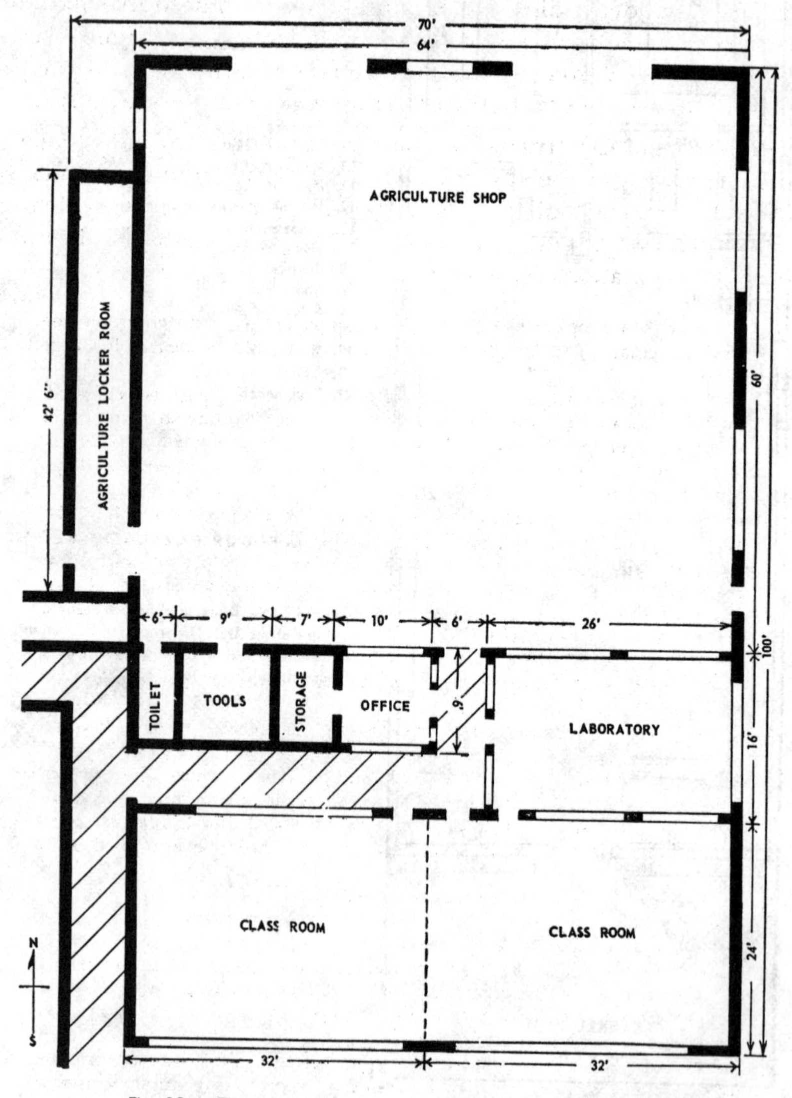

Fig. 32.4. Plans for the agriculture department at Marengo, Illinois.

AGRICULTURE MECHANICS SHOP

A functional agriculture mechanics program requires considerable space for the maintenance, repair, and adjustment of agricultural machinery and the construction of projects. Agriculture mechanics is an integral part of the instruction in agriculture, and each class usually receives some mechanics instruction each year. For these reasons, it is usually best for a vocational education in agriculture department to have exclusive use of its agriculture mechanics shop. The use of an agriculture mechanics shop for non-agriculture classes, bus storage, and general storage materially decreases the efficiency and effectiveness of an agriculture mechanics program.

Size and Shape—An agriculture mechanics shop should be 40′ to 50′ wide and 80′ to 100′ long, depending on community needs. A desirable minimum is 150 square feet of free floor space for each student in the largest class in a department, plus 1,400 square feet for permanent equipment. A shop narrower than 40′ does not permit efficient arrangement and use of space.

Basic Principles of Construction—There are a number of fundamental principles to be followed in the construction of an agriculture mechanics shop, regardless of the type of building used. These basic principles, which might be stated as approved practices in shop construction, should be indicated in the plans and specifications for a shop.

1. The *roof* in a shop should be properly supported so as to eliminate the need for pillars. The central portion of a shop should be cleared for large projects.
2. An *overhead door* at least 24′ to 27′ wide and 14′ to 16′ high is needed. It should be located at least 8′ from the corner of the building so as to permit a working area near the door. A *small entrance door* should be provided in a convenient location so as to eliminate the necessity of opening the large door every time the shop is entered.
3. The *windows* should be placed as near the ceiling as practical and 42″ to 44″ from the floor so that they will be far enough above the benches placed along the wall that the students working at these benches will not break the windows in front of them. The window area should be equal to at least 20 per cent of the floor space. Windowsills may slope at a sharp angle to prevent their use as shelves.
4. *Tool cabinet* space on the walls should be provided. The windows should be spaced so as to provide room for the tool cabinets which are to be placed on the walls.
5. The *floor* may be of concrete. Concrete floors should be properly bedded with a fill of gravel, tile, cinders, or sand to a depth of 4″ to 6″. The concrete should be applied over this fill to a depth of 6″ or more. The strength of the floor should be sufficient to support machines weighing 15 or more tons. One or two floor drains should be provided and located so as to drain the entire floor area, and these drains should be equipped with sump pumps.
6. A 20′ to 24′ *ceiling* is satisfactory for most shops.
7. The *electrical wiring* in a shop should provide convenience outlets along the walls at suitable intervals for plugging in equipment such as electric grinders, drills, soldering irons, arc welders, and circular saws, and extension cords for this equipment. Provision should be made for both 110- and 220-volt, single-phase and 220-volt, three-phase current. The 220-volt, single-phase current is needed to operate an arc welder. The 220-volt, three-phase current is needed to operate motors of ½ horsepower or larger. Long service cords may be avoided by providing duplex convenience outlets over work benches at 10′ to 15′ intervals. One or two conven-

ience outlets in the floor with a box which fits flush with the floor may be needed for power tools. Three or more rows of lights will be needed in a shop of average size, with each row being controlled by a separate switch. The lights should be placed near the ceiling and properly protected. Electrical service bars with 120 volts and 240 volts are recommended. There should be, for safety and other reasons, a master shut-off switch for all stationary power equipment.

8. An adequate *chimney* must be provided which will provide sufficient draft. If a forge is used, its pipe should be at least 10″ in diameter. Provision should also be made for removing the fumes from the arc welders. A hood for this purpose may be placed above the welding table.
9. An *exhaust fan* should be installed to remove the smoke and gases from the arc and acetylene welding areas and the forge area.
10. An *overhead beam* with a chain hoist for lifting heavy objects should be provided in the farm machinery area.
11. If a *ramp* leading to the large doorway is necessary, it should have not more than a 20 per cent slope. A drain should be placed at the foot of the ramp.
12. Adequate *chalkboard space* should be provided in a shop.
13. The *storage room* for a shop should be large. Many of the newer shops have storage rooms 20′ by 20′ to 26′. These larger storage rooms are used to store supplies, such as tools used only occasionally, and lumber. If the storage room is used for storing lumber, it should be long enough to handle 16-foot lengths of lumber.
14. An *all-weather driveway* should lead to the large overhead door in a shop so that machinery and equipment may be moved in and out of the shop at any time.
15. A *patio*, an all-weather surfaced area, adjacent to a shop's overhead door and enclosed by a non-climbable fence or wall, adds considerable work space and provides a place to store flammable materials and machinery. In many states, such areas may be used for several months each year. Many departments have areas of this type that are 2,400 square feet in size.
16. *Water service* should be provided for both exterior and interior use.

Fig. 32.5. An industrial type window with a screen on the outside is usually considered a desirable type of window for a vocational education in agriculture building.

OTHER FACILITIES

The nature of the educational program in agriculture has created a need for facilities in addition to a classroom and an agriculture mechanics shop. Many schools have provided their agriculture departments with offices, laboratories, greenhouses, conference rooms, storage rooms, toilets, washrooms, and locker rooms. A separate building for an agriculture department creates the need for separate toilets.

A school may also provide its department with one or more of the following facilities:

1. FFA chapter room or house.
2. Utility room for activities such as grinding feed and mixing feed.
3. Hatchery.
4. Freezer lockers.
5. Plant house.
6. Agricultural products processing rooms.

These latter facilities are not usually considered essential. The types of farming and agriculturally oriented businesses in a community determine the kind of facilities needed. For example, if a department is located in a horticultural area, there may be as great a need for a plant house and a greenhouse laboratory as there is a need for a soil testing or milk testing laboratory in another community.

Office—An office 10′ by 12′ is usually adequate for one teacher. Additional space is necessary for special teachers and in multiple-teacher departments. Some departments use offices as small conference rooms. If an office is to be used in this manner, additional space will have to be provided.

A door leading from an office to the outside of the building is very desirable. Young adults and older adult students will make many office calls if they can come to an office without passing through classes in session.

Conference Room—A conference room is very convenient for FFA committee meetings, for young and older adult committee meetings, for advisory council and advisory committee meetings, and for students wishing to do special work during class time. In a one-teacher department, the office may be expanded so that it may also be used as a conference room. In a multiple-teacher department, a separate conference room may be desirable because it may eliminate the need for one or more classrooms.

Laboratory—A laboratory for activities such as grain testing and soil testing is usually a part of an agriculture classroom. In a school where the department sponsors laboratory activities for the preparation of off-farm agriculture laboratory technicians, a separate laboratory is justified.

Toilet—Toilets located near both the classroom and the agriculture mechanics shop are needed. They are often placed between the classroom and the shop.

Washroom and Locker Room—Some agriculture departments have combination washrooms and locker rooms. In some of the newer buildings, however, the locker facilities and washing facilities are located in the agriculture mechanics shops. Placing these facilities in a shop conserves space.

CHAPTER

33

How to Equip and Arrange Classrooms and Laboratories

CLASSROOM EQUIPMENT

Kinds of Equipment—There are no rigid standards regarding the amount or type of classroom equipment needed, because the instructional needs vary in every state. There are some items of equipment, however, that should be found in every department:

1. Chalkboards.
2. Tables and chairs, rather than armchairs or desks, because tables can be used for laboratory work and for supervised study.
3. Cabinets for bulletins, notebooks, magazines, illustrative materials, books, seed samples, soil samples, and teaching apparatus.
4. Tack-boards.
5. Teacher's desk.
6. Filing cabinets.
7. Facilities for filing bulletins.
8. Demonstration table.

Tables and Chairs—Many prefer a two-student table 5′ long and 2′ wide. Others prefer a table 7′ long and 2′ wide which will accommodate three students. A table 28″ high is recommended. If the tables are of wood, they should be constructed of well seasoned lumber and built for permanency. The legs may be made of 4″ x 4″ lumber. Either a mortised or a beveled joint may be used at each corner. A very good inexpensive top for a table can be made by using pine lumber and covering it with a hard panel Celotex board, with Masonite, or with Formica. Such tables may be built by the students in shop classes.

If tables are purchased, folding, steel-legged tables are very satisfactory. Drawers are not needed in the tables because notebook racks, cases, and cabinets are usually provided in a classroom for the storage of materials used by the students. Drawers in tables become catchalls for wastepaper and for gum and candy wrappers. Enough tables are needed so that the students are seated on only one side of each table. It is usually desirable to have two extra tables which may be used for the display of teaching materials, for extra work space, or for unusually large classes. The chairs used in a classroom should be wooden or steel and constructed for maximum comfort. Folding chairs are not satisfactory. The legs of the chairs should be equipped with rubber tips or coasters to lessen noise.

Cabinets—Convenience is desirable in any kind of a cabinet, regardless of the type used. Cabinets should provide sufficient space for their intended use. Glass doors are very desirable in a cabinet that is to be used for books, bulletins, and seed samples. Often instructors keep their cabinets more neatly organized when the contents are visible at all times. Drawers may be provided for sheaf materials and for small bottles used for storing samples of soils and seeds.

A work counter along one wall of a classroom is needed for testing soil and grain and for performing other laboratory exercises. Cabinets are often placed below this work space or below bookcases and magazine racks.

A mouse-proof steel cabinet is very valuable for storing grain samples.

Chalkboards—Many of the new writing boards are not black. The most common color other than black is green. Writing on a green board is easily visible, and such a board is attractive and adds color to a room. The use of new colors is the reason for the change in name from "blackboard" to "chalkboard."

A chalkboard for an agriculture classroom of average size should be 20′ long and 42″ high. The bottom of a chalkboard should be 38″ from the floor. If a chalkboard is tilted out at the top, glare will be decreased. A light over a board will also help prevent glare.

A movable chalkboard on the principle of a double-hung window has many advantages. It doubles the amount of board space in proportion to the amount of wall space used. It provides a method of covering, until needed, material which has been placed on a board. A hinged, fan type, movable chalkboard and tack-board which swings like a door also has some advantages. One side of a movable section may be used as a chalkboard and the other side as a tack-board.

A chalkboard may have a rod of some sort along the top with movable clips so that illustrative material may be displayed to a class.

Tack-boards—A large amount of tack-board space is needed for agricultural education. Space is needed for each class, the FFA, "wanted" and "for sale" announcements, and general displays. The tack-board space should equal the chalkboard space in a classroom. Eighty square feet of tack-board space in a classroom can be used advantageously. This space may be located over the chalkboard, at the ends of the chalkboard, and at the sides or at the back of the classroom. Two or more tack-boards in a classroom are usually more useable than one tack-board with the same amount of space. A large amount of tack-board space may improve the acoustics of a classroom.

Cork is probably the best type of material for a tack-board. Other types of material are satisfactory, however. Some types of vegetable fiber boards are suitable. Soft white pine of the type used in drawing boards may be used.

Magazine Rack—Many kinds of magazine racks have been used in agriculture classrooms. Each has some advantages, but none seems to be entirely satisfactory. A desirable magazine rack should not use an excessive amount of floor space; it should display magazines attractively; it should be easily accessible; and it should provide for the storage of three or four back issues of each magazine. In many magazine racks, the magazines stand so straight that they bend forward at the top and the magazine display becomes very unattractive. Some teachers have done away with magazine racks and have hung their magazines on nails driven into moldings placed on the walls. This procedure displays magazines very attractively. The corners of magazines without stiff covers, however, often curl. The magazines must also be punched, and a good punch is required for the thicker magazines. This method of displaying magazines is illustrated in Figure 33.1. A magazine rack in combination with a bookcase or student notebook rack has some advantages. It places the magazines at a convenient height for use. Some teachers recommend magazine racks constructed with a space below each magazine shelf for the storage of the back issues of the magazines.

Fig. 33.1. An easy way of displaying magazines in a department of agriculture is by hanging them along a wall on hooks.

Notebook Rack—It is usually desirable for the vocational education in agriculture students in a school to leave their agriculture notebooks in the classroom. If the notebooks are left in the classroom, a desirable and efficient method of storage should be provided. The use of drawers for storage is not satisfactory. A rack in which the notebooks stand on end in individual slots is considered by most teachers to be the easiest and most efficient method of storage. Names may be placed alphabetically by classes on the edges of the shelves below the notebooks to identify the owners of the notebooks. A notebook rack is usually located near the main door in an agriculture classroom so that students may obtain their notebooks as they come to a class and replace them as they leave.

Bulletin Files—In an average department, space is needed for filing 4,000 to 5,000 bulletins. The use of legal size, four-drawer filing cabinets is one of the most common methods of filing bulletins. In a legal size filing cabinet, two rows of bulletins may be placed side by side. If steel filing cabinets are used, two four-drawer cabinets are usually sufficient.

Some departments have "built-in" filing cabinets, and some have wooden filing cabinets built in combination with general storage cabinets.

Sink—Every agriculture classroom needs a sink with plenty of work counter space on each side of it. A sink is needed for laboratory activities. The sinks installed in agriculture classrooms should be acid-proof and have hot and cold water connections. A sink 24" long and 20" wide, with a drain board, is usually satisfactory. A sink should be 34" above the floor, and a storage cabinet may be provided below it.

Exhibit or Display Cases—A display case is useful for exhibiting achievements of individual students, achievements of the FFA, models used in demonstrations, and preserved samples of parasites and diseased portions of animals. A display case is attractive, creates interest, and may be of considerable educational value. Many of the newer facilities for agricultural education have "built-in" exhibit or display cases in the hallways leading to the agriculture classrooms. For maximum value a display case must be kept neat, and the exhibits must be changed frequently.

Bookcases—Most departments keep their agricultural reference books in their classroom libraries for use during supervised study periods. Shelf space in a classroom for approximately 200 reference books is usually adequate if out-of-date books are frequently culled from the reference shelves. "Built-in" bookcases are very satisfactory. Placing book shelves at a convenient height is desirable. If "built-in" bookcases are not possible, a portable bookcase is inexpensive and may be constructed in an agriculture mechanics shop. Books may be more attractively displayed in a bookcase if the shelves are not too deep. Doors on a bookcase are unnecessary. Reference books are used frequently, and doors add to the time and confusion in obtaining books.

Picture Moldings—Most departments of agriculture have plaques, pictures, and banners which may be hung in their classrooms. These banners, pictures, and plaques may be fastened directly to a wall, but the most efficient and attractive method is the hanging of these items from picture moldings.

Classroom Desk—A teacher needs a desk or demonstration table in the classroom, even though there is a desk in the office. Some place is needed for storing attendance blanks and current materials. A table or stand with a top which may be tilted or slanted for a teacher's convenience is frequently provided in a department. This table or stand may also be turned to face the class during a demonstration and used for displaying materials being employed in the demonstration.

Steel File—A four-drawer, letter size, steel file is needed in a classroom for storing FFA records, clippings, and outsized bulletins. A card index file is needed for file cards and other teaching aids. More than one steel file may be needed, especially if additional filing space is not provided in a conference room or office.

Chart Cabinet—Storage of charts and posters is always a problem. Most drawers are not large enough for the storage of charts. If charts are rolled, they are bulky and difficult to use because they tend to reroll themselves while being used. Hanging charts in a chart cabinet is usually considered the most satisfactory method of storage.

Shades—A classroom for agriculture needs translucent shades so that the light glare may be regulated. Opaque shades are also needed so that the room may be darkened for movie and slide projection. In practically every department of agriculture, there is almost a daily need for using a projector of some type, although the amount of time a projector is used in any one class period may be small. A school may have a projection room, but to use this room every time there is a need for projecting a picture on a screen may be a waste of time.

Fans—Classrooms for agriculture are used throughout the summer for adult class meetings, young farmer class meetings, and FFA meetings. Fans are needed to cool agriculture classrooms during the hot summer months. Often meetings are at night and the classrooms used are closed during the day. Without fans these rooms are unbearably hot and stuffy. Exhaust fans are necessary equipment in most agriculture classrooms. Other fans may also be needed.

Screens—Since an agriculture classroom is used throughout the year, screens are indispensable. Windows have to be opened for air circulation. Without screens a classroom is soon swarming with flies and bugs, especially at night. Educators often deplore unsanitary conditions in their communities but do not insist on screens for their schoolroom windows. If houses need screens, so do schools.

Arranging the Equipment—The proper arrangement of the equipment in a classroom for effective instruction is important. The following suggestions for arranging equipment are based on observations made in many classrooms for agriculture:

1. The chalkboard should be located so that it may be easily seen and conveniently used by a class. The front of the room is usually the most desirable location.
2. The teacher's desk or demonstration table should be placed in the front of the room and located so that students may work around it.
3. Cabinets, exhibit cases, magazine racks, and bulletin racks may be placed along the side walls and at the rear of the room.
4. The study tables and chairs should be located so that students will not have to face the light. They should also be arranged so that the teacher will not have to face the light while leading a discussion.
5. The tables may be arranged in rows, one behind the other; in the form of a "U"; or in groups to provide for six to eight students working together. The arrangement will depend on the type of instruction being used, the number of students, the space available, the lighting, and the opportunity the stu-

dents have for facing the front of the room. All students should be seated so as to face the area where the teacher will be directing the discussion. For small group conferences the tables may be placed together so as to permit students to sit in a circle or square. The tables should be movable to permit them to be arranged to meet best the needs of the group using them. In adult classes it is desirable to have the tables grouped so as to permit the students to sit around them.

6. Tack-boards should be conveniently located where all students can see and have access to them.
7. The laboratory and other working areas may be in the back of the room.

STORAGE ROOM EQUIPMENT

Storage rooms in connection with classrooms are usually equipped with shelves, bins, and drawers of various sizes and shapes. If a storage room is equipped with a ladder fastened at the top to a track, then shelves, bins, and drawers may extend to the ceiling. Metal-lined drawers or steel cabinets are needed for storing grain and crop specimens so that they will be protected from rodents and insects. If these metal-lined drawers or steel cabinets are fitted closely, the contents may be treated with gaseous insecticides.

Drawers, shelves, bins, and cabinets may be specifically designed to accommodate the items of supply and equipment listed in a following section of this chapter. Accommodations for materials used frequently are usually constructed near the door of a storage room. Materials used infrequently may be placed in the less accessible areas of a storage room.

OFFICE–CONFERENCE ROOM EQUIPMENT

Furniture—Desk space is needed for each full-time teacher in a department. Typewriter desks are needed for the secretarial staff. Some departments have installed in their offices work counters which are supported by two-drawer steel cabinets.

A combination office–conference room will need at least four chairs. One of these may be the teacher's desk chair. If room is available, a folding conference table is a desirable addition to an office–conference room.

Storage—Filing cabinets are needed for filing materials and supplies used by the teachers. A storage cabinet for clothes, overcoats, and hats is needed unless a clothes closet is provided. A cabinet with shelves and drawer space is also needed for storing cameras, photographic supplies, stencils, paper, record books, postal cards, forms of various sizes, manila folders, a postal card mimeograph, and a ditto machine. A small bookcase is needed in an office–conference room for storing professional books, bound volumes of professional magazines, such as the *Agricultural Education Magazine*, and other books used primarily by the teacher or teachers in the department. Filing cabinets and other cabinets in an office–conference room should be equipped with locks. Items such as cameras are costly, and it is advisable to keep them under lock and key.

Equipment and Supplies—The following office equipment and supplies are primarily used by teachers and add to the effective and efficient operation of departments of agriculture:

1. *Telephone.*
   When it is possible to call an agriculture department by telephone, farmers, parents, and businesspersons call frequently on legitimate business, such as arranging for related individual instruction and for class meetings. A telephone is a time-saver for a teacher in arranging activities such as meetings, visits, and field trips. Telephones are justified in agriculture departments, even though they may not be justified in other school departments. A teacher should not be interrupted during class, except in an emergency, by a telephone call. Interruptions may be prevented by the routing of calls through the school's office during the day.
2. *Typewriter.*
   The secretarial staff and the teachers in a department need a typewriter for typing reports, letters, and publicity materials and for cutting stencils. The amount of correspondence and publicity and the number of reports and records originating from a department of agriculture are usually several times greater than those from any other department in a school.
3. *Calculating machine.*
   A calculating machine is useful in performing activities such as checking record books and totaling judging scores. Its use motivates farmers, off-farm agricultural workers, and students to keep and analyze records.
4. *Duplicating machines.*
   Duplicating equipment in a school is usually located in a central office. Inexpensive equipment may, however, be justified in a department for quick or emergency duplicating even though the bulk of the work is ordinarily done elsewhere. Most departments notify adult agricultural workers and young farmers of special meetings by postal card. A postal card mimeograph machine is useful in preparing these cards.
5. *Chalkboard.*
   A small chalkboard, 2½′ by 5′ or 6′, has many uses in an office–conference room. A chalkboard is an effective visual aid often needed during individual or small-group conferences.

Fig. 33.2. The desk file and telephone in the office–conference room in the department of vocational agriculture at Carlinville, Illinois.

6. *Tack-board.*
   A small tack-board, 2½′ by 5′, in an office–conference room may be used for current materials, such as announcements from the school's main office and notes to other teachers in the department.
7. *Sorting or desk file.*
   Figure 33.2 shows one type of sorting or desk file commonly used.
8. *Paper punch.*
9. *Stapler and staple remover.*
10. *Scissors.*
11. *Miscellaneous supplies.*
   When a teacher has an office, a supply of items such as manila folders, paper, examination booklets, erasers, paper clips, rubber bands, and chalk are usually kept in the office.

TEACHING AIDS

Equipment for Specific Areas of Instruction—The equipment a department should purchase for a specific area of instruction, such as soils, dairy, or horticulture, will depend on the following factors:

1. The needs, interests, and abilities of the students.
2. The number of students enrolled.
3. The finances available.
4. The ability of the instructor.
5. The content of the course.
6. The needs of the community.

The following is a partial list of equipment which teachers have found useful in teaching some of the more common areas of instruction. Tools and equipment usually found in an agriculture mechanics shop are not listed. It is assumed that these tools and equipment items may be obtained from the shop. This is not a minimum or a maximum list. Equipment is not listed more than once. For example, a soil auger is listed under "soils." A soil auger is needed in teaching ornamental horticulture but is not listed again under this heading.

Soils.

1—Farm level.
6—Lenses, hand.
1—Meter, moisture.
1—pH meter and probe.
12—Seamless tin soil cans, 8 oz.
1—Sieve set, .005, 1.0, 1.25, 1.5, and 2.0 mm. perforations.
1—Soil auger.
1—Soil class sample set.
1—Soil oven.
1—Soil sampling tube.
1—Soil sterilizer, electric.
1—Soil testing outfit with sufficient equipment and supplies for class use.
1—Soil thermometer.
2—Spades, soil sampling.
1—Steel tape, 100′.

Plants (including ornamental horticulture).

1—Air pressure duster.
1—Air pressure sprayer.

1—Axe.
—Black shade cloth.
—Buckets, water.
1—Budding knife.
1—Cable, electric heating, 60′, 360 w., 120 v.
6—Dibbles (may be made in shop).
1—Digger, post hole.
3—Flats.
1—Fork, manure.
1—Germinator, seed.
1—Grafting knife.
—Grafting thread and wax.
1—Hose, water, 100′.
1—Ladder, extension.
1—Ladder, step.
1—Mattock, cutter type.
1—Microscope.
—Mounts for plant and insect specimens.
1—Plastic sheet, 5 yd. x 200 yd., 4 mil polyethylene (soil fumigation).
1—Pruning saw, curved.
1—Pruning saw, straight.
1—Pruning shears, hand.
1—Pruning shears, 26″ long.
2—Rakes, garden.
1—Respirator, filter for sprays.
1—Saw, chain.
1—Scale, platform, ¼ to 1,000 lb.
1—Scale, utility, 60 lb.
—Seed mounts.
1—Shovel, round point.
1—Shovel, square point.
1—Sieve set, seed, perforations 1/25″ to 7/64″.
1—Sieve set, soil.
1—Spade.
1—Splicer, fence wire.
1—Stretcher, woven wire.
1—Tester, crop moisture.
—Tissue test equipment and supplies.
2—Tree pruners, long handle.
3—Tripod magnifiers.
1—Trowel, plant.
1—Truck, hand, two-wheel.
1—Wheelbarrow, 4 cu. ft.

Dairy Science.

1—Acid bottle, automatic.
6—Acid measures, 17.5 cc.
1—Acid waste jar.
2—Boxes for milk scales and bottles (homemade). (The number will depend on the number of persons testing dairy herds.)
1—Centrifuge, 24-bottle.
—Cow testing record forms.
12—Cream test bottles.
—Dehorning paste.
—Detergent powder.
3—Dividers, 4½″.
1—Glass marking pencil.
1—Harvard trip balance with weights (also may be used for soils and crops).
1—Hydrometer.
1—Interval timer.
1—Lactometer.
1—Mastitis testing equipment set.
—Milk preservative.

24—Milk sample jars. (The number will depend on the number of samples to be taken at any one time.)
2—Milk scales. (Several will be needed for junior dairy herd testing.)
6—Pipettes (milk).
1—Sediment tester.
12—Skim milk test bottles.
—Sulphuric acid for milk testing.
6—Test tube brushes.
24—Whole milk test bottles. (The number will depend on the number of students testing milk at one time.)
1—Wood-handle trocar.

Poultry.

1—Catching crate.
1—Catching hook.
4—Coops, wire exhibition.
1—Egg grader.
1—Egg scale.
1—Egg tester, homemade.
1—Killing knife.
1—Kitchen scale.
1—Posting set.
1—Toe marker.
1—Worming outfit.

Animal Science.

1—Artificial insemination equipment set.
1—Back fat probe.
1—Balling gun.
1—Branding equipment set.
1—Cattle squeeze.
1—Clippers for clipping needle teeth of pigs.
1—Dehorner.
1—Ear-notcher.
1—Ear tag tool.
1—Electric shearmaster with attachments.
1—Emasculator.
1—Grooming equipment set.
1—Heavy-duty animal scale, portable.
1—Hog bit and capsule gun for worming.
1—Hog holder (may be made in the farm shop).
1—Hoof clipper.
1—Hoof rasp.
1—Implanter pellet.
1—Knife, livestock.
—Livestock marking crayons.
1—Pig ringer with 100 rings.
1—Posting set.
1—Prod.
1—Scale and tripod.
—Specimen jars.
1—Syringe set.
1—Tattoo marker.
1—Thermometer.
1—Tooth nipper.
1—Trocar, cattle and hog.
1—Vaccination outfit (unless there is a state law prohibiting students from vaccinating livestock).
1—Veterinary thermometer.

Bees.

—Hives.
1—Hive tool set.

1—Honey processing equipment set.
    Color grader.
    Extractor.
    Uncapping machine.
    Waxmaster melter.
1—Pair of gloves, bee.
1—Smoker.
2—Veils.

Fish.

2—Aerators.
2—Aquariums and accessories.
1—Brood pond.
1—Depth-o-meter.
2—Fish tagging pliers.
8—Hip boots (pairs).
2—Scales.
1—Seine, 100′, 2″ mesh.
6—Traps.
4—Wash tubs.

Forestry.

3—Axes, brush.
3—Axes, single bit.
1—Cant hook.
1—Climber, tree.
1—Clinometer.
1—Diameter tape.
1—Increment borer.
3—Machetes with sheaths.
1—Meter, tally.
—Protective equipment to meet OSHA standards (hats, shoes, etc.).
3—Rakes, fire.
1—Saw, chain.
1—Saw, forester's.
1—Snake bite kit.
1—Survey rod.
3—Swatters, fire.
1—Tape, logger's.
1—Tie-down chain.
1—Tree injector.
1—Tree marking gun.
1—Tree scale stick.
1—Wedge, saw.

Agricultural Business.

1—Animal health sample set.
—Assorted agricultural products containers.
    Boxes.
    Field crates.
    Hampers.
    Tubs.
—Billing supplies.
1—Counter scale.
1—Display case.
1—Display window.
1—Feed sample set.
1—Fertilizer sample set.
1—Fungicide sample set.
1—Garden seed sample set.
1—Grain sample set.
1—Herbicide sample set.
1—Insecticide sample set.
—Labeling materials.

1—Meat sample set.
—Price boards.
—Representative tags, labels, empty sacks, or containers of feeds, seeds, fertilizers, and chemicals.
1—Sales counter.
—Sales pads.
1—Sign making set.
—Simulated agricultural materials packages.
1—Small cash register.
1—Volume measure set.
—Wall merchandising unit.

Audio-Visual Equipment—Almost every department of agriculture owns a projector or projectors which will handle slides and filmstrips. It is recommended that a department also own an overhead projector. A movie projector should be readily available. Some departments own movie projectors, but it is usually possible to share this type of projector with other departments in the school. A movable stand promotes the convenient use of these audio-visual aids. Some departments have movable stands with the bottoms enclosed for the storage of projectors, slides, and other visual aid equipment. A projection screen is essential.

Many departments believe that recorders are valuable pieces of equipment. Some departments record weekly or monthly programs which are sent by mail to their local radio stations. A recorder is frequently used in training public speakers and parliamentary procedure teams, and it may also be used in the training of special teachers and in the self-analysis of an instructor's teaching.

Some provision is needed for storing slides and filmstrips. A camera is a very valuable piece of equipment for a department of agriculture. Bantam or 35 mm. cameras are popular with teachers because the preparation of 2" x 2" slides is easy when this size camera is used. The use of cameras will be considered in more detail in Chapter 37. Visual aid supplies and materials and their use are also discussed in Chapter 37.

Miscellaneous Equipment and Supplies—The following miscellaneous equipment and supplies are valuable additions to a department:

1. Chalkboard pointer. (May be made in a department's agriculture mechanics shop.)
2. Clipboards. (Useful on field trips.)
3. Flannelboard. (May be made in a department's agriculture mechanics shop. For details, see Chapter 37.)
4. Platform scale.
5. First aid kit.

REFERENCE BOOKS

Importance of Reference Books—Having a variety of reference books in agriculture:

1. Provides suitable, up-to-date, and factual information and experimental data.
2. Provides plans for use in constructing equipment needed in connection with supervised occupational experience programs and home needs.
3. Provides step-by-step procedures in performing agricultural skills.
4. Promotes student enthusiasm and interest in agriculture.

Should a Text Be Used?—Textbook teaching as such cannot be justified in agriculture. When agriculture teaching is based on problems arising from supervised occupational experience programs, much detailed information which can be used in solving these problems is needed. A textbook broad enough to cover a course is usually so general that the detailed information for solving a particular problem is missing. Textbooks are also written so that they will be applicable over a large geographical area. Agriculture problems vary, however, among the different states, among the different areas in a state, and in some instances within a local community.

Textbooks are also usually written on some aspect of agriculture, such as soils, crops, livestock, vegetables, or a type of off-farm agricultural business. Problems arising from supervised occupational experience programs often cut across these areas of agriculture. Thus if a textbook were used, it would have to be jumbo sized, or the students would need to have several textbooks for each course. The solution is a variety of adapted reference books located in each agriculture classroom. *A textbook course is one of the best ways of killing a program of vocational education in agriculture. A teacher should never resort to it.*

In a specific agriculture course of a non-vocational nature, the use of a desirable textbook may be warranted. In courses of this type the objectives differ considerably from the objectives of vocational education in agriculture courses, making the use of textbooks more feasible.

What References to Secure—In evaluating an agricultural reference, there are a number of criteria to consider:

1. The year copyrighted.
2. Its adaptability to the supervised occupational experience programs and needs of the community.
3. The clearness, coverage, and organization of the material.
4. The number and quality of the illustrations.
5. Its authoritative value.
6. The amount of useable material.
7. Its apparent bias, prejudice, attitude, and philsophy.
8. Its cost.
9. The ability level for which it was written.

A reference must contain information pertaining to the agricultural activities and the supervised occupational experience programs most common in the community where it is to be used. Many state offices of agricultural education have lists of books recommended for use in their states. Teachers may consult the state list and review the books before purchases are made for their agricultural libraries.

Recent books should be secured so that the students will have up-to-date information. The science of agriculture is changing rapidly. In some fields a reference book may become out-of-date within a few years.

Number of References to Secure—Sufficient references are needed, covering all the necessary areas of instruction, so that the students in a class will not have to work together during supervised study periods because of a lack of reference materials. The number of books related to an area in technical agriculture, such as soils, should be at least equal to the number of students enrolled in the largest class in the department. For a class of 20 students, there is a need for at least 20 reference books in each of the technical areas, such as livestock, crops, soils, farm management, and agriculture mechanics. There will also be a need for one to five copies of a few specialized books on subjects such as weeds, artificial insemination, agriculture mechanics projects, and selected off-farm agricultural businesses.

Yearbooks—Every department of agriculture should have a complete set of the *U.S. Department of Agriculture Yearbooks* since 1970. These books contain valuable information as well as statistics that can be used as reference materials.

OTHER REFERENCE MATERIALS

Importance of Bulletins—Much valuable information is available in bulletins which may be secured for classroom and agriculture mechanics work. Bulletins are especially valuable for the following reasons:

1. They are written by persons who are specialists in their fields.
2. They often contain information which has not been published in book form.
3. They often contain specific and detailed information.
4. The information in the bulletins published by a state is adapted to the conditions existing in that state.
5. Many bulletins may be obtained without charge.

Sources of Bulletins—There are various sources from which bulletins may be secured:

1. Agricultural colleges and experiment stations in the state.
2. Other states.
3. U.S. Department of Agriculture and its various bureaus.
4. Agribusiness associations.
5. Various commercial concerns.

Number of Bulletins to Secure—A good supply of the bulletins from the home state should be available in every department. A department needs at least one copy of each bulletin used for class instruction for each student in the largest class in the department. For bulletins that are used infrequently, it may be adequate to have only one copy for every two students in the largest class. Some bulletins are too technical for general class work, but they should be available in a department for the instructor and the advanced students. A department usually maintains in its files one or two copies of the more technical bulletins that are used only occasionally. All bulletins in a department should be filed and should remain the property of the department.

It is difficult to determine useability of a bulletin by its title. Ordering single copies of bulletins and reviewing them before an order is placed for multiple copies constitute a desirable practice. Only up-to-date and useable bulletins should be ordered. A few well selected bulletins which are filed adequately are of more use than a large number of miscellaneous bulletins which are out of date or not filed.

Miscellaneous Collections—Catalogues, plans for buildings, slides, moving pictures, weeds, and other materials are usually collected for instructional purposes. Instructors may profitably spend time collecting, pressing, and mounting materials for future reference. See Chapter 37, "How to Prepare and Use Visual Aids." Many miscellaneous reference materials can be secured free, and other materials can be obtained at a small cost.

Importance of a Good Supply of Agricultural Magazines—Much valuable and up-to-date material is available in the better agricultural magazines. Many articles are written for these magazines by the leading authorities in the various agricultural areas. Experimental data are often released to these magazines before being published in bulletin form. Economic conditions are rapidly changing, and new discoveries are made daily; consequently, students must be educated to look for and study new information. This is one of the best types of education that can be given students to prepare them for solving the problems they may encounter in later life.

Paul W. Chapman has stated:[1] "The more thought and study we give to the matter, the sooner we reach the conclusion that the most valuable and worthwhile thing we can do for *our students is to help them form habits which will function in keeping their feet in the right pathway after they have left our classrooms, laboratories, and shops.*

"Is there any habit more important than that of reading the 'literature' pertaining to one's job?

". . . A number of the leading papers of the country have developed service features which make them of special interest to students in agriculture classes."

Number of Magazines and Papers to Secure—First consideration should be given the state or regional agricultural papers and magazines, since they more often contain data adapted for use in a community. One or two general agricultural magazines from other agricultural regions may well be included to let the students know what is being thought and done elsewhere. A few specialized agricultural magazines dealing with enterprises that need special emphasis in a community may also be included. Breed publications are examples.

Class members may also be encouraged to subscribe to specialized magazines which pertain to their supervised occupational experience programs.

Further Reference Materials—A daily newspaper containing market reports is very desirable. Students may be taught where to find market reports and how to interpret them. Students with livestock projects may keep records of the market prices of animals, and students having crop projects may keep records of the market prices of crops. Data from these daily records may be used for charts and graphs which show the variation in prices from week to week, from month to month, or from year to year.

Governmental news sheets and statistical and outlook reports are useful sources of data. Much valuable material is also found in trade and other periodical publications. An instructor should select carefully as many of these publications as practical. Many of them can be obtained free.

---

[1]Taken from an address by Paul W. Chapman, delivered before the Agricultural Education Section of the American Vocational Association.

Information Sheets—If a teacher is teaching in a community where a specialized type of agriculture is predominant, it may be difficult to find sufficient reference materials which are suitable. The teacher may need to assemble materials which are related to the specialized agribusiness activities in the community and have them mimeographed for student use. Several teachers may cooperate in the preparation of materials of this type.

Keeping the Library Up-to-Date—It is important that the agricultural library in a school be kept up-to-date. Bulletins and books which are out of date or which have been replaced with later editions should be discarded. If a school system objects to the burning of old books, a shelf, out of the reach of students, may be used for a library of books of historical value only. It is nearly impossible to teach new methods and new approved practices in agriculture when the only references available were written before these methods or practices were discovered. Teachers often permit students to use references which have become obsolete and which should be discarded.

The use of obsolete books, bulletins, and other materials not only wastes the students' time, but it is also dangerous. Young people, and even some adults, have great faith in what is written. They often do not consider whether the contents are valid or provide the best information presently available.

CHAPTER

34

How to Equip and Arrange an Agriculture Mechanics Shop[1]

Importance of Shop Equipment—Agriculture mechanics instruction cannot be conducted successfully without sufficient equipment. Equipment should not be purchased unless it fulfills a need, but an instructor must have adequate tools and equipment before effective instruction in agriculture mechanics can be provided.

Kinds of Equipment to Provide—The tools and equipment in an agriculture mechanics shop should be of the size, kind, and quantity necessary for the development of the abilities enrollees need in their work. The tools and equipment to provide depend on factors such as the following:

1. Course content.
2. Equipment already available in the shop.
3. Physical facilities (size, type, location of shop, and entryway).
4. Finances available.
5. Instructors available.
6. Number of persons to be educated.

A school needs to analyze its community carefully to determine the kind of tools and equipment necessary for an effective program in agriculture mechanics which will meet the needs and interests of the enrollees in high school courses and in courses for young and older adults.

The increased emphasis being given to soil and water management, agricultural machinery adjustment and maintenance, and the construction of labor-saving devices has created a need for specialized equipment.

---

[1]For a discussion on organizing, conducting, and evaluating an agriculture mechanics program, see Chapters 22, 23, and 42.

If an instructional program in agriculture mechanics is to meet the needs of both production agriculture and agribusiness, instruction must be provided in high school courses and in courses for young and older adults. This means that the tools and equipment in the agriculture shop must be adequate to meet the needs of these groups of students. Sufficient tools and equipment are essential in a shop so that young farmers may develop needed abilities in reconditioning farm machinery and in building labor-saving devices.

The Study of a Community—A teacher should study the local community, with the help of others, to determine the needs of production agriculture and agribusiness for agriculture mechanics.

A teacher should know the general needs in agriculture mechanics after analyzing, with the aid of others, the basic data about a community which are available from census reports and from local sources, such as the soil conservation district, the Extension Service, and business firms. In some situations, a teacher may need to supplement the data at hand by conducting a survey. After a teacher has studied the community, it should be possible to anticipate the kinds of experiences which the high school students will probably have in their supervised occupational experience programs. In established departments, a review of the records of former students' programs should also be helpful. A study of the agribusinesses in a community should also reveal agriculture mechanics areas in which enrollees will need training. As a result of such a study, a teacher should be in a position to recommend the kind of tools and equipment which will be required for effective instruction in agriculture mechanics.

Providing Good Tools and Equipment—*It is poor economy to purchase unknown brands of tools and equipment. It is also poor economy to purchase tools and equipment of inadequate size and substandard quality.* It is more desirable to have a few standard quality tools of adequate size and kind than to have a large number of "cheap" tools. *A teacher should always buy good quality tools and equipment of a desirable size.* Also, one should buy tools which carry a guarantee against breakage and poor quality of work. In requisitioning tools, complete specifications, such as numbers, sizes, and brands, must be given. The cheapest bid may not be the best buy.

GENERAL PURPOSE EQUIPMENT

Workbenches—All workbenches which are placed along a wall should be approximately 24″ wide and 32″ high. Since the heights of students vary, it may be desirable to have some workbenches 30″ high and others 34″ high. A 2″ plank top should be used. Two pieces 2″ thick by 8″ wide and one piece 2″ thick by 10″ wide, when fitted together, will make a very desirable top approximately 24″ wide. Benches should be well braced, sturdily constructed, and 6′ to 8′ long. Workbenches may be homemade.

If the benches are supported against a wall as shown in Figure 34.1, the housekeeping under the benches is facilitated. A roll-away rack that fits the angle under the bench may be used with a bench of this type. This rack may be used for storing lumber, iron, and tools.

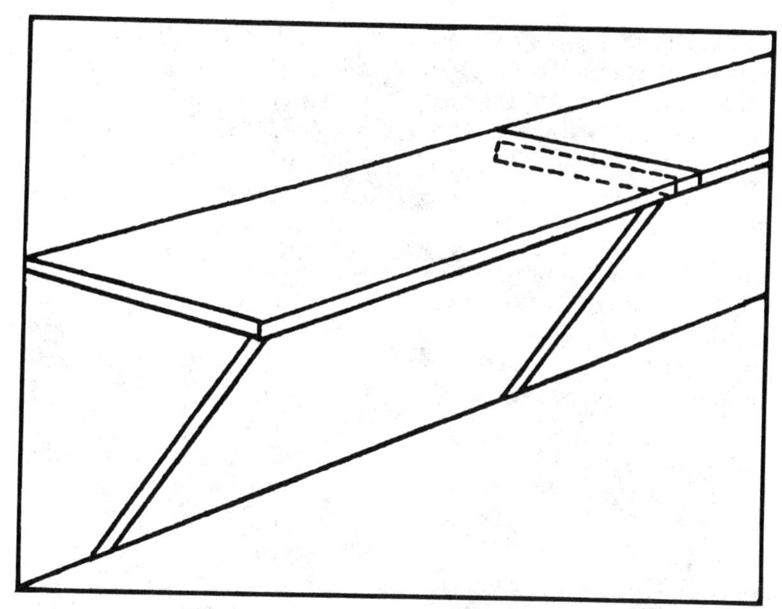

Fig. 34.1. Workbench supported by the wall.

Tool Storage—Cabinets which contain specific tools for a given kind of instruction and which are located in the work area in a shop are considered to be very desirable places to store tools. A tool room will not be needed when cabinets are used. Any tools or equipment which are used only occasionally can be kept in a storage room.

Tool Cabinets—The size of cabinets will depend upon the tools to be stored in them and the space available on the walls of a shop for hanging them. Shallow cabinets using 1″ x 6″ pieces for the top, bottom, and sides are satisfactory for storing most of the tools in a shop. They are attractive, they require a minimum of space, and the doors do not "sag" easily. Several cabinets of medium depth and size are more desirable than a few large cabinets.

Portable cabinets are becoming popular. They may be rolled to the areas of a shop where the tools in the cabinets are needed, and they may be placed in a storage room when these tools are not in use.

Forges—Gas forges are being used in many shops. They facilitate keeping a shop clean. A forge is used in a shop for economy in heating large pieces of metal.

Anvil Bases—Various kinds of anvil bases may be used. Some use a heavy chunk of wood; others use concrete. A concrete anvil base is preferred by most instructors because it is easier to keep in place and neater in appearance.

A concrete base may be cushioned by the placement of a 2″ block of wood on top of the concrete. Hooks may be placed on the side of an anvil base for a square, hardy, and tongs.

General Purpose Bench—It is desirable to have at least one portable general purpose bench in a shop. This bench may be equipped with two or more

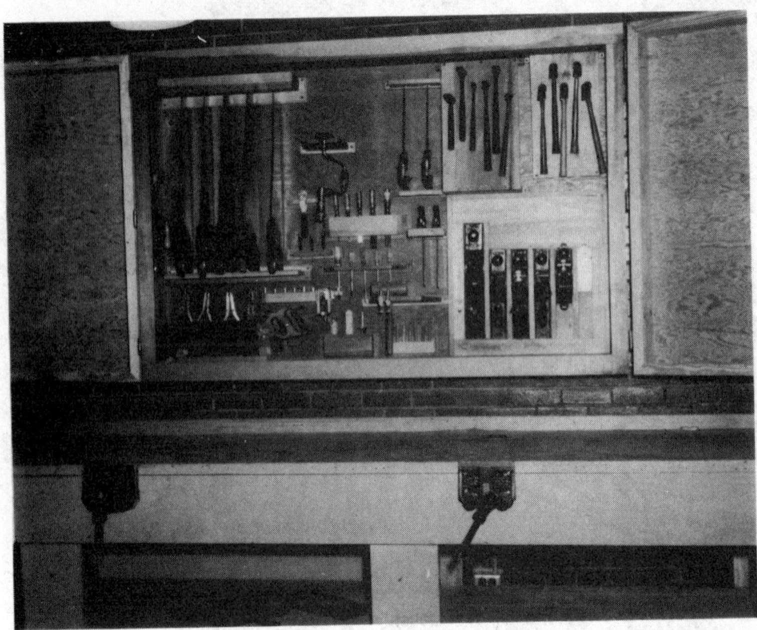

(Photo from L. C. Dalton, New Mexico)

Fig. 34.2. A wall cabinet placed over a workbench.

machinist's vises, a plumber's vise, and a blacksmithing vise. It should be covered with metal and should be of sturdy construction. The size will depend on local needs and space available. It should be at least 4′ wide.

Chalkboard—Every shop needs a chalkboard because it is not an economical use of time to return to a classroom every time a chalkboard is needed in teaching. The amount of board space needed in a shop is not as great as the board space needed in a classroom. A board 4′ by 6′ is usually sufficient. Some shops have their boards suspended from the ceiling so that they may be raised and lowered by pulleys. This type of board does not use wall space or floor space, which may then be used for workbenches or cabinets. A portable chalkboard may also be used in a shop. A portable board may be moved to the area of a shop in which the students are working.

Seating—Some provision for seating students in a shop during demonstrations is needed. Folding chairs are frequently employed because they may be stored away when not in use. A folding bleacher is a convenient way of seating students in a shop. It ensures good vision for all the students. It may also be stored in a small space. A three-tier bleacher 9′ long will seat 15 students.

Pipe and Iron Rack—If a shop has a walled or fenced-in patio or a covered shed, a pipe and iron rack may be placed in this area. Another possible location for it is on a wall inside a shop. Since standard pipe lengths are 21′ and standard iron lengths are 20′, the preferable length for a rack is 21′. If the horizontal supports are securely welded to uprights, the iron and pipe may be placed on a rack from one side.

Lumber Rack—Since storage space is usually a problem, vertical storage of lumber is growing in popularity. Horizontal storage space may be provided by placing a lumber rack along a wall. The preferable length of a lumber rack is 16′. The horizontal support arms on a lumber rack may be fastened to uprights so that lumber may be placed on the rack from one side. One tier of support arms may be floored so that short lengths of lumber may be stored on the rack.

First Aid Cabinet—A first aid cabinet is needed in a shop. An unused first aid cabinet may also be kept with the understanding that it will not be used except in an emergency. This ensures that necessary first aid supplies will be available for an emergency even though an item in the regular cabinet may be exhausted.

Drinking Fountain—Students in a shop work hard, and they frequently need drinks during a shop period. A drinking fountain in a shop adds to the efficiency of an agriculture mechanics program.

Industrial Washbasin—An industrial washbasin is usually considered to be the most desirable type. It is necessary for students to wash after working in a shop. Often all want to wash at once in a minimum period of time. The industrial washbasin permits a number of students to wash at one time. Since a spray of water is provided throughout a washing period, keeping the washbasin clean is facilitated.

Exhaust Fans—Exhaust fans are needed to eliminate smoke and fumes from a shop. Often these fans are installed in a shop at the time the shop is built. If not provided at this time, installation of fans is a simple job.

POWER EQUIPMENT

Grinder—A heavy duty power grinder is needed. It is recommended that it be equipped with two 10″ wheels and at least a 1-horsepower motor. Preferable location in a shop for a heavy-duty grinder is in a special area in which metal work and farm machinery work are done.

Drill Press—A floor type drill press which will drill to the center of 14″ material is a valuable addition to a shop's power equipment. It should be equipped with a ¾- to 1-horsepower motor. Some shops use portable electric drills mounted on stands in place of, or in addition to, floor type drill presses.

Air Compressor—An air compressor is needed for cleaning machinery and parts, for spray painting, for doing motor work, and for inflating tires. An air compressor may be located in a covered shed, patio, or tool room, with air lines leading to the various work areas. Air lines may be extended to all workbenches.

Power Saw—A shop may be equipped with a radial arm or tilting arbor saw, which should have a 12″ or 14″ blade and which should be powered with a 3-horsepower motor.

Other Power Equipment—Power hack saws, jointers, metal lathes, wood lathes, planers, belt and disc sanders, and band saws are sometimes found in agriculture mechanics shops. A shop should be equipped to do the mechanical jobs which farmers and other agricultural workers perform, or could profitably perform, on their farms or jobs. An agriculture mechanics shop is not a hobby shop, and it is not an industrial shop.

SHOP REFERENCES AND OTHER TEACHING AIDS

Importance of Shop Texts and References—Every agriculture mechanics class should be supplied with a number of references. Class study of activities such as welding or rafter cutting is handicapped without references. Two or three copies of each of three or four basic references are usually more useful than several copies of one basic reference.

Books Containing Desirable Plans—One of the problems in agriculture mechanics instruction is the securing of suitable project plans. Workers in production agriculture and agribusiness need many labor-saving devices. "Where can I get a plan?" is one of the first questions to arise when a new project is considered.[2]

TOOLS AND EQUIPMENT

A maximum class size of 15 students is assumed for the quantity of hand tools and equipment recommended in the following tables.

Carpentry Tools and Equipment—Table 34.1 is a suggested list of tools and equipment needed for teaching carpentry in agriculture courses.

Table 34.1. Suggested Tools and Equipment for Teaching Carpentry

Name of Tool	Size or Description	No.
Awl, scratch	6", 1/4 bar	4
Bar	Crow and tamping combination, 6', homemade	2
Bar	Nail, 10" claw	1
Bar	Pinch, 3' and 4' long	2 ea.
Bevel	Sliding T, 8" and 10"	1 ea.
Bit	Auger, 1/4" to 1" by 16ths, set	2
Bit	Countersink	2
Bit	Expansive, 7/8" to 3"	1
Bit	Screwdriver, assorted sizes	3
Bit	Wood boring, 1/4" to 3/4" by 16ths, set	1
Bob	Plumb	1
Brace	Ratchet bit, 10" sweep	2
Brush	Bench	12
Chalkline	50', reel and plumb bob	2
Chisel	Wood, 1/4" to 1 1/2" by 4ths, set	1

(Continued)

[2]*500 More Things to Make for Farm and Home* and *600 More Things to Make for the Farm and Home* can be purchased from The Interstate Printers & Publishers, Inc., Danville, Illinois.

Table 34.1 (Continued)

Name of Tool	Size or Description	No.
Clamp	Bar, 4′ and 5′	2 ea.
Clamp	C, 4″, 6″, 8″, 12″	1 ea.
Clamp	Saw	2
Cleaner, vacuum	2 HP	1
Divider	Wing, 8″ and 10″	1 ea.
Draw knife	10″	2
Dresser	Emery wheel	1
Drill	Automatic, and one set of bits	1
Drill, electric	3/8″, portable, reversible	2
Drill, electric	3/8″, portable, vari-speed	2
Drill, hand	1/4″	1
Driver	Ratchet, spiral, heavy-duty	1
File	Auger bit	3
File	Extra slim taper, 5 1/2″	6
File	Flat wood	2
File	Half-round cabinet, 10″	2
File	Slim taper, 6″	6
File, card	1 1/2″ x 5″	1
File handle	Assorted sizes, 0 to 4	19
Gauge	Marking	2
Grinder	Bench electric, wheel size 6″ or 8″	1
Hammer	Curved or straight, 16 oz.	12
Hatchet	Broad, 4 1/2″	1
Hatchet	Shingling	2
Knife	Putty, 1 1/4″	2
Knife	Utility, 6″, retractable point	2
Level	Builder's	1
Level	Carpenter's	1
Mallet	Wood	2
Miter box and saw	26″ x 4″ saw	1
Nail set	Assorted	1
Nail set	4″	1
Nipper	End cutting	1
Oiler	Hand	3
Plane	Block, 6″	1
Plane	Jack, 14″	4
Plane	Jointer, 22″	1
Pliers, fencing	10 1/2″	2
Router	1 1/2 HP, portable	1
Rule	Brass bound, non-folding, 2′	4
Rule	Folding, 6′	2
Rule	Steel tape, 6′	2
Saw	Compass, 12″	1
Saw	Crosscut, 8 and 10 point, 26″	2 ea.
Saw	Keyhole, 10″	1
Saw	Pistol grip	1
Saw	Rip, 5 1/2 and 6 point, 24″	1 ea.

(Continued)

Table 34.1 (Continued)

Name of Tool	Size or Description	No.
Saw	Tilting arbor, 12″ or 14″	1
Saw, radial arm	14″ blade, 3 HP	1
Saw vice		1
Screwdriver	4″, 6″, 8″, 10″	2 ea.
Screwdriver	Phillips, 0 to 4, set	1
Spoke shave	3″	1
Square	Carpenter's, 16″ x 24″	2
Square	Combination, 12″	2
Square	Try, 8″, all metal	6
Staple gun	½″, lever action, heavy-duty	1
Stone	Auger bit, 4″ x ½″	1
Stone	Combination oil, 7″ x 2″ x 1″, coarse and fine	4
Stone	Slip, medium and fine	2
Stone box	Oil, 7″ x 2″ x 1″	2
Tape	Steel, 50′ to 100′	1
Vise	Woodworking, rapid acting, 7″	6
Wrecking bar	Gooseneck, ¾″ x 30″	2

Concrete Tools and Equipment—Table 34.2 is a suggested list of tools and equipment needed for concrete work.

Table 34.2. Suggested Tools and Equipment for Teaching Concrete Work

Name of Tool	Size or Description	No.
Box	Measuring, 1 cu. ft.	1
Box, motor	9.2 cu. ft., homemade	1
Brick	Fluted rubbing, 1½″ x 3½″ x 8″	1
Bucket	5 gal., used container	5
Chalkline	Ball, cotton, 100′	1
Cone	Slump	1
Corner block	Plastic or aluminum	2 pr.
Drill	Star, ¼″, ½″, ¾″, 1″	1 ea.
Edger	Square corners and round corners	1 ea.
Float	Metal and wood	1 ea.
Groover	Concrete worker's	1
Hammer, electric	½″, heavy-duty	1
Hoe, motor	10″ width, long handle, two-hole	1
Hose, water	⅝″, 50′	1
Jointer	Cement	1
Level, mason's	48″	2
Line, mason's	250′, nylon	1
Mixer	4 cu. ft., rotating drum	1
Pad, knee		2 pr.
Pail	14 qt.	1
Platform	Mixing, homemade	1

(Continued)

Table 34.2 (Continued)

Name of Tool	Size or Description	No.
Scale, weight	100 lb., straight spring action	1
Screen	Assorted mesh sizes	1 ea.
Shovel	Square point	2
Tamper	Homemade	1
Trowel	Brick, 9″ and 11″, pointed	1 ea.
Trowel	Plastering, 11″	2
Trowel	Pointing, 6″	1
Wheelbarrow	5½ cu. ft.	2

Power and Machinery Tools and Equipment—Machinery and power equipment tools are essential in conducting a worthwhile agriculture mechanics program. Table 34.3 is a suggested list of tools and equipment needed for power and machinery instruction.

Table 34.3. Suggested Tools and Equipment for Teaching Power and Machinery Work

Name of Tool	Size or Description	No.
Anvil		1
Bearing scraper	Curved set	1
Bender, iron	Universal, complete with dies	1
Bleeder	Hydraulic brake	1
Brake, metal	48″, universal bench	1
Chain, log	¾″ x 14′	1
Charger, battery	80 amp.	1
Cleaner, parts	45 gal.	1
Cleaner, washer	High pressure pump	1
Compressor	Piston ring	1
Compressor	Single stage, air, horizontal type	1
Compressor	Valve spring	1
Creeper	Automobile	2
Cutter, bolt	30″	1
Drill, twist	High speed	1 set
Furnace, soldering	Three-burner	2
Gauge	Carburetor, float	1
Gauge	Cylinder	1
Gauge	Thickness	1
Grinder	Valve engine, hand	1
Grinder, right angle	Portable	1
Grinder, straight	Portable	1
Groove cleaner	Piston ring	1
Growler	Armature testing	1
Hoist	Safety, differential chain, ½ to 1 t.	1
Hone	Piston, pin	1

(Continued)

Table 34.3 (Continued)

Name of Tool	Size or Description	No.
Impact tool	½", portable electric	1
Indicator	Speed	1
Jack	Automotive heavy-duty, hydraulic	1
Lamp	Trouble, heavy-duty, automotive	2
Light	Neon timing	1
Micrometer	2" to 6" combination	1
Nibbler	16 ga., portable electric	1
Oiler, bench	⅓ pt.	2
Paint, spray	1 qt.	1
Pliers	Long nose, 6"	1
Pliers	Water pump	1
Press, hydraulic	25 t.	1
Puller	Clear, heavy-duty	1
Puller	Cylinder sleeve	1
Puller	Universal wheel	1
Reamer	Ridge, engine cylinder	1
Remover	Piston ring	1
Saw, abrasive cutoff	14" blade	1
Saw, metal cutting	Horizontal band	1
Screwdriver	Blade, Phillips	1 set
Screwdriver	Shock-proof, 4", 6", 8", 10"	2 ea.
Screw plate	Adjustable dies, taper taps	3 sets
Shear, metal	3/16"	1
Shear, metal	½"	1
Stand, safety	2 t.	6
Tester	Cleaner, spark plug	1
Tester	Storage battery cell	1
Valve	Refacer, electric (optional)	1
Valve	Seat grinding set	1
Valve lifter	Automotive, heavy-duty	1
Welder, arc	225 amp.	3–6
Welder, arc	250 to 300 amp.	1–2
Welder, mig	150 to 200 amp.	1
Welder, oxyacetylene		2
Wrench	Distributor set	1
Wrench	Open end, ¼" to ¾", set (alloy); metric set	1 ea.
Wrench	Socket, ¾" and square drive, 1⅛" to 2¼" by 32nds, set; metric set	1 ea.
Wrench	Socket-master, ½" and square drive, ⅜" to 1⅛" by 32nds, 12 point heavy-duty set; metric set	1 ea.
Wrench	Spark plug socket set	1
Wrench	Special mechanic's set, 7/16" to 1", 12 point; metric set	1 ea.
Wrench	Stud bolt puller	1
Wrench	Tappet set	1
Wrench	Tension	1

Metalworking Tools and Equipment—Table 34.4 is a list of tools and equipment needed for teaching hot and cold metal work.

Table 34.4. Suggested Tools and Equipment for Teaching Hot and Cold Metal Work

Name of Tool	Size or Description	No.
Anvil	Chilled face, 150 to 200 lb.	2
Anvil	Guard and sickle	1
Bit	Drill, twist, ¼″ to 1″ by 8ths, set	1
Brush	Wire wheel	1
Callipers	English, inside and outside	1 ea.
Callipers	Metric, inside and outside	1 ea.
Can	Squirt oiler, assorted sizes	3
Chisel	Cold, ¼″, ⅜″, ¾″, 1″	1 ea.
Chisel	Cold-eye, 1½″ blacksmith's handled	1
Chisel	Hot-eye, 1½″ blacksmith's handled	1
Clipper	Bolt, 30″ long	1
Divider	Wing, 8″	1
Dresser	Wheel	1
Drill	Electric, ½″ heavy-duty with stand	1
Drill	Press or post with three-jaw key or self-tightening chuck, two or more speeds	1
Extractor	Screw, "Ezyout" set	1
File	12″ double cut flat bastard	3
File	10″ double cut flat smooth	2
File	10″ flat mill bastard	3
File	5/16″, ⅜″, ½″ round bastard	1 ea.
File, card	Face with pick	4
Forge	30″ x 36″ x 6″	1
Gauge, drill point	6″, angle measurement	2
Gauge, drill size	Steel, 1/16″ to ½″ size	1
Goggles	Grinding, pair	3
Goggles	Oxyacetylene welding, pair	6
Grinder	Electric, wheel 10″ or 12″, face 1½″ to 2″	1
Grinder	Sickle, electric	1
Gun	Alemite	1
Gun	Oil and grease	1
Gun	Zerk, lever-type	1
Hammer	Ball peen, 1 lb.	2
Hammer	Ball peen, 2 lb.	1
Hammer	Cross peen, 2½ lb.	2
Hammer	Sledge, 6 to 8 lb.	2
Hardy	Shank to fit anvil	2
Helmet	Arc welder's	2
Ladle	Melting, assorted sizes	3
Lathe	Metal (optional)	1
Marking stamp	Steel figure set, for tool steel	1

(Continued)

Table 34.4 (Continued)

Name of Tool	Size or Description	No.
Micrometer		1
Pliers	Combination side cutting	4
Pliers	Long nose, 6″	2
Puller	Cotter pin	1
Punch	Aligning	2
Punch	Blacksmith's assorted	3
Punch	Center, machinist's assorted	3
Punch	Pin, machinist's assorted	3
Reamer	Burring, ¼″ to 2″	1
Reamer	Expansion, blade	1
Rivet set	4″ or 5″	1
Rule	Steel tape, 6′	2
Saw	Hack, adjustable frame	1
Saw, hole	¾″ to 2½″	1 set
Screwdriver	4″, 6″, 8″, 10″	2 ea.
Screw plate	N.C. and N.F.—¼″ to ¾″ by 16ths, set	1
Shield	Arc welder's	4
Square	Carpenter's steel, 8″ x 12″	2
Tongs	Bolt, ⅜″, ½″, ¾″, 20″ to 24″	2 ea.
Tongs	Plowshare, 24″	2
Tongs	Straight lip, 20″ to 24″	4
Vise	Blacksmith's, solid box, 50 to 100 lb.	1
Vise	Drill press, 6″ opening	1
Vise	Machinist's, 4¼″ jaw, swivel base	4
Wrench	Adjustable, open end, 8″	4
Wrench	Adjustable, open end, 10″, 12″, 18″ (alloy)	2 ea.
Wrench	Combination, box and open end, 5/16″ to ¾″, set; metric set	1 ea.
Wrench	Flex, ⅜″, ½″, ⅝″, ¾″, set	1
Wrench	Monkey, 12″ and 18″	1 ea.

Engine Maintenance and Repair Tools and Equipment—Table 34.5 is a list of tools and equipment needed for teaching engine maintenance and repair. Some of the tools in Tables 34.3 and 34.4 would also be used in engine maintenance and repair.

Table 34.5. Suggested Tools and Equipment for Teaching Engine Maintenance and Repair

Name of Tool	Size or Description	No.
Air hose, ¼″ x 25″	5 ply, braided rubber covered, ¼″ pipe fittings complete with DeVilbiss quick attach connections	2
Analyzer, exhaust gas	Air fuel, idle valves, propane and butane, portable	1
Bar, drag link, 16″	Separator for tie rods and links	1
Bar, pry, ¾″ x 18″	Rolling head and alignment point	1
Bar, pry, ¾″ x 24″	Round alignment point and pry wedge	2

(Continued)

Table 34.5 (Continued)

Name of Tool	Size or Description	No.
Battery carrier, 17″	Battery terminal post type, plastic strap	2
Battery cleaner	Battery terminal post cleaning tool, three-way	2
Battery filler, 1 qt.	Automatic, for water or battery acid	1
Brush, parts, 12″	Solvent, parts cleaning, 2½″ bristles	6
Bushing driver	Set of 13 collars and two mandrels in plastic box	1
Can, fuel, 5 gal.	Gasoline safety, 24 ga., seamless, no spill seal, trigger type pouring lip, safety screen, red color	1
Can, waste, 10 gal.	Oily waste disposal, 22 ga., safety lid, red color	2
Cutter, valve seat	Tool kit, valve seat reconditioning, cutter and pilots	1
Engine, 4 cycle, 1 cylinder, 3 HP	Air-cooled, recoil starter, air-vane governor	8
Extension cord, 50′	Flat industrial 12/3 conductor, safety orange color	4
Extractor, screw, no. 1–6	Spiral fluted, left hand spiral, set of six	1
Gauge, dial, 1″ range	0–100 reading, mounting pad on back	1
Gauge, feeler, .004″–.027″	Go–No Go thickness, precision ground, .002″ each step	4
Gauge, feeler, .04–.89 mm.	35 blades, flat hardened steel	2
Gauge, point	Ignition and spark plug Ignition point gauges & eight wire gauges, file, adjusting tool	4 ea.
Gauge, telescoping, ½″–6″	Set of five gauges (A, B, C, D, E) in plastic pouch	1
Grease gun, 1 lb.	Lever type, 10,000 psi cartridge or suction lead	2
Hone, cylinder, 1½″–3½″	Cylinder deglazing, flexible, self-aligning	1
Hone, cylinder, 2.0″–2.6″	For cylinder reconditioning, stones and storage box	1
Hydrometer	Battery testing, lead acid, 1,100–1,300 SPGN	2
Hydrometer	Radiator testing	1
Lamp, trouble, 25′ cord	OSHA approved, neoprene jacket, 18/3 cord	4
Oil measure, 2 qt.	Combination measure and pour spout, thumb control valve, lead coated steel	1
Punch gasket, ¼″–⅝″	Hollow punch set, not for metal, in plastic box, ¼″, 5/16″, ⅜″, 7/16″, ½″, 9/16″, ⅝″ cutters	1
Retrieving tool, 26″	Magnetic, for picking up steel and iron parts	1
Tachometer, 50–4,000 rpm	Dial type, 2% accuracy, cone-shaped tip	2
Tester, battery	6 to 12 v., 30-second test for rate and voltage drop	1
Tester, coil	Small engine magneto coil tester	1
Tester, engine	Engine tune-up kit, including inductive timing light, tach-dwell meter, vacuum gauge, compression tester, remote starter, instruction book, carrying case	2
Tester, ignition	Electronic ignition, 2- and 4-cycle, small and large engine	1
Tester, pressure cap	Engine cooling system	1
Tester, rpm	Small engine tachometer, electronic	1
Tools, special	Starter clutch wrench and flywheel holder	8
Wrench, adjustable, 8″	End wrench, adjustable jaw	1

(Continued)

Table 34.5 (Continued)

Name of Tool	Size or Description	No.
Wrench, adjustable, 10″	End wrench, adjustable jaw	1
Wrench, Allen, .028″–3/8″	Set of 15 short arm hex keys, plated	1
Wrench, ignition, 7/32″–7/16″	Set of eight miniature, open end	1
Wrench, oil filter	Self-adjusting strap wrench type	1

Arc and Oxyacetylene Welding Tools and Equipment—The tools and equipment listed in Table 34.6 are needed for teaching welding in agriculture mechanics.

Table 34.6. Suggested Tools and Equipment for Teaching Arc and Oxyacetylene Welding

Name of Tool	Size or Description	No.
Box	Electrode holder and scrap	1
Brush and scraper	Combination, 1½″ x 11″	2
Chipping tool	Hammer and brush combination	6
Clamp	9″ welding alignment	4
Clamp, C	4″, 6″, 8″	2 ea.
Cleaner, tip	Oxyacetylene	1 set
Gloves	Welder's	10 pr.
Helmet	Welding, No. 10 lens, lift front quick adjustment headgear	4
Lighter	Spark	2
Shield	Hand, No. 10 lens	2
Shield	Portable for welding table	1
Table	Arc welding	1
Table	Oxyacetylene	1
Truck	Cylinder	1
Welder	Electric, AC transformer type, 20 to 250 amp., 220 to 240 v., single phase	4
Welder	Oxyacetylene outfit	2

Plumbing Tools and Equipment—The tools and equipment listed in Table 34.7 are suggested for plumbing.

Table 34.7. Suggested Tools and Equipment for Teaching Plumbing

Name of Tool	Size or Description	No.
Bender, tubing	¼″ to 5/8″	1 set
Cutter, plastic	¼″ to 2 5/8″	1 set
Cutter, tubing	3/16″ to 5/8″	2 sets

(Continued)

Table 34.7 (Continued)

Name of Tool	Size or Description	No.
Die	Stock and die ratchet, 1/8" to 3/4"	1
Die	Stock and die ratchet, receding dies, 1" to 2"	1
Flaring tool	3/16" to 5/8"	2
Reamer	Tapered, 1/4" to 2"	1
Swaging tool	1/4" to 2 5/8"	1 set
Tap, pipe	1/8" to 3/4"	1 set
Torch, propane		2
Vise	Pipe, 1/8" to 3 1/2"	1
Vise stand		1
Wrench	Pipe, 10", 14", 18", 24"	1 ea.

Soldering and Sheet Metal Tools and Equipment—Soldering equipment is also needed in teaching electricity. The soldering and sheet metal tools and equipment listed in Table 34.8 are suggested.

Table 34.8. Suggested Tools and Equipment for Teaching Soldering and Sheet Metal Work

Name of Tool	Size or Description	No.
Awl	3 1/2" blade	2
Can	Gasoline, 1 gal. (safety)	1
Copper	Electric soldering	1
Copper	Soldering, 1 to 2 lb., pair	1
Divider, wing	12"	2
Furnace	Bench gas	1
Gauge, metal	Sheet metal and wire	1 ea.
Groover, hand	No. 4	2
Hammer	Tinner's medium	2
Handle	Soldering copper	12
Iron	Electric soldering, 300 w., diameter 9/16" to 1 1/8"	1 ea.
Mallet	Tinner's, 2 1/2" x 4 1/2", composition	2
Pliers, forming	8"	2
Rivet set	Size 7, 5, 3, 1	4
Rule, steel	1" x 36"	1
Seamer	Hand blade 3/4" x 3 1/2"	2
Shears	Bench, capacity 10 ga.	1
Snips	Tin, 12" duck bill and straight lip	1 ea.
Torch	Quart size, gasoline	1

Electricity Tools and Equipment—The soldering equipment used in teaching electricity is included in the list of equipment for soldering and sheet metal. The tools and equipment needed for electricity are listed in Table 34.9.

Table 34.9. Suggested Tools and Equipment for Teaching Electricity

Name of Tool	Size or Description	No.
Ammeter	0 to 50 amp.	1
Cable ripper	3¾″	5
Clamp	Electrician's splicing	1
Dipper	Soldering	1
Electrical supplies	Cable	
	Combination single-pole toggle switch and receptacle	
	Conduit	
	Duplex receptacle for switch box	
	Four-way toggle switches	
	Fuse box	
	Keyless shell sockets	
	Outlet boxes	
	Pendant switch current tap	
	Plaster ring	
	Plates for switches and receptacle	
	Porcelain duplex receptacles	
	Porcelain keyless receptacle	
	Porcelain pendant covers	
	Porcelain pull-chain receptacles	
	Remote control unit	
	Sill plate	
	Single-pole toggle switches	
	Surfex duplex convenience receptacle	
	Surfex keyless receptacles	
	Surfex pull receptacles	
	Surfex rosettes	
	Surfex single-pole dead-end switches	
	Surfex single-pole feed-through switches	
	Surfex three-way switches	
	Switch boxes	
	Three-way toggle switches	
	Weather head	
Hickey	Conduit-bending	1
Knife	Electrician's	6
Knockout	½″ to 1¼″	1 set
Pliers	Combination, side cutting, 8″	6
Pliers	Diagonal cutting, 8″	2
Pliers	Electrician's, 8″	2
Pliers, long nose	7″	4
Pliers, pump	10″	4
Soldering gun	325 w.	2
Tape	Tempered steel, electrical	1
Tool pouch	5″	2
Torch	Prest-o-lite, electrician's outfit	1
Voltmeter	AC portable, 5″ scale	1
Wattmeter	AC portable, 5″ scale	1
Wire stripper	5″	6

Soil and Water Management Tools and Equipment—The tools and equipment needed for teaching soil and water management are listed in Table 34.10.

Table 34.10. Suggested Tools and Equipment for Teaching Soil and Water Management

Name of Tool	Size or Description	No.
Arrow (pin), 3/16" x 14"	Enameled, surveyor's set of 11, red and white alternate color, with carrying ring	3 sets
Auger, soil, 2"	Solid 1/2" shaft, 42" long, wood handle	1
Level, farm, 20 power	Leveling instrument set, aluminum alloy frame, four leveling screws, azimuth 0°–90°; 15 min. vernier, with Fiberglas case and tripod and plumb bob, target and engineer's rod	1 set
Level, hand, 2 1/2 power	All purpose surface and sighting with carrying case	2
Level, universal, 26 power	Leveling instrument set, 12" telescope, 6 min. focus, four leveling screws, 110–120 sec./2 mm. level vial, azimuth graduated 0°–90°, vernier to 5 min., Fiberglas case with P-9010 tripod and plumb bob and 7690 engineer's rod and target.	2 sets
Pole, range, 8 1/2'	Two section, 1 1/8" diameter tubular steel, alternate color red and white on 1' gradients	2
Sampler, soil, 1" x 21"	Long push type, 14 1/2" profile opening	1
Tape, 100'	Chain tape, 5/16", width, .020" thickness, marked in ft. with ends marked in 10ths and 100ths	3

Painting and Glazing Tools and Equipment—Table 34.11 is a suggested list of tools and equipment for teaching painting and glazing.

Table 34.11. Suggested Tools and Equipment for Teaching Painting and Glazing

Name of Tool	Size or Description	No.
Brush	Paint, 2", 2 1/2", 3"	6 ea.
Brush	Stencil, 1", 1 3/8"	2 ea.
Cutter	Glass, circular, 2" to 12"	1
Cutter	Glass, single wheel	1
Cutter	Glass, turret wheel	1
Knife	Putty, 1 3/4", 2 1/2"	2 ea.
Sash tool	Size No. 4	1
Scraper	Paint, 3" blade	1
Stencil	Adjustable set and figure set, 1" letters	2 ea.

Leather Working Tools and Equipment—If, in a local community, the development of abilities to work with leather is needed, the tools and equipment listed in Table 34.12 are necessary.

Table 34.12. Suggested Tools and Equipment for Teaching Leather Work

Name of Tool	Size or Description	No.
Awl	Sewing, 12 needles	3
Awl	Stitching, 1¾" x 2¾"	12
Edging tool	Leather	1
Gauge	Draw, harness makers	1
Haft	Awl, assorted, set	1
Knife	Saddler's round	1
Knife	Skiving	2
Machine	Riveting, for tubular rivets	1
Punch	Leather, revolving, six-tube	1
Punch	Nail hole	1
Rivet set	No. 1 and No. 2	1 ea.
Tank	Washing, parts—homemade	1
Wheel	Pricking, ¾", 18 teeth	1

Drafting Tools and Equipment—The tools and equipment needed for teaching drafting are listed in Table 34.13.

Table 34.13. Suggested Tools and Equipment for Teaching Drafting

Name of Tool	Size or Description	No.
Drawing board, 16" x 21"	Basswood, metal edge	16
Scale, 12"	Architect's, triangular, plastic	16
Triangle, 8"	30°–60°, clear plastic	16
Triangle, 8"	45°–90°, clear plastic	16
T square, 21"	Wooden head with plastic insert in blade	16

Miscellaneous Tools and Equipment—The miscellaneous tools and equipment listed in Table 34.14 are needed for some of the minor phases of agriculture mechanics, such as fencing.

Table 34.14. Suggested Miscellaneous Tools and Equipment

Name of Tool	Size or Description	No.
Digger	Post hole	1
Sawhorse		4
Stretcher	Wire	1

Safety and First Aid Equipment—The safety and first aid equipment needed in an agriculture mechanics shop is listed in Table 34.15.

Table 34.15. Suggested Safety and First Aid Equipment for Agriculture Mechanics

Name of Tool	Size or Description	No.
Air nozzle, 5″	Compressed air, safety injector type, 30 psi max. discharge pressure	2
Brow band, adjustable	Cellulose sponge type, washable, 25/box	4 bx.
Cabinet, safety storage, 65″ x 43″ x 18″	Two-door, two shelves, double-wall construction 18 ga. steel, meets OSHA requirements	1
Cape, welder's, medium	Leather cape and sleeves	3
Ear inserts, universal	Foamed polymer, high-frequency sound, energy absorbing, noise silencing, in plastic container with chain	20 pr.
Face shield, 6″ x 12″	Clear acetate, .040″ thickness with adjustable headgear	6
Fire blanket, standard	In soft storage case, 64″ x 7½″ x 3″	2
Fire extinguisher, 10 lb.	Dry chemical, UL rating 4A-40BC	2
Fire extinguisher, 15 lb.	CO_2, UL rating 10BC, with hose and horn	1
First aid kit, for 25 students	Industrial quality	1
Glasses, safety, 46–48 mm.	Industrial quality, plastic frame, wire screen side shield, adjustable temple, meets ANSI Z87.1–1968 standards	–
Goggles, adjustable	Clear cover protection for Rx spectacles, fogless, soft plastic sides. Meets ANSI Z87.1–1968 standards	–
Goggles, adjustable	Gas welding, soft side with No. 5 shade lens, head strap, meets ANSI Z87.1–1968 standards	10
Helmet, adjustable	Arc welding, lightweight fiber, flip front with 2″ x 4¼″ No. 10 filter lens and cover lens, meets ANSI Z87.1 standards	10
Helmet, adjustable	Head protection (hard hat), meets ANSI Z87.1, Class A and Z89.2, Class B standards, yellow color, plastic	18
Respirator, dust	Disposable, non-toxic, meets NIOSH TC 23C-100 standards, 20 per box	2 bx.
Respirator, paint spray	Replaceable cartridge and filter, meets NIOSH TC 23C-100 standards	2
	Cartridge replacement for above, 3/box	1 bx.
	Filter replacement for above, 6/box	1 bx.
Tape, anti-slip, 2″ x 48′	White color, pressure sensitive	4
Tape, safety zone, 3″ x 36 yd.	Yellow color, pressure sensitive	4
Tape, warning, 1½″ x 18 yd.	Yellow and black stripes, pressure sensitive	1
Wearing apparel	Coveralls or shop coats, 100% cotton twill	–

ARRANGING THE EQUIPMENT IN A SHOP

Arrange Equipment Properly—Proper arrangement produces an attractive shop which stimulates student interest and facilitates the development of desirable abilities. Proper arrangement is also essential so that all space may be utilized. Some of the more common types of activities in a shop, such as the construction of trailers, feeders, and manure loaders and the maintenance and adjustment of machinery, require a large amount of space. More working area is usually needed in an agriculture mechanics shop.

Follow Basic Criteria—The following are a number of basic criteria for the arrangement of equipment in a shop. Teachers should:

1. Plan the overall arrangement to conform to the uses to be made of the shop. (Will it be used exclusively for instruction in agriculture mechanics classes, or will it be necessary to have other shop classes conducted in the same shop? In most states, agriculture mechanics shops are used entirely for agriculture mechanics classes.)
2. Consider safety factors in the arrangement of the equipment.
3. Provide the maximum amount of space for the construction and repair of large shop projects. (This means that as much of the central portion of the shop as possible should be left open.)
4. Provide for "dirty" work to be done in an area of the shop near a large doorway.
5. Have the cleaner types of work, such as carpentry, in a portion of the shop away from the forge, welding, and machinery repair areas.
6. Have suitable tools for a given job located near the place where the work is to be done.
7. Locate the equipment where adequate light is available.
8. Have a certain area for each specific activity or unit of instruction, such as metal work, electrification, forge work, welding, plumbing, and carpentry. This is important in locating tool cabinets.
9. Have the areas for sheet metal work and electrification adjoining, since there will be jobs in electrification which will involve soldering.

Decide on Location of Instructional Areas—There are a number of factors to consider in locating areas of instruction. The *first step* in deciding on the arrangement of the equipment in a shop is making an overall observation of the room relative to its possibilites for the major units of instruction. In the planning of a new building, the areas of instruction should be properly designated in the plans of the building.

The *second step* is deciding where to locate the forge and arc welders. The forge will have to be placed where it can be conveniently piped to a chimney. The arc welders should be located so a hood may be placed above them to carry off the fumes. It is desirable to locate the metalworking area in which these items of equipment will be used near a large doorway. This eliminates the necessity of moving machinery, tractors, and trucks great distances within a shop and keeps the grease, dirt, and grime near a large entrance and in the area where the floor drain is usually located. These arrangements facilitate cleaning a shop and keeping it clean.

The *third step* is locating the area for woodworking and carpentry. This area is usually located in the end of a shop opposite the large doorway.

The *fourth step* is deciding where to locate the other areas of instruction, such as plumbing, glazing, and electrification. These areas are commonly located along a wall between the carpentry and the metalworking areas.

The *fifth step* is determining where to locate the power equipment, such as the grinders, the drill press, and the circular saw.

The *sixth step* is locating suitable places for tool cabinets.

Place Equipment Along Walls—Authorities in agriculture mechanics agree that, insofar as possible, equipment should be placed along the walls of a shop so that the central portion of the shop will be open for the construction and repair of large projects.

The *workbenches* should be placed along the walls, although it may be desirable to have also one or two portable, general purpose benches (6′ to 8′ long). Portable benches may be needed for metal work and for activities in plumbing, such as cutting and threading pipe. A portable bench with two or more machinist's vises and a pipe vise may be placed in a shop in the metalworking area near the forge. The tops of portable benches should be covered with metal.

The *tool cabinets* should be placed above the benches, with specific tools in each cabinet for use in performing the jobs in the immediate area in which a cabinet is located; that is, the metalworking tools would be located in the area where metal work is done, welding equipment where welding is done, and woodworking tools where carpentry projects are constructed.

The *power tools*, such as the drill press and the floor-model electric grinders, may be placed along a wall. A heavy-duty electric grinder should be placed in the metalworking area near the forge. One light-duty, table-model grinder should be placed on a bench in the metalworking area and a second one placed on a bench in the carpentry area. The *circular saw* should be placed in the carpentry area and should be located so as to permit convenience in sawing.

The *welding equipment* may also be placed along a wall. A booth or screen should be used in connection with an arc welder to protect the eyes of persons other than those welding. Portable tables with screens may be used for arc welding and for oxyacetylene welding. When these tables are not in use, they may be placed along a wall. The *forge* should be placed along a wall. An iron rack may be placed near the forge. The forge and the welding equipment may be placed as a unit in one corner of a shop near a large doorway, or the forge may be placed near one corner and the welding equipment in an opposite corner.

Mark Off Location of Equipment—In planning where to place the equipment in a shop, it is desirable to mark on the floor, using chalk, what seems to be the most desirable location for each item of the equipment. The location of tool cabinets may be marked on the walls. If the planning regarding the location of equipment is done away from a shop, a floor plan may be drawn to scale on graph paper and the placement of equipment shown in the plan.

Rearrange Equipment in a Shop—Some teachers may be able to improve their agriculture mechanics facilities by rearranging the equipment. The basic steps previously mentioned should be followed in rearranging the equipment in a shop and in placing new equipment in a shop. Rearranging a shop is a good class project for students. They should be given an opportunity to help plan the rearrangement of the equipment.

First consideration in rearranging a shop should be given to the wall space available and to the way it is being used at the present time. Often the floor near the walls is cluttered with nonessential materials. Tool cabinets may extend to the floor when they could be placed above the benches. A bookcase or

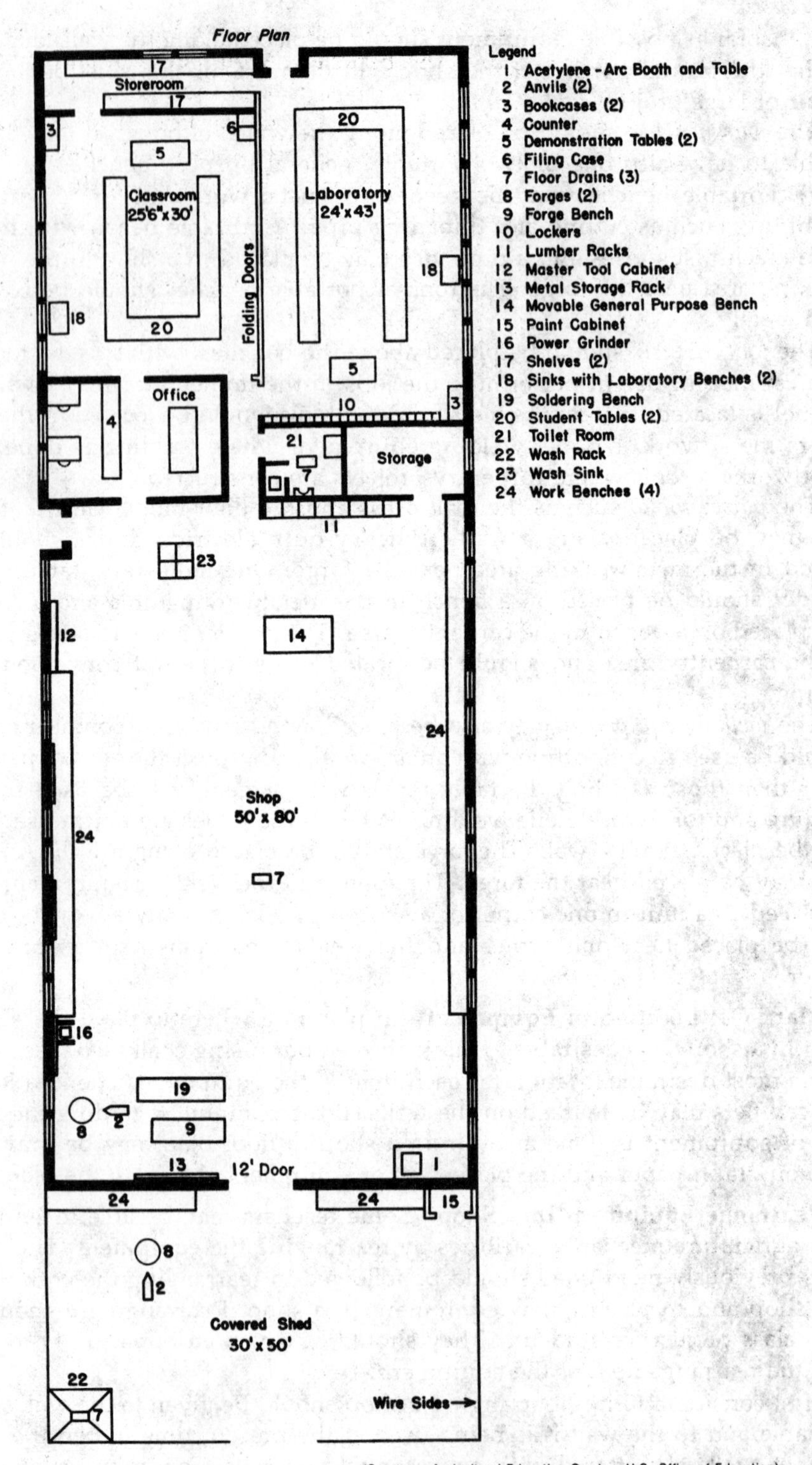

(Courtesy, Agricultural Education Service, U.S. Office of Education)

Fig. 34.3. A shop, classroom, and laboratory layout.

a supply cabinet may be sitting on the floor. Perhaps the bookcase or cabinet could be rebuilt and placed above the benches. A lumber rack and bins for storing small projects may be placed along the side of the room, while it may be possible to store small projects and lumber in the attic or in a separate room. Perhaps the workbenches have vises on both sides which prevent them from being placed against a wall, or the benches may be too wide to permit students to reach tools placed in cabinets above them.

It may be desirable to cut down wide benches to approximately 24″ in width. Perhaps the shop needs a good cleaning. Teachers are often surprised at the amount of space which can be made available in a shop through a program of reorganization and clean-up.

CHAPTER

35

How to Use School Land[1]

HISTORY

Early in the history of agricultural education in the United States, schools teaching agriculture often maintained farms on which their students received experience and instruction. Rufus Stimson, of Massachusetts, an early pioneering leader in agricultural education, introduced the home project as a functional procedure for gaining experience in farming. After the introduction of home projects, many schools sold or disposed of their land. Since that time, interest in school land has fluctuated. This fluctuation indicates that school land has definite advantages and definite disadvantages. Schools preparing persons for off-farm occupations requiring knowledge and skills in agriculture usually need school land laboratories on which opportunities for supervised occupational experiences may be provided.

PURPOSES AND ADVANTAGES

In communities having courses for farming where the enrollees live on farms, school land may be used to supplement the experiences obtained on the enrollees' home farms. The use of school land may enrich the farming experiences of these enrollees.

In a community offering agriculture courses with objectives other than the preparation for farming, and where many of the enrollees do not live on farms, school land is necessary as a laboratory.

Teachers of agriculture in a school that provides a school land laboratory usually indicate that they use the school land for the following purposes:

---

[1]The term "school land" is inclusive. It includes, for example, gardens, nurseries, forestry plots, arboretums, wood lots, ponds, conservation areas, and so forth.

1. To provide enrollees with worthwhile experiences and skills in agriculture that they would not otherwise have.
2. To demonstrate approved practices in agriculture.
3. To conduct quasi-experiments. True research is usually avoided. Quasi-experiments are sometimes used as a dramatic demonstration technique.
4. To provide occupational experiences in working and cooperating with others.
5. To provide an opportunity to coordinate classroom theory and practice. School land, because of its availability, often promotes coordination of agricultural theory and actual practice.
6. To promote supervised occupational experience programs. For example, a school may obtain a small amount of seed for an improved variety of a crop. This seed may be planted on school land. The seed produced may then be distributed to the enrollees.
7. To provide opportunities for supervised occupational experience programs for persons preparing for off-farm occupations requiring knowledge and skills in agriculture.
8. To provide opportunities for supervised occupational experiences in courses in agriculture with non-vocational objectives. Often the enrollees in these courses have had few agriculture experiences and have no opportunities to develop supervised occupational experience programs.
9. To earn money for an FFA chapter.
10. To publicize education in the agriculture program in the school.

The use of land as a laboratory is desirable. However, teachers in a rural community who work effectively with farmers are often able to arrange for the experiences needed by students on the farms in the community. In a rural community the opportunity that school land provides for demonstrating practices of potential value is probably the most worthwhile purpose mentioned. Here again, however, skillful teachers may be able to arrange for the demonstration of practices of potential value on the farms in their community.

The conducting of experiments on school land is a valid use of the land, but it should be remembered that experimentation is often costly, and a local department may not be able to afford possible losses. Teachers are also not usually trained to conduct experiments. If teachers do attempt to conduct experiments on school land, they should obtain the help of persons who know experimental procedures in agriculture. The operation of school land may provide many opportunities for students to work together cooperatively. It is not essential, however, that a school own land so that its students will have opportunities for cooperative experiences. A survey of FFA programs indicates that students have developed many ways of working together.

School land provides a laboratory for teaching the relationships between theory and practice, but good supervised occupational experience programs may also be used to provide for such teaching. The providing of seed for the supervised occupational experience programs of individuals is possible when a school operates land. This same purpose may be accomplished equally well, however, through a group, class, or FFA cooperative seed-producing project.

The provision of opportunities for supervised occupational experience programs for students who are enrolled in a vocational education for farming course is probably not a valid purpose for the operation of school land. If students do not have an opportunity to have a farming program or do not possess the means of acquiring facilities, their chances of becoming established in farming are very slight. If a department has a few students who may be able to become established in farming even though they lack opportunities

(Photo from Robert W. Walker, Pennsylvania)

Fig. 35.1. Plant identification. A land laboratory may be used as a convenient source of plant materials for instructional purposes.

for supervised farming programs, they can probably be placed on farms for experience.

The provision of opportunities for supervised occupational experiences for students who have inadequate facilities for such experiences but who are preparing for off-farm occupations requiring knowledge and skills in agriculture is a valid purpose for the operation of a school land laboratory. The operation of a school land laboratory is also a valid and effective way of providing opportunities for supervised occupational experiences for students in agriculture courses with non-vocational objectives.

The operation of school land may be a way for an FFA chapter to make money, but if a chapter pays all costs, including rent on land and labor costs, the profits will not usually be large. School land may provide publicity for an agricultural education program. It must be remembered, however, that this publicity may be good or bad. A community expects school land to be operated with efficiency and skill. If it is not, the community will criticize. It is apparent that school land serves valid purposes. However, other ways may often be found to accomplish some of these purposes.

Some Difficulties Encountered in School Land Operation—School land must be operated as a showplace in order to prevent criticism. Weeds must be controlled more carefully than on surrounding land. Seedbeds must be prepared especially well. Agribusiness must be conducted efficiently. This extra care cuts the possibility for profit. In fact, it may cost a school money to operate a school land laboratory.

Criticism may be received from parents and the public in a community when students work on the school land, even though they may be receiving valuable experiences which they do not receive at home. Often parents and the public assume that work done outside a schoolroom is not education. This type of criticism can usually be overcome if others are informed about the plan of operating the school land.

In order to operate school land properly, a school must hire competent labor. If a school operates a farm, a farm manager should be hired. The teacher of agriculture cannot be expected to take on this additional responsibility. A manager should have agricultural abilities nearly equal to those of an agriculture instructor. Such individuals are hard to find and must be paid substantial salaries. Often farm operators work only a 40- or 44-hour week, and it is impossible to operate a farm with no one on duty during much of the time.

Frequently, if the acreage of land operated by a department is small, custom workers are employed. Often it is difficult to complete a job at the correct time when the work is done by custom operators.

If the operation of school land by a department is successful, some persons in the community will discredit the results because they believe that excessive money has been expended to obtain these demonstrated results. If a school land operation makes money, the officials in the school may develop the habit of measuring the success of the department by the amount of profit received.

School land usually places an extra burden on the teacher or teachers of agriculture. This extra burden may result in decreased attention to individual supervised occupational experience programs and other important phases of a well balanced program of agricultural education.

With school land there is always the danger that the students will be exploited to perform a certain type of work beyond the point where it has educational value. Students who live on farms have often had experience with many of the operations performed on school land.

In some cases the financial risks involved in operating a school land laboratory are considerable. Teachers are under pressure to "make good." Therefore, they may make most of the managerial decisions, thus depriving the students of valuable learning experiences.

A school land laboratory is an educational facility. It is unfortunate when school officials or others urge teachers of agriculture to have school land laboratories simply as a way to use land which is part of enlarged school campuses. It is also unfortunate when school officials or others use profits as the chief measure of success of school land.

SCHOOL LAND MANAGEMENT

Policy—A department operating school land needs well developed policies regarding its operation. Overall policy regarding land operation may be formulated by a department's advisory council and submitted to the school authorities for their approval. The policy developed for the operation of school land should answer questions such as the following:

1. What are the purposes of a school land laboratory?
2. What is the primary purpose?
3. Who should manage the land?
4. How should students participate in the management of the land?
5. How should students participate in the physical operation of the land?

6. What part should the land laboratory operator, agriculture teachers, the advisory council, school authorities, students, and the community have in the management of the land?
7. What should be done with the profit earned from the land?
8. What capital investments should be made?
9. What policy should be followed when the land operation loses money?

After a policy statement for school land operation has been formulated by a department's advisory council and approved by the school authorities, it should be presented to the people of the community for their suggestions, criticisms, or approval. It may be published in the local newspapers and discussed at community meetings and family-night meetings. If criticisms or suggestions are obtained, the advisory council and the school authorities should reconsider the policies tentatively adopted. The final policy statement should be duplicated or printed and made available to students, parents, farmers, agribusiness workers, and others.

The advisory council for a department which operates school land will have to give some attention to policy for emergency or unanticipated situations which may develop. At the end of each year, the advisory council should evaluate the policies previously established. If revisions are made, these should be approved by the school authorities and the community before final adoption.

Some Precautions—School land should be operated for educational purposes. Profits should be of minor importance. School land should not be operated for the purpose of providing funds for the operation of agricultural education or an FFA chapter. Students should not be exploited in the physical operation of school land. It is possible for students to perform operations on school land to the point of diminishing educational returns. Student exploitation is one of the chief criticisms of school land operation. If students are asked to do work on school land that is not primarily of educational value for them, the work should be done before or after school hours, and the students should be paid a fair wage. It is good policy for teachers to observe this precaution carefully. If in doubt, the school should pay the students for their labor. Another rewarding policy for a department is not to spend more class time on school land than would be spent to teach the same things on a field trip to a farm or another agribusiness in the community.

Agriculture teachers are employed to provide agricultural education. They should not have responsibilities for performing and supervising the performance of operations on school land. If the school land laboratory for a department is a farm, a farm operator may be hired to perform farm operations. If the school land laboratory is a plot or a small acreage, it is usually necessary for the teachers to assume responsibility for supervising the performance of operations, which is one of the disadvantages of operating a school land laboratory. Teachers should not have a financial interest in the school's land laboratory operation.

Some Desirable Practices—If a school has a school land laboratory or if it is thought advisable to establish one, experience of departments operating school land indicates that the following practices are desirable:

1. The community is educated to view school land as a laboratory for agricultural education.
2. School authorities approve the policies regarding the operation of the school land laboratory.
3. The community is given an opportunity to share in policy formation regarding the operation of the school land laboratory.
4. The community is educated regarding the educational purpose of the school land laboratory.
5. The school land laboratory is operated as a business, and all laborers are paid a fair wage.
6. A farm operator is employed whenever the school land laboratory is of sufficient size to justify doing so.
7. Custom operators are employed, and paid a fair wage, when the employment of a farm operator is impractical.
8. Financial obligations are kept at a minimum.
9. The size and extent of operations on the school land laboratory are developed gradually.
10. The school land laboratory is maintained for demonstrational purposes instead of experimental purposes.

It is usually easier and simpler to produce crops, gardens, trees, fruits, ornamentals, and so forth on school land than it is to raise livestock. Raising livestock complicates and multiplies the problems involved. The purchase of farm machinery and equipment is not necessary when custom operators are used. In this way, the financial obligation can be kept low. Sometimes, when it is not practical to employ a farm operator, it is possible to lease the land to a farmer. This procedure solves not only the labor problem but also the farm machinery problem.

Many schools have found that school plots are as valuable and beneficial for plant and soil demonstrations as school farms are, and the responsibilities are much less.

TEACHING FACILITIES ON SCHOOL LAND

If school land is available, it may be used in a variety of ways. In addition to the more common uses, school land may provide opportunities for developing the following facilities:

1. Agriculture buildings and equipment.
2. Arboretum.
3. Nursery plot.
4. Turf demonstration plot.
5. Woodland demonstration plot.
6. Wildlife demonstration area.
7. Agricultural recreation demonstration area.
8. Garden demonstration area.
9. Landscaping and ornamental horticulture demonstration area.
10. Small fruit culture demonstration plot.
11. Pruning and grafting demonstration area.
12. Plant breeding demonstration plot.
13. Christmas tree plantation.
14. Plant propagation demonstration plot.
15. Pond development demonstration area.
16. Nature trails.
17. Cold frames.
18. Lath house.
19. Greenhouse.

CONCLUSIONS

The decision regarding the value of a school land laboratory is one that must be made locally. In some areas and under some conditions, school land laboratories are worthwhile and valuable additions to education in agriculture programs. If a school land laboratory is now available, teachers, with the help of others, should carefully develop the policies regarding its operation.

CHAPTER

36

How to File Bulletins and Other Teaching Aids

IMPORTANCE AND METHODS TO USE

Importance—A vast amount of valuable information is available in agricultural publications such as bulletins, magazines, charts, books, and illustrative materials. However, these materials must be filed in some way so that the teacher and the students can readily locate any information available in their department; otherwise, these publications merely take up space and are of little value. Every teacher should adopt a good filing system and keep definite files of any information deemed valuable for future use. The filing of agricultural publications is an important part of an agriculture teacher's work.

What to File—What to file must be determined by each instructor, but experience indicates that the following materials should usually be filed:

1. Bulletins containing information adapted to classroom, laboratory, and agriculture mechanics teaching.
2. Bulletins containing technical information.
3. Magazine articles and clippings from newspapers.
4. Illustrative materials.
5. Plans of items such as hog houses, hayracks, and labor-saving devices.
6. Charts and posters.
7. Pictures.
8. Correspondence.
9. Records and reports.
10. Records and printed materials of the FFA and other school-sponsored organizations.
11. Instructional materials.
12. Miscellaneous materials.

Methods of Filing—A number of methods with minor variations have been used in filing agricultural publications. The major systems used are the following:

1. The filing-box system.
2. The subject matter filing system.
3. The Dewey Decimal System.
4. The Agdex filing system.

Determining the System to Use—All systems of filing agricultural publications which have been developed so far have some advantages and some disadvantages. A teacher should attempt to anticipate the advantages and disadvantages of each system before choosing a method of filing for a department. A teacher's copying of the methods of filing used in other departments may not be a wise procedure. In determining a system to adopt, a teacher should consider the following questions:

1. Is the system easy to initiate?
2. Will the students be able to understand and use the system?
3. Will the system be easy to maintain?
4. Can the teacher and students quickly locate information related to a specific problem?
5. Can *all* materials related to a specific problem be found quickly and efficiently?
6. Does the system provide for adding new publications?
7. Is the system common in the area so that a new teacher in the department would understand it?
8. Is the system similar to the procedures used in other departments of the school, in the school's library, and in agribusiness so that students do not have to learn a new procedure in each location?
9. Is the system adaptable for use in the home library?
10. Is it possible to secure information, such as the source of a publication, date of a publication, number of copies, file number, station number, and author, without going to the publication itself?

Filing Equipment—The filing equipment needed depends on the system of filing adopted. If the filing-box system is used, a supply of boxes and shelf space are required. If one of the other systems is used, a special filing cabinet may be constructed, or a commercial filing cabinet may be purchased. When four-drawer metal filing cabinets are purchased, those of legal size are preferred because they are sufficiently wide to permit the filing of two rows of bulletins (normal size) in each drawer. A card file is needed for the card record of publications filed.

THE FILING-BOX SYSTEM

The filing-box system is one of the oldest methods of filing agricultural publications. It consists of grouping the various publications into units and placing each group in a separate filing box or compartment. A list of publications by boxes may be kept in a notebook.

The filing-box system is simple, easy to maintain, and easy for students to understand and use. It may promote wider reading because the students are forced to handle many bulletins in locating those desired. The system is gradually going out of use, however, because of its disadvantages, which are as follows:

1. Information related to a specific problem cannot be found without handling many or all of the publications in a box.
2. All materials related to a specific problem cannot be found quickly and efficiently.
3. When multiple copies of a publication are available, they become scattered among all the publications in a box or compartment.

In summary, the filing-box system is simple and easy to understand, but it requires more time to use after it has been established.

THE SUBJECT MATTER FILING SYSTEM

Subject matter filing is a refinement of the filing-box system. In this system the publications are filed by subject matter in consecutive order in filing cabinets or boxes. Each publication is given a number, and a record of the publications by subject matter headings is kept on cards in a card file. With this system, one may locate publications providing information related to a specific problem by going to the card file. The person may then locate the particular publication or publications quickly in the file cabinet without going through an entire box or compartment. The card file may be cross-indexed, making it possible to locate quickly all publications related to a specific problem. Multiple copies of any publication have the same number and are filed together in a cabinet. Thus, some of the disadvantages of the filing-box system are eliminated.

Determining Subject Matter Divisions—The first step in the organization of this plan is determining the main divisions to include in the system. After these divisions are selected, subdivisions may be chosen.

Making Guide Cards—After the various divisions have been determined, guide cards are made for the drawer or box in which the file cards are kept. One may locate quickly the principal subject headings and various levels of subdivisions by using guide cards of different colors and cuts. For example, the cards with a single cut might be blue; those with a half cut, salmon; and those with a third cut, buff. If a filing cabinet is used, a similar system of division cards may be developed for use within the cabinet itself.

Numbering Publications—The publications are grouped according to subject matter before numbering; that is, all publications on corn, all those on wheat, all those on sheep, and the like, are grouped. Then each subject may be assigned a certain consecutive series of numbers. For example, an instructor may allow the numbers 1 through 40 for alfalfa and 41 through 80 for corn. There may be only 15 bulletins on alfalfa to begin with, but the numbers 16 through 40 can be used as new publications on alfalfa are filed. If insufficient numbers are allocated, decimals may be used—for example, 80.1, 80.2, 80.3, or 80.01, 80.02, 80.03.

A gummed label may be placed in the upper right-hand corner of the cover page of each publication to be filed. The bulletins or circulars are numbered on these labels in consecutive order, or a number may be written on a bulletin without the use of a label. A stamper may be used to number publications. The number placed on a publication should be large enough to be seen easily.

Filling Out File Cards—Ordinarily 3″ x 5″ horizontally ruled file cards are used. Each card contains the following information: the number given to a publication; the number of copies of the publication; the title of the publication; the name of the author, if given; the year the publication was issued; and concise abbreviated information showing who issued the publication.

In some instances it is necessary to have two cards for the same publication. For example, two cards would be needed for "Growing Sorghum in Kansas"; one would be filed behind the guide card "Sorghum," a subdivision of "Grain Crops," and the other would be filed behind the guide card "Sorghum," a subdivision of "Forage Crops."

A list of all publications filed may also be kept in a permanent notebook. The entries in a notebook can very easily be recorded from the file cards. Some persons may prefer to record the information about the bulletins on file in a notebook instead of recording it on filing cards.

Placing Publications in Cabinets or Filing Boxes—After the bulletins are numbered and the file cards are properly filled out, the publications should be placed in cabinets or filing boxes in consecutive order. After this is done, each box or cabinet should be labeled and numbered according to the number of publications placed in each drawer or box. For instance, if the first drawer or box contains bulletins numbered from 1 to 41, it should be numbered "1 to 41."

THE DEWEY DECIMAL SYSTEM

The Dewey Decimal System is a more systematic, detailed, and refined subject matter filing procedure than the system just described. In the Dewey Decimal System, each subdivision is given a number, and the various publications in each subdivision are further identified by a combination of letters and numbers. This has the advantage of being the system most frequently used in school libraries and in other subject matter departments. It is also the system used in public libraries.

However, the Dewey Decimal System is seldom used in departments of agriculture in schools. The reason for this is not apparent. Perhaps it is because of the complexity of the system. Teachers of agriculture wishing to use the system may consult their school librarians for help.

THE AGDEX FILING SYSTEM

The Agdex filing system is a well accepted and widely used system of filing in agricultural education. Many institutions and other groups print the Agdex filing numbers on their publications when they are published. Thus part of the job is done in advance for the teachers using the Agdex system. It is the filing system most frequently recommended.

It is a comprehensive, complete numerical system for filing technical agricultural publications, agribusiness publications, and professional materials. It was developed in 1959 by Howard L. Miller for the National Project in Agricultural Communications, in cooperation with the Department of Agricultural Education of The Ohio State University. A publication describing the system in detail is available from the American Vocational Association (AVA). Also available from the AVA is a list of Agdex filing materials, including color coded divider sheets and color coded gummed labels.

Agdex is a subject classification procedure. Subjects are grouped under 10 subject areas. The indexing system is numerical, with each of the major subject areas allocated a block of 100 numbers. A color code is also used, which helps in identifying subject areas. About 15,000 numbers are available for classifying publications. Every number used represents a subject or topic. Publications in the Agdex system may be filed in steel filing cabinets. The system is ideally adapted for use with such cabinets.

In the Agdex system, publications are filed using both color coding and numerical identification classifications. The numerical identification classification has four major divisions. They are (1) agricultural enterprises, (2) agricultural science, (3) agricultural occupations, and (4) professional materials.

The following numbers are assigned to these four areas and to an open category:

Category	*Numbers Assigned*	*Color Code*
Open	000–099	
Agricultural Enterprises		
Field Crops	100–199	Green
Horticulture Crops	200–299	Coral
Forestry	300–399	Buff
Animal Science	400–499	Red
Agricultural Science		
Soils	500–599	Brown
Diseases	600–699	Blue
Engineering	700–799	Orange
Economics	800–899	Yellow
Agricultural Occupations	900–999	Gray
Professional Materials	.10–.90	White

Tens Digit—The tens digit of each number assigned is reserved for the further classification of the agricultural enterprise. For example, the field crops category may be further classified as follows:

Field Crops	
Field crops, general	100
Grain crops	110
Forage crops	120
Pastures	130
Oil and seed crops	140
Fiber crops	150
Roots and tubers	160
Sugar crops	170
Specialty crops	180
Open	190

The other categories are divided in a similar manner.

Units Digit—The units digit is reserved for categorizing the tens digit still further. For example, the grain crops area might be categorized as follows:

Field Crops	100
Grain crops	110
Corn	111
Wheat	112
Oats	113
Barley	114
Sorghum	115
Rice	116
Rye	117
Other	118
Open	119

The other tens digit categories may be further subdivided in a similar manner.

Fractions—The numbers placed on publications and on other filed materials are expressed as fractions. The numbers presented in the preceding paragraphs on the Agdex system would constitute the numerators of these fractions. The denominators of the fractions would designate enterprise practices, agricultural science categories, agricultural occupations subtitles, or professional materials subtitles.

The tens digit denominator categories for enterprise practices follow:

Category	*Number Assigned*
Production	00
Management	10
Culture	20
Varieties	30
Improvement	40
Harvesting	50
Storage	60
Processing	70
Product utilization	80
Open	90

The numerator numbers assigned to the agricultural occupations category are as follows:

Category	*Numerator Number Assigned*
Agricultural Occupations	900
Agricultural production	910
Agricultural supply	920
Agriculture mechanics	930
Agricultural products	940
Ornamental horticulture	950
Agricultural resources	960
Forestry	970
Open	980
Open	990

The denominator numbers assigned to the agricultural occupations category are as follows:

Category	*Denominator Number Assigned*
Career opportunities	00
Business procedures	10
Organization of agricultural:	
Business	20
Sales	30
Advertising	40
Customer service	50
Human relations	60
Stocking	70
Government regulations and laws	80
Open	90

The numerator numbers assigned to the professional materials category are as follows:

Category	*Numerator Number Assigned*
Administration	.10
Professional	.20
High school	.30
Occupational experience program	.40
FFA	.50
Continuing education—older adults, young adults	.60
Open	.70
Open	.80
Open	.90

The denominator numbers for professional materials designate the subtitles for the categories designated by the numerator numbers. The denominator subtitles for each numerator category would be different.

In numbering the agricultural science publications, a fraction is not used if the publication is not related to a certain agricultural enterprise. If the agricultural science publication is related to an agricultural enterprise, the agricultural enterprise number is used as the numerator and the agricultural science number is used as the denominator.

Thus, each publication or other piece to be filed is placed behind a color coded category divider card, and all items will have numbers placed on them. This will be a fraction for most items.

Below and on the next page are some examples of filing numbers:

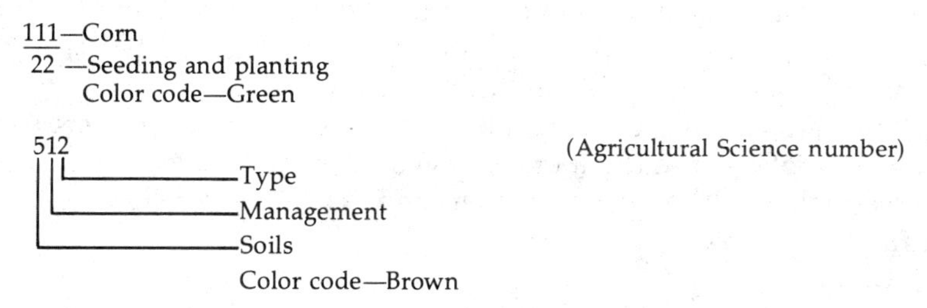

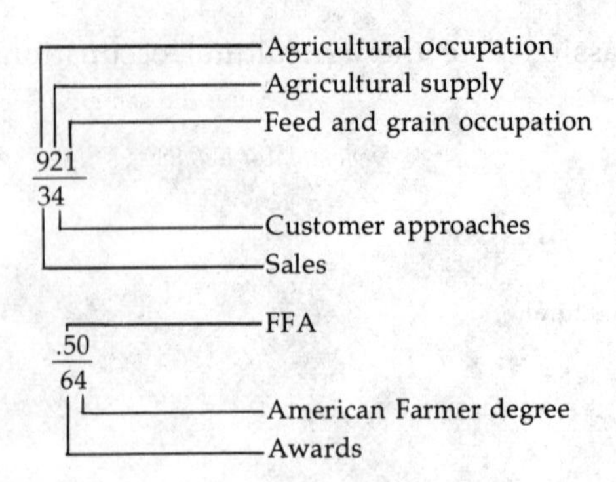

For a complete suggested numerical categorization of numerators and denominators and a detailed guide for using the Agdex filing system, one should obtain the Agdex guide publication from AVA.

LOCATOR CARD FILE

The following techniques apply to any numbered system of filing.

Cross-References—A publication on feeding swine may be listed in a subject matter card file under both *feeding* and *swine*. It takes only a short time to cross-reference a publication when it is filed, and it makes a subject matter card file much more valuable.

If duplicate cross-reference file cards for publications of a certain type are not considered necessary, cards may be inserted in the card file behind all the other possible headings, directing attention to other headings. For example, if red clover publications are not listed separately under the heading "Red clover," a card may be inserted behind this subdivision in the card file directing attention to the heading "Legumes," under which the red clover publications are listed.

Cards inserted in a subject matter card file directing attention to headings under which information pertaining to a subject may also be filed are a help to students in locating information regarding their problems. For example, a card may be inserted behind the heading "Swine" which states: "See also 'Feeding,' 'Diseases,' 'Parasites,' 'Farm buildings and conveniences,' 'Marketing,' 'Processing farm products,' 'Forage crops,' and 'Manures.'"

Station File—A station file is a card file which shows the source, kind, and number of all publications on file. Such a file may be developed for any numbered filing system. Figure 36.1 shows a station file card. On the top of a station file card are listed the source and kind of publication and the inclusive numbers of publications recorded on the card. The file number of a publication is listed at the right of the publication number.

Separate cards are needed for bulletins, circulars, and pamphlets because a station may duplicate the numbers on its circulars and bulletins. A station file is not essential, but Henderson, Rucker, and Witt list the following values for such a file:[1]

[1]Henderson, M. H., H. J. Rucker, and W. H. Witt, *Filing Agricultural Publications*, Vocational Agriculture Service, College of Agriculture, University of Illinois, Urbana–Champaign, p. 9.

1. "Such a file enables one to quickly determine whether or not a given publication is in the files.
2. "Using the station file cards also lessens the chance of filing the same publication under more than one file number.
3. "If you wished to know the file number of a publication previously filed, the station file will readily provide that number.
4. "When ordering publications you can quickly determine from the station file cards whether or not you have copies of the publications.
5. "You can prevent reordering publications that are out of print if you follow the practice of marking *OP* (out of print) after the file number of each publication when you are notified that it is out of print."

	Illinois Bulletins		300-349	
300	310	320	330	340
1	1	1	1	1
2	2–44	2	2–410	2
3	3	3	3	3
4	4	4	4	4
5–62	5	5	5	5
6	6	6	6	6
7	7	7–345	7	7
8	8	8	8	8–16
9	9	9	9	9

Fig. 36.1. Station file card.

FILING CLIPPINGS, CHARTS, AND POSTERS

Clippings—Numerous methods are used in filing articles. There is no best method—the main objective is to have a filing system. One very good practice is to purchase heavy manila paper and cut it so that when folded it will be of the size of an ordinary bulletin. A clipping may then be glued into a folder of this type, with the name of the article written on the outside of the folder and a number placed on the folder. A file card may then be filled out for it. While this involves time, it affords a very good way of keeping this material in good condition and readily available.

Some prefer not to remove an article from a magazine but to file the magazine and prepare a file card which tells the name of the article; the name, date, and page of the magazine; and the location of the magazine. Others prefer to file clippings in envelopes.

Clippings may be filed along with other publications when they are glued or stapled into folders the same size as the other publications, or when they are placed in envelopes.

Whatever system is used in a department, numbers should be stamped on all materials filed. The materials may then be recorded in the subject matter card file. Some teachers keep a separate card file of clippings, but this seems to be a duplication of files. When students go to a subject matter file, they should be able to find all materials on a subject without looking in another card file.

Charts and Posters—Charts and posters must be filed separately because of their size. A chart cabinet is recommended. If charts and posters are given numbers, information about them may be recorded on file cards which are included in the subject matter file.

A FILING SYSTEM FOR A TEACHER

A simple, yet adequate, filing system for a busy teacher of agriculture is a valuable aid in making teaching more systematic and more effective. One or two four-drawer steel file cabinets are recommended for a teacher's file of materials such as records, reports, course outlines, and FFA information. The file should be culled yearly and material not in present use removed to a transfer file or discarded. Transfer files may be expanded as needed. If the Agdex system is not used, the following procedures are suggested.

Correspondence—A teacher may file correspondence by using guide cards from A to Z with manila folders behind each guide. Material is filed according to person or subject.

Records—A stiff cardboard divider is generally used for each major heading. Manila folders may be used behind these dividers for subheadings and contents. The following major headings are suggested:

1. Advisory council records.
   a. Members.
   b. Minutes.
2. Data regarding community.
3. Departmental budget.
4. Departmental program.
5. Departmental policies.
6. Inventory.
7. Adult program.
8. Young farmer and other young adult programs.
9. Supervised occupational experience program.
10. Names and addresses.
11. Publicity.
12. Special events.

Reports—Reports will vary from state to state. The following reports are usually expected:

1. Monthly reports.
2. Supervised occupational experience program reports.
3. Adult program reports.
4. Young farmer and other young adult program reports.
5. Reports to local school officials.
6. Annual achievement reports.
7. FFA reports.

Instructional Materials—Instructional materials include items such as courses of study, teaching plans, and source units. Since this material will be used frequently, it should be located in a cabinet drawer that is at a convenient height.

FFA—The FFA materials may be filed alphabetically in manila folders. Some suggested headings are as follows:

President.
Vice-President.
Secretary.
Treasurer.
Reporter.
Adviser.
Chapter programs for meetings.
Contests.
Contests, district judging.
Contests, state judging.
Contests, public speaking.
Publicity.
Radio programs.
State chapter reports.
State FFA conventions.
State and American FFA degrees.
FFA information.
FFA program of work.
FFA achievement.
Initiations.
Leadership training.
Supervised occupational experience programs.
Manuals.
Membership lists.
Occupational records.
Parliamentary procedure.
Shows.
State Executive Secretary.

Miscellaneous—Lists, catalogues, maps, and regulations may be filed in manila folders under proper headings, such as the following:

List of available bulletins and circulars.
Book catalogues.
Equipment catalogues.
Seed catalogues.
Blueprints.
List of illustrative materials.
Special references for livestock and crops.
Map of community showing homes of students and bus routes.
Regulations of state board.
Professional bulletins and magazines.
Miscellaneous.

Personal Data—Most schools collect certain information regarding each student. Often agriculture departments collect additional information regarding their students and former students. This supplementary information usually indicates the home situations and the agriculture experiences of the students. Occupational data sheets for all present and former students are usually kept on file in agriculture departments. Frequently a department maintains a cumulative folder for each student currently enrolled.

Transfer Files—Correspondence, circular letters, and studies that must be kept should be placed in labeled manila folders soon after July 1 of each year and filed in transfer files. When all reports have been completed for a fiscal year, they should be put in one manila folder and filed under that year's heading in a transfer file drawer.

CHAPTER

37

How to Prepare and Use Visual Aids

PURPOSES AND KINDS OF VISUAL AIDS

Purposes of Audio-Visual Aids—Intelligent use of audio-visual aids will save teacher time and stimulate student interest. Audio-visual aids increase the retention of information and stimulate the development of understandings and attitudes. Most students remember what they see, hear, and read longer than what they only read. Charts are valuable in motivating goal-seeking and in evaluating outcomes. Aids which help students visualize abstract concepts and processes are especially valuable. Visual aids are also valuable in teaching manipulative skills. Teachers may use audio-visual aids to help students recognize a problem, to obtain information necessary to solve a problem, and to summarize a discussion.

Kinds of Audio-Visual Aids—Some of the audio-visual aids frequently used in agricultural education follow:

1. Movies.
2. Filmstrips.
3. Slides.
4. Overhead projection materials.
5. Photographs, especially those taken in the local community.
6. Preserved and mounted specimens.
7. Agricultural products and equipment.
8. Charts, graphs, and maps.
9. Models of various kinds.
10. Chalkboards.
11. Tack-boards.
12. Booths and displays.
13. Field trips and tours.
14. Demonstrations.

Schools should use every opportunity to secure suitable films and other visual aids of an educational nature to use in connection with their educational programs.

Sources of Materials—Teachers should preview the audio-visual aid materials they select to determine their educational value and their suitability for the uses they intend to make of them. There are a number of sources of visual aids:

1. The local community.
2. Commercial concerns, many of which have materials for free distribution.
3. State colleges of agriculture.
4. The U.S. Department of Agriculture and its various bureaus.
5. Agricultural supply companies having visual aids for sale.
6. The U.S. Superintendent of Documents, Washington, D.C.[1]
7. Breed associations.
8. Crop improvement associations.
9. Concerns or individuals handling photographs for sale.
10. The U.S. Department of the Interior.
11. The U.S. Department of Labor.
12. State government departments.
13. State and national associations.
14. Off-farm agribusiness associations.

Not all visual aids have sufficient educational value to justify their cost.

USING AUDIO-VISUAL AIDS

The unintelligent use of audio-visual aids may hinder, instead of aid, the learning process. In order to obtain good results, instructors must select types of aids adapted to the problems being studied. They must know what an audio-visual aid has to offer and understand when it will contribute most to the learning process. They must understand how to use audio-visual aids so that they will contribute to, and not hinder, learning.

Type of Aid to Use—There is no best type of audio-visual aid. The best aid to use in a teaching situation depends on the situation and what the students are attempting to learn. Teachers need to remember that movies and filmstrips are not the only types of audio-visual aids. Often examining actual objects (such as weed seeds or labor-saving devices) is preferable to looking at pictures. A well planned field trip or tour for a particular purpose may often be preferable to a movie intended to serve the same purpose. A working model may be easier to examine and understand than the actual object or a picture of the object. Often several types of audio-visual aids may be used during the study of a problem.

In a class studying weed control, five types of visual aids were used in a three-hour session. The class members first viewed a movie on weeds. This focused their attention on the problem. After discussing the movie, they observed 2″ x 2″ slides of some of the weeds in the community. The instructor illustrated on the chalkboard the root systems of the weeds being studied.

[1]*List of Available Publications of the United States Department of Agriculture,* U.S. Government Printing Office, Washington, D.C.

The instructor then asked the class to observe these same weeds more carefully by examining mounted specimens. The class then studied the seeds produced by these weeds. Through discussion and the use of a variety of visual aids, a thorough understanding of the weeds being studied was developed, and at the close of the class meeting, the members of the class voted to continue their study of these same weeds by going on a field trip during the next class session. Attention could have been focused on the weed problem by a field trip at the beginning of the study of weeds. However, since it was an adult group which was meeting during a busy season of the year, it was necessary to use the movie.

When to Use Aids—The use of an audio-visual aid to point up a problem, when that aid was designed only to supply information, usually hinders learning. For example, some audio-visual aids point up problems; others supply information necessary for solving problems. A filmstrip showing how to balance a ration for a cow may hinder learning if used before a group recognizes the need for balanced rations. The use of an audio-visual aid designed to point up a problem, when a group already recognizes the problem and desires additional information which will help solve the problem, also may hinder learning. For example, a movie focusing attention on the need for balanced rations may hinder progress when a class recognizes the need for balanced rations and is actively seeking information on how to balance rations.

There is no magic involved in the use of audio-visual aids. An aid should contribute to the learning process or not be used. This principle is often violated in the use of movies. Movies have to be ordered far in advance of their use. Often, when a movie arrives, the material it presents is not related to the problem being studied. If it is shown to a class anyway, the progress of the class may actually be retarded because the students are not prepared for viewing the movie and, therefore, receive little benefit from it. The movie also interrupts the problem being studied and may hinder its successful solution.

Some visual aids are designed for use during the teaching of a skill. For example, slides or filmstrips on rafter cutting may best be viewed as problems arise during the cutting of rafters. Often such an aid is used in advance of doing. The result is that the students are not ready for viewing the filmstrip or slides, or else the process is too involved to remember until the time for doing arrives. The sense of hearing may be reinforced by the sense of sight through the use of visual aids, but these two senses may need reinforcement from the senses of touch, smell, and taste. The use of an audio-visual aid as problems arise during an activity provides an opportunity for learning through all the senses.

Effective Use of Audio-Visual Aids—Audio-visual aids are tools and must be correctly used to produce desirable results. If best results are to be obtained, good tools must be used. Poor pictures or the projection of pictures in a lighted room may produce a reduction instead of an increase in the effectiveness of the instructional process.

A teacher should *preview* all audio-visual aids and thoroughly understand them before they are used. A class must be ready for the use of a visual aid. If a class wants information on the growing habits of a weed in order to decide on a program of control, it is ready for a movie on this subject. A teacher can, by skillful instruction, *prepare* a group or develop in a group the desire to understand the information a visual aid presents.

Visual aids are not entirely self-explanatory or understandable. Teachers must help groups *interpret* what they see. With slides, charts, or filmstrips, this interpretation may be accomplished while the aids are being viewed. With a movie, the interpretation of the content should immediately follow its showing. During a discussion and interpretation of a visual aid, the teacher should encourage the students to ask questions, clear up misunderstandings, and draw conclusions.

The last step in the use of a visual aid is to *apply* the information or understanding obtained to the solution of problems. Information and understanding obtained from a movie regarding the maintenance of the quality of milk, for example, should be used by the students in the solution of local problems in the maintenance of the quality of milk. A teacher may motivate use of information obtained from a movie by asking the students during the discussion period following the showing of the movie to draw conclusions regarding the applications of this information to their occupational experiences.

Advantages of Teacher-prepared Aids—Some of the best audio-visual aids are teacher-prepared.

Teacher-prepared aids have the following definite advantages:

1. They are designed to do specific jobs.
2. They are useable with the facilities available.
3. They belong to the teacher or the school, once they are prepared.
4. They are understood by the teacher.

TAKING STILL PICTURES

Local Pictures Desirable—Teachers can obtain effective teaching materials by taking pictures of supervised occupational experience programs, FFA activities, and other important production agriculture and agribusiness activities in a community. Teachers should not overlook opportunities to use pictures, local data, and other information pertaining to their local communities. Much of this information can be shown effectively through the use of 2″ x 2″ slides.

Taking Pictures—A 35 mm. or bantam camera is used for 2″ x 2″ slides. One of the first decisions a teacher has to make is: "Shall I use color or black and white film?" Color film is the best type for pictures of activities in which the scene should be given the major emphasis. Many teachers prefer black and white film to obtain prints for classroom exhibits, publication purposes, FFA scrapbooks, and individual collections.

Some departments have solved the problem of black and white film versus color film by having two cameras, a 35 mm. or bantam camera for color film and a reflex, Polaroid, box, or speed graphic camera for black and white film. If a department cannot afford two expensive cameras, good black and white pictures can be obtained with an inexpensive reflex camera.

If pictures are to be taken at night or inside, a flash attachment for a camera is essential. A close-up lens and a copying attachment are valuable accessories for copying charts, tables, and graphs and for taking close-ups of plants and specimens of various kinds.

PREPARING AND USING 2″ x 2″ SLIDES

Importance—Slides afford a teacher an opportunity to project a picture for an appropriate period of time and to discuss it in detail. Carefully selected and properly used slides are among the more important teaching aids in agriculture.

Preparing Slides—The preparation of 2″ x 2″ slides is very easy and requires little skill. The first essential is a good, clear negative. Following are a few suggestions regarding the preparation of slides. A teacher should:

1. Have a processing company prepare a positive film from the processed negative film. This job may be done by a local camera shop.
2. Secure the necessary slide binders. Slide binding kits provide binders, glasses for the front and back of each slide, and complete directions for binding.
3. Cut the positive frame to be mounted from the film and place it in a binder with the emulsion (dull) side up for black and white film and the shiny side up for color film, being careful not to scratch or otherwise mar the positive.
4. Label slides for future use.

Pictures may be taken of data and the negatives used for making slides. The black figures will show white and the white background will show black when projected on a screen. This eliminates the cost of having positives made from the negatives.

Teachers often have old filmstrips which they no longer use because most of the illustrations are out of date. There may be a few good frames in these filmstrips. These frames may be removed and placed in slide binders for future use.

Showing Slides—A projector with a 500-watt bulb and a 5″ focal length lens is satisfactory for general school use. A projector with a 1,000-watt bulb will project slides and filmstrips in a room which is not darkened.

The two types of projection screens in general use are the "beaded" and "mat white." A beaded screen has its surface covered with small glass beads. It is recommended for long, narrow rooms. Fixed relationships between the size of a screen and the size of the audience are recommended. The distance from a screen to the last row of seats should not be more than six times the width of the screen, and the distance to the first row of seats should not be less than two times the width of the screen.

MOUNTING AND USING PICTURES

Using Pictures—Some of the more effective uses of pictures are as follows:

1. *Classroom walls*—A few desirable pictures appropriately placed about a room help to make it more attractive. They should be related to the instructional program and replaced from time to time with other suitable pictures. A teacher should avoid covering the walls of the classroom with pictures.

2. *Class discussion*—Pictures related to a problem being discussed may be used for developing understandings.
3. *Public relations*—Pictures may be used in exhibits, news items, and magazine articles.

Enlargements (8″ x 10″ or 5″ x 7″) are more valuable for classroom displays and exhibits than the standard-size 3¼″ x 4½″ prints.

Using a Mounting Board—Various types of materials are used for mounting pictures. A stiff mounting board that will hold pictures firmly is usually preferred. A number of suitable cardboards may be purchased for this purpose. Some types of cardboard boxes may be cut up and used for mounting pictures.

Mounting Pictures—Pictures may be mounted and preserved in various ways:

1. *Library paste*—This method is not the most satisfactory, since pictures mounted in this way often have a tendency to draw and wrinkle.
2. *Rubber cement*—A non-wrinkling rubber cement designed especially for mounting pictures is desirable.
3. *Gummed tapes*—Gummed tapes may be purchased in a variety of colors and widths.
4. *Picture frames*—A few well selected pictures should be framed and hung in a classroom. Picture molding may be purchased and made into frames in an agriculture mechanics class.
5. *Shellac or plastic*—In preserving pictures which are not mounted behind glass or other protective covering, it is desirable to coat them. A thin coat of shellac consisting of one part shellac to one part denatured alcohol is usually satisfactory. A spray-on plastic available from photographic supply firms may also be used.

MOTION PICTURES

Value—Motion pictures are especially valuable in developing interest, in changing attitudes, in pointing up problems, and in developing generalizations. They are often not the best type of audio-visual aid for teaching facts or for developing skills. Motion pictures are usually best adapted for use in introducing or summarizing discussions.

Free, Rented, or Purchased Motion Pictures—Most motion pictures are too expensive to purchase. Teachers must, therefore, depend on free or rented films which are ordered and assigned to them for a definite period of time. This is a definite limitation in the use of motion pictures. It is difficult to anticipate the exact date when a motion picture will contribute to the progress of a class. As pointed out earlier, an audio-visual aid used at the wrong time may actually hinder the progress of a group of students.

The magnitude of the problem of obtaining films at a time when they can be used to advantage depends on the use made of motion pictures and the type of motion pictures used. Some of the motion pictures regarding the FFA are designed to develop interest in the FFA and to assist in the formulation of attitudes and generalizations about the FFA. Such pictures fit into the FFA program at almost any time. It is usually easier to use motion pictures with adults than with high school students. Meetings of adults are less frequent, and an instructor can anticipate and schedule motion pictures which will contribute to the progress of the class.

Even though an instructor plans carefully for the motion pictures needed and carefully anticipates the time they will be needed, a motion picture will occasionally arrive at the wrong time. When this happens, it may often be wise not to show the picture. Sometimes, when a motion picture arrives at the wrong time, it may be utilized at events such as FFA meetings and assembly programs.

Selecting Motion Pictures—An instructor should preview all motion pictures before showing. Titles are often very misleading. A free motion picture may contain advertising of a kind or to an extent that would make it undesirable for showing in a classroom.

Often someone in a community can be found who has a hobby of taking motion pictures. Such an individual is usually delighted to take local movies for the department when the film is furnished.

OVERHEAD PROJECTOR

An overhead projector produces images from transparent plastic, acetate sheets, or cellophane rolls. The overhead projector may be used in a lighted room. Materials may be prepared in advance for use, or the overhead projector may be used instead of a chalkboard.

The overhead projector is preferred as a visual aid by many teachers because materials for projection may be prepared quickly, easily, and inexpensively. The overhead projector will project color as well as black and white, and it is possible for the instructor to face the class or audience while using

(Photo from Robert W. Walker, Pennsylvania)

Fig. 37.1. An overhead projector provides a method of projecting that is useful in many situations.

the projector. The transparency sheets may be substituted for charts, and they are much easier to store.

SECURING, PREPARING, AND USING CHARTS

Importance of Charts—Someone has said, *"Chart it to teach it."* An adequate collection of well prepared charts covering appropriate materials is a valuable teaching aid. Charts are especially valuable in recording results obtained in supervised occupational experience programs. Such charts stimulate goal-seeking and the evaluation of results. A teacher should remember that charts may be placed on overhead transparencies.

Sources of Charts—Many of the most useful charts in a department are the ones made by, or under the supervision of, a teacher of agriculture and covering local activities and data. Charts especially designed for teaching agriculture are available for purchase. There are many commercial concerns which have charts for free distribution or for sale at a small charge. Several charts may be secured from the U.S. Superintendent of Documents, Washington, D.C., at a very small cost. Remittance to the Superintendent of Documents must be made by check or money order in advance of shipment.

Evaluation of Charts—In preparing charts or in selecting ready-made charts, a teacher should consider a number of questions:

1. Information provided:
   a. Do the data suit local conditions?
   b. Are the data reliable?
   c. Is the chart easily interpreted?
2. Mechanical make-up of a chart:
   a. Are the data well arranged?
   b. Are the data shown graphically?
   c. Are the letters large enough and well spaced?
   d. Does the chart present too many data?

If a chart does not meet these implied criteria, it may be best to discard it.

Who Should Prepare Charts?—Frequently there are students in an agriculture class who are capable of making very good charts. If not overdone, chart making by students stimulates interest and promotes learning. It is especially desirable for students to prepare charts pertaining to their individual occupational experience programs. In some instances an interested person outside a department may be employed to prepare a few charts.

Charts are easily made and require little time if adequate equipment is available.

Chart Materials to Use—Various kinds of materials may be used for charts:

1. Transparency sheets for overhead projector.
2. Sign cloth.
3. Unbleached muslin.
4. Vellum cloth.
5. Wrapping paper.
6. Stiff cardboard.
7. Window shades.
8. Chalkboard.

All the preceding kinds of materials have their merits and can be used for certain types of charts.

The method to use in making letters will depend on the time available, the type of chart, the use of the chart, and the materials available.

Chalkboard—A chalkboard may be used for temporary charts. Chalk may be treated so that it will not erase. It may be washed from a chalkboard, however. The following procedure for preparing treated chalk has been found satisfactory:[2]

1. *Selection of chalk*—Use only a soft chalk. Both colored and white chalk respond to the treatment equally well. The hard surfaced or dustless chalk is unsatisfactory.
2. *Preparation of sugar solution*—Use enough ordinary sugar in about 5 oz. of cold water to make a saturated solution. The solution is saturated if a small amount of the sugar remains undissolved after it has been vigorously shaken or stirred.
3. *Treatment*—Place a number of sticks of chalk in the solution. When bubbles no longer are given off from the chalk, which is usually the case after only a few minutes, remove the chalk and drain it thoroughly. After the surface moisture has evaporated, the chalk is ready to use. A reduction in the concentration of the sugar solution seems to reduce the permanency of the chalk. The lines appear full when this chalk is used but dry to normal appearance.
4. *Removal*—While it is not possible to erase this chalk with a dry eraser, it is easily removed with a damp cloth.
5. *Preservation of chalk*—Chalk which has been soaked in a sugar solution may be kept for an indefinite period if sealed in an airtight jar.

Cloth Materials—If a chart is to be rolled and extensively used, it should be made of durable materials. Book binders' vellum cloth is a high grade muslin with a filler which does not break or crack. Sign cloth is a desirable material, but it does not have the permanency of vellum cloth. The cost of muslin is much less than either of the other cloths, but it is less permanent. Since ink will run in bleached muslin, it is best to use an unbleached grade. If bleached muslin is used, it should be covered with a coat of white shellac which has been thinned with an equal part of denatured alcohol.

Wrapping Paper—If a temporary chart is needed, wrapping paper is an inexpensive and satisfactory material to use. A crayon or a felt-tip pen can be used to make letters on wrapping paper.

A teacher can use ordinary chalk on wrapping paper by covering the paper with a coat of white shellac thinned with an equal part of denatured alcohol, followed by a coat of chalkboard slating paint. Charts prepared in this way can be conveniently used in adult classes. An outline may be printed on the paper chalkboard and the remainder of the chart filled in as each point is discussed with an adult group. This type of chalkboard is especially desirable for use in a center where a permanent chalkboard is not available. The chart materials can be erased and the paper chalkboard used over and over again.

Window Shades—An inexpensive window shade may be used for a chart. A shade may be shellacked, using one part white shellac and one part denatured alcohol, and coated with chalkboard slating paint. Chalk may then be used on the shade for charting materials. Such charts can be conveniently carried and easily unrolled to expose all or a part of the charted materials.

---

[2]Courtesy, V. J. Morford, Department of Agricultural Engineering, Iowa State University.

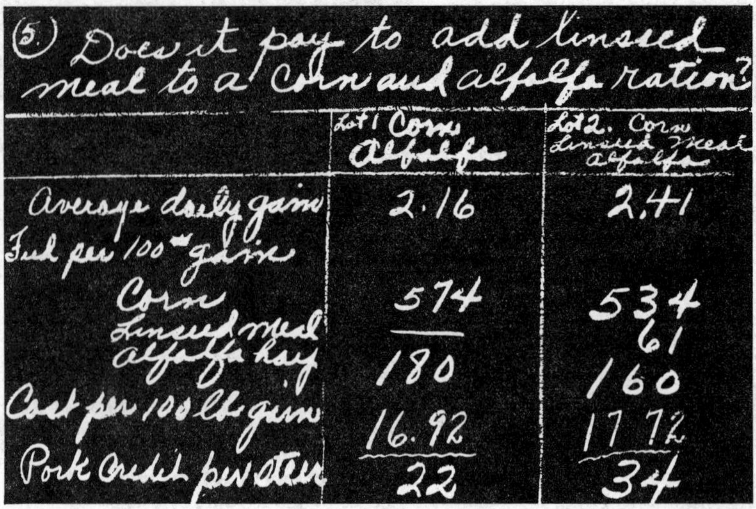

(5) Does it pay to add linseed meal to a corn and alfalfa ration?

	Lot 1 Corn Alfalfa	Lot 2. Corn Linseed meal Alfalfa
Average daily gain	2.16	2.41
Feed per 100# gain		
Corn	574	534
Linseed meal	—	61
alfalfa hay	180	160
Cost per 100 lb gain	16.92	17.72
Pork Credit per steer	22	34

(Photo from V. J. Morford, Iowa)

Fig. 37.2. This chart was made on heavy brown wrapping paper that was sealed with one coat of clear shellac thinned with an equal part of alcohol. It was then given one coat of liquid chalkboard slating. The soft chalk used in its preparation was treated with a saturated sugar solution. This chart does not blur in handling but is readily erased with a damp cloth.

Diagrams and lettering may be traced on light-colored shades with India ink or Speedball ink, using a Style B Speedball pen or a specially designed pen or pencil for lettering. Shades can be used in a variety of ways. They may be used as backgrounds for almost any kind of chart. Stick-on letters or freehand lettering may be effectively used on shades.

Graphic Charts—One of the best ways of comparing various types of data is by graphs. Various forms may be used in making graphs:

1. Bars.
2. Squares.
3. Circles.
4. Curves.
5. Dots.
6. Pictures.

The form to use will depend on the use to be made of a graph. Bar graphs are relatively easy to prepare, yet they are attractive and easily interpreted. Circle graphs are attractive but require more time to make than bar graphs. Trends may be shown on graph paper, which may be purchased in rolls. Graphs are relatively simple to make, yet they are attractive and easily understood.

Mounting Commercial Charts—Many charts can be obtained free but may soon be destroyed if not mounted. One effective method of mounting a chart which is to be rolled is to tack the bottom of the chart to the flat side of a piece of half-round wood. The top of the chart may be fastened between two pieces of half-round or between two pieces of flat moulding board. A black shoelace may then be tacked to the back of the top of the chart and used to hang it up. When the chart is rolled, the shoelace may be tied around it.

Another effective method of mounting a chart is similar to the one recommended for pictures. A chart is placed on a piece of stiff cardboard and framed by using gummed tape. The teacher can prepare a chart for hanging on a wall by punching two small holes near the top, inserting two shoe eyes, and riveting them in place. Shoe eyes of various sizes may be secured from a local shoe repair shop.

Flannelboard—Flannel makes an effective chart or bulletin board background. A flannelboard is constructed by stretching a good grade of cotton outing flannel tightly over a firm background, such as a composition board or a piece of heavy cardboard. Sandpaper, felt, felted paper, or pieces of flannel will stick to this flannelboard without an adhering agent.

If pictures, diagrams, or forms are to be attached to a flannelboard, pieces of flannel, sandpaper, felted paper, or felt may be attached to the backs of these items. A flannelboard may be used in teaching, and a chart or picture may be developed during a class discussion. With a flannelboard, any teacher can give an illustrated lecture.

Cotton outing flannel comes in various colors. One color may be used on one side and another color on the other side of a board. The color of the flannel background should be suited to the color of the items placed on a board.

In placing material on a board, the picture or other item may have to be rubbed against the flannel background to make it stick. Brushing the flannel background with a stiff brush facilitates sticking. If the flannel background is stretched tautly, the flannelboard may be hung perpendicular to the floor. The use of felted paper is the cheapest method of backing items placed on a flannelboard. Sandpaper backing works better, however. A fine to medium sandpaper may be used. Cotton yarn also sticks very well to a flannelboard, and it may be used to connect pictures and other items. Since yarn comes in various colors, its use adds color to a flannelboard.

Using Charts—Charts may be used in a variety of ways. They can be effectively used in connection with FFA demonstrations and in high school and adult classes. Most charts should be exhibited only while they are being used. There are some charts, however, such as an FFA program of work chart, that may be kept on a wall in a classroom during an entire year.

Filing Charts—If a chart cannot be found, it is of no value. If it is found but badly wrinkled, it may be very unattractive and its usefulness greatly decreased. Consequently, it is important that some system be developed for filing and storing charts. For a discussion of procedures for filing charts, see Chapter 36.

CHALKBOARD

Chalkboards are among the oldest and most used visual aids. The drawings in Figures 37.3 and 37.4 were developed by L. O. Armstrong of North Carolina State University at Raleigh, and they present some of the principles regarding the effective use of chalkboards.

For instructions regarding the procedure for making chalkboards out of wrapping paper and other materials, see the previous sections in this chapter.

1
Make the drawing *too* small.

2
Make a large drawing—the students in the back row do not have field glasses.

3
Draw continuously until the entire picture is completed. This takes too long. The students don't know what you are leading up to, and they don't know what they should be doing. They get restless, stop wondering what is coming next, lose any interest which may have developed, and are likely to start playing. One value of a chalk-talk is that the students are carried along step by step. A completed drawing throws the entire story at them all at once.

4
Stand aside, face the students, and let them in on the secret; tell them what the lines represent.

5
Turn to the board and draw one or two more lines.

6
Stand in front of the drawing. After all, it should be a fairly good picture—why hide it?

7
Stand aside, face the students, and tell them the how, why, where, and when; point out relationships. Take them along with you; keep their interest.

Fig. 37.3. Effective use of the chalkboard. (See also Fig. 37.4.)

8
Try to draw elaborate works of art showing all details. You are not an artist, and this is not a class in art. Even if you are an artist, the excess art hides the lesson.

9
Keep your drawing simple; use only those lines necessary to make the lesson clear and concrete. Omit unessential details.

10
Apologize for being unskilled as an artist; the students have observed, or will observe, this fact.

11
Execute a well planned chalk-talk. Practice it prior to class time; know how to draw it, how to use it, and what to say. Remember—make a large drawing; draw one or two bold, firm lines at a time; stand aside; face the class.

12
Talk to the board—the students will miss part of what you have to say, possibly a very important part.

13
Sketch rapidly and silently—then face the class to explain. Glance over your shoulder to locate the spot to which you wish to point, but face the class to talk.

Fig. 37.4. Effective use of the chalkboard. (See also Fig. 37.3.)

TACK-BOARD

Tack-boards, if properly used, are an effective visual aid. A cluttered tack-board will not be used by students, and it will be an eyesore. For effective use, a tack-board must be organized. "For sale" and "wanted" bulletins, for example, should always appear in the same location. Only current material should be placed on a tack-board. Exhibits placed on a tack-board should be changed frequently. If tack-boards are organized properly, changed frequently, and kept neat and current, the students will develop the habit of consulting them before each class meeting.

For a discussion of the location of tack-boards, see Chapter 33, "How to Equip and Arrange Classrooms and Laboratories," and Chapter 34, "How to Equip and Arrange an Agriculture Mechanics Shop." For a discussion of the principles of developing exhibits which may be placed on a tack-board, see the section on exhibits in this chapter.

COLLECTING AND PRESERVING INSECTS

Importance of Collecting—A good collection of insects, properly mounted and labeled, is a valuable teaching aid. A collection of the common insects found in a community affords valuable illustrative materials which may be used in high school, and in young and older adult classes. Average farmers or workers in an agriculturally oriented business do not have extensive knowledge of insects. They often know there is some kind of moth or worm attacking crops, but they often do not know the name of the pest involved. Consequently, teaching the life cycles, characteristics, and habits of insects, which must be known in order to control them, is an important part of the instructional program in agriculture.

Killing Insects for Mounting—After an insect has been caught, some method of killing is needed that will not damage the appearance of the specimen. Ethyl acetate may be used for killing insects in a killing bottle. The vapor from ethyl acetate kills an insect in a short time. If ethyl acetate is not available, nail polish remover may be used. A cork should be placed tightly in the bottle so that the bottle will be airtight. Various sizes of killing bottles may be used. Some prefer to have two sizes, small bottles about ¾" to 1" in diameter and 3" to 5" long and larger bottles about 2" to 3" in diameter and 6" to 8" long.

Labeling—A good grade of white paper should be used for labels. The printing should be carefully done, using India ink, and a uniform system of labeling should be followed. Printed labels are often used. A variety of sizes of labels can be purchased.

Mounting Boxes—Numerous types of boxes may be used for mounting insects. Regardless of the kind used, the insects must be kept dry, the box must be tightly sealed to prevent other insects from entering and eating the mounted specimens, and the specimens should be kept in a dark place to preserve their color. Mounting boxes may be secured from commercial concerns. One may use cigar boxes as temporary mounting boxes by placing a layer of some soft material, such as cork, in the bottom of the boxes to which the specimens may be pinned. Homemade boxes may be made with sliding glass tops. Drawers may also be used for storing insects.

Fumigation Materials—Mounted specimens must be protected from other insects. A shallow container in which a small amount of carbon tetrachloride or carbon bisulphide has been placed may be stored with the specimens. One of the best fumigants to use is paradichlorobenzene, which is a white crystalline substance. A small amount of this fumigant may be placed with the specimens.

Liquid Preservatives—The following suggestions regarding liquid preservatives for insect specimens were made by Glenn Bressler of Pennsylvania.[3] He found this liquid preservative to be satisfactory:

Alcohol, 95% solution	150 cc.
Commercial Formalin	50 cc.
Glacial acetic acid	15 cc.
Water	250 cc.
Glycerine	A few drops

In the experience of Mr. Bressler, it has been found desirable to place the solution in 9 cc. and 17 cc. glass vials with cork stoppers. When an insect is caught, it is dropped into one of the vials. No special killing process is necessary, since the solution does the killing as well as the preserving. The name of the insect may be written with pencil on a piece of paper and placed on the inside of the vial. This method of collecting and preserving is simple and requires very little time.

Preserving in Plastic—Commercial concerns now have for sale a liquid plastic in which specimens may be embedded. A specimen embedded in plastic may be examined and seen from all angles.

COLLECTING AND PRESERVING PLANT AND ANIMAL MATERIALS

What to Collect—Following is a list of materials which are often collected by teachers of agriculture for use in their teaching:

1. Seeds of local crops.
2. Sheaves of grains grown locally.
3. Important weeds found locally.
4. Weed seeds produced locally.
5. Fertilizers used locally.
6. Commercial protein concentrates.
7. Ingredients in feed mixtures.
8. Ingredients in fertilizer mixtures.
9. Crop rodents, such as gophers.
10. Spray materials.
11. Root crops.
12. Materials for treating seed.
13. Fungi, such as rust and smut.
14. Plants with common diseases.
15. Samples of local soils.
16. Samples of local rocks and minerals.
17. Diseased organs of animals.
18. Internal parasites of animals.
19. Samples of agricultural chemicals.
20. Samples of commercial products.

---

[3]Bressler, Glenn, "Preserving Insect Specimens," *Agricultural Education Magazine,* Vol. 17, No. 7, p. 127.

Pressing Plants—In pressing plants, each plant should be neatly arranged so that its roots, stem, leaves, flowers, and seed will be visible. The roots should be washed until free of dirt. If a weed is too large for mounting, a part of the stem may be removed. Ordinary newspapers or blotters may be satisfactorily used in pressing plants. Each plant should be placed between sheets of newspaper or between blotters. These are then placed in a press. Paper commonly used in magazines is generally too smooth to absorb the moisture from a plant and, for best results, should not be used.

Preserving Fleshy Fruits or Roots—Specimens such as carrots, beets, or plant nodules can best be preserved in preservative fluids. Ordinary fruit jars with glass tops are very satisfactory for this purpose. A 5 or 6 per cent solution of 40 per cent formaldehyde is a good preservative to use. All specimens should be carefully washed before being placed in the jars.

Preserving Seeds—Before seeds are placed in containers for storing, they should be free of all impurities and foreign materials. They should also be free of insect pests and fungi. It is best to treat the seeds with carbon bisulphide or formaldehyde before storing. Treatment may not be necessary if the seeds are known to be free of insects or larvae. Various methods may be used in storing and preserving seeds. One of the most common methods is to place the seeds in small jars.

Preserving Animal Specimens—Immersion of animal specimens in a formaldehyde solution is a simple method of preservation. One part of 40 per cent formaldehyde solution and nine parts of water make a satisfactory solution for most specimens. In preserving animal tissues for exhibition purposes, it may be necessary to use a more complex formula and system of preservation. For example, in preserving worms, a solution of 45 per cent ethyl alcohol and 10 per cent Formalin is often recommended.

EXHIBITS

Teachers are often expected to provide exhibits. These exhibits may consist of window displays, assembly displays, booths, or floats. Time for preparing these exhibits is usually limited. If students are to produce an acceptable exhibit in a minimum amount of time, it is necessary to have certain supplies on hand. The following supplies are recommended:

1. Background paper of various colors.
2. Paste-on letters of various sizes.
3. Stencils.
4. Crystal flakes of various colors.
5. Spotlights.
6. Small electric motors.
7. China pencils.
8. Speedball pens and India ink.
9. Poster paint (various colors) and brushes.
10. Small spray gun.
11. Some 8″ x 10″ glossy prints and 2″ x 2″ slides.
12. A case for exhibiting 2″ x 2″ slides.
13. Cardboard and sign cloth.
14. Petal paper.
15. Felt-tip marker with self-contained ink supply.

One principle to remember in preparing an exhibit is that people learn from exhibits through what they see. Very few people take the time to read the printed material in an exhibit. Keep the reading material to a minimum. Actual working models probably make the most effective exhibits.

FIELD TRIPS AND TOURS

Field trips and tours have always been extensively used in agricultural education. They are effective visual aids and must not be neglected as newer types of visual aids become available. For a discussion of the techniques of conducting effective field trips, see the guide for evaluating field trips in the section on evaluating teacher activities in Chapter 40, "How to Evaluate and Test in a High School Program."

DEMONSTRATIONS

A demonstration is a teaching technique which makes extensive use of the sense of sight. For a discussion of effective demonstration procedures, see Chapter 4, "What Is Good Teaching?"

TELEVISION PROGRAMS

The opportunities teachers of agriculture have to use television programs as an audio-visual aid in instructing their students are limited. Often programs of interest are not presented at convenient times for viewing by a class. It is often impossible to arrange for a class to meet at the time a program is presented. Since the persons enrolled in agriculture classes are limited in number, few closed circuit television programs or special series programs are designed or suitable for agriculture students.

Television does offer opportunities for presenting to others agricultural information and public relations information regarding agricultural education. Television stations must use a certain percentage of their time for educational programs. Station managers welcome opportunities to present programs prepared by teachers, FFA members, and adult class members. Presenting a television program occasionally is a worthwhile educational experience for persons enrolled in agriculture classes. It motivates students, creates enthusiasm, and acts as a means of acquiring knowledge and competence in agriculture and in public speaking.

AUDIO AIDS

Recorder—A recorder may be used to train public speakers and parliamentary procedure teams. It may be used to train judging teams in giving oral reasons. Radio programs may be recorded and used over and over as a source of information in the classroom.

Many good radio programs concerning agriculture are scheduled early in the morning, at noon, or at night. If a recorder is available, they may be recorded for class use when they are not broadcast during class time.

Teachers may record some of their classes as a means of evaluating their teaching. Recordings may be made at state, regional, or county agricultural meetings and later used in high school, young farmer, and adult classes. Interviews with specialists at state, regional, and county meetings may also be recorded and used later. A recording of an interview with an agribusiness worker may be made that will correlate with pictures taken at the place of employment.

At present, a magnetic tape recorder seems to be the most satisfactory type of recorder for school use. A tape recording is easily edited, and a new recording may be made over an old recording. The new recording erases the previous recording. A tape may be used over and over, or a recording may be kept for a relatively long period of time.

Radio—Many agriculture departments in schools present programs over local radio stations. Some departments have assumed responsibility for programs scheduled regularly. Radio programs presented by an agriculture department provide a very effective means of communicating to the public information and announcements regarding the high school program, the FFA, and the adult program. They also constitute an effective teaching technique. The youth and adults who assist in the preparation and presentation of programs learn a great deal.

Teachers and students may use a radio in a classroom for obtaining market reports and for listening to occasional programs. A radio is of more value when a recorder is also owned. A classroom radio is not essential equipment, but it can probably be justified because of its low cost.

Public Address System—A portable public address system is a valuable audio aid to use on field trips and tours. It is especially valuable with large groups. When a portable public address system is used, the persons in the back of the group can hear as well as those in the front.

ACQUIRING VISUAL AIDS IN AGRICULTURE MECHANICS

Sources of Material—Many commercial concerns in the agricultural equipment field have for free distribution many desirable visual aids. Many valuable visual aid materials in the agriculture mechanics area can also be secured locally or be prepared by teachers and students.

What to Prepare—There are many kinds of materials which an instructor may collect and mount for class use. Following are a few examples:

1. Various kinds of common hardware, such as nails and bolts.
2. Common materials used in building construction.
3. Various samples showing the results of correct and incorrect procedures.
4. Samples of finishes on wood.
5. Rope exhibits showing common uses of rope.
6. Samples of soldering jobs.
7. Samples of welding jobs—arc, mig, tig, oxyacetylene, and forge.
8. Models of labor-saving devices.

9. Samples of numerous supplies, such as welding rods, flux, turpentine, and red lead.
10. Small shop projects.
11. Pipe fittings and plumbing parts.
12. Samples of metals.
13. Electrical equipment, such as wiring materials, switches, receptacles, and appliances.
14. Farm equipment parts.

Charts—Following are a few examples of topics for charts relating to agriculture mechanics that may be developed:

1. Safety precautions in agriculture mechanics.
2. Good housekeeping.
3. Methods of cleaning brakes.
4. Objectives of agriculture mechanics.
5. Lumber grades and prices.
6. Different angles to use in sawing.
7. Suggestions on using tools.
8. Nails, bolts, and screws.
9. Phases of agriculture mechanics.
10. Achievements (record chart).
11. Improvement projects in agriculture mechanics.

Sound Films and Slides—Sound films and filmstrips on the mower, plow, grain drill, cultivator, tractor, and other types of farm machinery are available. These films are especially valuable in developing interests, understandings, and manipulative skills and in stimulating better care and maintenance of farm equipment.

Pictures of local agriculture mechanics activities may be taken and made into 2″ x 2″ slides, as suggested in a previous section of this chapter. There are

Fig. 37.5. A display case in the corridor outside an agribusiness classroom and agriculture mechanics shop.

a number of commercial concerns which have agriculture mechanics films available on a loan basis to schools. Some colleges have similar services.

Filing Materials—Some provision should be made for the protection of all visual aids. At the same time, they should be easily available for use. A case may be designed for carrying certain illustrative materials to and from centers where adult courses are offered.

PART

Administering and Evaluating Agricultural Education

CHAPTER

38

How to Manage Education in Agriculture

The comments in this chapter are directed to teachers of agriculture. The contents are not specifically designed to assist school administrators in directing education in agriculture, but many of the general principles presented may be of value to them.

WORKING WITH OTHERS

Importance—Ability to work with others is one of the secrets of success in the management of education in agriculture. A teacher does not live an isolated life. A teacher has to work with people: school authorities, boards of education, other teachers, supervisors, other professional agricultural education workers, young farmers, adult students, high school students, and parents. Success or failure is dependent on the ability to work with the people in these various groups.

Basic Principles—A song refrain goes: "Don't do something to someone else that you wouldn't want done to you." The Golden Rule is: "Whatsoever ye would that men should do unto you, do ye even so to them." A proverb advises: "Put yourself in their place." These statements present the basic principle for working with others. If this basic principle is followed, teachers will be punctual, loyal, dependable, understanding, self-confident, cheerful, sympathetic, friendly, and courteous. They will allow others to share in the planning of activities that will immediately or eventually affect them. They will always attempt to give credit to those who deserve credit, and they will use praise when it is deserved. Before acting they will consider the effect of their actions on the feelings of others. Honesty in all things will be the policy.

Promises will be kept, and the seeking of special privileges will be avoided. Instead, added service—a little extra—will be provided whenever possible. Responsibility will be given to others, and the authoritarian approach will be avoided. Co-workers and others will be kept informed. Neat and clean appearance will be practiced. Vulgar speech will be avoided. In self-evaluation, the assumption will be accepted that the critics may be right.

These virtues have been presented to nearly all teachers since childhood. They are not new ideas, and all teachers have developed some skill in working with others. No teacher is perfect. Every teacher can improve, but increased skill results only from the conscious practice of the basic principles until they become habits and from the thinking through of what these virtues mean when translated to specific situations. The basic principles of working with others will be considered in relation to specific situations in the following sections.

School Administrators—Most school administrators try to the best of their ability to operate good schools, and they also practice to the best of their ability the principles of working with others. They usually have definite ideas regarding what is a good school, and they see a faculty as a team designed to produce such a school. All teachers are expected by administrators to do their share of routine duties, and considerable importance is usually placed on dependability and promptness. Administrators also expect teachers to be loyal to the school system in which they are teaching. Administrators try to be fair, and being fair is usually interpreted as not giving any one teacher special privileges which are denied the others. This sometimes results in a conflict between a teacher of agriculture and an administrator, because what the teacher considers basic to good education in agriculture may be considered a special privilege by the administrator. Conflicts are certain to arise if both parties refuse to try to understand the attitudes, outlooks, value systems, and pressures under which the other works.

A teacher may eliminate, prevent, or alleviate conflicts by trying to understand the problems of administrators and the pressures under which they work. Administrators will usually do all they can to assist teachers of agriculture in developing their program if the teachers will keep them fully informed. Administrators will support an approved practice in the teaching of agriculture if they understand why the practice is desirable. They cannot produce miracles, however, and there are often reasons why an approved practice cannot be put into effect immediately. Administrators may be unable to obtain the finances required for carrying out a practice immediately. It may also be necessary for them to educate the faculty or board regarding the value of a new practice before it is instituted. However, if teachers want their administrators to "go to bat" for them, they will have to conduct themselves and their program so that the administrators will desire to assist them in every way possible.

Keep administrators informed. It is embarrassing for them not to be informed. Teachers should clear their absences from their jobs during the summer for summer school and conferences and during the school year for conferences and meetings.

Relationships with school administrators are usually good when teachers of agriculture observe the following practices:

1. Maintain discipline.
2. Maintain neat appearances.
3. Accept a fair share of school "chores."
4. Avoid "unclean" speech and irritating habits.
5. Avoid going "over the head" of the administrators.
6. Arrange for necessary absences in advance.
7. Provide necessary reports and records promptly and accurately.

Teachers may learn the problems and the value system of their administrators through frequent conferences with them. Most administrators appreciate being consulted frequently about the problems, activities, and results of their departments of agricultural education.

A written annual program and a written annual report are devices for informing administrators and board members concerning education in agriculture. A discussion of annual reports will be presented in a following section of this chapter.

In many sections or districts of the United States, teachers of agriculture have sponsored dinner conferences for their administrators as a means of creating a better understanding of education in agriculture by administrators and as a means of discussing the complaints of administrators regarding agricultural education. Administrators may also be invited to attend the conferences of the teachers of agriculture in a district or section.

The questions often discussed at meetings with administrators are as follows:

1. Who should be served by a program of agricultural education?
2. For what agricultural education purposes should state and national funds be accepted?
3. What should be the purposes of a public school program of agricultural education?
4. What kind of courses in production agriculture and agribusiness should be provided to implement these purposes?
5. How should the courses in agriculture be evaluated?
6. What should be emphasized in the courses with vocational objectives and in the courses with non-vocational objectives?
7. How much emphasis should be given to the adult courses in agriculture?
8. What should be the maximum size of classes?
9. How may the teachers of agriculture provide educational services in agriculture to other teachers?
10. How should teachers of agriculture be paid for their summer work?

School Board—It may be considered unethical in a community for a teacher to negotiate directly with the school board regarding the implementation or interpretation of board policies unless requested to do so by the school administrators. Teachers should take their problems directly to the administrators. Administrators do not formulate policies, but they are responsible for executing them. If teachers believe they have a problem that should be presented to the school board, they may diplomatically suggest this procedure to the administrators. If a school or department lacks policies, an advisory council may be used to initiate proposals for policies for presentation to the school board via the administrators.

Other Teachers in the School—Jealousy over salaries is a frequent cause of conflicts among teachers in a school. Teachers of agriculture are especially vulnerable, for their total salary may be higher than the salaries of other teachers because they work during the entire year. Teachers of agriculture should avoid gossiping about the salaries of fellow teachers. Conflicts over salaries are at a minimum in schools where each teacher's salary is based on a formula developed by the teachers, and each teacher's place in this salary schedule is his/her own business. If other teachers in the school want to discuss salaries, the teachers of agriculture should explain the basis for their salaries and then change the subject. Gossiping over salaries is dangerous.

Another frequent cause of conflict in a school staff is teacher load, especially the extracurricular load. A teacher may alleviate this conflict by encouraging the school staff and the administrators in the school to decide teaching and extracurricular loads in faculty meetings where each faculty member's duties are outlined and assigned. If this procedure is followed, each faculty member knows the teaching and extracurricular load of every other faculty member. If teachers of agriculture believe that their loads are excessive when compared with the loads of other teachers, they can voice their grievances at this time. Meetings to decide work loads should be very democratic.

Teachers of agriculture cannot shirk nonacademic duties, such as monitoring the halls and working at school events, and still be popular with other teachers. However, they need to educate the other teachers regarding their programs so that they will not expect too much from them. An annual report and a record of the time spent on each activity are procedures for educating other teachers regarding an agriculture teacher's program.

Other Agriculture Teachers in a Department—For a discussion of some of the details involving relationships with other teachers of agriculture in a department, see the section in this chapter on multiple-teacher departments.

State Agency for Vocational Education—Sending reports on time contributes to good relationships. An attempt to encourage the type of program of agricultural education sponsored by a state agency is also appreciated.

When a state supervisor visits a department, it is for the purposes of checking to see whether the contract between the state and the school is being observed, and helping the teachers improve the program. During a visit of a state supervisor, teachers should conduct their work in a normal manner. No special preparations or changes should be made. The filing system, records, reports, and supervised occupational experience program plans and records should be made available to the supervisor.

Teachers are not obligated to provide housing or meals for supervisors, because the supervisors have expense accounts and do not expect this service from teachers. A supervisor usually desires to confer with the teachers sometime before leaving a school. The teachers may ask when the supervisor desires this conference and arrange their schedule for the day accordingly.

Teachers of Agriculture in Neighboring Schools—The maintenance of good relationships with teachers in neighboring schools is not usually a problem. A teacher must accept responsibility for a fair share of the cooperative activities of the teachers of agriculture in the area and must also be willing to accept the majority decisions of the teachers for operating these cooperative activities. Publicity materials should not downgrade the activities of other agriculture departments.

Teachers' Associations—Teachers' associations provide a systematic and organized method for teachers to work together. Teachers will receive from an association as much as they put into it. Membership in a teachers' association is one way of showing other teachers that an instructor is willing to cooperate with them. An obligation of membership is faithful attendance at meetings. Attendance at conferences of a teachers' association is a method of professional improvement, and it gives a teacher a chance to work with other teachers.

Other Agricultural Education Agencies—Taking full credit for results in which other agricultural education agencies have had a part, and scheduling meetings which conflict with the meetings of other agencies are the most common causes of conflict with these agencies. In publicizing their programs and their results, teachers will promote good relationships by indicating the part other agencies may have had in producing the results obtained. All conflicts of meeting dates cannot be avoided, but teachers can keep the other agencies informed regarding the meeting dates of young farmer courses and other adult courses. Teachers can also ask for the meeting dates of the other agencies before they schedule their own courses.

Occasional conferences with the representatives of the other agencies also promote good relationships. Promotion of the programs of other agencies through announcements of their meetings in classes is usually appreciated. Observing memoranda of understanding regarding the type of program which vocational education in agriculture is supposed to offer is essential for good relationships.

Vocational Division or Department—Teachers of agriculture often are a part of a division or department of vocational education. This department is composed of all the vocational teachers in the school, such as agriculture teachers, industrial teachers, business teachers, health occupations teachers, home economics teachers, and so forth. A director of vocational education is often employed as administrator of the total vocational program. An agriculture program must be operated in harmony with the total vocational program. To accomplish this, teachers of agriculture need to attend vocational teachers' staff meetings called by the local director of vocational education and actively participate in the development of vocational education policies and procedures. Agriculture teachers need to cooperate with vocational teachers to avoid excessive duplication of instruction and of facilities. Agriculture teachers need to keep the local director of vocational education and other vocational teachers adequately informed of policies and procedures in agriculture. Undue credit for results obtained needs to be avoided to prevent the jealousy of other vocational teachers. Agriculture teachers need to give adequate credit to other vocational teachers for their efforts.

Community—For a discussion on how to work with the people in a community, see Chapter 11, "How to Develop a Desirable Public Relations Program."

MULTIPLE-TEACHER DEPARTMENTS

Working together is the key to successful relationships. Sharing in planning is essential. Definite division of responsibilities and acceptance of responsibilities by each of the teachers in a department are also essential. Giving all teachers in a department an opportunity to participate in a large percentage of the activities of the department is conducive to the mental health of the teachers. This does not mean that all the teachers in a department must share in each activity every time it occurs. It does mean, however, that if a teacher is designated to teach the agricultural science course one year, another teacher, if qualified, might teach this course the following year. The participation of a teacher in several activities in a department over a period of years prevents some activities from developing more prestige value than others. It also keeps teachers "on their toes," and it keeps teaching from becoming monotonous.

A permanent head of a department is not essential. A chairperson of a department with time allotted to administer the department is essential, however. All teachers in a department should be on the same salary schedule.

One problem in multiple-teacher departments is the duplicating of visits to homes and jobs. A father may be enrolled in an adult course taught by one teacher, a brother may be enrolled in a young farmer course taught by another teacher, and a sister may be enrolled in a high school course taught by still another teacher. This situation results in home visits being made by three teachers. Some multiple-teacher departments have tried to solve this problem by dividing the school district into territories and delegating the home visits in each territory to one teacher. This is not an entirely satisfactory procedure because students need to be supervised by their own teachers. Each problem situation involving a number of teachers visiting one home has to be solved as an individual problem. No blanket solutions seem to be satisfactory.

Teachers in multiple-teacher departments have to be more careful about keeping records and putting supplies and tools back in place than they would need to be if they were in single-teacher departments. The many successful multiple-teacher departments indicate that the advantages outweigh the problems. Many teachers would rather work in a multiple-teacher department than in a single-teacher department.

Department Chairperson—The final selection of a chairperson is usually the prerogative of the school administration, but the administrators should consult with all the teachers in the department before making the selection. The chairperson should be responsible for coordinating all the activities in agriculture, should serve as the liaison with the school administrators, and should provide leadership for the program in agriculture within and outside the school. The chairperson needs to be allocated time for these duties. He/she needs to conduct regular meetings of the staff to plan and evaluate activities.

The chairperson needs to delegate responsibilities to other staff members in agriculture. Each staff member should be responsible for coordinating the work in one or more of the major components of the department program, such as the FFA program, the high school program, the young adult program, or the older adult program.

The chairperson needs to consult the staff prior to giving staff members major assignments of responsibility. Assignments of jobs and responsibilities should be based on the interests, experiences, and abilities of the staff members. Major assignments should be approved by the appropriate school administrator. In many cases this may be the local director of vocational education in the school system. Care needs to be exercised that there is a division of labor so that all staff members are not expected to do everything. Discretion is needed, for example, in determining the number of teachers assigned to attend, or who feel obligated to attend, fairs, contests, award meetings, and so forth.

The short- and long-range program in agriculture needs to be developed cooperatively by all the teachers in the department. The chairperson and the teachers need to seek the advice of advisory committees. Teachers need to propose the program in their respective areas of assigned responsibility. Their proposed programs need to be discussed and revised, approved, or rejected by the entire staff. After the program is approved by the staff, it should be presented to the appropriate school administrator, often the local director of vocational education, for approval.

The chairperson needs to obtain the cooperation of all staff members in developing the budget for agriculture. The chairperson should then present the proposed annual budget request to the school administrators. An important job in a multiple-teacher department is keeping good inventory records. The chairperson needs to delegate specific inventory tasks to staff members. The inventory file needs to be maintained by the chairperson in the department's office.

Records and Reports—The department chairperson needs to coordinate the keeping of records and the making of reports. However, the teacher assigned a job should be responsible for keeping the records and submitting appropriate reports to the chairperson. Cumulative records of students should be kept by all teachers in the department office, and these records should be available to all teachers. The chairperson should submit all required state and federal reports, after appropriate clearance from the administration of the school. A file of these reports should be kept in the department office.

Facilities and Equipment—The chairperson needs to assume responsibility, in accordance with departmental procedures, for the coordination of the use, care, and maintenance of facilities and equipment in the agriculture department. However, all teachers need to accept responsibility for the care and maintenance of the building and of the equipment they use.

Public Relations—One staff member needs to be designated to coordinate the public relations efforts in agriculture, but all staff members need to provide supportive help to the coordinator. An attempt should be made to give equal and appropriate recognition to all phases and events of the program in agriculture. The staff should decide on the agencies in the community with which cooperative relationships would be sought and maintained. The responsibility for maintaining these relationships needs to be divided in an equitable manner among staff members.

Teaching—All teachers in the department need to be involved in deciding teaching assignments. It is advisable to provide for some team teaching in basic courses so that students can become acquainted with all the teachers of agriculture. Students enrolling in several courses in agriculture over a period of years need to have an opportunity to be taught by more than one teacher.

To the extent possible, dependent on other assignments, the teaching load needs to be equalized among the teachers. Specific assignments need to be based on interests, competence, and experience.

Occupational Experience Supervision—All teachers in a department should have responsibility for occupational experience supervision. To the extent feasible, teachers need to supervise the occupational experiences of the students they are teaching. This guideline applies to both high school youth and older adult students. Uniform records need to be kept by all teachers supervising the occupational experiences of the students. These records, at a minimum, need to include dates of supervisory visits, types of experiences observed, persons contacted, problems discussed, and recommendations made.

Departmental Procedures—All teachers in a department, along with appropriate administrators, need to be involved in the development of departmental procedures. The procedures should be put in written form and should be available to all concerned. These procedures need to be reviewed, interpreted, and revised as needed at periodic intervals at staff meetings.

Written procedures regarding discipline are especially important. All teachers in a department of agriculture need to attempt to implement these procedures uniformly.

New Teachers—New teachers are officially selected by the school. However, all teachers in the agriculture department need to have input into the selection of additional or replacement teachers. The chairperson needs to coordinate this input and must be the person to transmit the input to the school administrators. An attempt needs to be made to select new teachers who are compatible with present teachers, who have abilities and interests which complement those of present teachers, and who can work in harmony with present teachers.

Program Evaluation—Periodically, internal and external evaluations of a program need to be made. All teachers in a department should be involved in planning and conducting these evaluations.

Adult Education—All teachers in a department need to have responsibility for teaching young or older adults. Their assignments need to be definite, such as teaching a young adult course, a farm business management course, or an agriculture mechanics course. To the extent feasible, the assignments for teaching adults need to be equalized among the teachers.

In managing a multiple-teacher department of agriculture, it is often helpful to prepare and display a chart of the responsibilities of each teacher. Form 38.1 is an example of such a chart.

Form 38.1. Responsibilities of Agriculture Teachers

Responsibility	Teachers				
	Chair-person 1	2	3	4	Special Teachers
1. Teaching high school courses					
a.	X				
b.		X			
c.			X		
d.				X	
e.				X	
f.			X		
g.		X			
2. Teaching adult courses					
Young farmer course				X	
Farm business management course					X
Commodity course		X			
Agriculture mechanics course	X				
Off-farm agribusiness course			X		
3. FFA					
Business meetings	X				
Banquet			X		
Degrees		X			
Contests				X	
Awards		X			
4. Public relations	X				
5. Greenhouse			X		
6. Shop				X	
7. Land laboratory		X			
8. Office	X				
9. Supervised occupational records and reports	X				
10.					
11.					
12.					
13.					
14.					
15.					

MANAGEMENT OF TIME

Teachers of agriculture and most other people never have time to do all the work that needs to be done. In order to prevent undue strain and to accomplish the maximum amount of work, teachers need to set priorities regarding their work and to organize the use of their time. In other words, they need to plan carefully the use of the time they have and then force themselves to follow their plans. Without a plan, teachers may jump from job to job and accomplish little. Long-time and annual plans for the use of teacher time are needed. Teachers need to make monthly, weekly, and daily time management plans.

The work of a department of agricultural education is so complex and so demanding that a plan for budgeting the time of a teacher among various jobs is very helpful. This plan regarding the organization of time may be a part of a department's annual written program. Following are the personnel assignments included in an annual plan for education in agriculture prepared by a department chairperson.

• • •

PERSONNEL ASSIGNMENT

First Teacher	*No. of Hours*
a. Chairperson of department—some administrative and supervisory responsibilities	100
b. Two agribusiness courses (36 students)	972
c. FFA chapter adviser	50
d. Adult class (25 farmers)	500
e. Supervision of adult programs	175
f. Landlady program	50
g. Young farmer class instruction and supervision	575
h. Routine school duties (not in class program)	100
i. Professional (required by state)	50
j. General (shop maintenance, etc.)	100
k. Cooperating with other agencies	100
l. Section fair	10
Second Teacher	
a. Basic agriculture course (15 students)	360
b. Adult program	475
c. Agribusiness course (two sections, 32 students)	540
d. Occupational experience program visitation and supervision	654
e. General (shop maintenance, etc.)	100
f. Assisting FFA committees	50
g. Judging contests	50
h. Section fair	10
i. Professional (required by state)	50
j. Young farmer program (one section)	100
k. Routine school duties	100
l. Vacation	—

• • •

Form 38.2 is a detailed time budget for two adult courses.

Form 38.2. Time Budget for Two Adult Farmer Courses

Activities and hours required, monthly	July	Aug.	Sept.	Oct.	Nov.	Dec.	Jan.	Feb.	Mar.	Apr.	May	June	Total
Adult agribusiness management class instruction	15		8			12	15	12		4		8	74
Individual instruction	30	24	24	70	60	50			50	50	72	70	500
									Total				574
Adult agriculture mechanics class instruction									15	15			30
Individual instruction							12	6		6			24
									Total				54

BUDGETS AND INVENTORIES

Budget—Some public school administrators give their departments of agriculture definite budgets each year for supplies and equipment. Other administrators seem to object to indicating definite amounts for budgets. These latter administrators may believe that if definite amounts are budgeted, their teachers will spend that much money whether or not the supplies and equipment are needed. Whether or not a department has a definite budget, the teachers will profit from preparing and submitting a detailed budget to the administrators. This detailed budget should be submitted at the end of one school year for the following year.

A budget showing a breakdown between consumable items and additions to equipment is preferred. Explanations of the reasons for items in a budget may also be a part of a budget statement. If plans for purchases in a budget are distributed throughout a year, the budget may receive more favorable consideration because the income of most schools is distributed throughout a year.

No definite amount can be established as a desirable budget for an agriculture department. The size of budgets is a local problem and depends on many factors. When teachers prepare and submit detailed budgets, with good reasons for them, they may be surprised to find how much money they can obtain for maintaining and improving their departments.

Inventory—An annual inventory is needed. Items of equipment will be lost and will wear out. An inventory is an organized method of discovering needs and keeping a record of equipment. A normal loss of equipment is expected each year by administrators. If this loss is reported every five years instead of every year, however, it may seem excessive.

RECORDS AND REPORTS

Records—For a discussion of records needed by a teacher of agriculture and for a system of filing these records, see Chapter 36, "How to File Bulletins and Other Teaching Aids."

Annual Reports—It is a common practice for departments in business and industrial concerns to submit annual reports. This is also becoming a regular practice in more and more departments of agriculture. An annual report is a part of evaluation and a method of recording results obtained in evaluation studies. An annual report is also a method of informing all concerned about a school's department of agriculture. It is important that reports be *accurate* and that they be filed *on time*, for the sake of one's reputation, future job mobility, and so forth.

An annual report may include the following items:

1. *Community study.*
   a. Studies made.
   b. Methods of studying a community.
   c. Conditions discovered.
2. *Objectives.*
   a. Restatement of objectives.
   b. Major objectives for the year.
3. *Evaluation.*
   a. Evaluations carried out.
   b. Results of evaluation studies.
4. *Program planning.*
   a. Copy of program for the year completed.
   b. Copy of program for the coming year.
   c. Ideas for making program planning and the use of the programs more practical.
5. *Relationships.*
   a. Relationships developed with the rest of the school.
   b. Relationships developed with other agricultural education agencies.
   c. Relationships developed with others.
6. *Advisory council.*
   a. Number of members.
   b. Number of meetings during the year.
   c. Minutes of council meetings.
   d. Values derived from use of the council.
7. *Enrollment.*
   a. High school classes (number, enrollment).
   b. Young farmer and other young adult classes (number, enrollment).
   c. Classes for older adults (number, enrollment).
8. *FFA chapter.*
   a. Membership.
   b. Copy of annual program.
   c. New developments.
   d. Accomplishments.
9. *Supervised occupational experience program.*
   a. Number and kinds of activities and net earnings.
   b. Number and kinds of improvement projects, new practices, and agricultural skills.
   c. Placement for experience.
10. *Guidance and placement.*
    a. Studies of the need for farmers and other agricultural workers in the community.
    b. Percentage, of students of preceding year who are not in school, who are employed.
    c. Number of high school students and young farmers established in farming or other occupations requiring knowledge and skills in agriculture.
    d. Provisions for providing systematic guidance.

CHAPTER

39

How to Evaluate a Program of Education in Agriculture

INTRODUCTION

Program Planning and Evaluation—Evaluation is closely linked with planning and carrying out a program of agricultural education. Outcomes should be evaluated in terms of the objectives formulated. The expected outcomes should be carefully analyzed to determine the types of evidence which would indicate that the objectives are being realized. Methods should be developed for securing evidence which reveals the degree to which the outcomes are attained.

Why Is Evaluation Necessary?—It is important to evaluate the total agricultural education program in order to:

1. Find out the strengths and weaknesses of the program.
2. Help to evaluate the effectiveness of individual teachers' activities.
3. Determine ways and means of improving the program.

Evaluating a program occasionally helps keep a teacher alert and working for the improvement of the program. It also helps keep the advisory groups interested in the program.

Recognition must also be given to the fact that a program of agricultural education is being evaluated all the time by those who are affected directly and indirectly by it. Unorganized evaluation may be unjust because it is usually superficial, partial, and very possibly based on objectives in conflict with those adopted for the program. A complete evaluation based on valid objectives discourages evaluations based wholly on aspects of the program such as teacher's actions, discipline, winnings at fairs, or attendance at adult courses. Systematic and valid evaluations focus attention on the program and away from the measurement of the teacher alone. This is as it should be, because a teacher is the victim of the situation and is never wholly responsible for results or lack of results. Systematic evaluations take a teacher off the "hot spot." The teacher and the advisory council, as representatives of a community, should assist in the evaluation of a program by establishing standards, providing guidance, and conducting evaluation studies.

Who Should Participate in Evaluation?—Since a program of agricultural education is being continually evaluated by school administrators, school board members, teachers, farmers, agribusiness workers, and other interested persons in a community, an effort must be made to bring them or their representatives into the systematic evaluation process so that evaluation will be based on valid objectives. The following persons and groups or their representatives should be systematically used in evaluating a program:

1. Persons from outside the community who represent the state, national, and world needs for good education in agriculture.
2. The advisory council.
3. Adult class members.
4. Young farmers and other young adult class members.
5. Workers in off-farm jobs requiring knowledge and skills in agriculture.
6. High school students.
7. Parents.
8. The board of education.
9. School administrators and other teachers, especially vocational teachers.
10. The general public.

When Should a Program Be Evaluated?—Evaluation is a continuous process. The evaluation process begins as a part of program planning. The development of objectives becomes meaningful as methods and criteria for evaluating them are considered. There are certain times when more systematic evaluations should be made. A systematic measuring, analyzing, recording, and reporting of results should be an annual affair.

GUIDES TO USE IN EVALUATION

Evaluating Ways and Means—Evaluation may be based upon a program of agricultural education, upon ways and means, and upon the results of a program. Ways and means may or may not be connected with results and, by themselves, are not valid criteria. Evaluation of ways and means need not be discarded, however, but should be only a part of a total evaluation. One way of evaluating ways and means would be to compare them with ideals, approved practices, and standards which are recognized as valid in agricultural education. It may be wise to obtain professional educators to work with the teachers, the advisory council, and the community in conducting this phase of the evaluation process. Outsiders at this point may help the local people develop the "yardstick" of approved practices and standards for measuring their program. Some of the ways and means which might be evaluated follow:

1. Facilities and equipment.
2. Teachers: professional training, tenure, experience, professional interests, and activities.

3. Teaching procedures.
4. Courses for adults.
5. Courses for young farmers and other young adults in agriculture.
6. Courses for high school students.
7. The advisory council.
8. Departmental records.
9. Clerical assistance.
10. Travel expenses.
11. The written program of work.
12. The summer program.
13. The FFA program of work.
14. Community activities of teachers.
15. Costs.

Comparison of ways and means of the program with those of other communities may be one desirable evaluation device.

Evaluating Outcomes—Measuring outcomes is the best way of determining progress toward educational objectives. It is also the most difficult. The outcomes in which we are interested are the change and growth of individuals toward educational objectives. Change and growth of individuals in agricultural education are often measured indirectly by measuring changes in agriculture. Caution must be exercised in using this procedure because a change in agriculture may not indicate progress toward educational objectives. The change may have resulted from imitation, subsidies, unusual weather, epidemics, new varieties, or other causes. Evaluation of outcomes in agriculture, if used with judgment and as a part of a broad evaluation program, is of value. Some of the following efficiency factors have been found to be of value as "yardsticks" for measuring outcomes in agricultural production:

Objective: Ability to produce farm commodities efficiently.

1. Dairy.
   a. Pounds butterfat per cow (305 days, 2X, ME).
   b. Services per conception.
   c. Average calving interval.
   d. Percentage of cows calving from August to November.
2. Poultry.
   a. Eggs per layer per year.
   b. Eggs produced per layer in September.
   c. Percentage of mortality.
   d. Percentage of birds removed as poor layers.
   e. Pounds of feed per dozen eggs.
   f. Percentage of eggs marketed in highest quality grade.
3. Swine.
   a. Percentage of live pigs farrowed raised to weaning time.
   b. Average number of pigs raised per litter.
   c. Litter weight at 56 days.
   d. Average weight per pig at 56 days.

Long-time outcomes, which are more likely to be indicative of educational growth than short-time outcomes, may be used as a check on short-time results.

Criteria similar to *efficiency factors* in agricultural production may also be developed to evaluate progress toward educational objectives. Following are a few examples of criteria for vocational education in agriculture for farming:

Objective: Ability to produce farm commodities efficiently.

1. Dairy.
   a. Attitude of the community toward selected approved practices in dairying.
   b. Understanding of the relationship between the use of essential approved practices and production in dairying.
   c. Knowledge of essential approved practices in dairying.
   d. Acquaintance with the literature on dairying.
   e. Interest in dairying.
   f. Use of skills in dairying.
   g. Vision of possibilities in dairying.
   h. Understanding of aptitudes in dairy farming.
   i. Desire to produce a high-quality product.

Setting Standards—If the evaluative criteria previously suggested are to be used in evaluation, standards of performance have to be established as units of measurement. Knowledge must also be obtained regarding the status at the time the educational program was started if progress is to be determined. As an example, let us consider the standards needed for the criterion, pounds of butterfat per cow (305 days, 2X, ME). For this criterion it would be desirable to know the average for the state and community, and it would be desirable to know what the upper 10 per cent of the cows in the state and community produced. If these standards are known, a measurement of pounds of butterfat per cow may be interpreted. Standards regarding attitudes, knowledge, understanding, and interest are sometimes best expressed in descriptive terms.

Evaluating the Total Program—All phases of agricultural education should be included in an evaluation program. The following headings may be used for evaluating a comprehensive program:

1. Long-time plan for the local program.
2. High school instruction.
   a. Supervised occupational experience programs.
   b. Courses of study.
   c. FFA activities.
   d. Time allocated.
   e. Teaching procedures.
3. Young farmer and other young adult instruction.
   a. Supervised occupational experience programs.
   b. Courses of study.
   c. Organization.
   d. Teaching.
4. Adult farmer instruction.
   a. Related farmer activities.
   b. Courses of study.
   c. Organization.
   d. Teaching.
5. Instruction for off-farm jobs requiring knowledge and skills in agriculture.
   a. Preparatory.
   b. Upgrading.
6. Non-vocational phases of the agricultural education program.
7. Teachers.
   a. Qualifications.
   b. Relationships.
8. Students.
   a. Selection.
   b. Information.
9. Agriculture rooms and equipment.
10. Agriculture shop.
11. Follow-up and establishment.

Collecting Data—There is a vast amount of data useable for evaluation purposes which may be easily collected. There is usually considerable information on file in a department which is very helpful in evaluating the program. This information is included in the following materials:

1. Written plans, including long-time plans and course outlines for the program.
2. Records of approved practices adopted.
3. Records of efficiency measures of production achieved.
4. Records of visits to individuals.
5. Records of high school students' activities, including occupational experience programs, agriculture mechanics, FFA, and classroom activities.
6. Lists of former students now established in farming and in off-farm agricultural occupations requiring knowledge and skills in agriculture.
7. Records indicating investments in farming or agriculturally oriented businesses.
8. Records and accomplishments of young and adult farmers and other adults who have received education in the department.
9. Records of home shops established.
10. "Before" and "after" pictures.

U.S. census reports by minor civil divisions may be analyzed to obtain production rates and trends. Evaluation may necessitate the collection of additional information not now available from departmental records, from other agencies, or from state and national reports. Two other types of information which have been found of value for evaluation purposes are records of farmers, off-farm agribusiness entrepreneurs, and former students, and estimates and opinions of farmers, agribusiness workers, and others.

Records, other than financial records, are not difficult to obtain from farmers and from agricultural businesses. Adult students, as well as high school students, should keep and provide records for evaluation purposes. Records of results pertaining to efficiency factors and the use of approved practices should be expected from all students.

Often desirable information is not available in the form of records. For example, farmers may not have records regarding pounds of butterfat (305 days, 2X, ME), or weight of pigs at 56 days. The only thing that can be done in a situation such as this is to rely on estimates and opinions until records can be established.

A survey of non–class members may be necessary to obtain data regarding the community in general. These data can then be used in comparing the results of class and non–class members.

Studying the progress of all persons in a community who are engaged in agricultural pursuits—both farmers and off-farm agricultural workers—has certain advantages. It helps in the assessment of the indirect effects of teaching. Often persons in a community who have not been instructed adopt the practices of those who have been instructed, but they adopt them one or two years later than the persons who have been enrolled in courses. Studying such progress also provides a check on the teaching done, because comparisons between those taught and those not directly taught are possible. Finally, it helps to keep a teacher thinking about the entire community and not just in terms of those enrolled in courses.

For a further discussion of how to collect data, see the section on determining needs in Chapter 10.

Conducting Surveys—The use of surveys has been indicated several times as a means of collecting data. There are many techniques in the use of surveys that make them more valid, more reliable, and easier to use. The use of sampling instead of surveying the whole population decreases the work involved but does not reduce the reliability of a survey if certain precautions are taken to ensure that the sample is representative of the community. Stratified random sampling is usually best, since a check is made to see that the sample selected is representative of factors such as:

1. Geographical distribution.
2. Age.
3. Types of agribusinesses and farms.
4. Number of owners and number of employees.
5. Nationality.
6. Training in agricultural education.
7. Sex.

A teacher usually does not have the time to survey many agricultural businesses and farms. Returns from mailed surveys are often very low, thus making results of questionable value. Therefore, one of the best ways of securing information from non–class members is to have class members conduct the surveys. Adults enrolled in courses, young farmer association members, and FFA members have successfully conducted surveys in many schools. Certain principles should be followed in conducting surveys:

1. The members of the group conducting a survey should understand the value and use of the information gathered. They should desire the information as much as the teacher does. The need for the information should develop from class work, and those conducting a survey should have a part in the construction of the survey form.
2. No one person should be asked to spend much time conducting a survey. Usually each person should be expected to contact only two or three persons.
3. The group conducting a survey should collect and analyze first the information from one another. This will create a better understanding of the values and the uses of the data.
4. Each person should collect information from neighbors who will cooperate.
5. Survey forms should be short. Usually there should be few enough questions so that they can be put on a 4″ x 6″ card.
6. Reports should be made of the analysis of data to those supplying information. This will make future surveys easier.
7. Survey forms should be so constructed that little writing is needed in answering.
8. Each question should be analyzed as to its purpose. This will eliminate unnecessary questions.
9. The questions should be answerable.

Opinion surveys may also be desirable to discover changes in attitude, interest, and understanding related to specific objectives of a department.

Making Evaluation Studies—Some of the data which departments of agriculture have found very useful for evaluation purposes follow:

1. Percentage of graduates of high school classes engaged in farming or in off-farm jobs involving agricultural knowledge and skill.
2. Percentage, of students of preceding year who are not in school, who are employed.
3. Number of approved practices adopted by students.

4. Quality of supervised occupational experience programs of students.
5. Change in relative importance of farm enterprises.
6. Trend in relative importance of farm enterprises.
7. Change in value of farm machinery per farm.
8. Change in number of livestock.
9. Change in number of acres of legumes.
10. Change in number of acres of cropland harvested.
11. Change in average production per unit of crops and livestock.
12. Change in percentage of net income that comes from crops and livestock.
13. Change in number of acres harvested of different crops.
14. Change in production value per productive work unit.
15. Change in number, type, size, and quality of agriculturally oriented business firms in the community.
16. Change in knowledge of agriculture among persons not involved in agriculture.

Using Self-evaluation—Teachers should use self-evaluation devices occasionally in order to determine ways and means of improving proficiency in teaching.

A common self-evaluation technique is to obtain the opinions of class members regarding the teacher's effectiveness. The following four forms have been used by teachers to obtain the opinions of their students.

Form 39.1. Evaluation of Teaching Effectiveness

1. To what extent has this course forced you to think?

( ) Very much ( ) A good deal ( ) Average
( ) Less than average ( ) Very little

2. To what extent has this course captured your interest?

( ) Very much ( ) A good deal ( ) Average
( ) Less than average ( ) Very little

3. To what extent do you regard this course as being practical and useful to those students for whom it is specifically planned?

( ) High ( ) A little above average ( ) Average
( ) Less than average ( ) Little

4. How often was the material presented clearly and logically?

( ) Always ( ) Usually ( ) Sometimes ( ) Seldom ( ) Never

5. How would you describe the attitude and responsiveness of this class as a whole toward this course?

( ) Very favorable ( ) Fairly favorable ( ) Average
( ) Slightly favorable ( ) Highly unfavorable

6. If another course similar to this one were offered, would you enroll?

( ) Definitely ( ) Probably ( ) Probably not ( ) Definitely not

Comments:

Form 39.2. Teacher Rating by Students[1]

Please answer the following questions sincerely, fairly, and carefully. Your answers will in no way have any influence on your grade. Do not sign your name. A summary will be made by the students. The instructor will see only the summary.

1. Considering all school teachers with whom you have taken work, how would you rank the instructor in this course?
   ( ) Among the best ( ) Very good ( ) Average
   ( ) Rather poor ( ) Among the poorest

2. To what extent does the work of the instructor impress you as indicating mastery in the field of this course?
   ( ) Very markedly ( ) Markedly ( ) Average ( ) Little ( ) Very little

3. Considering faults the course has had, where would you locate them? (Check as many as necessary.)
   ( ) In the subject matter
   ( ) In the instructor's mastery
   ( ) In the class itself
   ( ) In the instructor's method
   ( ) In the instructor's personality

4. In attitude toward students, would you say that the instructor is:
   ( ) Invariably considerate and courteous?
   ( ) Generally considerate and courteous?
   ( ) Sometimes inconsiderate and discourteous?
   ( ) Frequently rude and discourteous?

5. With reference to a liberal, tolerant, and progressive attitude, would you say that the instructor:
   ( ) Welcomes honest differences in viewpoint?
   ( ) Is biased on some things but usually tolerant?
   ( ) Is entirely intolerant and resentful of different viewpoints even though honest?

6. With reference to a sense of proportion, would you rate the instructor as being:
   ( ) Well balanced—not overcritical or oversensitive—having very good sense of relative values?
   ( ) Fairly well balanced—having fairly good sense of values?
   ( ) Overcritical, extremely sensitive—having very poor sense of relative values?

7. Make a list of your instructor's strongest points and weakest points.

Strongest	*Weakest*
1. ______	1. ______
2. ______	2. ______
3. ______	3. ______
4. ______	4. ______
5. ______	5. ______

8. If you were asked to evaluate the instructor's work in the course in terms of the scale used in evaluating students' work, what would you assign as a grade?
   ( ) A ( ) B ( ) C ( ) D ( ) F

	Excellent		Average		Poor
Personal Characteristics:	5	4	3	2	1
1. Appearance					
2. Qualities of leadership					

(Continued)

Form 39.2 (Continued)

	Excellent		Average		Poor
	5	4	3	2	1
3. Willingness to cooperate					
4. Enthusiasm					
5. Dependability					
6. Courtesy and refinement in personal relationships					
7. Personality					
8. Behavior					
9. Interest in others					
10. Receptivity to others' problems					
11. Cheerfulness					
12. Self-confidence					
13. Quality of voice					
14. Sincerity					
15. Persistence					
16. Health					
Personal Abilities:					
1. Oral English					
2. Written English					
3. Initiative					
4. Ability to work with others					
5. Ability to adapt to situations					
6. Ability to learn					
7. Attitude toward criticism					

[1]Adapted from an evaluation form used by Kenneth Diehl, Illinois.

Form 39.3. Comments on Course

1. Name of course:
2. Favorable comments:
3. Unfavorable comments:
4. What recommendations do you wish to make as to ways of improving courses of this type or as to the desirability of courses of this type?

Form 39.4. Evaluation of Course by Class Members

1. Parts of course of most value:
2. Parts of course of least value:
3. To what extent did you accomplish what you hoped to accomplish?
4. Other comments:

CHAPTER

40

How to Evaluate and Test in a High School Program

The careful evaluation of programs in local high schools and in area vocational centers is essential. It provides a "box score" of progress. It motivates interest and makes objectives meaningful. It is not, however, a teacher's responsibility alone but the responsibility of all concerned. See Chapter 39, "How to Evaluate a Program of Education in Agriculture," for a discussion of the general techniques of evaluation. The following discussion will deal mainly with the techniques useful in evaluating progress, supervised occupational experience programs, the FFA, and teacher effectiveness.

One of the principal values of the measurement of student progress is the information it provides teachers regarding the effectiveness of their teaching. If a student has not learned, the teacher has not taught. Measurement may also serve as a yardstick of progress for a student if the student fully understands and accepts the measurement procedures. The best way of obtaining this understanding and acceptance is through teacher-student planning of objectives and evaluation.

Teacher-student planning of measurement devices and the frequent use of these devices will stimulate teachers and students to formulate definite objectives in terms of individual needs. Teacher-student planning of measurement devices should also help teachers and students locate the weaknesses and strengths of their programs and decide on ways and means of improving their programs. Teacher-student planning of evaluation procedures will develop desirable teacher-student relationships. A teacher cannot afford to be autocratic in planning and using measurement devices. For a discussion of techniques of teacher-student planning, see Chapter 4, "What Is Good Teaching?"

EVALUATING STUDENTS

What to Evaluate—Evaluation procedures should be designed to measure changes in ability in terms of the objectives developed. Changes in ability are manifested in changes in phases of behavior such as the following:

1. Interests.
2. Attitudes.
3. Ideals.
4. Appreciations.
5. Desirable habits.
6. Understandings.
7. Fundamental information.
8. Problem-solving.
9. Managerial skills.
10. Manipulative skills.
11. Planning.
12. Self-confidence and leadership.

Procedures to Use in Evaluation—The best measurement of a change in ability is the reaction of an individual when confronted with a real-life situation. What students do with their supervised occupational experience programs is usually one of our best indications of changes in abilities. Any measurement device, however, measures a product of a change in ability and not the change itself; therefore, measurement devices must be used with care. Measurement of changed behavior as indicated by supervised occupational experience programs may even be an inaccurate indication of change in ability.

Health, cooperation of parents, cooperation of the employer, and facilities available may affect the quality of a supervised occupational experience program, and an excellent program does not necessarily reflect the development of desired abilities. A student may have an excellent supervised occupational experience program, for example, because the parents are doing the planning and the work necessary for developing a successful program.

Real-life situations which may be used in measuring changes in ability do not always present themselves at opportune times for evaluating progress. This creates a desire on the part of teachers and students for shortcuts. The following are some of the "shortcuts" which have been used:

1. Performance (or practical) tests.
2. Oral responses and examinations.
3. Written examinations.
4. Daily evaluations.
5. Notebooks.
6. Record books.
7. Self-evaluation by students.
8. Individual scorecard and check lists.
9. Completed jobs or projects.
10. Home visits.
11. Personal interviews and observations.

Constructing Tests—Pencil and paper tests are among our principal "shortcuts" for measuring changes in ability. It should always be remembered, however, that they are shortcuts and that results of tests should be used only until more valid and reliable results are available, such as progress in the supervised occupational experience programs.

Pencil and paper tests have to be constructed with care because they determine indirectly what a student learns. For example, when tests emphasize principles and generalizations, the students concentrate their attention on these principles and generalizations and disregard nonessential details which are soon forgotten and which can always be located in a reference book when needed. When tests emphasize details, the students also emphasize details and often neglect principles and generalizations. Teachers must constantly guard against emphasizing details in examinations because a test of this type is often easier to prepare than one measuring the knowledge and understanding of principles and generalizations. A test should not call for long lists of "factors" or "points." A student may have the knowledge and understanding required to solve a certain type of problem but still be unable to recall a long list of factors or points.

Types of Written Examinations—There are various types of examinations, but they may be classified into three general groups:

1. *Essay Type Tests*—This type consists of questions requesting the students to state in full, compare, describe, or tell what they know. In this type of examination, students are free to write what they choose. A teacher cannot score this type of examination mechanically but must evaluate it subjectively. It tests the students' ability to recall and may stimulate reorganization of ideas and thus improve expression. It is probably our best pencil and paper procedure for measuring ability to solve problems. Problems presented in an essay examination also provide an opportunity to measure understanding if the problems have not been discussed previously.
2. *Standardized Tests*—This type of test is generally in printed form and has been "standardized" after it was given to a large number of students. Standardized tests are usually marketed through publishing companies. There are few standardized tests available in agriculture. One reason for the lack of standardized achievement tests in agriculture is that practices vary greatly from community to community.
3. *Objective Tests*—In this type of examination, the students are requested to complete statements, to cross out incorrect statements, to underline correct statements, to check true-false statements, and to match related items. An examination of this type may be scored objectively and mechanically. It is an excellent device for measuring a student's recognition and recall of information. There are numerous advantages claimed for this kind of examination:
   a. It is quickly and easily scored.
   b. It eliminates bluffing by students, since the answers must be either correct or incorrect.
   c. A variety of types may be used.
   d. Most students prefer an objective test.
   e. It permits the use of a large number of questions, thus allowing a more extensive sampling of subject matter.
   f. It is scored objectively; therefore, the opinion of a teacher does not enter into the scores.
   g. Slow writers have a better chance to complete an objective test.

An objective test requires considerable time to prepare, and a copy must be duplicated for each student. The time which is lost in developing the questions for an objective test is regained in scoring, because this type of examination requires much less time to score than an essay type examination.

Objective tests may also have some disadvantages. They often tend to emphasize memorization instead of understanding. They do not indicate students' ability to organize their thinking or their ability to express themselves in writing. A student may become "test-wise" regarding objective tests unless they are expertly constructed. A student who has the ability to memorize easily usually has a distinct advantage in taking an objective test.

Some Variations in Objective Tests—Some of the more common variations in objective tests are as follows:

True-False Type

Directions to students—Some of the following sentences are true, and some are false. Put a plus sign (+) before each true statement; put a minus sign (−) before each false statement. Do not guess!

1. Brown Leghorns lay brown eggs.
2. Infertile eggs are best for storage purposes.
3. Minorcas lay large white eggs.
4. Perches should be arranged one above the other.

Guiding Principles to Follow in Constructing and Scoring a True-False Test

1. Have at least 50 questions, about half of them true, half of them false.
2. A student's score equals the number of correct answers minus the number of incorrect answers (S = C − I). This method presumably takes care of guessing.
3. Avoid using items which are partly true and partly false.
4. Avoid using double negatives—they may confuse the students.
5. Avoid "specific determiners" which serve as clues to answers. For example, questions containing "always" and "never" are usually false; comparison questions are usually true; questions with "cause or reason" clauses are usually false.
6. Avoid using questions containing two or more ideas.
7. Avoid using trick or catch questions.

Completion Type

Directions to students—Certain words have been left out of the following sentences. Usually just one word has been omitted. Fill in the blanks to complete the statements.

1. The correct incubation temperature is ______ degrees F.
2. Fifty laying hens should have about ______ pounds of scratch feed daily.
3. Caponizing should be done when the birds are about ______ old. They should be deprived of food and water for about ______ before the operation.

Guiding Principles to Follow in Constructing and Scoring a Completion Test

1. Each blank should call for a single idea, the most significant word or phrase.
2. Make all blanks the same length.
3. Score by giving one point for each blank correctly filled.
4. Avoid using "a" or "an" immediately before a blank.

Multiple Choice Type

Directions to students—Following are some incomplete statements. Five words or phrases are given after each. One of these five words or phrases correctly completes the statement. Write the number of the correct answer on the line before the statement.

_______ 1. The Holsteins come from (1) England, (2) Scotland, (3) Holland, (4) Switzerland, (5) Denmark.
_______ 2. Average Jersey milk tests about (1) 3%, (2) 4%, (3) 5%, (4) 5.5%, (5) 6%.
_______ 3. Jerseys are noted for (1) quantity of milk, (2) hardiness, (3) large veal calves, (4) quiet disposition, (5) quality of milk.

Guiding Principles to Follow in Constructing and Scoring a Multiple Choice Test

1. Use at least four or five responses whenever possible to minimize the chance of guessing correctly.
2. When five responses are given, the score equals the number of correct answers. When three responses are given, the score equals the number of correct answers minus half the number of incorrect answers ($S = C - ½I$).
3. Choose responses so that some or all will have some degree of plausibility.
4. Avoid the use of "a" or "an" as the final word before a response. One of these articles would serve as a clue to the answer.
5. Vary the location of the correct response in the list of possible responses.

Matching Type

Directions to students—From column B choose the items which match or are connected with items in column A, and place the corresponding numbers on the lines.

A	*B*
_______ Duroc-Jersey.	1. Black with white belt.
	2. Corn meal.
_______ Chester White.	3. Lard breed, red color.
	4. White color, drooping ears.
_______ Hampshire.	5. White color, stiff ears.
_______ Protein concentrate.	6. Tankage.
	7. Corn stover.
_______ Protein roughage.	8. Alfalfa hay.

Guiding Principles to Follow in Constructing and Scoring a Matching Test

1. Use between 10 and 20 pairs of items for the most effective test.
2. Have an excess number of items in one column to prevent answering by the process of elimination.
3. Avoid clues such as having some words singular and some plural.
4. Score by giving one point for each pair correctly marked.

Measuring Understanding—It is essential that we measure understanding. If we do not, some students may memorize information without developing any effective understanding of the information. Understanding is necessary if information is to be useable in new situations. A student, for example, may memorize a spray formula without knowing what is meant by a word used in the formula. Without this understanding, the memorization of the formula would have little value.

A new problem not previously studied but involving the use of information presented in class requires in its solution both knowledge and understanding. A teacher may wish to measure knowledge and understanding separately. The teacher may do this by inserting first a few questions to measure knowledge of the information, followed by a new problem involving the use of this information.

The measurement of understanding is possible in both the essay and objective type tests. It is usually easier for a novice in test construction, however, to design an essay question in the form of a new problem than it is to design an objective question that will measure understanding.

Criterion Referenced Testing—A recent innovation in testing that is receiving much attention is *criterion referenced testing*. The attention it is receiving is probably closely related to the recent emphasis on performance or behavioral objectives, which are discussed in Chapter 5. "Criterion referenced testing" refers to the way the test results are interpreted.

Until recently, most test results were interpreted in terms of some norm such as the student's position or relative placing in a class, or the student's position or relative placing in some outside group. In standardized tests the student's score is in relation to some well defined group on a national, regional, or state level. When test results are interpreted in this way, it is termed *norm testing*.

When test results are interpreted in terms of the performance or behavior of the student, it is termed *criterion referenced testing*. A criterion referenced test indicates the performance level of the student. It tells the teacher and the student specifically what the student can do and at what level the student can perform a task, such as cleaning and preparing pieces of metal for welding, or planning farmstead wiring.

Criterion referenced tests do not indicate the position of performance in terms of other students. They measure the student's abilities to perform tasks on jobs according to predetermined levels or standards. Criterion referenced testing is relatively easy to develop and administer if good performance or behavioral objectives have been developed prior to the testing process. Good performance or behavioral objectives clearly indicate the acceptable standards or levels of performance. For example, if the performance objectives stated that the student, shown the 10 most common weeds in the community growing in pots in the greenhouse, would be able to identify them, the test would be interpreted in a manner such as the following:

1. The student was able to identify all of the weeds shown,
2. The student was able to identify 90 per cent of the weeds shown, or
3. The student was able to identify half of the weeds shown.

A criterion referenced test is interpreted in terms of what a student can do. It is not interpreted in terms of the student's performance in comparison with the performance of other students. A criterion referenced test, as its name implies, refers to the criterion statements in the performance or behavioral objectives.

EVALUATING STUDENTS' SUPERVISED OCCUPATIONAL EXPERIENCE PROGRAMS

There are several reasons why occupational experience programs should be effectively evaluated. An effective evaluation of an occupational experience program (1) helps the student and the teacher make improvements in the program, (2) provides evidence of the "growth" the student has made in connection with the program, (3) provides for self-evaluation by the student, and (4) indicates to the teacher the ways and means of improving the instruction in agriculture.

Experience programs provide many opportunities for measuring effectively the results of instruction. Many teachers, in determining final grades in agriculture, place considerable emphasis on individual occupational experience programs. Determining in advance the percentage of a final grade that will be based on the occupational experience program is not possible, however, because circumstances beyond the student's control that will affect the program may develop.

When occupational experience programs are considered in determining grades, teachers must remember that these programs measure abilities indirectly. A teacher using occupational experience programs to measure changes in abilities must check to see whether each student has had an opportunity to reflect changes in ability through the program. If a student has, for some reason beyond his/her control, not been able to reflect change in ability through the occupational experience program, some substitute measure of change in ability has to be used.

In the evaluation of individual occupational experience programs, there are a number of criteria which may be checked. Often a teacher bases most of the evaluation on the number of activities completed in the program. The number of activities completed is only one outcome of an occupational experience program. Following is a list of some of the other outcomes of occupational experience programs that should be evaluated:

1. The achievement of goals and efficiency factors of production.
2. The development of managerial abilities and manipulative skills.
3. The development of basic understandings.
4. The development of desirable habits.
5. The development of problem-solving abilities.
6. The development of attitudes, interests, ideals, and appreciations.

A simple check sheet for use in evaluating occupational experience programs may be developed by class members as one procedure for evaluating all phases of their occupational experience programs. The check sheet illustrated in Form 40.1 is one possible type.

The achievements of a student may also be compared to standards or goals of productive efficiency to discover degree of achievement. In a swine project, for example, a student may formulate the following goals of productive efficiency. Achievements in swine production may be evaluated in terms of these goals:

1. Number of pigs raised per litter, eight.

Form 40.1. A Check Sheet for Individual Occupational Experience Programs

Name ______________________ School Year ______________

Criteria (abbreviated)	Good	Fair	Poor
1. Attaining proficiency in agriculture			
2. Making progress			
3. Earning money, saving and using it wisely			
4. Having an interest in agriculture			
5. Developing self-confidence and managerial responsibility			
6. Contributing to family living			
7. Developing desirable habits and attitudes			
8. Developing plans and putting them into action			
9. Developing improvements			
10. Developing abilities in cooperation			
11. Developing desirable relationships with parents			
12. Improving agriculture in the community			
13. Carrying all activities to completion			
14. Using a large number of approved practices			
15. Starting the program early in the year			
16. Preparing a budget for each entrepreneur activity			
17. Using desirable financial business procedures			
18. Keeping complete and accurate records			
19. Performing agriculture mechanics activities			
20. Using or selling all products effectively			
21. Conducting entrepreneur activities			
22. Conducting improvement projects			
23. Performing supplementary practices			
24. Developing desirable school-community relationships			
25. Achieving objectives			
26. Developing desirable employer-employee relationships			
27. Achieving goals and efficiency factors of production			
28. Understanding how to do each job			
29. Developing problem-solving ability			
30. Utilizing exploratory experiences			

2. Average weight of pigs at 56 days, 50 pounds.
3. Average litter weight at 56 days, 400 pounds.
4. Average amount of pork per sow at six months, 2,000 pounds.
5. Amount of feed used per pound of pork, 4 pounds.

A chart based on these goals, such as the one shown in Form 40.2, may be developed with the students. Such charts stimulate considerable interest and provide many opportunities for evaluating results and for determining what

Form 40.2. Goals of Productive Efficiency and Achievements in Swine Production Projects for the Year 19____[1]

Name	No. of Sows	No. of Pigs Raised per Sow		Avg. Litter Wt. at 56 Days (Lbs.)		Avg. Wt. per Pig at 56 Days (Lbs.)		Lbs. of Pork per Sow at 6 Mo.		No. of Days to Produce Market Hogs		Lbs. of Feed per Lb. of Pork		Feed Cost per 100 Lbs. of Pork		Labor Income per Sow	
		Goal	Ach'd	Goal	Ach'd	Goal	Ach'd	Goal	Ach'd	Goal	Ach'd	Goal	Ach'd	Goal	Ach'd	Goal	Ach'd
Jones, John (Example)	2	8	9	360	450	45	50	2,000	2,250	170	170	4	3.6	$10	$9	$45	$50
Thomas, Mary																	
Walker, Ray																	
Young, Bill																	
Average																	

[1]A chart of this kind may be developed with the students having production projects in swine early in the school year, at the time they are setting up goals of productive efficiency for their swine projects. As the projects develop, the individual achievement columns may be completed, and the students may compare their results.

improvements should be made the following year. Charts of a similar kind may also be developed for other activities in occupational experience programs.

Evaluating Placement for Experience—Some criteria should be developed for evaluating the accomplishments of students placed on farms or in agriculturally oriented businesses to receive desirable agriculture experiences. Many of the experiences obtained by a student placed on a farm or in an agriculturally oriented business should be new to the student. Following are some of the types of evidence that may be considered in evaluating a student placed for experience:

1. New and approved management jobs learned.
2. New and approved operative jobs performed.
3. New and approved skills mastered.
4. Evidence of industry.
5. Habits formed and attitudes developed.
6. Evidence of dependability and honesty.
7. Managerial responsibilities developed.
8. Achievement of objectives established by the student before placement.

In addition to students' experience as employees, they may have opportunities to conduct one or more entrepreneur activities under the supervision of the teacher and the employer. If a student placed on a farm for experience does have an opportunity to develop a farming program while on the farm, many of the criteria used in evaluating farming programs may be used to evaluate this phase of the experience. Both the teacher and the employer should evaluate a student. The employer may be asked to prepare a written statement of appraisal of the student. The teacher should also evaluate the employer, using criteria such as the following:

1. Did the employer cooperate with the teacher?
2. Was the employer fair to the student?
3. Did the employer provide opportunities for the student to participate in a large number of varied activities?
4. Did the employer stress safety?
5. Did the employer provide desirable working conditions?
6. Did the employer abide by the agreement regarding wages and types of experience provided?
7. Did the employer use desirable training procedures?
8. Did the employer provide an opportunity for the student to conduct entrepreneur activities?

An evaluation of an employer aids a teacher in determining the desirability of placing other students with that employer.

Evaluating Experiences for Off-Farm Agricultural Occupations—The supervised occupational experiences for off-farm occupations requiring knowledge and skills in agriculture would involve experiences with plants, animals, soils, agricultural distribution, agricultural services, agricultural processing, agriculture mechanics, farm management, forestry, and agricultural leadership. These may be provided by placement for experience or through school greenhouses, nurseries, land laboratories, and shops. The general principles of evaluation presented previously would apply. Teachers, however, should consider carefully the facilities and opportunities available in evaluating occupational experience programs for off-farm occupations requiring knowledge and skills in agriculture.

Evaluating Agriculture Mechanics Activities—A student will probably participate in a number of agriculture mechanics activities in connection with the supervised occupational experience program. Here again, a teacher, in evaluating a student's agriculture mechanics program, may be inclined to think in terms of the completed project. This, however, is but one phase of appraising achievement in agriculture mechanics. Following are some of the items which should also be considered:

1. Accuracy and completeness of planning.
2. Choice of suitable materials.
3. Type of project and degree of difficulty.
4. Relationship to the total occupational experience program.
5. Quality of work.
6. Skills developed.
7. Amount of work done.
8. Selection and use of tools and equipment.
9. Ability to form judgments and solve problems.

Students should be encouraged to include a number of agriculture mechanics activities in their supervised occupational experience programs and to develop a number of managerial and manipulative abilities related to these activities.

Student Self-evaluation—Students should be encouraged to evaluate their own accomplishments. Following are some questions which may be used in evaluating a supervised occupational experience program:

1. Am I following my plan?
2. Am I keeping complete and accurate records?
3. Am I following the necessary safety precautions?
4. Am I doing all the labor in connection with my program?
5. Am I using appropriate approved practices in my program?
6. Am I giving proper thought to the expansion of my program?
7. Do I have adequate responsibility for carrying on my program?
8. Am I reading suitable references to keep me up-to-date?
9. Am I using all my opportunities for conducting a comprehensive program?
10. Am I making satisfactory progress?
11. Am I conducting my program to the best of my ability?
12. Am I developing a number of abilities not previously developed?
13. Am I cooperating with my teacher to the fullest extent possible?
14. Am I making sufficient use of my teacher?
15. Were the plans for my individual projects adequately written, with the necessary specific information on how to perform each job?

Evaluating Supervised Occupational Experience Programs—Teachers, in evaluating programs of supervised occupational experience, may compare their practices and results in developing and supervising occupational experience programs with recommended practices and results such as the following:

1. The instructor, before the beginning and again near the end of the school year, confers with the parents, employers, and students regarding the students' supervised occupational experience programs.
2. The supervised occupational experience programs are initiated near the beginning of the school year.

3. The projects initiated and conducted are compatible with the agricultural activities in the community.
4. The projects initiated and conducted are compatible with the students' needs, interests, and abilities.
5. Supervisory visits are planned in advance and made systematically, especially at crucial or critical times.
6. Instruction is based upon the problems arising in the supervised occupational experience programs.
7. Instruction is geared to promote satisfactory establishment in an occupation requiring knowledge and skills in agriculture.
8. The supervised occupational experience programs contribute to community improvement.

EVALUATING FFA ACTIVITIES

When to Evaluate—A chapter program should be evaluated at the end of the year to determine what has been achieved in terms of the objectives and goals established. However, there should be frequent evaluations of the progress of the program and the development of the chapter as a whole. The officers of a chapter should meet to discuss what is being done and to consider how to improve the chapter's program. Evaluation is a continuous process, and all members of a chapter should participate in the evaluation of their chapter.

What to Evaluate—All phases of a local FFA organization should be evaluated, including items such as chapter meetings, entertainment, participation by members, officers, the program of work, and accomplishments. Evaluation questions on chapter operation that may be used as a guide are as follows:

1. Are the officers selected on the basis of special qualifications? Do they meet frequently to plan work and receive assistance?
2. Are school authorities and others concerned consulted and kept informed regarding the activities of the chapter?
3. Does the chapter have a written program of work formulated by the members? How much of last year's program was completed?
4. Is there a committee functioning on each division of the present program of work?
5. Does the chapter have a written budget based primarily on the program of work and a sound plan developed for securing the necessary funds with which to operate?
6. Is the expenditure of chapter funds properly safeguarded?
7. Do most of the members get experience in the work of the chapter, and do they have definite responsibilities that contribute to its success or failure?
8. Does the chapter possess the standard meeting equipment, and if so, is it properly mounted and protected?
9. Has a satisfactory system of chapter records and reports been developed?
10. Is at least one planned meeting held each month, with sufficient time available to take care of all chapter business? Is the program for each chapter meeting posted in advance? Is accepted parliamentary procedure followed?
11. Does the chapter name an executive committee with power to act for the chapter when necessary?
12. Do most of the students enrolled in agriculture courses belong to the chapter? Are qualified members advanced systematically to higher degrees of membership?
13. What percentage of the membership attends meetings regularly?

14. Do most of the members know what they should know about FFA? Is systematic, continuous leadership training given to all members?

These questions evaluate ways and means only and not outcomes. The scorecard in the following section suggests a procedure for evaluating outcomes. Evaluation of ways and means is a "shortcut" in evaluation. The evaluation of outcomes should be made as soon as possible and whenever possible. Ways and means may or may not be associated with outcomes.

Scorecards for Evaluating—Scorecards, sometimes called point systems, are often used to evaluate activities in the FFA. The National Chapter Contest described in Chapter 20, "How to Develop an FFA Program of Activities," is evaluated by a scorecard. Most local FFA point systems or scorecards, however, have been designed to evaluate individual members. Members obtaining a certain number of points usually receive some kind of an award. The scorecard, therefore, really becomes a basis for a local contest. A scorecard or point system, if properly developed, may have some value for evaluating members' activities in the FFA. Many scorecards are now in existence.

Following is an example of a portion of a scorecard or point system of little or negative value:

	No. of Points
Attendance at meetings	5
Purchase of FFA jacket	10
"A" grade in agriculture course	25
State FFA degree	10
American FFA degree	20
Participation in earning and saving activities	10
Serving in lunch stand at football games	10

This scorecard or point system as an evaluation device can be criticized in a number of ways. First, it is not based on educational objectives. Second, purchase of an FFA jacket may give no indication of a desirable attitude or interest in the FFA. Third, quality of an activity is not considered. For example, participation in earning and saving activities gives no indication of the quality of participation. Fourth, points for the American and State FFA degrees provide for an award on top of an award. This point system also provides for awarding points twice. A member who earns a State or American FFA degree has already earned points for the activities which helped the member earn the advanced degree. Fifth, there is evidence of a lack of logical reasoning behind the number of points awarded for the various items.

Developing an effective and valid scorecard requires considerable teacher-student planning. The first step is a decision regarding the interests, attitudes, and abilities which should be developed through the FFA. Some of these abilities may be the ability to become established in an agricultural occupation, the ability to work with others, and the ability to provide leadership. After a decision has been made regarding objectives, some of the evidences of progress toward these objectives may be listed. A decision may then be made regarding the relative importance of each objective and the maximum number of points to be allowed on the scorecard for the accomplishment of each objective. The following portion of a scorecard or point system is an example of the kind of scorecard that results when these procedures are used:

	Max. No. of Points	Points Claimed by Student	Points Allowed Student by FFA
I. Ability in agriculture.	50		
A. Evidences of this ability.			
1. Comprehensive occupational experience program.			
2. Continuous program.			
3. High level of efficiency.			
4. Complete and accurate records.			
5. Improvement projects.			
6. Supplementary practices.			
7. Exploratory experiences.			
8.			
9.			
10.			
11.			
II. Ability to work with others.	50		
A. Evidences of this ability.			
1. Attendance at meetings.			
2. Behavior at meetings.			
3. Participation in meetings.			
4. Committee service.			
a.			
b.			
c.			
5.			
6.			

If a scorecard of this type is used, some system needs to be established for approving, for not approving, or for adjusting claims by students for points. A committee of FFA members may be appointed to perform this job. Students may be requested to appear before a committee to justify their claims. If a student believes that the committee is incorrect in its allotment of points, an appeal to the FFA executive committee may be made. A final appeal might be made to the teacher.

This subjective procedure of approving and adjusting claims provides a means of evaluating the quality of activities. For example, if a student claims points for the ability to work with others and lists as evidence of this ability attendance at all FFA meetings, the committee may not allow the points because of the student's misbehavior at the meetings. The misbehavior at the meetings would indicate to the committee that the student had not developed the ability to work with others. The committee may allow 20 points to one student for three occupational experience activities and 25 points to another student for the same number of activities. The reason for the difference may be the effort which each student has expended in conducting the activities. The difference may also be due to the size, scope, and quality of the activities.

In using this type of scorecard, each student keeps records and presents claims for points to a committee. This partially eliminates the criticism that scorecards or point systems involve a teacher in too much record keeping. The committee system takes a teacher "off the spot."

A scorecard or point system, however, must develop through teacher-student planning. It cannot originate from a teacher and be imposed on the students.

EVALUATING TEACHER ACTIVITIES

Evaluation Guides—Teachers need to evaluate their procedures and results constantly. Following are some guides for evaluating classroom instruction, field trips, and demonstrations.[1]

Form 40.3. A Guide for Evaluating Classroom Instruction in Agriculture

Suggestions for Using the Guide

The guide for evaluating classroom instruction is divided into four major headings as follows:

I. Evaluating the Short-Time Teaching Plan.
II. Evaluating the Class Discussion.
III. Evaluating the Assignment.
IV. Evaluating the Supervised Study.

In the use of this guide for evaluation, it is not assumed that all parts will be utilized at any one time. In fact, it is likely that each teacher will wish to concentrate on the portion in which the greatest need for improvement is felt. For example, the teacher may wish to utilize only the portion on evaluating the teaching plan (Part I).

Under the column headed "Rating," use one of the following symbols—A, B, C, or N. The symbols mean:

A. Highly satisfactory.
B. Present to some extent; fairly adequate.
C. Absent (when it should be included); inadequate.
N. Does not apply in this particular classroom situation.

Under the column headed "Comments," briefly describe the situation which justifies the rating, if this seems desirable.

Date ______________ School ______________ Class ________

Unit of instruction being taught ______________________________

	Rating	Comments
Part I. Evaluating the Short-Time Teaching Plan (preferably written)		
A. Objectives:		
1. Are stated in terms of student growth and performance		
2. Appear attainable and challenging		
3. Contribute to the major objectives of agricultural education		
4. Imply achievements related to programs of supervised occupational experience		
5. Have been formulated jointly by students and teacher		
B. Problem or job:		
1. Is clearly stated		

(Continued)

[1]Forms 40.3, 40.4, and 40.5 are revisions of forms originally developed by G. P. Deyoe.

Form 40.3 (Continued)

	Rating	Comments
2. Contributes to the attainment of objectives		
3. Has originated from the students		
4. Is related to the needs in supervised occupational experience programs		
5. Is appropriate in scope		
6. Is appropriate in difficulty		
C. Interest approach:		
1. Includes questions or other provisions for arousing interest at the start		
2. Arouses thinking early in the discussion		
D. Key questions for use in guiding the discussion:		
1. Lead forward in the solution of the problem		
2. Are varied sufficiently to provide flexibility for meeting situations which can be anticipated		
3. Include "why" and "how" questions which provide for appraisals of quality of thinking		
4. Provide for appraisals of related experiences outside of class		
5. Provide for appropriate summaries		
6. Provide for application to supervised occupational experience programs		
E. Teaching aids listed:		
1. Are appropriate for the problem under consideration		
2. Are varied sufficiently to provide for situations likely to arise		
3. Are varied sufficiently to provide for individual differences in learning ability		
F. Assignment or "next step":		
1. Is stated as a problem or part of a problem previously discussed		
2. Is such that it is likely to emerge from the class discussion		
3. Provides for variations in accordance with individual needs and capabilities		
4. Provides for references and other study materials		
5. Is compatible with home and employment conditions		
6. Is likely to contribute to the effective development of supervised occupational experiences		
Part II. Evaluating the Class Discussion		
A. Developing interest:		
1. Interest was developed at the start		
2. Interest was sustained throughout		

(Continued)

Form 40.3 (Continued)

	Rating	Comments
3. Interest was developed through:		
a. Arousing a feeling of need		
b. Appealing to natural impulses (such as desire for approval, curiosity, emulation)		
c. Utilizing experiences of students ...		
d. Using appropriate teaching aids		
e. Other means (write in)		
B. Conducting the discussion:		
1. Questions asked by the teacher promoted thinking		
2. Students themselves asked many questions		
3. All or most students contributed to the discussion		
4. Contributions of students were based on sound evidence		
5. Contributions were critically evaluated by the class		
6. Experiences were utilized in drawing inferences		
7. All important aspects of the problem were considered		
8. Sound conclusions were drawn		
9. Ideas were summarized into a new pattern or into new relationships		
10. Forward connections were made		
11. Applications to programs of supervised occupational experience were in evidence		
12. The teacher was able to proceed with little or no direct reference to written plans		
13. The students were conscious of their progress toward objectives		
Part III. Evaluating the Assignment		
A. The assignment was made at the appropriate time		
B. The assignment "grew out" of the discussion		
C. The assignment involved the formulation of purposes or objectives in which the teacher and the students shared		
D. The assignment involved the help of the students in making plans for solving the problems		
E. The assignment was adapted to the stage of development of the students		
F. The assignment was likely to contribute to the development of supervised occupational experience programs		

(Continued)

Form 40.3 (Continued)

	Rating	Comments
Part IV. Evaluating the Supervised Study		
A. Supervised study was a natural outgrowth of class discussion		
B. Students maintained interest in what they were doing		
C. Students understood what they were supposed to be doing		
D. Students made definite progress in solving the problems under consideration		
E. Students, in using source materials:		
1. Used various sources available		
2. Intepreted materials properly		
3. Showed increasing facility in using source materials		
F. The teacher worked with small groups and with individuals to:		
1. Help evaluate progress		
2. Stimulate and encourage their work		
3. Help interpret materials, find source materials, and overcome other difficulties		
4. Help make appropriate applications to supervised occupational experience programs		
5. Develop special assignments, when desirable		

Form 40.4. A Guide for Evaluating a Field Trip in Agriculture

Place visited ____________ Date ____________

Class or classes included ____________ No. who went ____________

Purposes or objectives of this trip ____________

Criteria or "Approved Practices"	Rating		
	Superior	Fair	Poor
A. Purposes or objectives:			
1. The purposes were clear and definite			
2. The students shared in formulating the purposes of the trip			
3. The purposes were such that this field trip is especially desirable as a teaching device			
B. Preliminary preparation:			
1. It was evident that students were oriented to the need for this trip, especially in relation to their supervised occupational experience programs			

(Continued)

Form 40.4 (Continued)

Criteria or "Approved Practices"	Rating		
	Superior	Fair	Poor
2. Appropriate questions to be asked and observations to be made were developed with the class			
3. Responsibilities to be assumed by participants were discussed and delegated			
4. Specific directions were developed for all phases of the trip			
5. Preliminary arrangements were made at the places visited			
6. Arrangements for transportation were carefully made			
7. Proper arrangements were made with the school administration and school staff			
C. Conduct of trip:			
1. Student responsibility was assumed as planned .			
2. A high degree of interest was shown throughout the trip			
3. Student participation was in keeping with the nature of the trip			
4. Students made appropriate notations and observations			
5. Proper courtesies were extended to the persons at the place visited			
6. The time schedule was kept as planned			
D. Outcomes and results:			
1. The students participated in evaluating the trip ..			
2. The students participated in summarizing the trip and in drawing appropriate conclusions			
3. This field trip contributed significantly to programs of supervised occupational experience through the development of necessary skills, knowledge, approved practices, awareness of new problems, or broadened programs			
4. New interests resulting from the trip were in evidence through informal comments, extended reading, and contributions in agriculture and other classes			
5. The students showed growth in ability to plan for and participate in later field trips			

Evaluation of Supervisory Activities—It is desirable for a teacher to appraise supervisory activities occasionally. Following are some possible criteria:

1. Am I visiting the homes and places of employment of students at crucial times in their occupational experience programs?
2. Have I done a good job of teaching while supervising?
3. Have I checked diaries and record books on each of my visits?
4. Have I left suitable recommendations on each of my visits?
5. Have I visited the students' employers or the students' homes frequently enough?
6. Have I done a sufficient amount of effective planning before visiting?
7. Have I made satisfactory arrangements for visits in all cases?
8. Have I helped the students solve their current problems on my visits?
9. Have I talked to the parents and employers on my visits?
10. Have I discussed the possibilities for expanding the students' programs?

Form 40.5. A Guide for Evaluating Teacher Demonstrations in Agriculture Courses

School ______________________ Class __________ Date ______________

Demonstration performed by ______________________ Evaluated by __________

Unit of instruction and problem or job being taught ______________________

____

Name of this demonstration ______________________________

____

Objective or objectives of this demonstration ______________________

____

Criteria or "Approved Practices"	Rating		
	Superior	Fair	Poor
1. Suitable materials and equipment were available			
2. Equipment was in good condition			
3. It was evident that students were oriented to the need for this instruction, especially in relation to supervised occupational experience programs			
4. Appropriate objectives were developed with the students			
5. Necessary precautions were indicated			
6. Essential details were emphasized			
7. Proper use and care of equipment were emphasized			
8. The demonstration was performed with skill and precision			
9. Appropriate standards of accuracy were emphasized			
10. Principles basic to important steps were developed .			
11. Appropriate devices for arousing and sustaining interest were evident throughout			
12. Student participation added to the effectiveness of the demonstration			
13. Important steps were summarized effectively			
14. Forward connections were made and next steps indicated			

11. Have I developed desirable family and employer relationships?
12. Have I checked the students' plans for their programs and made recommendations for necessary changes on each of my visits?
13. Have I helped the students to develop manipulative skills and abilities on my visits?
14. Have I observed the activities in the students' programs?
15. Have I made a list of problems while visiting which may be discussed in the classroom?
16. Have I spent sufficient time in the classroom having students write complete and detailed plans for their occupational experience programs?

Forms for use with students in evaluating the teacher's activities are presented in Chapter 39 in the section on self-evaluation.

CHAPTER

41

How to Evaluate Programs for Young and Older Adults

INTRODUCTION

Principles—Many of the principles and techniques of evaluation are presented in Chapter 39, "How to Evaluate a Program of Education in Agriculture," and in Chapter 40, "How to Evaluate and Test in a High School Program." These chapters should be reviewed before an attempt is made to evaluate agricultural education programs for young and older adults.

Objectives and Evaluation—Evaluation should be based on the objectives of the total agricultural education program for adults and on the specific objectives of each course. One way of making objectives meaningful and effective is to determine procedures for measuring progress toward their accomplishment. Evaluation, to be worthwhile, must be continuous. It has to be a part of the teaching process. It is not just something that is done at the end of a course or program. Evaluation of a course at its completion is but one phase of a total evaluation process. Evaluation at the completion of a program is a summing up of results. What is learned is of little or no value except for its implications for future programs. When a course or program is finished, it is then too late to make it more effective and worthwhile.

EVALUATION BY CLASS MEMBERS

Written Tests—Adults do not readily accept the right of a teacher to test their understanding and knowledge through the use of written tests. Some teachers have given tests to adult students, however, as a means of motivating self-evaluation by class members. If a test is given with the understanding that the teacher will not collect the test papers, adults will use the test as a means of pointing up their own knowledge or lack of knowledge. When this technique is used, it is generally at the beginning of a course to illustrate the need for additional information.

Records—Adult students should expect, and be encouraged, to keep records of their results. The analysis of records of results is an excellent method of evaluation. A teacher may improve the effectiveness and practicality of all courses by encouraging the students to keep records and by basing the instruction on the weaknesses and strengths indicated by the records.

For example, in a course on swine feeding, the adult students should keep records of the amounts and kinds of feed used and the results obtained as measured by weight increases. In a course on pasture improvement, the adult students may keep records of treatments used and the results obtained as measured by pounds of livestock produced per acre. If a teacher considers with the students the records that should be kept which will help them evaluate their results, functional and meaningful types of records may be developed and used for all types of courses.

Analysis of Results—Adults will not keep records unless they are to be used. Results as indicated by records may be compared with average and superior results. This comparison usually motivates class members to analyze their results to discover why they are higher or lower than the results obtained by others.

Approved Practice Inventory—One of the expected outcomes of the instruction of adults is the understanding developed regarding various approved practices. Individual acceptance of a practice may be checked by the use of an approved practice inventory. The use of such an inventory may also be used to motivate the adoption of approved practices. Form 41.1 is an example of a portion of an approved practice inventory used in a soils course for adult farmers. Approved practice inventories may also be developed for adults en-

Form 41.1. Approved Practice Inventory

Approved Practices	Being Done Effectively	Needs Improvement	Plan to Do	Could Not Use
1. Test soil in each field and apply needed limestone.				
2. Spread manure as it accumulates.				
3. Conserve manure by use of shelter.				
4. Use approximately 50 pounds of superphosphate to each ton of manure.				
5. Inoculate sweetclover before seeding.				
6. Clip sweetclover in November of the first year.				
7. Plow under sweetclover when 6″ to 8″ high the second year.				

rolled in off-farm agribusiness courses. Form 41.2 is an example of such an inventory.

Form 41.2. Approved Practice Inventory for an Off-Farm Agribusiness Course

Approved Practices	Being Done Effectively	Needs Improvement	Plan to Do	Could Not Use
1. Study operation manuals for jobs assigned.				
2. Keep accurate records required in agribusiness.				
3. Analyze time required to do each job and attempt to reduce time required.				
4. Be friendly and helpful to customers.				
5. Emphasize quality of work.				
6. Get to work on time.				
7. Keep days off to a minimum.				
8. Give appropriate reports as needed to supervisor.				

Progress Inventory—In courses that continue over a period of time, it is possible to motivate class members to measure their progress in the adoption of approved practices. Form 41.3 is a portion of a progress inventory used with a young farm operators' course.

Form 41.3. Progress Inventory

Please supply the information asked for on each item. Write in the number of acres or rods involved. If you credit your association for help with the job you have done, please indicate that also by placing a check mark in the parentheses at the right.

1. Grass waterway established or started (rods) .... ________ ( )
2. Contour field operations performed (acres) .... ________ ( )
3. Soil samples taken for testing (acres) .... ________ ( )
4. Soil tested (acres) .... ________ ( )
5. Soil maps prepared for lime, phosphate, and potash needs (acres) .... ________ ( )
6. Applied lime according to needs as shown by tests (acres) .... ________ ( )
7. Applied phosphate according to needs as shown by tests (acres) .... ________ ( )
8. Selected and used mixed fertilizer most nearly meeting crop needs as shown by soil tests (acres) .... ________ ( )
9. Applied fertilizer to pastures according to needs as shown by tests (acres) .. ________ ( )
10. Seeded legumes to be plowed down for soil improvement (acres) .... ________ ( )
11. Mowed pasture to control weeds (acres) .... ________ ( )
12. Rotated pasture to secure greater livestock gains or milk production (acres) .... ________ ( )
13. Disked and re-seeded pasture (acres) .... ________ ( )
14. Sowed legume-grass mixture for pasture, hay, or soil improvement (acres) .... ________ ( )
15. Applied superphosphate to wheat (acres) .... ________ ( )

Opinion Surveys—Adults are usually too appreciative of the efforts of a teacher to criticize the program, even in a constructive manner. Constructive criticism will not be obtained unless systematically sought through some method of allowing and motivating class members to present their opinions anonymously. Form 41.4 is an opinion survey that has been used to obtain the ideas of class members regarding the adult program in agribusiness education in which they were enrolled.

Form 41.4. Opinion Survey for Adult Courses

	Circle Your Answer	
1. What specific subjects would you like to have covered if these courses were continued next year?		
a.		
b.		
c.		
d.		
e.		
2. Do you believe that you and the group have benefited enough from the classes that they should be continued?	Yes	No
3. Do you favor continuation of the classes if they were handled in the same manner as they were this year?	Yes	No
4. What improvements would you suggest?		
a.		
b.		
c.		
d.		
e.		
5. What did you obtain from the courses that you attended this year that you intend to make use of in your situation?		
a.		
b.		
c.		
d.		
e.		

For examples of other types of opinion surveys, see Chapter 39, "How to Evaluate a Program of Education in Agriculture." Several forms are presented in that chapter, in the section on self-evaluation.

Forms 41.5, 41.6, and 41.7 presented in the following section may also be used to assist class members in planning and evaluating their own programs.

EVALUATIONS BY ADVISORY GROUPS, TEACHERS, AND OTHERS

Advisory councils and committees provide a teacher with effective devices for obtaining evaluations of adult programs. The advisory council and committees for a department may be used to evaluate progress of courses, teaching procedures, plans, and results. The teacher should actively seek their evaluations during the progress of, and at the completion of, each course for adults.

Evaluation of the Total Program—An advisory council should annually evaluate the total program of education in agriculture for adults. One meeting a year of the advisory council and of each advisory committee for a department may be profitably used in the evaluation of the adult program. These meetings on evaluation would be in addition to the time usually devoted to evaluation at council and committee meetings. One way of evaluating an adult program is to compare the program with approved practices and standards for adult programs in agriculture. No group of approved practices and standards can be forced on an advisory council or its committees, but an evaluation program may be greatly facilitated if teachers and administrators supply the advisory groups and the community with lists of accepted practices and standards. Advisory groups should discuss such lists item by item to see whether they accept each practice or standard presented and to discover whether the practice or standard applies to their local situation. Form 41.5 is a list of criteria for a comprehensive adult program.

Form 41.5. A Guide for Evaluating a Comprehensive Program of Education in Agriculture for Adults

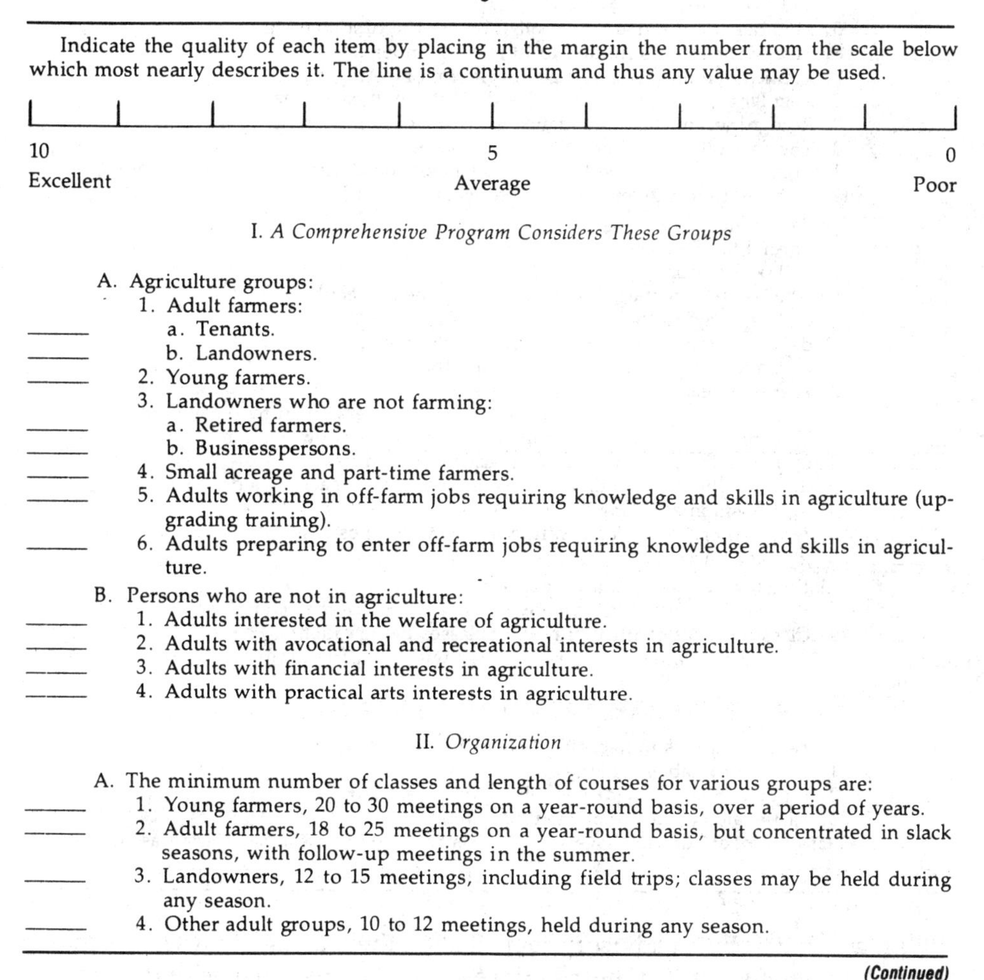

Indicate the quality of each item by placing in the margin the number from the scale below which most nearly describes it. The line is a continuum and thus any value may be used.

10	5	0
Excellent	Average	Poor

I. *A Comprehensive Program Considers These Groups*

A. Agriculture groups:
1. Adult farmers:
______ a. Tenants.
______ b. Landowners.
______ 2. Young farmers.
3. Landowners who are not farming:
______ a. Retired farmers.
______ b. Businesspersons.
______ 4. Small acreage and part-time farmers.
______ 5. Adults working in off-farm jobs requiring knowledge and skills in agriculture (upgrading training).
______ 6. Adults preparing to enter off-farm jobs requiring knowledge and skills in agriculture.

B. Persons who are not in agriculture:
______ 1. Adults interested in the welfare of agriculture.
______ 2. Adults with avocational and recreational interests in agriculture.
______ 3. Adults with financial interests in agriculture.
______ 4. Adults with practical arts interests in agriculture.

II. *Organization*

A. The minimum number of classes and length of courses for various groups are:
______ 1. Young farmers, 20 to 30 meetings on a year-round basis, over a period of years.
______ 2. Adult farmers, 18 to 25 meetings on a year-round basis, but concentrated in slack seasons, with follow-up meetings in the summer.
______ 3. Landowners, 12 to 15 meetings, including field trips; classes may be held during any season.
______ 4. Other adult groups, 10 to 12 meetings, held during any season.

(Continued)

Form 41.5 (Continued)

B. Needs determined by:
1. Advisory council through:
_____ a. Analyzing census reports, community surveys, and other data.
_____ b. Personal contacts.
_____ c. Experiences of advisory council members.
_____ 2. Experience of the agriculture teacher.

C. Courses:
_____ 1. Needs and interests of prospective students are considered by the advisory council and by the advisory committees.
2. A long-time program is planned:
_____ a. Initial priority is given to the area of greatest need.
_____ b. Courses for various groups, e.g., dairy, swine, grain, and off-farm agribusinesses, are planned in a long-time program in order of need.

_____ D. Classes are offered in community centers.

E. Individual courses meet the following criteria:
_____ 1. Each course is a unit, not a series of unrelated topics.
_____ 2. Field trips and follow-up meetings are an organized part of every course.
_____ 3. Courses are composed of out-of-school people.
_____ 4. Members are definitely enrolled as class members and have certain responsibilities and privileges.
_____ 5. Members of a course are enrolled before the first meeting.
_____ 6. Size of the class is limited to 10 to 30 members.
_____ 7. Public announcement is made of the first meeting date.
_____ 8. Regular attendance is stressed—roll is taken at each meeting.
_____ 9. Recognition of class attendance is given at each meeting.
_____ 10. The agriculture teacher visits the enrollees.
_____ 11. Consideration is given to recreational and social activities and problems.
_____ 12. Definite time and length of meetings are determined.

F. Special teachers:
1. Special teachers are:
_____ a. Local persons.
_____ b. Successful managers or operators in the subject to be taught.
_____ c. Respected in the community.
_____ d. Competent and willing to learn from others.
_____ e. Competent in getting along with others.
2. A special teacher:
_____ a. Attends instruction classes for special teachers given by the agriculture teacher.
_____ b. Is taught to understand the objectives of the adult program.
_____ c. Is taught to use democratic teaching procedures.
_____ d. Is taught to understand course materials and teaching aids.
_____ e. Assists in enrolling adults.
_____ f. Visits each enrollee a minimum of three times.
_____ g. Keeps necessary records.

G. Relationships to other educational activities:
_____ 1. Teachers of adults cooperate with the program of the school.
_____ 2. Classes do not conflict with other classes being taught.
_____ 3. A definite relationship is maintained with the community's educational program.

III. *Facilities*

A. Classes have access to necessary school facilities:
_____ 1. Classroom (tables, chairs).
_____ 2. Library (books, magazines, illustrative material).
_____ 3. Visual aids (slides, movies, projectors).
_____ B. Class members do not have to use certain facilities at the same time as high school classes.

An evaluation by an advisory council and others using Form 41.5 would be an evaluation of ways and means. Since outcomes are of overall importance, a council may wish to devise methods of measuring outcomes. One method of measuring outcomes is the comparison of results obtained by class members in the phase of agriculture being taught with the results obtained by non–class members. This may be done through the analysis of existing local data, census reports, and surveys.

For additional suggestions regarding devices for measuring outcomes, see Chapter 39, "How to Evaluate a Program of Education in Agriculture."

Evaluation of a Young Farmer Program—Form 41.6 is a list of criteria which may be useful to a young farmer committee and a teacher in evaluating the ways and means of conducting a young farmer program.

Form 41.6. A Guide for Evaluating a Young Farmer Program

Indicate the quality of each item by placing in the margin the number from the scale below which most nearly describes it. The line is a continuum and thus any value may be used.

10	5	0
Excellent	Average	Poor

I. *Class Organization*

A. School officials:

_____ 1. The school administration and the board of education have been fully informed of the purposes of, and the program for, young farmers.

_____ 2. School officials aided in deciding how to finance the program.

B. Advisory council:

_____ 1. An advisory council is used to aid the teacher in planning the program.

_____ 2. The council aids in determining the need for a young farmer program.

_____ 3. The number of young people available for a young farmer program is determined by a young farmer committee of the council.

_____ 4. The committee is representative of the young farmers in the community.

_____ 5. The committee determines the interests, farming status, and home situation of the prospective members.

_____ 6. The committee enrolls the members before the first class meeting.

_____ 7. The committee issues membership cards to members. The secretary of the advisory committee sends postal cards to all members two days before the first meeting, as a reminder of the meeting.

C. Teacher:

_____ 1. Application for holding the course, if required, is made to the state agency for vocational education.

_____ 2. The teacher arranges a centrally located place of instruction.

_____ 3. The teacher places young farmer meeting dates on the school calendar.

_____ 4. The teacher has at least one period during the day which can be devoted to the young farmer program.

_____ 5. Farm visits are made to enrolled members prior to the first meeting.

_____ 6. Letters are mailed to all class members at least two weeks before the first meeting of the course.

_____ 7. The teacher uses at least one newspaper article to announce the program to the public.

D. Class:

_____ 1. Class committees are appointed to handle recreation and refreshments.

_____ 2. Capable officers and leaders are elected (this would apply to a local young farmer organization).

_____ 3. Class members know they are enrolled and pledge to attend regularly.

_____ 4. A minimum of 15 meetings is planned (the goal is 25 to 30 meetings a year).

_____ 5. The class helps to plan the year-round program, with special events and seasonal meetings being provided.

(Continued)

Form 41.6 (Continued)

_____ 6. The class is open to all persons becoming established in farming.
_____ 7. The class assists in planning a course for a three- or four-year period.
_____ 8. Each young farmer class contains not more than 20 to 25 students and not less than 10. Agriculture mechanics classes do not exceed 15.

II. *Teaching Methods*

_____ 1. Instruction is based on the interests and needs of the group.
_____ 2. Teaching plans are developed in writing for each problem.
_____ 3. Individual instruction is given to class members during class time.
_____ 4. Outside speakers are used as consultants rather than as lecturers.
_____ 5. Visual aids are used.
_____ 6. Long-time plans are made to carry the young farmers to and into adult classes.
_____ 7. Provision is made for the development of abilities in problem-solving and manipulative skills.
_____ 8. Extensive use is made of the conference method in teaching.
_____ 9. The problem method of teaching is used.
_____ 10. Field trips or tours are taken.
_____ 11. Teaching is goal-centered rather than subject-centered.
_____ 12. Outside agencies and resources are used (SCS, county agent).
_____ 13. Instruction is seasonal.
_____ 14. Good teaching facilities are provided at all teaching centers.
_____ 15. Rapport is created in class.

III. *Supervised Farming*

_____ 1. Farms are visited a minimum of three times.
_____ 2. A minimum of six hours of individual instruction is given on the farm.
_____ 3. Individuals keep records and accounts to measure their progress in farming.
_____ 4. The farming programs expand in scope and breadth.
_____ 5. The teacher and the group strive to find ways and means to finance the farming programs of those who need help.
_____ 6. Each young farmer and the teacher plan and organize a farming program.
_____ 7. Programs contribute to the conservation of soil and other natural resources.
_____ 8. Programs improve the farming and farm living on the home farms.

IV. *The Program of the Young Farmer Chapter*
(For Use If a Local Young Farmer Organization Exists)

_____ 1. The program is primarily educational and contributes to the needs of the members.
_____ 2. The program includes a variety of educational activities.
_____ 3. The program includes a variety of social and recreational activities.
_____ 4. The program includes a variety of leadership activities.
_____ 5. The program includes a variety of community service activities.
_____ 6. The program provides for assistance to, and cooperation with, other farm organizations.
_____ 7. The program helps to acquaint members with government agricultural services.
_____ 8. The program aids in building desirable public relationships in the community.
_____ 9. The program contains a calendar of activities developed by the members with the aid of the teacher.
_____ 10. The program provides instruction in social problems.
_____ 11. The program is systematically correlated with other community programs.
_____ 12. The program is varied enough to provide opportunity for each individual member to exercise initiative and special abilities.
_____ 13. The program provides for democratic participation by all the members (through committee work, etc.).

V. *Follow-Up*

_____ 1. Young farmers are visited during critical times of the year.
_____ 2. Farm tours are taken on which members see one another's programs.
_____ 3. Several summer meetings are held.
_____ 4. The teacher aids the young farmers in placement.

Some teachers and advisory committees are motivated and better able to evaluate ways and means if a series of questions is developed regarding the conduct of the program. If a teacher and advisory groups desire to use a method other than the technique presented in Form 41.6, the question procedure might be used. Following is a suggested list of questions which may be used in evaluating the method of conducting a young farmer program:

1. Was the course content closely related to the supervised farming programs?
2. Was the course supplemented by social, recreational, and citizenship activities which contribute toward establishment as desirable citizens in a rural community?
3. Was the instruction given in a location convenient for the enrollees?
4. Were suitable and adequate facilities provided?
5. Did the instruction extend over a period of 12 months?
6. Was an advisory committee used?
7. Were the special instructors adequately supervised by the teacher of vocational agriculture?
8. Did the students participate in planning and conducting the course?
9. Were objectives formulated in terms of desired abilities to be developed?
10. Were teaching plans carefully and completely developed in writing?
11. Are plans for instruction of young farmers over a period of years in effect?
12. Does the school administration support the young farmer program?
13. Has the general public been sufficiently informed concerning the program?
14. Do farmers and the general public support the program?
15. Has an adequate follow-up program been developed and put into effect?

The advisory groups and the teachers for a department should not be satisfied merely with an evaluation of ways and means. Outcomes of instruction should also be evaluated. Following is a series of questions that should be answered regarding outcomes of instruction:

1. Are the young farmers progressing toward establishment in farming on a satisfactory basis?
2. Does the farming program of each class member provide for the accumulation of assets either for a partnership at home or for establishment in some other farming status?
3. Do the farming programs of the young farmers indicate appropriate and adequate training?
4. Have satisfactory working relationships and understandings with parents and others been developed?
5. Do the farming programs include cooperative activities that will assist the class members toward progressive establishment in farming?
6. Have the young farmers adopted and put into effect a large number of approved practices as a result of the instruction?

For techniques of collecting information necessary for answering the preceding questions, see Chapter 39, "How to Evaluate a Program of Education in Agriculture," and Chapter 40, "How to Evaluate and Test in a High School School Program."

Evaluation of an Adult Course in Agriculture—Form 41.7 is a list of criteria which may be useful to a committee and a teacher in evaluating the procedures used in conducting an adult course in agriculture. This list of criteria should not be considered as valid for all situations. These criteria may be profitably used, however, to stimulate a committee and a teacher to study their own situation.

Form 41.7 may be used for courses for off-farm workers and entrepreneurs in agribusiness, or for adult farmer courses.

Form 41.7. A Guide for Evaluating an Adult Course in Agriculture

Indicate the quality of each item by placing in the margin the number from the scale below which most nearly describes it. The line is a continuum and thus any value may be used.

10 Excellent	5 Average	0 Poor

I. *Planning*

1. Suitable facilities for instructors are available at the location of the class:
_____ a. Graphs.
_____ b. Charts.
_____ c. Slides.
_____ d. Projection machines.
_____ 2. Group instruction is planned to extend over 12 months of the year.
_____ 3. The total number of meetings is decided by the group, but the number is not less than 10.
_____ 4. Time of meetings is decided by the members of the group.
_____ 5. The instructor studies written plans of previous years and makes necessary revisions before teaching a given unit.
_____ 6. Plans are based on the needs of the members of the class.
_____ 7. The instructor and class members share in making teaching plans which are based on members' problems.
_____ 8. Plans include objectives.
_____ 9. Plans specify ways and means of attaining objectives.
_____ 10. Plans define the activities of the instructor and members of the class.
_____ 11. Plans include a list of the facilities needed.
_____ 12. Plans include a list of manipulative skills, approved practices, and understandings needed to fulfill the objectives.
_____ 13. Plans include ways of determining progress toward objectives.
_____ 14. Plans are flexible to provide for individual differences and for varying situations.
_____ 15. Members of the class know and understand the objectives of the course.
_____ 16. The instructor and students continuously evaluate progress toward objectives.
_____ 17. Short-time teaching plans are made for each meeting.

II. *Determining Objectives*

_____ 1. Objectives are formulated jointly by class members and the instructor.
_____ 2. Objectives arise out of the occupational experiences, needs, and interests of the members of the class.
_____ 3. Objectives are stated in terms of student growth and performance.
_____ 4. Objectives are attainable.
_____ 5. Objectives are challenging.
_____ 6. Objectives contribute to the major objectives of vocational education in agriculture.
_____ 7. Objectives imply achievements related to the agricultural activities of the members of the class.
_____ 8. Objectives are definite and clear to all.
_____ 9. Objectives are considered and accepted by all.
_____ 10. Objectives are related to the objectives of the total educational system.

III. *Developing and Maintaining Interest*

_____ 1. Discussion is based on experiences and needs of the learners and related to the activities in which the learners are engaged.
_____ 2. Specific problems faced by members of the class are recognized and identified.
_____ 3. Broad problems are subdivided into more specific ones.

(Continued)

Form 41.7 (Continued)

_____ 4. Realistic problems of adults are used in class as a teaching device.
_____ 5. Members of the class participate freely in all class activities.
_____ 6. Questions by the instructor are usually directed to the entire group.
_____ 7. The instructor usually employs impersonal comparisons.
_____ 8. A variety of appropriate teaching devices, such as audio-visual facilities, is used.
_____ 9. A certificate of completion is awarded at the end of the course.
_____ 10. Responsibility is delegated by the instructor to members of the class.
11. Various group techniques are used:
_____ a. Buzz sessions.
_____ b. Panel discussions.
_____ c. Role playing.
_____ d. Forums.

IV. *Conducting the Discussion*

_____ 1. The discussion proceeds in an informal atmosphere.
_____ 2. Problems are drawn from actual experience and are properly identified.
_____ 3. Members understand and accept a problem for discussion.
_____ 4. Group experiences are used to formulate tentative solutions.
_____ 5. Members are led to recognize the need for more accurate information.
_____ 6. Discussion is oriented toward solution and action at all times.
_____ 7. Resource persons serve as consultants and guides.
_____ 8. The class is brought into discussion soon after the opening of a meeting.
_____ 9. All points of view are considered from several angles.
_____ 10. Arguments are shifted to an unbiased person.
_____ 11. Members with strong feelings are given a chance to "blow off."
_____ 12. The instructor guides the discussion.
_____ 13. Timid members are encouraged to participate.
_____ 14. Questions directed to the instructor are often returned to the class.
_____ 15. Judicious praise is given for class contributions.
_____ 16. Experimental method is used.
_____ 17. Solutions are formulated by class members.
_____ 18. Forward steps and connections are indicated.

V. *Presenting Demonstrations*

_____ 1. Need for a demonstration is recognized by the class.
_____ 2. The class determines objectives.
_____ 3. A demonstration is presented as a problem.
_____ 4. The class participates in demonstrations by suggesting next steps.
_____ 5. Appropriate materials and equipment are available.
_____ 6. Use and care of equipment are explained.
_____ 7. Precautions and details are emphasized.
_____ 8. Basic principles are explained.
_____ 9. Demonstrations are performed within full view of each member of the class.
_____ 10. The instructor uses skill and precision in demonstrating.
11. Appropriate devices are available and utilized:
_____ a. Pictorial charts.
_____ b. Models.
_____ c. Diagrams.
_____ 12. Demonstrations are performed slowly.
_____ 13. A tryout for each student is provided.
_____ 14. Forward connections and steps are indicated.

VI. *The Field Trip*

_____ 1. The purposes of field trips are clear and definite.
_____ 2. The members share in formulating the purpose of, and procedures for, a trip.
_____ 3. The purposes justify a trip.
_____ 4. Members of the class are oriented to the need for a field trip.

(Continued)

Form 41.7 (Continued)

_____ 5. Appropriate observations and questions to be answered are developed with the class.
_____ 6. Responsibilities to be assumed by members of the class are discussed and delegated.
_____ 7. Specific directions are developed.
_____ 8. Arrangements are made in advance with appropriate personnel at the places to be visited.
_____ 9. Arrangements for a field trip are made with the school administrators.
_____ 10. Student participation is maintained throughout a trip.
_____ 11. Appropriate notations and observations are made during a field trip.
_____ 12. Courtesies are extended appropriate persons at the places visited.
_____ 13. Conclusions concerning a trip are developed by the class.
_____ 14. Forward connections and appropriate steps are indicated.

VII. *Individual Instruction*

_____ 1. The instructor makes regular visits for the purpose of providing individual instruction.
_____ 2. Teaching is carried to the doing level.
_____ 3. New and approved practices are supervised.
_____ 4. Results of approved practices are checked.
_____ 5. A check list of approved practices is used.
_____ 6. Group tours are made to individual farms and agricultural businesses.
_____ 7. Photographs are used to compare results.
_____ 8. Opinion polls are used by the instructor.
_____ 9. The instructor promotes recognition of new problems by enrollees.
_____ 10. New interests are created.
_____ 11. The instructor encourages enrollees to implement broader programs.
_____ 12. The instructor encourages enrollees to use the resources of the community.
_____ 13. Local leadership is developed.
_____ 14. The instructor visits each class member a minimum of six hours a year.
_____ 15. At least four visits a year per enrollee are made.

For teachers and advisory groups who desire to evaluate the ways and means of conducting an adult course through the use of questions regarding procedures, the following partial list of questions is suggested. Notice that the questions duplicate many of the items in Form 41.7.

1. Were specific objectives outlined in terms of the needs of the enrollees?
2. Was the course content based on the immediate problems of the enrollees?
3. Did the enrollees have a part in selecting the course and the content of the course?
4. Did the instruction provide for the development of the abilities needed by the enrollees?
5. Was the course sufficiently limited to be thoroughly covered?
6. Did the instruction assist the enrollees in reaching the specific objectives outlined for the course?
7. Was the instruction carefully and thoroughly planned?
8. Did those involved carefully review the local situation in deciding on the course to be offered?
9. Was the course of study closely related to the agricultural activities of the enrollees?
10. Were improvement projects carried out?
11. Was a strategic place in the community selected for offering the instruction?
12. Were adequate facilities provided?
13. Was the special instructor qualified to teach the course?
14. Was the conference procedure extensively used in conducting discussions?
15. Was an effective plan of local supervision put into action?

16. Was an effective follow-up program completed?
17. Was an extensive and effective publicity program used?
18. Did the instruction include social and citizenship activities?
19. Did the instruction extend over 12 months?
20. Were complete records kept and placed on file?
21. Was the instruction a part of a community program in adult education?

Evaluation of procedures or of ways and means is a "stopgap" method of evaluation. It is a type of evaluation that may be used until enough time has elapsed to make the evaluation of outcomes possible. Procedures may be evaluated as "excellent," but if desirable outcomes in terms of changed behavior do not materialize, the purpose of the instruction has not been reached. Some of the questions that may be asked which will provide evidence that desirable changed behavior has resulted are as follows:

1. Did the instruction result in improved practices and improved living?
2. Did enrollees, as a result of instruction, repair machinery, construct labor-saving devices, or process food produced?
3. Did the enrollees select and adopt a number of suitable approved practices?
4. Was a long-time program in the area of instruction developed by each class member?

Comparison with Programs of Adult Education in Agriculture in Other Communities—One evaluation technique useful in broadening the horizon regarding vocational education in agriculture for adults is to compare a local program with programs in other communities. Another technique is to invite outsiders to evaluate the local program.

CHAPTER

42

How to Evaluate in Agriculture Mechanics

The appraisal and evaluation of an agriculture mechanics program and of the achievements of individuals in the program are essential. Such evaluation aids the community, board members, administrators, teachers, and students in recognizing the value of a program in agriculture mechanics for all groups. It helps all concerned to understand the program. Evaluation helps students to see their mistakes, and it stimulates effort toward objectives. Evaluation is also of value to an instructor because it helps in discovering the strengths and weaknesses of the instruction. It stimulates all concerned to develop definite, meaningful objectives.

EVALUATING A PROGRAM

Chapter 39, "How to Evaluate a Program of Education in Agriculture," may be reviewed for a discussion of the general principles of evaluation. A discussion of (1) how program planning and evaluation are related, (2) why evaluation is necessary, (3) who should participate in evaluation, and (4) when to evaluate will not be presented in this chapter but may be found in Chapter 39.

Outcomes—The outcomes of a program in agriculture mechanics are indicated by behavior changes in people of the community served. An evaluation of changes in behavior is often difficult. Important changes in behavior do not occur quickly. The best evaluations are made some time after a program has gone into effect. Outcomes should be evaluated in terms of the objectives formulated for the program in agriculture mechanics. Let's assume that one of the objectives is the development of abilities of agribusiness workers to repair and construct equipment by welding. One approach in measuring progress toward this objective might be to determine the quantity of welding done at present as compared with the amount done in previous years. An indirect evidence might be the number of welding rods used in the community during a year. One could obtain this evidence by surveying the community, or by surveying sales agencies selling welding rods to the agribusinesses of the community. Appraisals of the skills in agriculture mechanics used on farms and elsewhere and the attitudes of farmers and other agricultural workers may also indicate outcomes of a program in agriculture mechanics.

Evaluating Ways and Means—Methods, or ways and means, of carrying out a program of agriculture mechanics may or may not be related to outcomes and, therefore, should not be used as the only measurement of such a program. A careful evaluation of ways and means is often useful as a part of a total evaluation program. Evaluation of ways and means can be accomplished quickly and may be of value prior to the time an evaluation of outcomes is undertaken. One may evaluate ways and means by comparing them with ideals, approved practices, and standards usually accepted as valid in agriculture mechanics.

Some of the questions to consider in evaluating the *ways and means of conducting a program of agriculture mechanics* are as follows:

1. Is instruction provided for high school students, young farmers, adult farmers, and other workers requiring knowledge and skills in agriculture mechanics?
2. Are sufficient courses offered to meet the needs of out-of-school groups?
3. Do high school students receive adequate education in all phases of agriculture mechanics?
4. Do students have opportunities to develop the abilities needed to conduct their supervised occupational experience programs?

Some of the questions to consider in evaluating *facilities* are as follows:

1. Are tools and equipment available for teaching the jobs which farmers and other agricultural workers in the community should perform?
2. Are supplies available for performing the more common jobs which farmers and other agricultural workers should perform?
3. Are the amount of floor space and the arrangement of the shop adequate to serve the number of persons in the community who desire instruction?
4. Does the shop afford favorable working conditions?
5. Can assembled agricultural machinery be brought into the shop?
6. Are adequate storage facilities provided?
7. Is definite provision made for replacement, maintenance, and purchase of tools and equipment?
8. Are the safety facilities adequate?

Some of the questions to consider in evaluating *teaching procedures* are as follows:

1. Is teacher-student planning used?
2. Are definite objectives developed with students for their work in agriculture mechanics?
3. Are plans made with students for measuring their progress in agriculture mechanics?
4. Are democratic teaching procedures used?
5. Is the teaching based on the agricultural activities of the students?
6. Are the students ready for the content of the agriculture mechanics program?

7. Do students learn by doing?
8. Is adequate instruction provided at the students' homes or jobs?

EVALUATING INDIVIDUAL ACHIEVEMENT

Chapter 40, "How to Evaluate and Test in a High School Program," presents the general principles of evaluating individual achievement. Chapter 40 also presents many detailed suggestions regarding measurement techniques. These general principles and details regarding measurement techniques will not be repeated in the following section, but the application of these principles and measurement techniques to the evaluating of individual achievement in agriculture mechanics will be considered.

What to Evaluate—Evaluation of individual achievement should be continuous. When individuals are working on projects, they should be motivated to attempt to measure their progress in terms of objectives and standards acceptable to them. The acceptance of objectives, standards, and evaluation techniques should be given continued attention as work on a project advances. Attention of students should also be directed to the evaluation of the concomitant results of the program in agriculture mechanics. Some of these concomitant results are as follows:

1. The development of desirable interests, ideals, appreciations, and understandings.
2. The development of desirable habits of industry.
3. The development of managerial and operative abilities needed in agriculture mechanics.
4. The acquisition of fundamental information pertaining to agriculture mechanics.
5. The development of self-confidence and mechanical resourcefulness.
6. The development of problem-solving abilities.

Procedures to Use in Evaluation—There are a number of desirable ways of appraising individual progress and achievement in agriculture mechanics, such as:

1. Examinations.
2. Oral responses.
3. Daily evaluation.
4. Student notebooks or workbooks.
5. Performance tests.
6. Completed jobs or projects.
7. Activities put into practice on the farm or job.
8. Self-evaluation.

Adults and high school students will cooperate in the use of any or all of these procedures if they are allowed to share in developing objectives, standards, and evaluation techniques. Students often suggest pencil and paper tests as a means of evaluating progress toward their objectives if the teacher asks for suggestions for determining their progress.

Grading—Adults do not usually receive formal grades in agriculture mechanics courses. This situation does not eliminate the necessity of evaluation. It may, however, create a more desirable climate for evaluation. Formal grading of high school students is expected, and techniques must be developed for creating the correct attitude toward a grade.

If evaluation is continuous and if the students share in the process, grading will be accepted and welcomed. Most teachers of agriculture mechanics allow some time daily for helping students evaluate their progress. If students are concerned about their final grades, the instructor may need to help them translate the daily evaluation of their work into letter grades. An instructor should interest such students in objectives as a means of eliminating interest in grades as ends in themselves. Daily evaluations in agriculture mechanics have the following advantages:

1. They stimulate an instructor to observe carefully the work of students each day.
2. They give an instructor a definite check on each day's accomplishments.
3. They create interest.
4. They stimulate the students to do more and better work.
5. They afford a basis for more accurate final grading.
6. They give an instructor an opportunity to discover weaknesses in the instruction.

When work is evaluated daily, the instructor may move around the shop before the close of the shop period and discuss with each student the quality and quantity of the work that day. The instructor needs to be careful not to dominate this discussion. Students need to be led to evaluate their own work. The task is to guide this evaluation through skillful questioning. Such questions as the following may be asked:

1. What have you accomplished today?
2. What difficulties have you encountered?
3. What improvements could you make?
4. How could you have done better?
5. Are you satisfied with the quality of your work?

The instructor may help students evaluate their work by indicating near the end of the discussion the good points of the work for the day. The instructor should strive to get students to recognize their own weaknesses. The instructor has to be careful not to alienate interest by causing the students to "lose face."

The instructor and the students in a class in agriculture mechanics should develop together objectives and evaluation techniques that will give consideration to the following points in determining grades:

1. The attitude and desire to remain at a job.
2. The use and care of tools.
3. The quality of work.
4. The amount accomplished.
5. The type of project.
6. The ability of the student.

Some students may work hard, keep on the job, and yet not accomplish much. Of course, some can do more than others. This should be considered in grading. In evaluating achievement in agriculture mechanics, the instructor should give recognition to the work done outside of class.

Appendix

APPENDIX

THE NATIONAL VOCATIONAL EDUCATION (SMITH-HUGHES) ACT

(Public Law 347, Sixty-fourth Congress—S. 703)

SEC. 1.

AN ACT to provide for the promotion of vocational education; to provide for cooperation with the States in the promotion of such education in agriculture and the trades and industries; to provide for cooperation with the States in the preparation of teachers of vocational subjects; and to appropriate money and regulate its expenditure.

BE IT ENACTED BY THE SENATE AND HOUSE OF REPRESENTATIVES OF THE UNITED STATES OF AMERICA IN CONGRESS ASSEMBLED, That there is hereby annually appropriated out of any money in the Treasury not otherwise appropriated, the sums provided in sections two, three, and four of this act, to be paid to the respective States for the purpose of cooperating with the States in paying the salaries of teachers, supervisors, and directors of agricultural subjects, and teachers of trade, home economics, and industrial subjects, and in the preparation of teachers of agriculture, trade, industrial, and home economics subjects; and the sum provided for in section seven for the use of the Federal Board for Vocational Education for the administration of this act and for the purpose of making studies, investigations, and reports to aid in the organization and conduct of vocational education, which sums shall be expended as hereinafter provided.

SEC. 2. That for the purpose of cooperating with the States in paying the salaries of teachers, supervisors, or directors of agricultural subjects there is hereby appropriated for the use of the States, subject to the provisions of this act, for the fiscal year ending June thirtieth, nineteen hundred and eighteen, the sum of $500,000; for the fiscal year ending June thirtieth, nineteen hundred and nineteen, the sum of $750,000; for the fiscal year ending June thirtieth, nineteen hundred and twenty, the sum of $1,000,000; for the fiscal year ending June thirtieth, nineteen hundred and twenty-one, the sum of $1,250,000; for the fiscal year ending June thirtieth, nineteen hundred and twenty-two, the sum of $1,500,000; for the fiscal year ending June thirtieth, nineteen hundred and twenty-three, the sum of $1,750,000; for the fiscal year ending June thirtieth, nineteen hundred and twenty-four, the sum of $2,000,000; for the fiscal year ending June thirtieth, nineteen hundred and twenty-five, the sum $2,500,000; for the fiscal year ending June thirtieth, nineteen hundred and twenty-six, and annually thereafter, the sum of $3,000,000. Said sums shall be allotted to the States in the proportion which their rural population bears to the total rural population in the United States, not including outlying possessions, according to the last preceding United States census: *Provided*,----

SEC. 3. That for the purpose of cooperating with the States in paying the salaries of teachers of trade, home economics, and industrial subjects there is hereby appropriated for the use of the States, for the fiscal year ending June thirtieth, nineteen hundred and eighteen, the sum of $500,000; for the fiscal year ending June thirtieth, nineteen hundred and nineteen, the sum of $750,000; for the fiscal year ending June thirtieth, nineteen hundred and twenty, the sum of $1,000,000; for the fiscal year ending June thirtieth, nineteen hundred and twenty-one, the sum of $1,250,000; for the fiscal year ending June thirtieth, nineteen hundred and twenty-two, the sum of $1,500,000; for the fiscal year ending June thirtieth, nineteen hundred and twenty-three, the sum of $1,750,000; for the fiscal year ending June thirtieth, nineteen hundred and twenty-four, the sum of $2,000,000; for the fiscal year ending June thirtieth, nineteen hundred and twenty-five, the sum of $2,500,000; for the fiscal year ending June thirtieth, nineteen hundred and twenty-six, the sum of $3,000,000; and annually thereafter, the sum of $3,000,000. Said sums shall be allotted to the States in the proportion which their urban population bears to the total urban population in the United States, not including outlying possessions, according to the last preceding United States census: *Provided*,----

That not more than twenty per centum of the money appropriated under this act for the payment of salaries of teachers of trade, home economics, and industrial subjects, for any year, shall be expended for the salaries of teachers of home economics subjects.

SEC. 4. That for the purpose of cooperating with the States in preparing teachers, supervisors, and directors of agricultural subjects and teachers of trade and industrial and home economic subjects there is hereby appropriated for the use of the States for the fiscal year ending June thirtieth, nineteen hundred and eighteen, the sum of $500,000; for the fiscal year ending June thirtieth, nineteen hundred and nineteen, the sum of $700,000; for the fiscal year ending June thirtieth, nineteen hundred and twenty, the sum of $900,000; for the fiscal year ending June thirtieth, nineteen hundred and twenty-one, and annually thereafter, the sum of $1,000,000. Said sums shall be allotted to the States in the proportion which their population bears to the total population of the United States, not including outlying possessions, according to the last preceding United States census: *Provided*,----

SEC. 5. That in order to secure the benefits of the appropriations provided for in sections two, three, and four of this act, any State shall, through the legislative authority thereof, accept the provisions of this act and designate and create a State board, consisting of not less than three members, and having all necessary power to cooperate, as herein provided, with the Federal Board for Vocational Education in the administration of the provisions of this act. The State board of education, or other board having charge of the administration of public education in the State, or any State board having charge of the administration of any kind of vocational education in the State may, if the State so elects, be designated as the State board, for the purposes of this act.

In any State the legislature of which does not meet in nineteen hundred and seventeen, if the governor of that State, so far as he is authorized to do so, shall accept the provisions of this act and designate or create a State board of not less than three members to act in cooperation with the Federal Board for Vocational Education, the Federal Board shall recognize such local board for the purposes of this act until the legislature of such State meets in due course and has been in session sixty days.

Any State may accept the benefits of any one or more of the respective funds herein appropriated, and it may defer the acceptance of the benefits of any one or more of such funds, and shall be required to meet only the conditions relative to the fund or funds the benefits of which it has accepted. *Provided*, That after June thirtieth, nineteen hundred and twenty, no State shall receive any appropriation for salaries of teachers, supervisors, or directors of agricultural subjects, until it shall have taken advantage of at least the minimum amount appropriated for the training of teachers, supervisors, or directors of agricultural subjects, as provided for in this act, and that after said date no State shall receive any appropriation for the salaries of teachers of trade, home economics, and industrial subjects until it shall have taken advantage of at least the minimum amount appropriated for the training of teachers of trade, home economics, and industrial subjects, as provided for in this act.

SEC. 6. That a Federal Board for Vocational Education is hereby created, to consist of the Secretary of Agriculture, the Secretary of Commerce, the Secretary of Labor, the United States Commissioner of Education, and three citizens of the United States to be appointed by the President, by and with the advice and consent of the Senate. One of said three citizens shall be a representative of the manufacturing and commercial interests, one a representative of the agricultural interests, and one a representative of labor. The board shall elect annually one of its members as chairman. In the first instance, one of the citizen members shall be appointed for one year, one for two years, and one for three years, and thereafter for three years each. The members of the board other than the members of the Cabinet and the United States Commissioner of Education shall receive a salary of $5,000 per annum.

The board shall have power to cooperate with State boards in carrying out the provisions of this act. It shall be the duty of the Federal Board for Vocational Education to make, or cause to have made, studies, investigations, and reports, with particular reference to their use in aiding the States in the establishment of vocational schools and classes and in giving instruction in agriculture, trades, and industries, commerce and commercial pursuits, and home economics. Such studies, investigations, and reports shall include agriculture and agricultural processes and requirements upon agricultural workers; trades, industries, and apprenticeships, trade and industrial requirements upon industrial workers, and classification of industrial processes and pursuits; commerce and commercial pursuits and requirements upon commercial workers; home management, domestic science, and the study of related facts and principles; and problems of administration of vocational schools and of courses of study and instruction in vocational subjects.

When the Board deems it advisable such studies, investigations, and reports concerning agriculture, for the purposes of agricultural education, may be made in cooperation with or through the Department of Agriculture; such studies, investigations, and reports, concerning trades and industries for the purposes of trades and reports concerning commerce and commercial pursuits, for the purposes of commercial education, may be made in cooperation with or through the Department of Commerce; such studies, investigations, and reports concerning the administration of vocational schools, courses of study, and instruction in vocational subjects may be made in cooperation with or through the Bureau of Education.[1]

The Commissioner of Education may make such recommendations to the Board relative to the administration of this act as he may from time to time deem advisable. It shall be the duty of the chairman of the board to carry out the rules, regulations, and decisions which the board may adopt. The Federal Board for Vocational Education shall have power to employ such assistants as may be necessary to carry out the provisions of this act.

SEC. 7. That there is hereby appropriated to the Federal Board for Vocational Education the sum of $200,000 annually, to be available from and after the passage of this act, for the purpose of making or cooperating in making the studies, investigations, and reports provided for in section six of this act, and for the purpose of paying the salaries of the officers, the assistants, and such office and other expenses as the board may deem necessary to the execution and administration of this act.

SEC. 8. That in order to secure the benefits of the appropriation for any purpose specified in this act, the State board shall prepare plans, showing the kinds of vocational education for which it is proposed that the appropriation shall be used; the kinds of schools and equipment; courses of study; methods of instruction; qualifications of teachers; and, in the case of agricultural subjects, the qualifications of supervisors or directors; plans for the training of teachers; and, in the case of agricultural subjects, plans for the supervision of agricultural education, as provided for in section ten. Such plans shall be submitted by the State board to the Federal Board for Vocational Education, and if the Federal Board finds the same to be in conformity with the provisions and purposes of this act, the same shall be approved. The State board shall make an annual report to the Federal Board for Vocational Education, on or before September first of each year, and on the work done in the State and the receipts and expenditures of money under the provisions of this act.

SEC. 9. That the appropriation for the salaries of teachers, supervisors, or directors of agricultural subjects and of teachers of trade, home economics, and industrial sub-

[1]Name changed to Office of Education, October 3, 1929.

jects shall be devoted exclusively to the payment of salaries of such teachers, supervisors, or directors having the minimum qualifications set up for the State by the State board, with the approval of the Federal Board for Vocational Education. The cost of instruction supplementary to the instruction in agriculture and in trade, home economics, and industrial subjects provided for in this act, necessary to build a well-rounded course of training, shall be borne by the State and local communities, and no part of the cost thereof shall be borne out of the appropriations herein made. The moneys expended under the provisions of this act, in cooperation with the States, for the salaries of teachers, supervisors, or directors of agricultural subjects, or for the salaries of teachers of trade, home economics, and industrial subjects shall be conditioned that for each dollar of Federal money expended for such salaries, the State or local community, or both, shall expend an equal amount for such salaries; and that appropriations for the training of teachers of vocational subjects, as herein provided, shall be conditioned that such money be expended for maintenance of such training, and for each dollar of Federal money so expended for maintenance, the State or local community or both shall expend an equal amount for the maintenance of such training.

SEC. 10. That any State may use the appropriations for agricultural purposes, or any part thereof allotted to it, under the provisions of this act, for the salaries of teachers, supervisors, or directors of agricultural subjects, either for the salaries of teachers of such subjects in schools or classes or for the salaries of supervisors or directors of such subjects under a plan of supervision for the State to be set up by the State board, with the approval of the Federal Board for Vocational Education. That in order to receive the benefits of such appropriations for the salaries of teachers, supervisors, or directors of agricultural education such education shall be that which is under public supervision or control; that the controlling purpose of such education shall be to fit for useful employment; that such education shall be of less than college grade and be designated to meet the needs of persons over fourteen years of age who have entered upon or who are preparing to enter upon the work of the farm or of the farm home; that the State or local community, or both, shall provide the necessary plant and equipment determined upon by the State board, with the approval of the Federal Board for Vocational Education, as the minimum requirement for such education in schools and classes in the State; that the amount expended for the maintenance of such education in any school or class receiving the benefit of such appropriation shall not be less annually than the amount fixed by the State board, with the approval of the Federal Board, as the minimum for such schools or classes in the State; that such schools shall provide for directed or supervised practice in agriculture, either on a farm provided for by the school or other farm, for at least six months per year; that the teachers, supervisors, or directors of agricultural subjects shall have at least the minimum qualifications determined for the State by the State board, with the approval of the Federal Board for Vocational Education.

SEC. 11. That in order to receive the benefits of the appropriation for the salaries of teachers of trade, home economics, and industrial subjects the State board of any State shall provide in its plan for trade, home economics, and industrial education that such education shall be given in schools or classes under public supervision or control; that the controlling purpose of such education shall be to fit for useful employment; that such education shall be of less than college grade and shall be designed to meet the needs of persons over fourteen years of age who are preparing for a trade or industrial pursuit or who have entered upon the work of a trade or industrial pursuit; that the State or local community, or both, shall provide the necessary plant and equipment determined upon by the State board, with the approval of the Federal Board for Vocational Education, as the minimum requirement in such State for education for any given trade or industrial pursuit; that the total amount expended for the maintenance of such education in any school or class receiving the benefit of such appropriation shall be not less annually than the amount fixed by the State board, with the approval of the Federal Board, as the minimum for such schools or classes in the State; that such schools or classes giving instruction to persons who have not entered upon employment shall require that at least half of the time of such instruction be given to practical work on a useful or productive basis, such instruction to extend over not less than nine months per year and not less than thirty hours per week; that at least one-third of the sum appropriated to any State for the salaries to teachers of trade, home economics, and industrial subjects shall, if expended, be applied to part-time schools or classes for workers over fourteen years of age who have entered upon employment, and such subjects in a part-time school or class may mean any subject given to enlarge the civic or vocational intelligence of such workers over fourteen and less than eighteen years of age; that such part-time schools or classes shall provide for not less than one hundred and forty-four hours of classroom instruction per year; that evening industrial schools shall fix the age of sixteen years as a minimum entrance requirement and shall confine instruction to that which is supplemental to the daily employment; that the teachers of any trade or industrial subject in any State shall have at least the minimum qualifications for teachers of such subject determined upon for such State by the State board, with the approval of the Federal Board for Vocational Education: *Provided*, That for cities and towns of less than twenty-five thousand population, according to the last preceding United States census, the State board, with the approval of the Federal Board for Vocational Education, may modify the conditions as to the length and hours of instruction per week for schools and classes giving instruction to those who have not entered upon employment, in order to meet the particular needs of such cities and towns.

SEC. 12. That in order for any State to receive the benefits of the appropriation in this act for the training of teachers, supervisors, or directors of agricultural subjects, or of teachers of trade, industrial, or home economics subjects, the State board of such State shall provide in its plan for such training that the same shall be carried out under the supervision of the State board; that such training shall be given in schools or classes under public supervision or control; that such training shall be given only to persons who have had adequate vocational experience or contact in the line of work for which they are preparing themselves as teachers, supervisors, or directors, or who are acquiring such experience or contact as a part of their training; and that the State board, with the approval of the Federal Board, shall establish minimum requirements for such experience or contact for teachers, supervisors, or directors of agricultural subjects and for teachers of trade, industrial, and home economics subjects; that no more than sixty per centum nor less than twenty per centum of the money appropriated under this act for the training of teachers of Vocational subjects to any State for any year shall be expended for any one of the following purposes: For the preparation of teachers, supervisors, or directors of agricultural subjects, or the preparation of teachers of trade and industrial subjects, or the preparation of teachers of home economics subjects.

SEC. 13. That in order to secure the benefits of the appropriations for the salaries of teachers, supervisors, or directors of agricultural subjects, or for the salaries of teachers of trade, home economics, and industrial subjects, or for the training of teachers as herein provided, any State shall, through the legislative authority thereof, appoint as custodian for said appropriations its State treasurer, who shall receive and provide for the proper custody and disbursements of all money paid to the State from said appropriations.

SEC. 14. That the Federal Board for Vocational Education shall annually ascertain whether the several States are using, or are prepared to use, the money received by them in accordance with the provisions of this act. On or before the first day of January of each year the Federal Board for Vocational Education shall certify to the Secretary of the Treasury each State which has accepted the provisions of this act and complied therewith, certifying the amounts which each State is entitled to receive under the provisions of this act. Upon such certification the Secretary of the Treasury shall pay quarterly to the custodian for vocational education of each State the moneys to which it is entitled under the provisions of this act. The moneys so received by the custodian for vocational education for any State shall be paid out on the requisition of the State board as reimbursement for expenditures already incurred to such schools as are approved by said State board and are entitled to receive such moneys under the provisions of this act.

SEC. 15. That whenever any portion of the fund annually allotted to any State has not been expended for the purpose provided for in this act, a sum equal to such portion shall be deducted by the Federal Board from the next succeeding annual allotment from such fund to such State.

SEC. 16. That the Federal Board for Vocational Education may withhold the allotment of moneys to any State whenever it shall be determined that such moneys are not being expended for the purposes and under the conditions of this act.

If any allotment is withheld from any State, the State board of such State may appeal to the Congress of the United States, and if the Congress shall not direct such sum to be paid, it shall be covered into the Treasury.

SEC. 17. That if any portion of the moneys received by the custodian for vocational education of any State under this act, for any given purpose named in this act, shall, by any action or contingency, be diminished or lost, it shall be replaced by such State, and until so replaced no subsequent appropriation for such education shall be paid to such State. No portion of any moneys appropriated under this act for the benefit of the States shall be applied, directly or indirectly, to the purchase, erection, preservation, or repair of any building or buildings or equipment, or for the purchase or rental of lands, or for the support of any religious or privately owned or conducted school or college.

SEC. 18. That the Federal Board for Vocational Education shall make an annual report to Congress, on or before December first, on the administration of this act and shall include in such report the reports made by the State boards on the administration of this act by each State and the expenditure of the money allowed to each State.

Approved, February 23, 1917.

Selected Portions of
THE VOCATIONAL EDUCATION AMENDMENTS OF 1976

(Public Law 94-482—Oct. 12, 1976)

VOCATIONAL EDUCATION

PART A—STATE VOCATIONAL EDUCATION PROGRAMS

DECLARATION OF PURPOSE

SEC. 101. It is the purpose of this part to assist States in improving planning in the use of all resources available to them for vocational education and manpower training by involving a wide range of agencies and individuals concerned with education and training within the State in the development of the vocational education plans. It is also the purpose of this part to authorize Federal grants to States to assist them—

(1) to extend, improve, and, where necessary, maintain existing programs of vocational education,

(2) to develop new programs of vocational education,

(3) to develop and carry out such programs of vocational education within each State so as to overcome sex discrimination and sex stereotyping in vocational education programs (including programs of homemaking), and thereby furnish equal educational opportunities in vocational education to persons of both sexes, and

(4) to provide part-time employment for youths who need the earnings from such employment to continue their vocational training on a full-time basis,

so that persons of all ages in all communities of the State, those in high school, those who have completed or discontinued their formal education and are preparing to enter the labor market, those who have already entered the labor market, but need to upgrade their skills or learn new ones, those with special educational handicaps, and those in postsecondary schools, will have ready access to vocational training or retraining which is of high quality, which is realistic in the light of actual or anticipated opportunities for gainful employment, and which is suited to their needs, interests, and ability to benefit from such training.

Subpart 1—General Provisions

STATE ADMINISTRATION

. . . .

(b) (1) Any State desiring to participate in the programs authorized by this Act shall also assign such full-time personnel as may be necessary to assist the State board in fulfilling the purposes of this Act by—

(A) taking such action as may be necessary to create awareness of programs and activities in vocational education that are designed to reduce sex stereotyping in all vocational education programs;

(B) gathering, analyzing, and disseminating data on the status of men and women, students and employees in the vocational education programs of that State;

(C) developing and supporting actions to correct any problems brought to the attention of such personnel through activities carried out under clause (B) of this sentence;

(D) reviewing the distribution of grants by the State board to assure that the interests and needs of women are addressed in the projects assisted under this Act;

(E) reviewing all vocational education programs in the State for sex bias;

(F) monitoring the implementation of laws prohibiting sex discrimination in all hiring, firing, and promotion procedures within the State relating to vocational education;

(G) reviewing and submitting recommendations with respect to the overcoming of sex stereotyping and sex bias in vocational education programs for the annual program plan and report;

(H) assisting local educational agencies and other interested parties in the State in improving vocational education opportunities for women; and

(I) making readily available to the State board, the State and National Advisory Councils on Vocational Education, the State Commission on the Status of Women, the Commissioner and the general public, information developed pursuant to this subsection.

(2) From the funds appropriated to carry out subpart 2, each State shall reserve $50,000 in each fiscal year to carry out this subsection.

(3) For the purpose of this subsection, the term "State" means any one of the fifty States and the District of Columbia.

. . . .

(g) (1) Each eligible recipient receiving assistance under this Act to operate vocational education programs shall establish a local advisory council to provide such agency with advice on current job needs and on the relevancy of courses being offered by such agency in meeting such needs. Such local advisory councils shall be composed of members of the general public, especially of representatives of business, industry, and labor; and such local advisory councils may be established for program areas, schools, communities, or regions, whichever the recipient determines best to meet the needs of that recipient.

. . . .

NATIONAL PRIORITY PROGRAMS

SEC. 110. (a) For each fiscal year, at least 10 per centum of each State's allotment under section 103 shall be used to pay 50 per centum of the cost of vocational education for handicapped persons.

(b) (1) For each fiscal year, at least 20 per centum of each State's allotment under section 103 shall be used to pay 50 per centum of the cost of vocational education for disadvantaged persons (other than handicapped persons), for persons who have limited English-speaking ability, and for providing stipends authorized under section 120(b) (1) (G).

(2) From the funds used by a State pursuant to paragraph (1), each State shall use an amount equivalent to the same percentage of the funds reserved pursuant to that paragraph as the population aged fifteen to twenty-four, inclusive, having limited English-speaking ability is to the total population of the State aged fifteen to twenty-four, inclusive, for providing vocational education for such persons with limited English-speaking ability, except that such amount shall not exceed the full sum used pursuant to paragraph (1).

(c) For each fiscal year, at least 15 per centum of each State's allotment under section 103 shall be used to pay 50 per centum of the cost of vocational education for (1) persons who have completed or left high school and who are enrolled in organized programs of study for which credit is given toward an associate or other degree, but which programs are not designed as baccalaureate or higher degree programs, and (2) persons who have already entered the labor market, or are unemployed, or who have completed or left high school and who are not described in paragraph (1).

(d) Each State shall use, to the maximum extent possible, the funds required to be used for the purposes specified in subsections (a) and (b) to assist individuals described in those subsections to participate in regular vocational education programs.

PAYMENTS TO STATES

SEC. 111. (a) (1) The Commissioner shall pay, from the amount available to each State for grants under this part (except subpart 5) to eligible recipients, an amount equal to—

(A) 50 per centum of the cost of carrying out its annual program plan as approved pursuant to section 109, other than programs and activities for persons described in section 110;

(B) 50 per centum of the cost of vocational education programs for persons with special needs described in section 110(a), (b), and (c); and

(C) 100 per centum of the cost of vocational education programs described in sections 122(f), 133(b), and 140;

except that in the case of the Trust Territory of the Pacific Islands and American Samoa, such amount shall be equal to 100 per centum of such expenditures.

(2) (A) In addition, the Commissioner shall pay, from the amount available to each State for administration of State plans appropriated under section 102(d), an amount equal to the Federal share of the cost of administration of such plan.

(B) For the purpose of this paragraph, the Federal share for any fiscal year shall be 50 per centum, except that (1) for fiscal year 1978 it shall be 80 per centum and for fiscal year 1979 it shall be 60 per centum, and (2) whenever the Commissioner determines in exceptional circumstances that for the fiscal year preceding fiscal year 1978 State and local expenditures for vocational education in a State exceed ten times the Federal expenditure for vocational education in that State, and that the State has an appropriate, economic, and efficient State administration of the program, the Commissioner shall set the Federal share for fiscal year 1978 for that State in excess of the Federal share specified in clause (1), but not to exceed 100 per centum.

(b) (1) No payments shall be made in any fiscal year under this Act to any local educational agency or to any State unless the Commissioner finds, in the case of a local educational agency, that the combined fiscal effort per student or the aggregate expenditures of that agency and the State with respect to the provision of vocational education by that agency for the fiscal year preceding the fiscal year for which the determination was made was not less than such combined fiscal effort per student or the aggregate expenditures for that purpose for the second preceding fiscal year or, in the case of a State, that the fiscal effort per student or the aggregate expenditures of that State for vocational education in that State for the fiscal year preceding the fiscal year for which the determination was made was not less than such fiscal effort per student or the aggregate expenditures for vocational education for the second preceding fiscal year.

(2) No payments shall be made in any fiscal year under this Act to any postsecondary educational institution unless the Commissioner finds that the aggregate amount or the amount per student spent by such institution from current funds for vocational education purposes for the fiscal year preceding the fiscal year for which the determination was made was not less than such amount spent by such institution from current funds for the second preceding fiscal year.

FEDERAL AND STATE EVALUATIONS

SEC. 112. (a) In order for the Federal government to assist the States in operating the best possible programs of vocational education—

(1) the Commissioner shall within four months of the receipt of a State's annual program plan and accountability report transmit to that State board an analysis of such plan and report, including suggestions for improvements in the State's programs and findings contained in any program or fiscal audits performed in that State pursuant to paragraph (2); and

(2) the Bureau of Occupational and Adult Education shall, in at least ten States a fiscal year during the period beginning October 1, 1977, and ending September 30, 1982, conduct a review analyzing the strengths and weaknesses of the programs assisted with funds available under this Act within those States; and the Department of Health, Education, and Welfare shall, in the same period, conduct fiscal audits of such programs within those States.

(b) (1) In order for the States to assist local educational agencies and other recipients of funds in operating the best possible programs of vocational education—

(A) each State shall, during the five-year period of the State plan, evaluate the effectiveness of each program within the State being assisted with funds available under this Act; and the results of these evaluations shall be used to revise the State's programs, and shall be made readily available to the State advisory council; and

(B) each State shall evaluate, by using data collected, wherever possible, by statistically valid sampling techniques, each such program within the State which purports to impart entry level job skills according to the extent to which program completers and leavers—

(i) find employment in occupations related to their training, and

(ii) are considered by their employers to be well-trained and prepared for employment,

except that in no case can pursuit of additional education or training by program completers or leavers be considered negatively in these evaluations.

(2) Each State, in formulating its plans to fulfill these requirements, shall annually consult with the State advisory council which shall assist the State in developing these plans, monitor the evaluations conducted by the State, and use the results of these evaluations in compiling its annual report required by section 105.

(c) The Commissioner shall prepare and submit annually to the Congress, within nine months of the termination of each fiscal year, a report on the status of vocational education in the country during that fiscal year. This report shall include data on the information elements developed in the national vocational education data reporting and accounting system and an analysis of such data, and a summary of the findings of the reviews and audits required by paragraph (2) of subsection (a) and of the evaluations performed pursuant to paragraphs (1) and (2) of subsection (b).

Subpart 2—Basic Grant

AUTHORIZATION OF GRANTS AND USES OF FUNDS

SEC. 120. (a) From the sums made available for grants under this subpart pursuant to section 103, the Commissioner is authorized to make grants to States to assist them in conducting vocational education programs in accordance with the requirements of this subpart.

(b) (1) Grants to States under this subpart may be used, in accordance with five-year State plans and annual program plans approved pursuant to section 109, for the following purposes:

(A) vocational education programs;

(B) work study programs as described in section 121;

(C) cooperative vocational education programs as described in section 122;

(D) energy education programs as described in section 123;

(E) construction of area vocational education school facilities;

(F) support of full-time personnel to perform the duties described in section 104(b);

(G) the provision of stipends, subject to the restriction contained in paragraph (2), which shall not exceed reasonable amounts, as prescribed by the Commissioner pursuant to regulations, for students entering or already enrolled in vocational education programs, if those students have acute economic needs which cannot be met under work-study programs;

(H) placement services for students who have successfully completed vocational education programs, subject to the restriction contained in paragraph (2);

(I) industrial arts programs where such programs will assist in meeting the purposes of this Act;

(J) support services for women who enter programs designed to prepare individuals for employment in jobs which have been traditionally limited to men, including counseling as to the nature of such programs and the difficulties which may be encountered by women in such programs, and job development and job followup services;

(K) day care services for children of students in secondary and postsecondary vocational education programs;

(L) vocational education for—

(i) persons who had solely been homemakers but who now, because of dissolution of marriage, must seek employment;

(ii) persons who are single heads of households and who lack adequate job skills;

(iii) persons who are currently homemakers and part-time workers but who wish to secure a full-time job; and

(iv) women who are now in jobs which have been traditionally considered jobs for females and who wish to seek employment in job areas which have not been traditionally considered for job areas for females, and men who are now in jobs which have been traditionally considered jobs for males and who wish to seek employment in job areas which have not been traditionally considered job areas for males; and

(M) construction and operation of residential vocational schools as described in section 124.

(2) No funds shall be used for the purposes specified in subparagraph (G) or (H) of paragraph (1) unless the State board first makes a specific finding in each instance of funding that the funding of this particular activity is necessary due to inadequate funding in other programs providing similar activities or due to the fact that other services in the area are inadequate to meet the needs.

WORK STUDY PROGRAMS

SEC. 121. (a) Funds available to the States under section 120 may be used for grants to local educational agencies for work-study programs which—

(1) are administered by the local educational agencies and are made reasonably available (to the extent of available funds) to all youths in the area served by such agency who are able to meet the requirements of paragraph (2);

(2) provide that employment under such work-study programs shall be furnished only to a student who (A) has been accepted for enrollment as a full-time student in a vocational education program which meets the standards prescribed by the State board and the local educational agency for vocational education programs assisted under this Act, or in the case of a student already enrolled in such a program, is in good standing and in full-time attendance, (B) is in need of the earnings from such employment to commence or continue his vocational education program, and (C) is at least fifteen years of age and less than twenty-one years of age at the commencement of his employment, and is capable, in the opinion of the appropriate school authorities, of maintaining good standing in his vocational education program while employed under the work-study program;

(3) provide that, pursuant to regulations of the Commissioner, no student shall be employed under such work-study program for more than a reasonable number of hours in any week in which classes in which he is enrolled are in session, or for compensation which exceeds payments under comparable Federal programs, unless the student is attending a school that is not within a reasonable commuting distance from his home, when the compensation may be set by the Commissioner at a higher level;

(4) provide that employment under such work-study program shall be for the local educational agency or for some other public or nonprofit private agency or institution; and

(5) provide that, in each fiscal year during which such program remains in effect, such agency shall expend (from sources other than payments from Federal funds under this section) for the employment of its students (whether or not in employment eligible for assistance under this section) an amount that is not less than its average annual expenditure for work-study programs of a similar character during the three fiscal years preceding the fiscal year in which its work-study program under this section is approved.

(b) Each State in operating work-study programs from funds made available under section 120 shall—

(1) adopt policies and procedures which assure that Federal funds used for this purpose will be expended solely for the payment or compensation of students employed pursuant to the work-study programs meeting the requirements of subsection (a); and

(2) set forth principles for determining the priority to be accorded applications from local educational agencies for work-study programs, which principles give preference to applications submitted by local educational agencies serving communities having substantial numbers of youths who have dropped out of school or who are unemployed, and provide for undertaking such programs, insofar as financial resources available therefor make possible, in the order determined by the application of such principles.

(c) Students employed in work-study programs assisted pursuant to this section shall not by reason of such employment be deemed employees of the United States, or their service Federal service, for any reason.

COOPERATIVE VOCATIONAL EDUCATION PROGRAMS

SEC. 122. Funds available to the States under section 120 may be used for establishing or expanding cooperative vocational education programs through local educational agencies with the participation of public and private employers. Such programs shall include provisions assuring that—

(a) funds will be used only for developing and operating cooperative vocational programs as defined in section 195(18) which provide training opportunities that may not otherwise be available and which are designed to serve persons who can benefit from such programs;

(b) necessary procedures are established for cooperation with employment agencies in identifying suitable jobs for persons who enroll in cooperative vocational education programs;

(c) provision is made, where necessary, for reimbursement of added costs to employers for on-the-job training of students enrolled in cooperative programs, provided such on-the-job training is related to existing career opportunities susceptible of promotion and advancement and which do not displace other workers who perform such work;

(d) ancillary services and activities to assure quality in cooperative vocational education programs are provided for, such as preservice and inservice training for teacher coordinators, supervision, curriculum materials, travel of students and coordinators necessary to the success of such programs, and evaluation;

(e) priority for funding cooperative vocational education programs through local educational agencies is given to areas that have high rates of school dropouts and youth unemployment;

(f) to the extent consistent with the number of students enrolled in nonprofit private schools in the area to be served, whose educational needs are of the type which the program or project involved is to meet, provision has been made for the participation of such students;

(g) Federal funds used for the purposes of this section will not be commingled with State or local funds; and

(h) such accounting, evaluation, and followup procedures as the Commissioner deems necessary will be provided.

. . . .

EXEMPLARY AND INNOVATIVE PROGRAMS

SEC. 132. (a) Funds available to the States under section 130(a) may be used for contracts, as part of the comprehensive plans of program improvement mentioned in section 131(a), for the support of exemplary and innovative programs, including—

(1) programs designed to develop high quality vocational education programs for urban centers with high concentrations of economically disadvantaged individuals, unskilled workers, and unemployed individuals;

(2) programs designed to develop training opportunities for persons in sparsely populated rural areas and for individuals migrating from farms to urban areas;

(3) programs of effective vocational education for individuals with limited English-speaking ability;

(4) establishment of cooperative arrangements between public education and manpower agencies, designed to correlate vocational education opportunities with current and projected needs of the labor market; and

(5) programs designed to broaden occupational aspirations and opportunities for youth, with special emphasis given to youth who have academic, socioeconomic, or other handicaps, including—

(A) programs and projects designed to familiarize elementary and secondary school students with the broad range of occupations for which special skills are required, and the requisites for careers in such occupations; and

(B) programs and projects to facilitate the participation of employers and labor organizations in postsecondary vocational education.

(b) Every contract made by a State for the purpose of funding exemplary and innovative projects shall give priority to programs and projects designed to reduce sex stereotyping in vocational education and shall, to the extent consistent with the number of students enrolled in nonprofit private schools in the area to be served whose educational needs are of the type which the program or project involved is to meet, provide for the participation of such students; and such contract shall also provide that the Federal funds will not be commingled with State or local funds.

(c) The annual program plan and accountability report covering the final year of financial support by the State for any such program or project shall indicate the proposed disposition of the program or project following the cessation of Federal support and the means by which successful or promising programs or projects will be continued and expanded within the State.

CURRICULUM DEVELOPMENT

SEC. 133. (a) Funds available to the States under section 130(a) may be used for contracts for the support of curriculum development projects, including—

(1) the development and dissemination of vocational education curriculum materials for new and changing occupational fields and for individuals with special needs, as described in section 110; and

(2) the development of curriculum and guidance and testing materials designed to overcome sex bias in vocational education programs, and support services designed to enable teachers to meet the needs of individuals enrolled in vocational education programs traditionally limited to members of the opposite sex,

(b) No contract shall be made pursuant to subsection (a) unless the applicant can demonstrate a reasonable probability that the contract will result in improved teaching techniques or curriculum materials that will be used in a substantial number of classrooms or other learning situations within five years after the termination date of such contract.

VOCATIONAL GUIDANCE AND COUNSELING

SEC. 134. (a) Not less than 20 per centum of the funds available to the States under section 130(a) shall be used to support programs for vocational development guidance and counseling programs and services which, subject to the provisions of subsection (b), shall include—

(1) initiation, implementation, and improvement of high quality vocational guidance and counseling programs and activities;

(2) vocational counseling for children, youth, and adults, leading to a greater understanding of educational and vocational options;

(3) provision of educational and job placement services, including programs to prepare individuals for professional occupations or occupations requiring a baccalaureate or higher degree, including followup services;

(4) vocational guidance and counseling training designed to acquaint guidance counselors with (A) the changing work patterns of women, (B) ways of effectively overcoming occupational sex stereotyping, and (C) ways of assisting girls and women in selecting careers solely on their occupational needs and interests, and to develop improved career counseling materials which are free;

(5) vocational and educational counseling for youth offenders and adults in correctional institutions;

(6) vocational guidance and counseling for persons of limited English-speaking ability;

(7) establishment of vocational resource centers to meet the special needs of out-of-school individuals, including individuals seeking second careers, individuals entering the job market late in life, handicapped individuals, individuals from economically depressed communities or areas, and early retirees; and

(8) leadership for vocational guidance and exploration programs at the local level.

(b) Each State which chooses to fund activities described in paragraph (1) or (2) of subsection (a) of this section shall use those funds, insofar as is practicable, for funding programs, services, or activities by eligible recipients which bring individuals with experience in business and industry, the professions, and other occupational pursuits into schools as counselors or advisors for students, and which bring students into the work establishments of business and industry, the professions, and other occupational pursuits for the purpose of acquainting students with the nature of the work that is accomplished therein, and for funding projects of such recipients in which guidance counselors obtain experience in business and industry, the professions, and other occupational pursuits which will better enable those counselors to carry out their guidance and counseling duties.

VOCATIONAL EDUCATION PERSONNEL TRAINING

SEC. 135. (a) Funds available to the States under section 130(a) may be used to support programs or projects designed to improve the qualifications of persons serving or preparing to serve in vocational education programs, including teachers, administrators, supervisors, and vocational guidance and counseling personnel, including programs or projects—

(1) to train or retrain teachers, and supervisors and trainers of teachers, in vocational education in new and emerging occupations;

(2) which provide in-service training for vocational education teachers and other staff members, to improve the quality of instruction, supervision, and administration of vocational education programs, and to overcome sex bias in vocational education programs;

(3) which provide for exchange of vocational education teachers and other personnel with skilled workers or supervisors in business, industry, and agriculture (including mutual arrangements for preserving employment and retirement status and other employment benefits during the period of exchange), and the development and operation of cooperative programs involving periods of teaching in schools providing vocational education and of experience in commercial, industrial, or other public or private employment related to the subject matter taught in such school;

(4) to prepare journeymen in the skilled trades or occupations for teaching positions;

(5) to train and to provide in-service training for teachers and supervisors and trainers of teachers in vocational education to improve the quality of instruction, supervision, and administration of vocational education for persons with limited English-speaking ability and to train or retrain counseling and guidance personnel to meet the special needs of persons with limited English-speaking ability; and

(6) which provide short-term or regular-session institutes designed to improve the qualifications of persons entering or reentering the field of vocational education in new and emerging occupational areas in which there is a need for such personnel.

(b) A State may include in the terms of any grant or contract under this section provisions authorizing the payment, to persons participating in the training programs supported under this section, of such stipends (including allowances for subsistence and other expenses for such persons and their dependents) as the Commissioner may determine, pursuant to regulations, consistent with prevailing practices under comparable programs.

GRANTS TO ASSIST IN OVERCOMING SEX BIAS

SEC. 136. Funds available to the States under section 130(a) may be used to support activities which show promise of overcoming sex stereotyping and bias in vocational education.

. . . .

Subpart 4—Special Programs for the Disadvantaged

SPECIAL PROGRAMS FOR THE DISADVANTAGED

SEC. 140. (a) From the sums made available for grants under this subpart pursuant to sections 102 and 103, the Commissioner is authorized to make grants to States to assist them in conducting special programs for the disadvantaged (as defined in section 195(16)) in accordance with the requirements of this subpart.

(b) (1) Grants to States under this subpart shall be used, in accordance with five-year State plans and annual program plans approved pursuant to section 109, for allocation within the State to areas of high concentrations of youth unemployment and school dropouts, and shall be used to pay the full cost of vocational education for disadvantaged persons.

(2) Such funds may be granted to eligible recipients only if (A) to the extent consistent with the number of students enrolled in nonprofit private schools in the area to be served whose educational needs are of the type which the program or project involved is to meet, provision has been made for the participation of such students, and (B) effective policies and procedures have been adopted which assure that Federal funds made available under this subpart to accommodate students in nonprofit private schools will not be commingled with State or local funds.

. . . .

Subpart 4—Emergency Assistance for Remodeling and Renovation of Vocational Education Facilities

PURPOSE

SEC. 191. It is the purpose of this part to provide emergency assistance, for a limited period of time, to local educational agencies in urban and rural areas which are unable to provide vocational education designed to meet today's manpower needs due to the age of their vocational education facilities or the obsolete nature of the equipment used for vocational training, in order to assist such agencies in the modernization of facilities and equipment and the conversion of academic facilities necessary to assure that such facilities will be able to offer vocational education programs which give reasonable promise of employment, including the remodeling and renovation of such facilities to make the facilities comply with the requirements of the Act of August 2, 1968, commonly known as the Architectural Barriers Act of 1968.

. . . .

Part C—Definitions

DEFINITIONS

SEC. 195. As used in this Act—

(1) The term "vocational education" means organized educational programs which are directly related to the preparation of individuals for paid or unpaid employment, or for additional preparation for a career requiring other than a baccalaureate or advanced degree; and, for purposes of this paragraph, the term "organized education program" means only (A) instruction related to the occupation or occupations for which the students are in training or instruction necessary for students to benefit from such training, and (B) the acquisition, maintenance, and repair of instructional supplies, teaching aids and equipment; and the term "vocational education" does not mean the construction, acquisition or initial equipment of buildings, or the acquisition or rental of land.

(2) The term "area vocational education school" means—

(A) a specialized high school used exclusively or principally for the provision of vocational education to persons who are available for study in preparation for entering the labor market, or

(B) the department of a high school exclusively or principally used for providing vocational education in no less than five different occupational fields to persons who are available for study in preparation for entering the labor market, or

(C) a technical or vocational school used exclusively or principally for the provision of vocational education to persons who have completed or left high school and who are available for study in preparation for entering the labor market, or

(D) the department or division of a junior college or community college or university operating under the policies of the State board and which provides vocational education in no less than five different occupational fields, leading to immediate employment but not necessarily leading to a baccalaureate degree, if it is available to all residents of the State or an area of the State designated and approved by the State board, and if, in the case of a school, department, or division described in (C) or (D), if it admits as regular students both persons who have completed high school and persons who have left high school.

(3) The term "school facilities" means classrooms and related facilities (including initial equipment) and interests in lands on which such facilities are constructed. Such term shall not include any facility intended primarily for events for which admission is to be charged to the general public.

(4) The term "construction" includes construction of new buildings and acquisition, expansion, remodeling, and alteration of existing buildings, and includes site grading and improvement and architect fees.

(5) The term "Commissioner" means the Commissioner of Education.

(6) The term "Secretary" means the Secretary of Health, Education, and Welfare.

(7) The term "handicapped", when applied to persons, means persons who are mentally retarded, hard of hearing, deaf, speech impaired, visually handicapped, seriously emotionally disturbed, crippled, or other health impaired persons who by reason thereof require special education and related services, and who, because of their handicapping condition, cannot succeed in the regular vocational education program without special education assistance or who require a modified vocational education program.

(8) The term "State" includes, in addition to the several States, the District of Columbia, the Commonwealth of Puerto Rico, the Virgin Islands, Guam, American Samoa, and the Trust Territory of the Pacific Islands.

(9) The term "State board" means a State board designated or created by State law as the sole State agency responsible for the administration of vocational education, or for supervision of the administration of vocational education in the State.

(10) The term "local educational agency" means a board of education or other legally constituted local school authority having administrative control and direction of public elementary or secondary schools in a city, county, township, school district, or political subdivision in a State, or any other public educational institution or agency having administrative control and direction of a vocational education program.

(11) The term "State educational agency" means the State board of education or other agency or officer primarily responsible for the State supervision of public elementary and secondary schools, or, if there is no such officer or agency, an officer or agency designated by the Governor or by State law.

(12) The term "postsecondary educational institution" means a nonprofit institution legally authorized to provide postsecondary education within a State for persons sixteen years of age or older, who have graduated from or left elementary or secondary school.

(13) The term "eligible recipient" means a local educational agency or a postsecondary educational institution.

(14) The term "National Advisory Council" means the National Advisory Council on Vocational Education continued under section 162.

. . . .

(16) The term "disadvantaged" means persons (other than handicapped persons) who have academic or economic handicaps and who require special services and assistance in order to enable them to succeed in vocational education programs, under criteria developed by the Commissioner based on objective standards and the most recent available data.

(17) The term "low-income family or individual" means such families or individuals who are determined to be low-income according to the latest available data from the Department of Commerce.

(18) The term "cooperative education" means a program of vocational education for persons who, through written cooperative arrangements between the school and employers, receive instruction, including required academic courses and related vocational instruction by alternation of study in school with a job in any occupational field, but these two experiences must be planned and supervised by the school and employers so that each contributes to the student's education and to his or her employability. Work periods and school attendance may be on alternate half days, full days, weeks, or other periods of time in fulfilling the cooperative program.

(19) The term "curriculum materials" means materials consisting of a series of courses to cover instruction in any occupational field which are designed to prepare persons for employment at the entry level or to upgrade occupational competencies of those previously or presently employed in any occupational field.

(20) For the purposes of this Act, the term "administration" means activities of a State necessary for the proper and efficient performance of its duties under this Act, including supervision, but not including ancillary services.

CERTIFICATE OF INCORPORATION, THE FUTURE FARMERS OF AMERICA FOUNDATION, INCORPORATED

We, the undersigned, citizens of the United States and majority citizens and residents of the District of Columbia, desiring to associate ourselves as a corporation, pursuant to the provisions of Title 29, Chapter 6 of the 1940 Code Laws for the District of Columbia, do certify as follows:

FIRST:

The name of the corporation shall be "The Future Farmers of America Foundation, Incorporated."

SECOND:

The term for which it is organized shall be perpetual.

THIRD:

The principal office of the said Corporation shall be located at 3227 Vista Street, Northeast, Washington, D.C.

FOURTH:

The objects and purposes of "The Future Farmers of America Foundation, Inc." are to receive, maintain and hold, by bequest, devise, gift, or otherwise, either absolutely or in trust, for any of its purposes, any property, real or personal, fund or funds, without limitations as to amount or value; to convey such property and to invest and reinvest any principal; and to deal with and expand the income and/or principal of the Corporation for such educational activities and in such manner as in the judgment of the Board of Trustees will stimulate and promote the best interests of students and former students of vocational education in agriculture on a local, State, or national basis. As an amplification of said purposes and without in any way limiting the same or the discretion of the Board of Trustees, it is contemplated that said funds may be expended:

(a) To financially assist deserving students of vocational agriculture, and young farmers under 30 years of age who were former students of vocational agriculture, through loans or grants in becoming satisfactorily established in a farming occupation;

(b) To promote and stimulate interest in agricultural leadership among students of vocational agriculture;

(c) To promote and develop interest on the part of the general public in vocational agriculture, including farm mechanics, and activities of the Future Farmers of America and New Farmers of America.

(d) To provide prizes and awards to deserving students who have achieved distinction in vocational agriculture, including farm mechanics activities, on a local, State, or national basis, and to administer, direct, or supervise the granting of same.

(e) To publish an annual report of the activities of the Corporation, including a statement of receipts and expenditures, and to print such other documents, pamphlets, or bulletins as may be approved from time to time by the Board of Trustees.

FIFTH:

The Corporation is not for profit and shall have no capital stock.

SIXTH:

The private property or private funds of the incorporators or members of the Board of Trustees shall not be subject to the payment of corporate debts.

SEVENTH:

The direction and management of the affairs and business of the Corporation, including the control and disposition of its property and funds, shall be vested in a Board of Trustees, fifteen in number, except for the first year as specified in Article Nine, and composed of the Chief and the four Regional Agents of the Agricultural Education Service in the U.S. Office of Education, the National Executive Secretary and the National Treasurer of the Future Farmers of America, and the four State Supervisors of Agricultural Education who are elected on a regional basis to serve on the National Advisory Council of the Future Farmers of America, together with four other persons who shall be originally named, chosen, appointed, or elected in accordance with the method prescribed in the by-laws of the Corporation.

EIGHTH:

No portion of the property, real or personal, nor any part of the income or principal of the Corporation shall inure to the benefit of any member of the Board of Trustees, officer, or employee of the Corporation or to any individual having a personal or private interest in the activities of the Corporation nor shall any such member of the Board of Trustees, officer, or employee, or individual receive or be lawfully entitled to receive any pecuniary profit from the operations thereof, except reasonable compensation for services rendered by employees of the Corporation, and such necessary travel or other expenses as may be incurred by employees or members of the Board of Trustees, or both, while discharging their official duties and responsibilities as said employees or members of the Board of Trustees.

NINTH:

The Corporation shall be under the supervision and control of eleven Trustees for the first year of its existence, and their names are as follows: William T. Spanton, Charles H. Lane, A. Webster Tenney, James H. Pearson, Dudley M. Clements, Elmer J. Johnson, Dowell J. Howard, Robert E. Cammack, Ralph A. Howard, Louis M. Sasman, and Stanley S. Richardson.

Witness the following signatures and seals this 28th day of March, 1944.

WILLIAM T. SPANTON (SEAL)

FRANK W. LATHROP (SEAL)
RAYMOND WM. GREGORY (SEAL)

DISTRICT OF COLUMBIA, ss:

I, Sylvia D. Carlson, a Notary Public in and for the District of Columbia, do hereby certify that William T. Spanton, Frank W. Lathrop, and Raymond W. Gregory, parties to a certain Certificate of Incorporation bearing date on the 28th day of March, 1944, and hereto annexed personally appeared before me, in said District, the said William T. Spanton, Frank W. Lathrop, and Raymond W. Gregory being personally well known to me as the persons who executed the said Certificate of Incorporation, and acknowledged the same to be their act and deed.

Given under my hand and seal this 28th day of March. A.D. 1944.

SYLVIA D. CARLSON,
Notary Public of D.C.

(NOTARY SEAL)

OFFICE OF THE RECORDER OF DEEDS

District of Columbia

THIS IS TO CERTIFY that the foregoing is a true and verified copy of the Certificate of Incorporation of the

FUTURE FARMERS OF AMERICA
FOUNDATION, INCORPORATED

and of the whole of said Certificate of Incorporation, as filed in this Office the 29th day of March, A.D. 1944.

IN TESTIMONY WHEREOF, I have hereunto set my hand and affixed the seal of this Office this 29th day of March, A.D. 1944.

WM. J. THOMPKINS,
Recorder of Deeds, D.C.

(SEAL)

INCORPORATION OF THE FUTURE FARMERS OF AMERICA

(Public Law 740, Eighty-first Congress—S. 2868)
(Chapter 823—Second Session)

SEC. 1

AN ACT to incorporate the Future Farmers of America, and for other purposes. *Be it enacted by the Senate and House of Representatives of the United States of America in Congress assembled,* That the following persons: William T. Spanton, Washington, District of Columbia; Dudley M. Clements, College Park, Maryland; Herbert B. Swanson, Washington, District of Columbia; R. Edward Naugher, Arlington, Virginia; Elmer J. Johnson, Arlington, Virginia; Rodolph D. Anderson, Columbia, South Carolina; Earl H. Little, Concord, New Hampshire; Bert L. Brown, Olympia, Washington; and Ralph A. Howard, Columbus, Ohio, are hereby created a body corporate by the name of Future Farmers of America (hereinafter referred to as the "corporation") and by such name shall be known and have perpetual succession and the powers and limitations contained in this Act.

SEC. 2. The persons named in the first section of this Act are authorized to meet to complete the organization of the corporation by the selection of officers, the adoption of regulations and bylaws, and the doing of such other acts as may be necessary for such purpose.

SEC. 3. The objects and purposes of the corporation shall be—

(1) to create, foster, and assist subsidiary chapters composed of students and former students of vocational agriculture in public schools qualifying for Federal reimbursement under the Smith-Hughes Vocational Education Act or the Vocational Education Act of 1946 (Public Law 347, Sixty-fourth Congress, and Public Law 586, Seventy-ninth Congress), and associations of such chapters in the several States and Territories of the United States;

(2) to develop character, train for useful citizenship, and foster patriotism, and thereby to develop competent, aggressive rural and agricultural leadership;

(3) to create and nurture a love of country life by encouraging members to improve the farm home and its surroundings, to develop organized rural recreational activities, and to create more interest in the intelligent choice of farming occupations;

(4) to encourage the practice of thrift;

(5) to procure for and distribute to State associations, local chapters, and members all official Future Farmers of America supplies and equipment;

(6) to publish an official magazine and other publications for the members of the corporation;

(7) to strengthen the confidence of farm boys and young men in themselves and their work, to encourage members in the development of individual farming programs, and to promote their permanent establishment in farming by (a) encouraging improvement in scholarship; (b) providing prizes and awards to deserving students who have achieved distinction in vocational agriculture, including farm mechanics activities on a local, State, or national basis; and (c) assisting financially, through loans or grants, deserving students in all-day vocational agriculture classes and young farmers under thirty years of age who were former students in all-day vocational agriculture classes in becoming satisfactorily established in a farming occupation; and

(8) to cooperate with others, including State boards for vocational education, in accomplishing the above purposes; and to engage in such other activities, consistent with the foregoing purposes, determined by the governing body to be for the best interests of the corporation.

SEC. 4. The corporation shall have power—

(1) to sue and be sued, complain, and defend in any court of competent jurisdiction;

(2) to adopt, use, and alter a corporate seal;

(3) to choose such officers, managers, agents, and employees as the business of the corporation may require;

(4) to adopt and alter bylaws and regulations, not inconsistent with the laws of the United States or any State in which such corporation is to operate, for the management of its property and the regulation of its affairs, including the establishment and maintenance of local chapters and State associations of chapters;

(5) to contract and be contracted with;

(6) to take and hold by lease, gift, purchase, grant, devise, or bequest any property, real or personal, necessary for attaining the objects and accomplishing the purposes of the corporation, subject to applicable provisions of law of any State (A) governing the amount or kind of real and personal property which may be held by, or (B) otherwise limiting or controlling the ownership of real and personal property by, a corporation operating in such state;

(7) to transfer and convey real or personal property;

(8) to borrow money for the purposes of the corporation, issue bonds therefor, and secure the same by mortgage, subject to all applicable provisions of Federal or State law;

(9) to use the corporate funds to give prizes, awards, loans, and grants to deserving students and young farmers for the purposes set forth in section 3;
(10) to publish a magazine and other publications;
(11) to procure for and distribute to State associations, local chapters, and members all official Future Farmers of America supplies and equipment;
(12) to adopt emblems and badges; and
(13) to do any and all acts and things necessary and proper to carry out the objects and purposes of the corporation.

SEC. 5. The headquarters and principal offices of the corporation shall be located in the District of Columbia, but the activities of the corporation shall not be confined to that place but may be conducted throughout the various States, Territories, and possessions of the United States. The corporation shall maintain at all times in the District of Columbia a designated agent authorized to accept service of process for the corporation, such designation to be filed in the office of the clerk of the United States District Court for the District of Columbia. Notice to or service upon such agent, or mailed to the business address of such agent, shall be deemed sufficient notice or service upon the corporation.

SEC. 6. Eligibility for membership in the corporation and the rights and privileges of members shall, except as provided in this Act, be determined according to the bylaws of the corporation. In the conduct of official business of any local chapter each member shall have one vote. In the conduct of the official business of any State association each qualified delegate of a local chapter shall have one vote.

SEC. 7. (a) The national officers of the corporation shall be a student president, four student vice presidents (one from each of four regions of the United States established in the bylaws for purposes of administration of the corporation), a student secretary, an executive secretary, a treasurer, and a national advisor.
(b) The national student officers of the corporation shall comprise a board of student officers. It shall be the duty of such board to advise and make recommendations to the board of directors with respect to the conduct of the activities and business of the corporation.
(c) The national officers of the corporation shall be elected annually by a majority vote of the delegates assembled in the annual national convention from among qualified members of the corporation, except that the national advisor shall be the Chief of the Agricultural Education Service, Office of Education, Federal Security Agency, the executive secretary shall be a member of that service, and the treasurer shall be an employee or member of a State agency that directs or supervises a State program of agricultural education under the provisions of the Smith-Hughes Vocational Education Act or the Vocational Education Act of 1946 (Public Law 347, Sixty-fourth Congress, and Public Law 586, Seventy-ninth Congress).
(d) In the conduct of the business of the annual national convention each qualified delegate shall have one vote.

SEC. 8. (a) The governing body of the corporation, which shall exercise the powers herein granted to the corporation, shall be a board of directors composed of: (1) the Chief of the Agricultural Education Service, Office of Education, Federal Security Agency, who shall act as chairman; (2) four staff members in the Agricultural Education Service, Office of Education, Federal Security Agency; and (3) four State supervisors of agricultural education.
(b) The terms of office of members of the board and the method of selection of such members, other than ex-officio members, shall be prescribed by the bylaws of the corporation.
(c) The board shall meet at least once each year at such time and place as may be prescribed by the bylaws. The annual report of the board shall be presented at such meeting. Special meetings of the board may be called at any time by the chairman.
(d) The Board may designate the chairman and two members of his staff as a governing committee which, when the board is not in session, shall have and exercise the

powers of the board subject to its direction and have the power to authorize the seal of the corporation to be affixed to all papers which may require it.

(e) The board of directors which shall serve until the first board is selected as provided in this Act shall be composed of the nine persons named in the first section of this Act.

SEC. 9. (a) No part of the income or assets of the corporation shall inure to any member, officer, or director, or be distributable to any such persons except upon dissolution and final liquidation of the corporation as provided in section 15 of this Act.

(b) The corporation shall not make loans to its officers, directors, or employees. Any director who votes for or assents to the making of a loan to an officer, director, or employee of the corporation, and any officer who participates in the making of such a loan shall be jointly and severally liable to the corporation for the amount of such loan until the repayment thereof.

(c) This section shall not preclude prizes, awards, grants, or loans to student officers and members meeting the criteria established by the board of directors for selecting recipients of such benefits.

SEC. 10. The corporation, and its members, officers, and directors, as such, shall not contribute to or otherwise support or assist any political party or candidate for elective public office.

SEC. 11. The corporation shall be liable for the acts of its officers and agents when acting within the scope of their authority.

SEC. 12. The corporation shall have no power to issue any shares or stock, or to declare or pay any dividends, its objects and purposes being solely educational.

SEC. 13. The corporation shall keep correct and complete books and records of account and shall also keep minutes of the proceedings of its members, the board of directors, and committees having any authority under the board of directors; and it shall also keep a record of the names and addresses of its members entitled to vote. All books and records of the corporation may be inspected by any member or his agent or attorney at any reasonable time.

SEC. 14. (a) The financial transactions shall be audited annually by an independent certified public accountant in accordance with the principles and procedures applicable to commercial corporate transactions. The audit shall be conducted at the place or places where the accounts of the corporation are normally kept. All books, accounts, financial records, reports, files, and all other papers, things, or property belonging to or in use by the corporation and necessary to facilitate the audit shall be made available to the person or persons conducting the audit; and full facilities for verifying transactions with the balances or securities held by depositors, fiscal agents, and custodians shall be afforded to such person or persons.

(b) A report of such audit shall be made by the corporation to the Congress not later than January 15 of each year. The report shall set forth the scope of the audit and shall include a verification by the person or persons conducting the audit of statements of (1) assets and liabilities, (2) capital and surplus or deficit, (3) surplus or deficit analysis, (4) income and expense, and (5) sources and application of funds.

SEC. 15. Upon final dissolution or liquidation of the corporation and after the discharge or satisfaction of all outstanding obligations and liabilities, the remaining assets of the corporation shall be used by the board of directors for the benefit of students of vocational agriculture, or be transferred to some recognized educational foundation.

SEC. 16. The corporation, and its duly authorized chapters and associations of chapters, shall have the sole and exclusive right to use the name of Future Farmers of America and the initials FFA as representing an agricultural membership organization and such seals, emblems, and badges as the corporation may lawfully adopt.

SEC. 17. As a condition precedent to the exercise of any power or privilege granted to the corporation under this Act, the corporation shall file in the Office of the Secretary of the State, or similar officer, in each State and in each Territory or possession of the United States in which subordinate associations or chapters are organized, the name and post office address of an authorized agent in such State, Territory, or possession upon whom legal process or demands against the corporation may be served.

SEC. 18. The United States Commissioner of Education, with the approval of the Federal Security Administrator, is authorized to make available personnel, services, and facilities of the Office of Education requested by the board of directors of the corporation to administer or assist in the administration of the business and activities of the corporation. The personnel of the Office of Education shall not receive any compensation from the corporation for their services, except that travel and other legitimate expenses as defined by the Commissioner of Education and approved by the board of directors of the corporation may be paid. The Commissioner, with the approval of the Administrator, is also authorized to cooperate with the State boards for vocational education to assist in the promotion of the activities of corporation.

SEC. 19. The corporation may acquire the assets of the Future Farmers of America, a corporation organized under the laws of the State of Virginia, and of the Future Farmers of America Foundation, Incorporated, a corporation organized under the laws of the District of Columbia, upon discharging or satisfactorily providing for the payment and discharge of all of the liabilities of such corporations.

SEC. 20. The provisions of this Act shall take effect on the filing, in the office of the clerk of the United States District Court for the District of Columbia, of affidavits signed by the incorporators named in the first section of this Act to the effect that the Virginia corporation known as the Future Farmers of America has been dissolved in accordance with law, but only if such affidavits are filed within one year from the date of enactment of this Act.

SEC. 21. The right to alter, amend, or repeal this Act is hereby expressly reserved.

Approved August 30, 1950.

Index

INDEX